D1616719

**Series Editor: R. Bruce Lindsay**
**Brown University**

**PUBLISHED VOLUMES**

UNDERWATER SOUND / *Vernon M. Albers*
ACOUSTICS: Historical and Philosophical Development / *R. Bruce Lindsay*
SPEECH SYNTHESIS / *James L. Flanagan and L. R. Rabiner*
PHYSICAL ACOUSTICS / *R. Bruce Lindsay*
MUSICAL ACOUSTICS, PART I: Violin Family Components / *Carleen M. Hutchins*
MUSICAL ACOUSTICS, PART II: Violin Family Functions / *Carleen M. Hutchins*
ULTRASONIC BIOPHYSICS / *Floyd Dunn and William D. O'Brien*
VIBRATION: Beams, Plates, and Shells / *Arturs Kalnins and Clive L. Dym*
MUSICAL ACOUSTICS: Piano and Wind Instruments / *Earle L. Kent*

Additional volumes in preparation

A BENCHMARK® Books Series

# MUSICAL ACOUSTICS
## Piano and Wind Instruments

Edited by

**EARLE L. KENT**

Copyright © 1977 by **Dowden, Hutchinson & Ross, Inc.**
Benchmark Papers in Acoustics, Volume 9
Library of Congress Catalog Card Number: 76-20464
ISBN: 0-87933-245-X
PHYSICS
6241-1354 ✓

All rights reserved. No part of this book covered by the copyrights hereon may be reproduced or transmitted in any form or by any means—graphic, electronic, or mechanical, including photocopying, recording, taping or information storage and retrieval systems—without written permission of the publisher.

79 78 77 1 2 3 4 5
Manufactured in the United States of America.

LIBRARY OF CONGRESS CATALOGING IN PUBLICATION DATA

Main entry under title:
Musical acoustics : piano and wind instruments.
(Benchmark papers in acoustics ; 9)
Bibliography: p.
Includes index.
ISBN 0-87933-245-X
1. Music—Acoustics and physics—Addresses, essays, lectures. 2. Piano—Construction—Addresses, essays, lectures. 3. Wind instruments—Construction—Addresses, essays, lectures. I. Kent, Earle Lewis, 1910-
ML3805.M885 786.2'1 76-20464
ISBN 0-87933-245-X

Exclusive Distributor: Halsted Press
A Division of John Wiley & Sons, Inc.
ISBN: 0-470-98972-6

M L
3805
M885
PHYS

# SERIES EDITOR'S FOREWORD

The "Benchmark Papers in Acoustics" constitute a series of volumes that make available to the reader in carefully organized form important papers in all branches of acoustics. The literature of acoustics is vast in extent and much of it, particularly the earlier part, is inaccessible to the average acoustical scientist and engineer. These volumes aim to provide a practical introduction to this literature, since each volume offers an expert's selection of the seminal papers in a given branch of the subject, that is, those papers that have significantly influenced the development of that branch in a certain direction and introduced concepts and methods that possess basic utility in modern acoustics as a whole. Each volume provides a convenient and economical summary of results as well as a foundation for further study for both the person familiar with the field and the person who wishes to become acquainted with it.

Each volume has been organized and edited by an authority in the area to which it pertains. In each volume there is provided an editorial introduction summarizing the technical significance of the field being covered. Each article is accompanied by editorial commentary, with necessary explanatory notes, and an adequate index is provided for ready reference. Articles in languages other than English are either translated or abstracted in English. It is the hope of the publisher and editor that these volumes will constitute a working library of the most important technical literature in acoustics of value to students and research workers.

The present volume, Musical Acoustics: Piano and Wind Instruments, has been edited by Earle L. Kent, consulting engineer, who has for a long time been professionally active in the field of musical acoustics. Its 28 seminal articles cover, in thorough fashion, progress in the physics of the piano as well as of brass and woodwind instruments. Emphasis is laid on both the fundamental physical properties of such instruments and their practical application in music. Though due attention is paid to historical background, all the papers reprinted are of twentieth-century origin, and over half of them have appeared since 1950. The detailed commentaries by a distinguished authority in the field greatly enhance the utility of this volume and its value to all who are involved with musical problems in the area covered.

R. BRUCE LINDSAY



7775

# PREFACE

The aim of this volume of the Benchmark Series is to carry forth the concept of the other volumes, which reflect a concerted, worldwide search, review, selection, and distillation of the primary literature contained in previously published and unpublished material.

Wind instruments, and even pianos, appear to be relatively simple devices. Yet the science of sound, as it relates to these instruments, is quite complex. The musician is an acoustical part of wind instruments. Piano construction is varied and more complex than it may appear. Subjective evaluation of the acoustics of these instruments is related to the objective studies. These facts make it quite difficult to evaluate broad work done by the authorities in this field. I have tried to select material which seemed to be the most accurate technically and at the same time the most in touch with the subjective and practical elements involved. At least 18 other papers related to those in this volume are in previously published volumes of the Benchmark Series. The other volumes are: *Acoustics: Historical and Philosophical Development* (1973); *Physical Acoustics* (1974), both edited by R. Bruce Lindsay; and *Musical Acoustics, Part I* (1975), edited by Carleen M. Hutchins. The reader will find these volumes useful supplements to this volume.

Much credit is due Hermann von Helmholtz, John W. Strutt (Lord Rayleigh), H. Bouasse, D. J. Blaikley, Dayton C. Miller, and other pioneers in this field of musical acoustics. It is impressive to note their insight and the painstaking work they did without the sophisticated technical tools available today. Their work is cited often in the papers selected for this volume but this alone may not reflect the credit they deserve. To adequately condense the published volumes of their contributions in a single volume and leave room for more recent work is beyond my ability.

A considerable amount of the work done in musical acoustics has not been published. Much of what has been published has been done as an avocation—a labor of love—by interested individuals working independently. These people also deserve more credit than space limitations permit. Many good papers are not included. Less than one-tenth of the items available in the literature, and a very much smaller percentage of printed pages, can be contained in this volume.

I have been privileged to work with many people who have contributed to my understanding of musical acoustics. Also, they have greatly influenced my selections for this volume. I cannot name all of the musicians, music educators, and scientists with whom I have worked, and to whom I am greatly indebted. Arthur H. Benade worked with me as a consultant when I was directing wind instrument research for C. G. Conn, Ltd. He was very helpful then and during the years since. The late O. Hugo Schuck, the late Thomas H. Long, Robert W. Young, John C. Webster, Jody C. Hall, Paul Bert, Clyde Lockwood, Jr., Richard Lazure, Robert Cannon, Charles Walter, and James W. Coleman, Sr. were very helpful as co-workers in the former research department at C. G. Conn. Helmut Fuchs, Stuttgart, and Klaus Fenner, Bad Hersfeld, were quite helpful to me while I was in Germany. James Engelhardt, Braunschweig, Germany, has been a help with translations.

Also, I am indebted to my wife, Nina, for her assistance in proof reading and for her tolerance during the time I have spent in the preparation of this volume.

EARLE L. KENT

# CONTENTS

## PART II: ACOUSTICS OF BRASS INSTRUMENTS

## PART III: ACOUSTICS OF WOODWINDS

# CONTENTS BY AUTHOR

# INTRODUCTION

Music is an important part of all cultures. It ranges from simple folk tunes to music that is extremely complex in style and structure. Pictorial material, preserved writings and a few ancient musical instruments indicate that musical instruments have been a part of human activity since its beginning.

The earliest musical instruments were dependent upon available materials and limited technical knowledge. Little is known about how some instruments originated. One might speculate that some began with the observation of sounds produced by nature. For example, the fundamental principle of the flute may have been discovered by observing the sound made by the wind blowing across the top of a broken reed. The flute, in its simplest form, was well known in ancient Greece and Egypt. It probably dates back to prehistoric times. The principle of the double-reed musical instruments could have been learned by the discovery that sound could be produced by blowing on a hollow reed that had become collapsed at one end. Specimens of double-reed instruments have been found in ancient Egyptian tombs dating back to 3700 B.C.

The genealogy of cup-mouthpiece instruments can be traced in the records of kings and princes among the Chinese, Egyptians, Greeks, and Romans. The trumpet probably was the first such instrument.

The ancients had their psaltery, lyre, lute, and harp. Vegetable fiber or some similar material found in nature probably was first used to string such instruments; but cut, or flat, wire is as old as history. Cut wire of gold is mentioned in Exodus 39:3. Although drawn wire can be traced back as far as 1270 A.D., such hand-drawn wire was soft and not well suited for stringed instruments.

While music and musical instruments have been important for centuries, the scientific development of musical instruments has been relatively slow. Some of the earliest scientists took significant interest in the physics of musical tones and the instruments that produced them. Yet very little use has been made of this early work. The development of musical instruments has generally depended upon the availability of improved materials and a slow evolution of improvements by empirical methods.

There are physical, physiological, and psychological elements in the production of music. The physical portion includes musical instruments with their mechanical and acoustical components. A scientific approach to the acoustics of musical instruments requires due consideration of the physiological and psychological influences as well as the physics involved.

Music is an art; and the artistic characteristics of musicians influence the development of musical instruments. Tradition, training, physiological limitations, creative imagination, and prejudices are elements of the design, construction, and use of musical instruments.

Music is a living event and its dynamics must receive careful consideration. A scientific analysis of steady tones, for example, reveals little important information about the complex nature of musical sounds. The clarity of definition of music that is usually sought by engineers in the reproduction of music is not necessarily related to the best interest of the musician in the production of music. Lack of appreciation of this has been a considerable handicap in the development of some electronic musical instruments. Scientists who have made carefully conducted studies of musical instruments have sometimes arrived at incomplete or erroneous conclusions when adequate consideration is not given the dynamics of the musician, the instrument, and the music.

Many musicians and music educators are reluctant to accept change. They may want something new as long as it is not different—an attitude that affects improvements in musical instruments and the introduction of new instruments. Since music is an art, the musician may be quite sensitive to public opinion about his or her musicianship. If this is the case, feelings of insecurity can cause opposition to any tinkering with the status quo. An exception is the musician who is constantly seeking the innovation that will, at last, unleash his "true" musical ability. This attitude causes complaints about any existing instrument or music hall.

Some inaccurate information about musical instruments has been propagated in print or by hearsay. It is difficult for musicians, music educators, and the general public to disprove false assumptions, faulty theories, or misleading statements. This is a handicap in the education of musicians and in the design of their instruments.

Some mechanical or acoustical improvements that could be made in instruments are not made for practical reasons. If, for example, the acoustical characteristics of a wind instrument are modified to make better intonation possible, the manufacturer is likely to find that a trained musician will not like it. The musician who has become accustomed to pampering an instrument with poor intonation will need to make considerable adjustment in playing an instrument with an improved response. A change in the appearance of a brass instrument, such as the diameter of its bell, or making a cornet look like a trumpet, can provoke a negative reaction. The manufacturer of musical instruments tries to anticipate what will sell in profitable quantities. The buyers pick and choose from what is offered by the manufacturers.

Scientific knowledge has been growing at an extremely rapid rate in recent years. Large sums of money and many man-hours have gone into accomplishments that seemed impossible a few years ago. Men have walked on the moon. Scientific instruments explore outer space. Transportation, communication, and data processing have undergone fantastic changes in a short time. As important and universal as music is, there is little evidence that similar progress has been made, or is being made, in the application of science to musical instrument design. Notable exceptions are electronic musical instruments and the efforts of the Catgut Acoustical Society for the violin family.[1] Considerable engineering ingenuity has gone into the manufacturing processes and factory equipment for producing musical instruments; and competition has provided the incentive to keep costs as low as possible and to maintain uniformity in the products.

The number and kind of patents granted give some indication of the scientific efforts being made regarding the acoustics of pianos and wind instruments. Only a small amount of other basic information has been published by the manufacturers. Most of the technical matter has been published by people outside the music industry. Those people generally work independently.

In 1947, Harvey Fletcher proposed that an Institute of Musical Science be formed to provide a scientific basis and the techniques whereby music might contribute more fully to the aesthetic life of a greater number of people.[2] His suggestions included a wide range of activity intended to promote the best interests of musicians and music lovers. No such institute was formed. Perhaps Dr. Fletcher's proposal was too visionary, too broad, or just ahead of its time. The same year, Harold Burris-Meyer pointed out the importance of acoustics in music and the increasing interdependence of science and the art of music.[3] He wrote, "Defined in physical terms, music is an acoustical phenomenon. The field of acoustics includes all phases of music from the time the basic concept is first given actuality in any form by the composer, until the listener has reacted to the performance. . . . The scientific method has been applied to the art to make possible an unlimited audience. This is an important accomplishment, but it is a limited one. It has only made more listeners. It has not made better music."

Others have seen the value of a cooperative effort being made in the broad interest of music. Little has come from their suggestions and efforts in this regard. The Catgut Acoustical Society is a notable example of what can be done. A small number of interested physicists, chemists, musicians, and music lovers joined together informally to pool their efforts to learn more about the acoustics of violins and to find ways and means to produce better and less costly instruments in the violin family. They did not wait for the government or a well-endowed university to establish the needed function.

Acousticians interested in music and musical instruments meet together informally at the meetings of the Committee on Musical Acoustics when the Acoustical Society of America holds its semiannual meetings. Those attending the meetings exchange information of general interest related to musical acoustics. The meetings often are interesting and informative and give some element of cohesion to the independent efforts of those working in the field. For several years, an effort to publish a newsletter was made by the chairman of the committee. The paper was sent to any interested person and was intended to expand the effectiveness of the brief informal meetings of the committee.

Over two hundred technical people from the piano industry and its suppliers met at meetings in 1916, 1917, and 1918 in Chicago and in 1919 in New York to discuss the technical aspects of piano tone production. This cooperative effort was under the auspices of the American Steel & Wire Co. of Chicago.[4] Those present exchanged practical views of piano acoustics. They hoped their quest for better information would result in better pianos.

The Piano Technicians Guild holds national and regional meetings regularly to exchange technical information related to piano acoustics in order to promote better maintenance and rebuilding of pianos in the field.

In May 1965, there was an unprecedented meeting of nearly 500 piano manufacturers, acousticians, musicologists, piano teachers, and music lovers in Berlin, Germany. The Fördergemeinschaft Klavier, a federation of associations in the piano industry (teachers, artists, and music lovers) held the first European Piano Congress with the motif, "The Pianoforte in Past, Present and Future."[5] Twenty countries were represented by those in attendance at the technical sessions. The meetings gave the opportunity for all of those interested in the piano to exchange information through lectures, study groups, platform discussion, conferences, exhibits, demonstrations, and motion pictures. Those involved hoped it would be the beginning of a much needed cooperative effort and that similar conventions would follow. Since Berlin was once the capitol of piano making it was a fitting setting for the first such congress. The effort has not been repeated, but there is some cooperative effort toward piano research by federal and state governments and the piano manufacturers in Germany. The French Government sponsors some musical instrument research also.

The acoustics of pianos and wind instruments is a broad and complex field. Much remains to be learned in it. It is hoped that this volume can be helpful in providing useful information about the subject.

## REFERENCE NOTES

1. The Catgut Acoustical Society, Inc., was founded by the late Frederick A. Saunders. Its permanent secretary is Mrs. Carleen M. Hutchins, 112 Essex Avenue, Montclair, N.J. 07042. More information can be found in *Musical Acoustics, Part I,* Carleen M. Hutchins (ed.), Stroudsburg, Pa.: Dowden, Hutchinson & Ross, 1975, p. 455.
2. H. Fletcher, "An Institute of Musical Science—A Suggestion," *J. Acoust. Soc. Am.,* **19,** 527–531 (1947).
3. H. Burris-Meyer, "The Place of Acoustics in the Future of Music," *J. Acoust. Soc. Am.,* **19,** 532–534 (1949).
4. Stenographic report of the proceedings of the piano technicians conference, Chicago 1916, 1917, 1918, and New York 1919, reprinted in *Piano Tone Building,* Vestal, N. Y.: Vestal Press, 1974.
5. *Europiano Kongress Berlin 1965 Dokumentation,* Frankfurt am Main: Fördergemeinschaft Klavier, e.v. 1966.

Part I

# PIANO ACOUSTICS

# Editor's Comments on Paper 1

## 1 BLACKHAM

*The Physics of the Piano*

Blackham presents some historical background of the piano and a general overview of its construction and its functioning. This article and the nine following it present basic information regarding the acoustics of pianos.

It may be helpful for the reader to keep in mind some information regarding the piano that is implied but perhaps not clearly stated in these papers.

1. Partials are termed "inharmonic" or "anharmonic" if their frequencies are not integer multiples of the fundamental frequency. The fact that partials are not harmonic should not necessarily indicate poor tone quality. This is brought out more fully in Paper 9.

2. Pianos vary considerably in size from a small spinet to a large concert grand. They also vary in the quality of design and construction. One should use caution in arriving at broad conclusions based upon a study of small samples. Pianos that are well designed, constructed, and maintained can produce tones that vary greatly in maximum intensity, in decay characteristics, and in the relative magnitudes of the partials in tones. Construction variations within a given piano and in different pianos include: the hardness, speaking length, diameter, and tension of strings; the stiffness, tightness, uniformity, and length of windings on wound strings; the tuning of strings in unison groups; the hardness, shape, and weight of hammers; the strike line of hammers; the dwell time of hammers on strings; the shape and impedance of the boundaries of string speaking lengths; the length and damping of nonspeaking string portions; the effectiveness of the dampers; the acoustic response of the bridge–soundboard combination; and the efficiency and recovery characteristics of the key–action combination.

3. The piano string serves as the primary element in piano tone production. This simple-appearing device establishes the fundamental frequency of the tone, its timbre, and its power potential. The tones have "life" and "warmth" and are capable of great musical expression. They are very much more complex than the simple-appearing structure might imply. It might be said that it is about as difficult to synthesize a piano tone as it would be to synthesize a tomato.

4. Some of the construction information given in Paper 1 applies to grand pianos. Piano actions and some other details are different in vertical pianos.

Blackham was a research assistant to Harvey Fletcher at the time Paper 1 and Paper 9 were written. He established a private school of music in 1965 at Nephi, Utah where he teaches and performs.

# 1

*Copyright © 1965 by Scientific American, Inc. All rights reserved.*

Reprinted with permission from *Sci. Am.*, 88–96, 99 (Dec. 1965)

# The Physics of the Piano

by E. Donnell Blackham

[*Editor's Note:* Illustrations were rendered in color in original publication.]

Almost every musical tone, whether it is produced by a vibrating string, a vibrating column of air or any other vibrating system, consists of a fundamental tone and a number of the higher-pitched but generally fainter tones known as partial tones or overtones. The complex sound produced by this combination of separate tones has a timbre, or characteristic quality, that is determined largely by the number of partial tones and their relative loudness. It is timbre that enables one to distinguish between two musical tones that have the same pitch and the same loudness but are produced by two different musical instruments. A pure tone—one that consists solely of the fundamental tone—is rarely heard in music.

It is widely believed that the partial tones produced by all musical instruments are harmonic—that their frequencies are exact whole-number multiples of the frequency of a fundamental tone. This certainly holds true for all the woodwinds and under certain conditions for many of the stringed instruments, including the violin. It is only approximately true, however, in the most familiar stringed instrument: the piano. The higher the frequency of the partial tones of any note on the piano, the more they depart from a simple harmonic series. In our laboratory at Brigham Young University my colleagues and I, under the direction of Harvey Fletcher, have succeeded in measuring with considerable precision the degree to which the modern piano is inharmonic and have demonstrated the importance of this factor in determining the distinctive quality of the piano's tone.

a

b

c

**IDEAL STRING, that is, one without any stiffness, can be made to vibrate at many different frequencies: the fundamental frequency (*a*) produces a pure tone, rarely heard in music, whereas higher-pitched partial tones, or overtones, are produced by harmonic vibrations (*"b" and "c"*), whose frequencies are whole-number multiples of the fundamental frequency.**

**SIMULTANEOUS VIBRATION of a string at two or more different frequencies is normal for stringed instruments. Here the string vibrates at the fundamental frequency and the second partial frequency (*"a" and "c" in upper illustration*). In the piano the stiffness of the strings causes higher partials of a complex tone to depart from the simple harmonic series.**

The physics of the piano can best be understood by first reviewing the evolution of the modern piano and its principal components. Archaeological evidence shows that primitive stringed instruments existed before the beginning of recorded history. The Bible refers several times to an instrument called the psaltery that was played by plucking strings stretched across a box or gourd, which served as a resonator. A similar instrument existed in China some thousands of years before the Christian era. In the sixth century B.C. Pythagoras used a simple stringed instrument called the monochord in his investigation of the mathematical relations of musical tones. His monochord consisted of a single string stretched tightly across a wooden box. It was fitted with a movable bridge that could divide the string into various lengths, each of which could vibrate freely at a different fundamental frequency.

Another important component of the modern piano—the keyboard—did not arise in conjunction with a stringed instrument but with the pipe organ. The organ of Ctesibus, perfected at Alexandria in the second century B.C., undoubtedly had some kind of keyboard. The Roman architect Vitruvius, writing during the reign of Augustus Caesar, describes pivoted keys used in the organs of his day. In the second century A.D. Hero of Alexandria built an organ in which the valves admitting air to the pipes were controlled by pivoted keys that were returned to their original position by springs.

We do not know who first conceived the idea of adding keys to a stringed instrument. From this obscure beginning there eventually evolved in the 15th century the clavichord. In the early clavichords a piece of metal mounted vertically at the end of the key acted both as a bridge for determining the pitch of the string and as a percussive device for producing the tone [*see upper illustration on page 92*]. Since one string could be used to produce more than one tone, there were usually more keys than strings. A strip of cloth was interlaced among the strings at one end in order to damp the unwanted tone from the shorter part of the string.

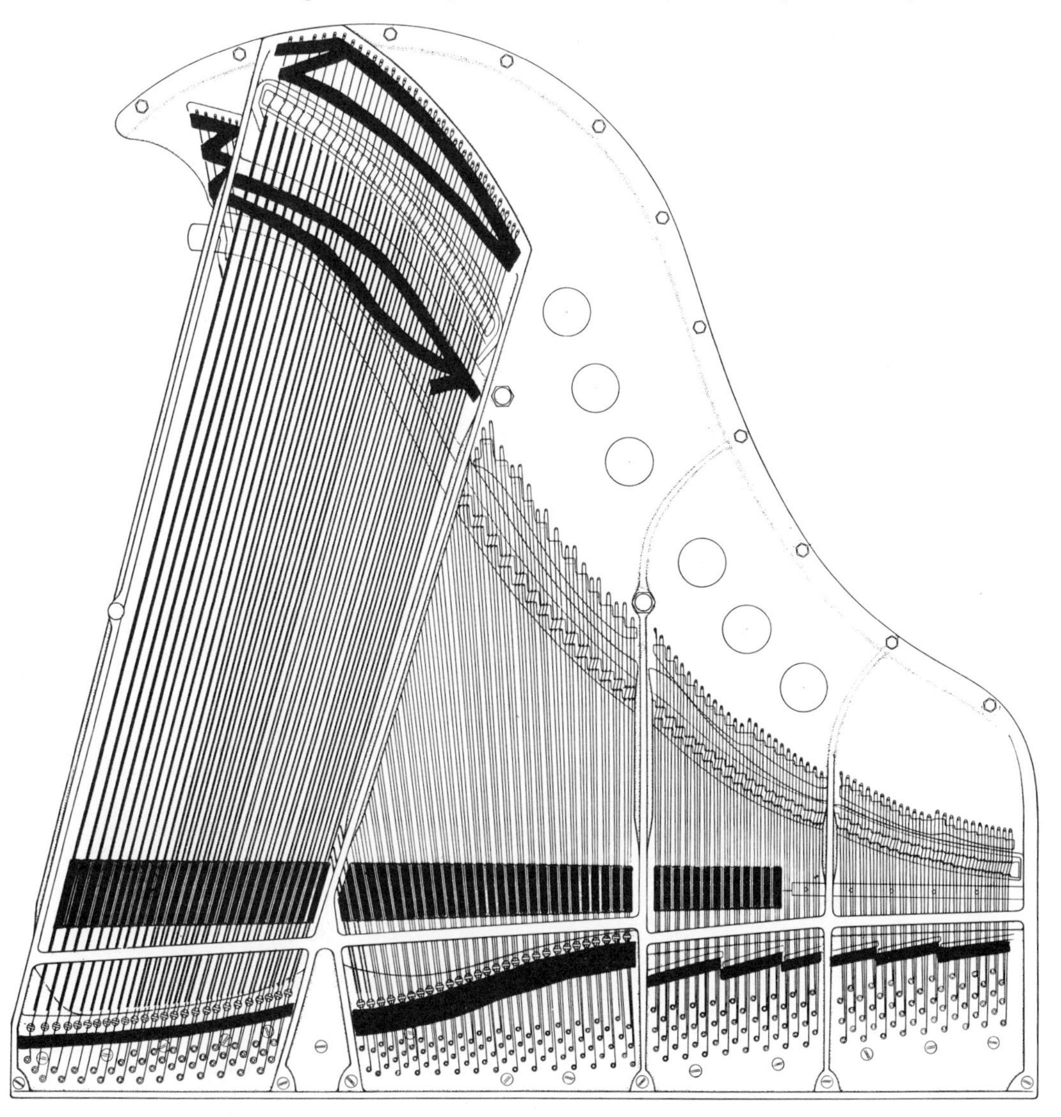

**TOP VIEW of the interior of a modern "baby grand" piano shows the powerful construction of the full cast-iron frame, which sustains the tremendous tension exerted by the strings. In this particular piano the frame, which is cast in one piece, weighs about 250 pounds and sustains an average tension of some 50,000 pounds; in a larger concert-grand piano the frame weighs as much as 400 pounds and sustains an average tension of 60,000 pounds. The strings are made of steel wire with an ultimate tensile strength of from 300,000 to 400,000 pounds per square inch. In order to make the bass strings (*left*) vibrate slower and thus produce a lower pitch, they are wrapped in copper or iron wire; two such wrappings are often used in the extreme bass. In all modern pianos the bass strings are "overstrung" in order to conserve space and to bring them more nearly over the center of the soundboard. Starting from the treble, or right-hand, end of the keyboard there are 60 notes with three strings each, then 18 notes with two strings each and finally, in the extreme bass, 10 notes with only one string each. Larger pianos have more strings but the same total number of notes: 88. Rectangular black objects in a row near the bottom are the heads of the dampers. Parts made of felt are in color. Strips of cloth interlaced among the strings at top damp unwanted tones from the short parts of the strings beyond the bridge (*see illustration on next page*).**

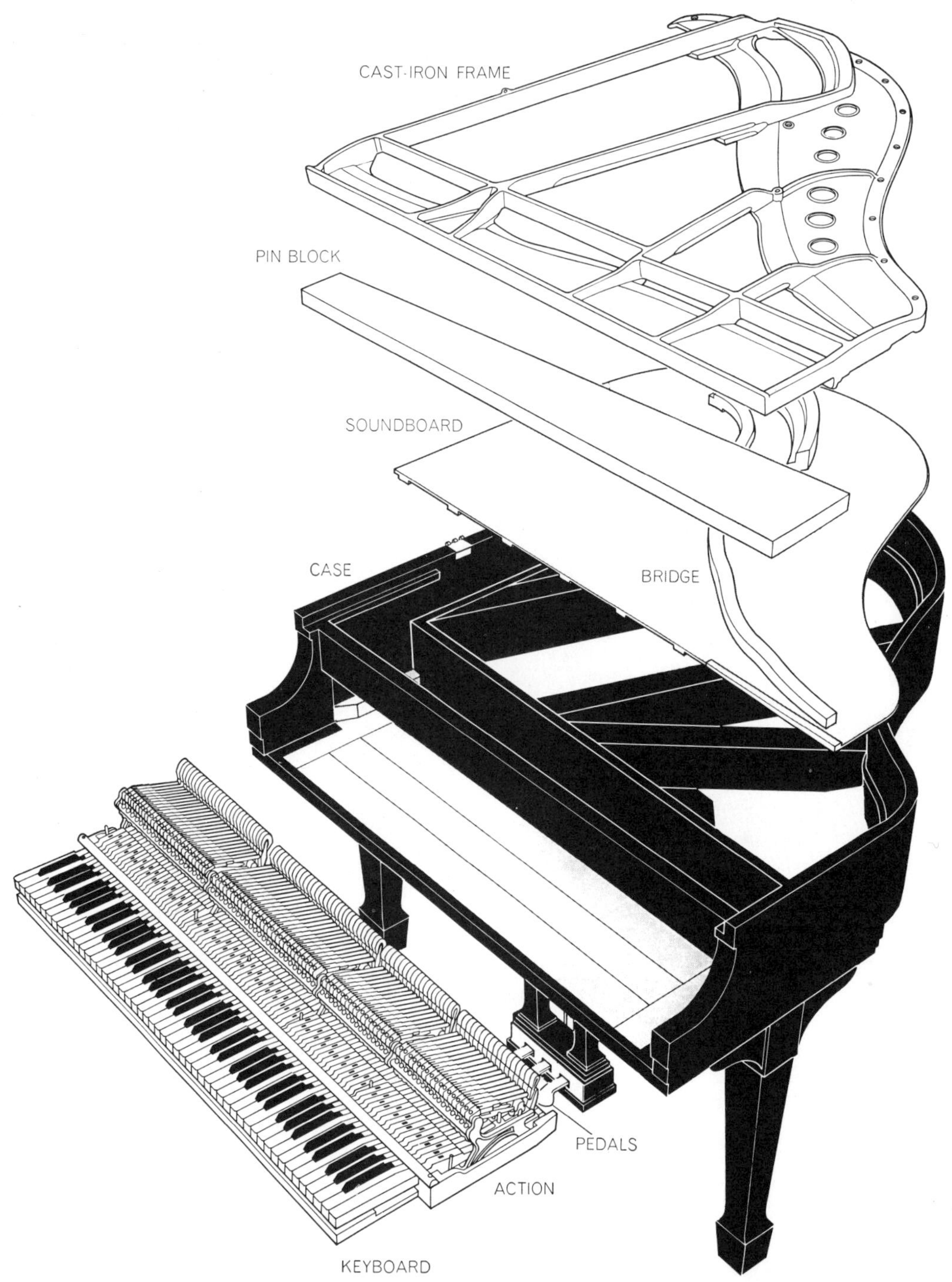


**EXPLODED VIEW** of the baby-grand piano depicted from above on the preceding page shows the relations of several main components. The keyboard (*bottom left*) has 88 keys divided into seven and a third octaves. Each octave has eight white keys for playing the diatonic scale (whole notes) and five raised black keys for playing the chromatic scale (whole notes plus sharps and flats). Connected to the keyboard is the action, which includes all the moving parts involved in the actual striking of the string. Three pedals (*bottom center*) serve to control the dampers in the action. When a key is struck, the hammer sets the strings in vibration and, after a very short interval known as the attack time, sound is translated by means of a wooden bridge to the soundboard, from which it is radiated into the air. During the attack time sound is also radiated to a lesser degree from both the strings and the bridge.

Several essential characteristics of the modern piano are inherited from the clavichord. The clavichord had metal strings, a percussive device for setting the strings in vibration, a damping mechanism and also an independent soundboard: the board at the bottom of the case did not also serve as the frame for mounting the strings. Moreover, although the tone of the clavichord was weak, the instrument allowed for the execution of dynamics, that is, for playing either loudly or softly.

**JURY composed of both musicians and nonmusicians was asked to distinguish between recordings of real piano tones and synthetic ones. When the synthetic tones were built up of harmonic partials, the musicians on the jury were able to distinguish 90 percent of these tones from real piano tones; the nonmusicians, 86 percent. When inharmonic partials were used, results showed that in most cases both the musicians and the nonmusicians were guessing; both groups identified only about 50 percent of the tones correctly. In this photograph two members of the jury are listening to tones in an anechoic, or echoless, chamber.**

At about the same time another forerunner of the modern piano was in process of development. In the spinet, or virginal, longer strings were introduced to produce a louder tone. Now the metal percussive device of the clavichord was no longer adequate to produce vibration in the strings. Instead the strings were set in motion by the plucking action of a quill mounted at right angles on a "jack" at the end of the key [*see lower illustration on next page*]. When the key was depressed, the jack moved upward and the quill plucked the string. When the jack dropped back, a piece of cloth attached to it damped the vibration of the string.

Around the beginning of the 16th century experiments with still longer strings and larger soundboards led to the development of the harpsichord. Although this instrument was essentially nothing more than an enlarged spinet, it incorporated several important innovations that have carried over to the modern piano. The wing-shaped case of the harpsichord is imitated by that of the grand piano. The stratagem of using more than one string per note in order to increase volume was adopted for the harpsichord by the middle of the 17th century. The harpsichord also had a "forte stop," which lifted the dampers from the strings to permit sustained tones, and a device for shifting the keyboard, both of which are preserved in the modern piano.

The invention of the piano was forecast by inherent defects in both the clavichord and the harpsichord. Neither the spinet nor the harpsichord was capable of offering the composer or performer an opportunity to execute dynamics. The clavichord, on the other hand, allowed a modest range of dynamics but could not generate a tone nearly as loud as that of the harpsichord. Attempts to install heavier strings in order to increase the volume of either instrument were futile; neither the metal percussive device of the clavichord nor the quill of the harpsichord could excite a heavy string. Moreover, the cases of these early instruments were not strong enough to sustain the increased tension of heavier strings.

A remedy for these defects was provided by the Italian harpsichord-maker Bartolommeo Christofori, who in 1709 built the first hammer-action keyboard instrument. Christofori called his original instrument the "piano-forte," meaning that it could be played both softly and loudly. The idea of having the strings struck by hammers was probably suggested to him by the dulcimer, a stringed instrument played by hammers held in the hands of the performer. Christofori recognized that his new instrument would need a stronger case to withstand the increased tension of the heavier strings. By 1720 an improved model of the pianoforte included an escapement device that "threw" the free-swinging hammer upward at the string and also a back-check that regulated the hammer's downward return [*see upper illustration on page 93*]. An individual damper connected to the action of the hammer was provided for each note.

For a century and a half after Christofori's first piano appeared inventors worked to improve the new instrument, particularly its novel hammer action. Several other types of action were developed, some new and others modeled closely on Christofori's original. Pianos were built in a variety of forms: traditional wing-shaped pianos, square pianos, upright pianos and even a piano-organ combination.

Among the major innovations toward the end of this period was the full cast-

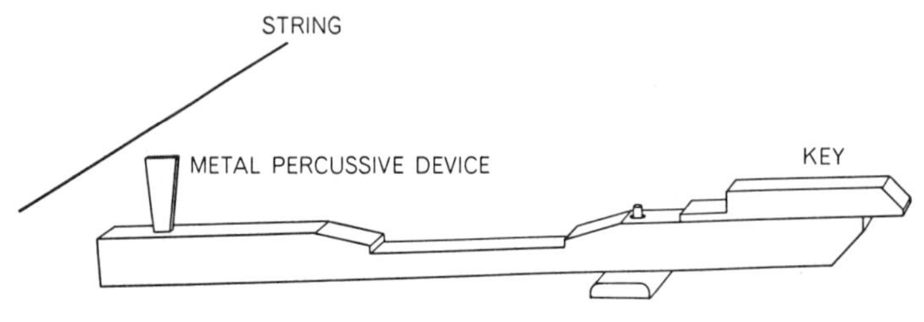


**CLAVICHORD ACTION** included one essential feature found in all modern pianos: a percussive device for setting the strings in vibration. A piece of metal mounted vertically at the end of the key acted both as a bridge for determining the pitch of the string and as a percussive device for producing the tone. Since one string could be used to produce more than one tone, there were usually more keys than strings. A strip of cloth was interlaced among the strings at one end to damp the tone from the shorter part of the string.

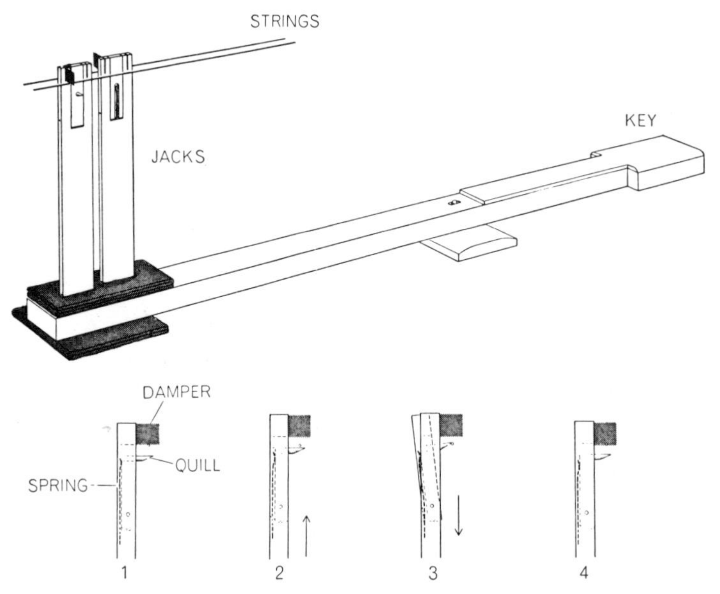


**HARPSICHORD ACTION** was capable of producing a louder tone than that of the clavichord, but, unlike the clavichord, it did not allow for the execution of dynamics, that is, for playing either loudly or softly. The strings were set in motion by the plucking action of a quill mounted at right angles on a "jack" at the end of the key. When the key was depressed, the jack moved upward and the quill plucked the string. When the jack dropped back, a piece of cloth attached to it damped the vibration of the string. The stratagem of using more than one string per note was adopted in the harpsichord in the 17th century.

iron frame. Constant striving for greater sonority had led to the use of very heavy strings, and the point was reached where the wooden frames of the earlier pianos could no longer withstand the tension. In 1855 the German-born American piano manufacturer Henry Steinway brought out a grand piano with a cast-iron frame that has served as a model for all subsequent piano frames. Although minor refinements are constantly being introduced, there have been no fundamental changes in the design or construction of pianos since 1855.

A part of the piano that has received a great deal of attention from acoustical physicists is the soundboard. Some early investigators believed the sound of the piano originated entirely in the soundboard and not in the strings. We now know that the sound originates in the strings; after a very short interval, called the attack time, it is translated by means of a wooden bridge to the soundboard, from which it is radiated into the air. During the attack time sound is also radiated to a lesser degree from both the strings and the bridge. In the late 19th century Frederick Mathushek and his associates proved that the quality of a piano's sound was not influenced by the transverse, or horizontal, vibrations of the soundboard. They glued together two soundboards so that the grain of one was at right angles to the grain of the other, thereby eliminating any transverse vibrations, and found that the quality of the sound was not affected by this arrangement. The behavior of the soundboard has also been analyzed theoretically by a number of eminent physicists, including Hermann von Helmholtz, but such analyses have added nothing to the principles of soundboard construction arrived at empirically by the builders of the early clavichords and harpsichords.

The development of the full cast-iron frame gave the sound of the piano much greater brilliance and power. The modern frame is cast in one piece and carries the entire tension of the strings; in a large concert-grand piano the frame weighs 400 pounds and is subjected to an average tension of 60,000 pounds. In order to maintain the tension of the strings each string is attached at the keyboard end to a separate tuning pin, which passes down through a hole in the frame and is anchored in a strong wooden pin block. Since the piano would go out of tune immediately if the tuning pins were to yield to the tremendous tension of the strings, the pin block is built up of as many as 41 cross-grained layers of hardwood.

The keyboard of the modern piano is constructed on essentially the same principles that had been fully developed before the 15th century. The standard keyboard has 88 keys divided into seven and a third octaves, the first note in each octave having twice the frequency of the first note in the octave below it. Each octave has eight white keys for playing the diatonic scale (whole notes) and five raised black keys for playing the chromatic scale (whole notes plus sharps and flats). In all modern pianos the white keys are not tuned exactly to the diatonic scale but rather to the equally tempered scale, in which the octave is simply divided into 12 equal intervals.

The moving parts of the piano that are involved in the actual striking of the string are collectively called the action [*see lower illustration on opposite page*]. One contemporary piano manufacturer asserts that the action in one of his pianos has some 7,000 separate parts. Nearly all modern actions are versions of Christofori's original upward-striking ones, which took advantage of the downward force of gravity for the key's return. Some workers have experimented with downward-striking actions, so far without success.

Early in the history of piano-building the hammers were small blocks of wood covered with soft leather. The inability of leather to maintain its resiliency after many successive strikings led eventually to the use of felt-covered hammers. If the felt is too hard and produces a harsh tone, it can be pricked with a needle to loosen its fibers and will produce a mellower tone. If the tone is too mellow and lacks brilliance, the felt can be filed and made harder.

A standard piano has three pedals that serve to control the dampers. The forte, or sustaining, pedal on the right disengages all the dampers so that the strings are free to vibrate until the pedal is released or the tones die away. The sostenuto pedal in the middle sustains only the tones that are played at the time the pedal is depressed; all the other tones are damped normally when their respective keys are released. The "soft" pedal on the left shifts the entire action so that the hammers strike fewer than the usual number of strings, decreasing the loudness of the instrument.

The most interesting part of the piano from the standpoint of the acoustical physicist is of course the strings. The strings used in pianos today are made of steel wire with an ultimate tensile strength of from 300,000 to 400,000 pounds per square inch. Additional weight is needed to make the bass strings vibrate slower and so generate sounds of lower pitch; this is provided by wrapping the steel wire with wire of

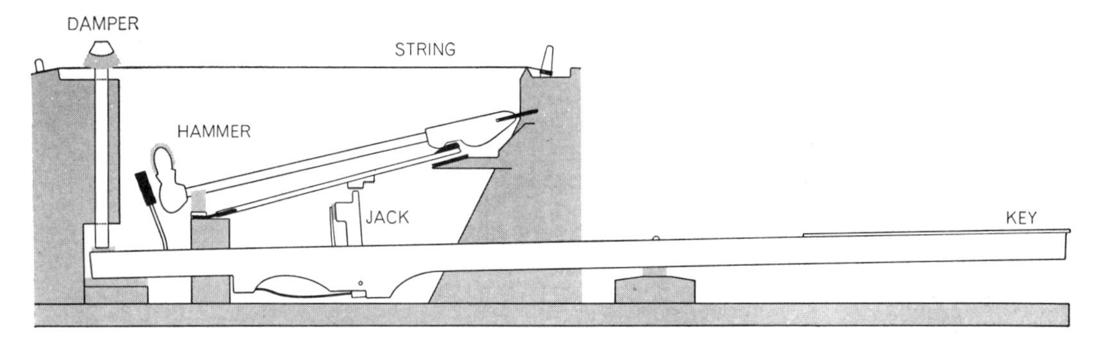


**CHRISTOFORI ACTION, invented by Bartolommeo Christofori in the early 18th century, was the first hammer action and the prototype of all modern piano actions. It included an escapement device that "threw" the free-swinging hammer upward at the string and also a back-check that regulated the hammer's downward return. An individual damper connected to the action of the hammer was provided for each note. Christofori called his instrument the "piano-forte," meaning it could be played either softly or loudly.**

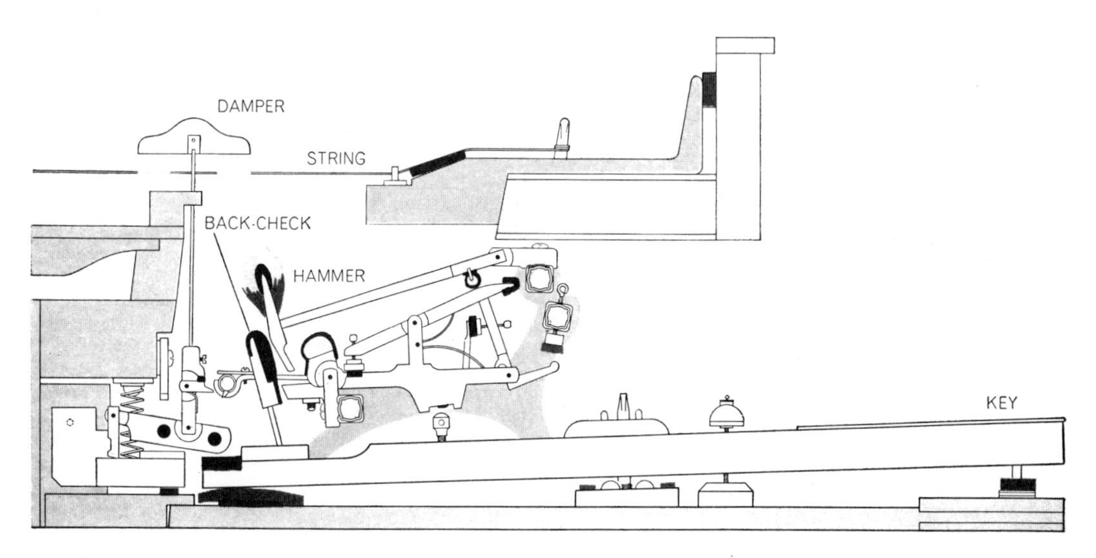


**MODERN PIANO ACTION is modeled closely on Christofori's original upward-striking actions, which took advantage of the downward force of gravity for the key's return. Unlike the early hammers, which were small blocks of wood covered with soft leather, the modern hammer is covered with felt. If the felt is too hard and produces a harsh tone, it can be pricked with a needle to loosen its fibers and will produce a mellower tone. If the tone is too mellow and lacks brilliance, the felt can be filed and made harder.**

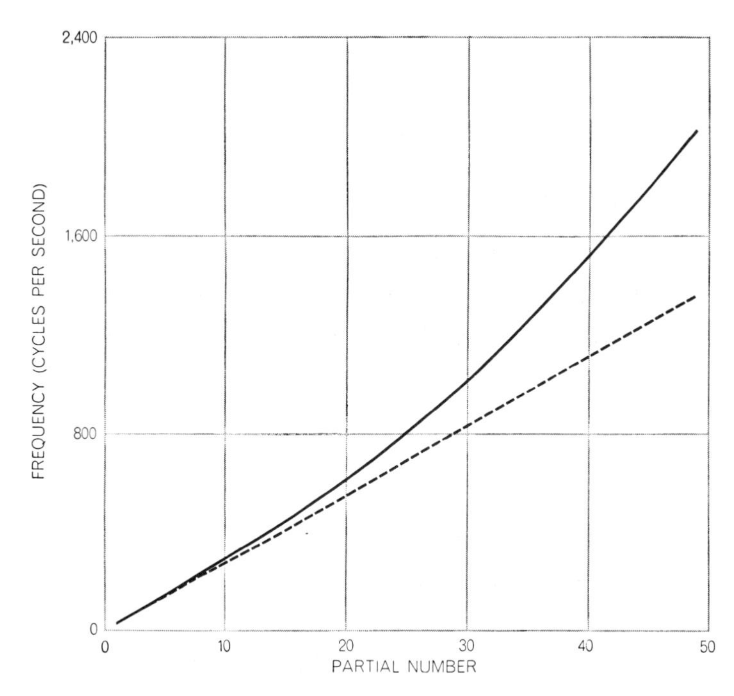


**INHARMONICITY of a real piano tone is evident in this graph, based on data obtained from an electronic analysis of the partial tones of the lowest note on the piano keyboard (an *A*). The partials of the real piano tone (*solid line*) become increasingly sharper—that is, higher in frequency—compared with the partials of a pure harmonic tone (*broken line*).**

copper or iron. Two such wrappings are often used in the extreme bass.

The vibration of a string that is attached securely at both ends is caused by a restoring force—a force that seeks to return the string to its original position after it has been displaced from that position. In a string that lacks stiffness the partial tones set up under the influence of the restoring force will be harmonic. In the piano the stiffness of the strings affects the restoring force to such a degree that some of the partials generated are not harmonic. This effect was known to Lord Rayleigh, who took it into account in formulating his classic equations for vibrating strings in the late 19th century. Many other investigators have since worked on the problem; our current effort is a continuation of the same line of inquiry.

Part of our program includes a series of tests in which a jury composed of both musicians and nonmusicians is asked to distinguish between recordings of real piano tones and synthetic ones. The synthetic tones are made by a bank of 100 audio-frequency oscillators that can be tuned to cover a range of from 50 to 15,000 cycles per second. Fine tuning is achieved by means of an attenuator connected to each oscillator circuit; the attenuator covers a range of 50 decibels, 10 decibels being a tenfold increase or decrease in the intensity of sound. With this apparatus it is possible to build up synthetic tones that represent a wide variety of partial-tone combinations. Real piano tones can be closely imitated by tuning a separate oscillator to the precise frequency and intensity associated with each partial tone of the real tone. The complex synthetic tone thus generated can then be fed into an "attack and decay" amplifier in order to give it the attack-and-decay characteristics found in the real piano tone.

In our early tests the synthetic tones were arbitrarily built up of harmonic partials. The musicians on the jury were able to distinguish 90 percent of these tones from real piano tones; the nonmusicians, 86 percent. In later tests synthetic tones built up of inharmonic partials were used. Results from these tests showed that in most cases both the musicians and the nonmusicians were guessing; both groups identified only about 50 percent of the tones correctly. Whenever a synthetic tone and a real tone were judged to be identical, we could give a description of the quality of the real tone based on our knowledge of the quality of the synthetic tone.

Recorded piano tones can also be analyzed directly by means of a conventional audio-frequency analyzer that is adjusted to pass only a narrow band of frequencies (about four cycles per second). The analyzer is set at different frequencies until it registers a maximum response for the particular partial being analyzed. A pure tone from one of the oscillators is then sent through the analyzer, and its frequency is adjusted until it gives a maximum response at the same setting as that of the real partial. An electronic counter is used to measure the frequency of the oscillator tone to an accuracy of within about a tenth of 1 percent. This frequency is assumed to be the frequency of the real partial being analyzed.

A sample of this kind of analysis for the lowest note on the piano keyboard (an *A*) is given in the illustration at the left. It is evident that the partials of the real piano tone become sharper—that is, higher in frequency—compared with the partials of a pure harmonic tone. The 16th partial, for example, is a semitone sharper—half a step higher—than it would be if it were harmonic. The 23rd partial is more than a whole tone sharp, the 33rd partial is more than two tones sharp and the highest partial in the analysis, the 49th, is 3.65 tones sharp.

In addition to the fact that the piano's tones are generally inharmonic, the partials of any particular note tend to vary considerably in loudness. This variation is called the harmonic structure of the tone, or in the case of the piano, the partial structure. One way to analyze the partial structure of a piano tone is to measure the maximum response of each partial as it passes through the audio-frequency analyzer. This method was used to obtain the partial structure of the four *G*'s shown in the illustration on the opposite page.

The foregoing method does not yield the most accurate description of the partial structure of a piano tone, because the structure is continuously changing. When a piano string is struck by its hammer, its response reaches a maximum an instant later. From this moment on the tone dies away as the string gradually ceases to vibrate. Because the ear perceives the entire tone dying away uniformly, it might seem that all the partials of the tone die away at an equal rate. An examination of the decay curves of individual partials proves that this is not the case [*see illustration on next page*]. It is obvious from these curves that if the partial structure of a tone were measured at any given time, it would be different from the structure at any other time. Nonetheless, some authors still refer to a decay rate of a tone as so many decibels per second. In actuality the partials do not all decay at the same rate; in some cases they may even increase in intensity before starting to decay.

The tones used for our decay-time analyses were recorded in an ordinary music studio. It was thought at first that the irregular variations during decay might be related to the acoustic characteristics of the room or the piano. Accordingly the experiment was repeated in three different rooms: a normally reverberant studio, a very reverberant room and an anechoic, or echoless, chamber. The irregularities in the decay curves were present in all three rooms [*see illustration on page 99*].

One of the main advantages of our synthetic-tone system is that it can be used to produce synthetic tones identical with one another and with a real tone except for certain selected characteristics. For example, a group of synthetic tones can be produced that differ only in attack time, the time required for the loudness of the tone to reach its first maximum after the hammer strikes the string. By presenting such a group of tones to our jury we were able to determine that for the *G* just above middle *C* the attack time has to be between zero and .05 second to sound like the *G* on a piano. An attack time in the range of from .05 to .12 second made the note seem questionable, and one longer than .12 second made it sound decidedly unlike a *G* struck on a piano. For lower notes the required attack time tended to be longer; for higher notes it tended to be shorter.

Synthetic tones can also be produced that are identical with one another and with a real tone in every respect except decay time, the time required for the string to stop vibrating after it has reached its maximum loudness. For an undamped *G* above middle *C* the decay time required for the synthetic tone to sound piano-like was between two and 5.5 seconds. Again acceptable decay times were longer for lower notes and shorter for higher notes.

Another procedure is to give synthetic tones a piano-like attack and decay but

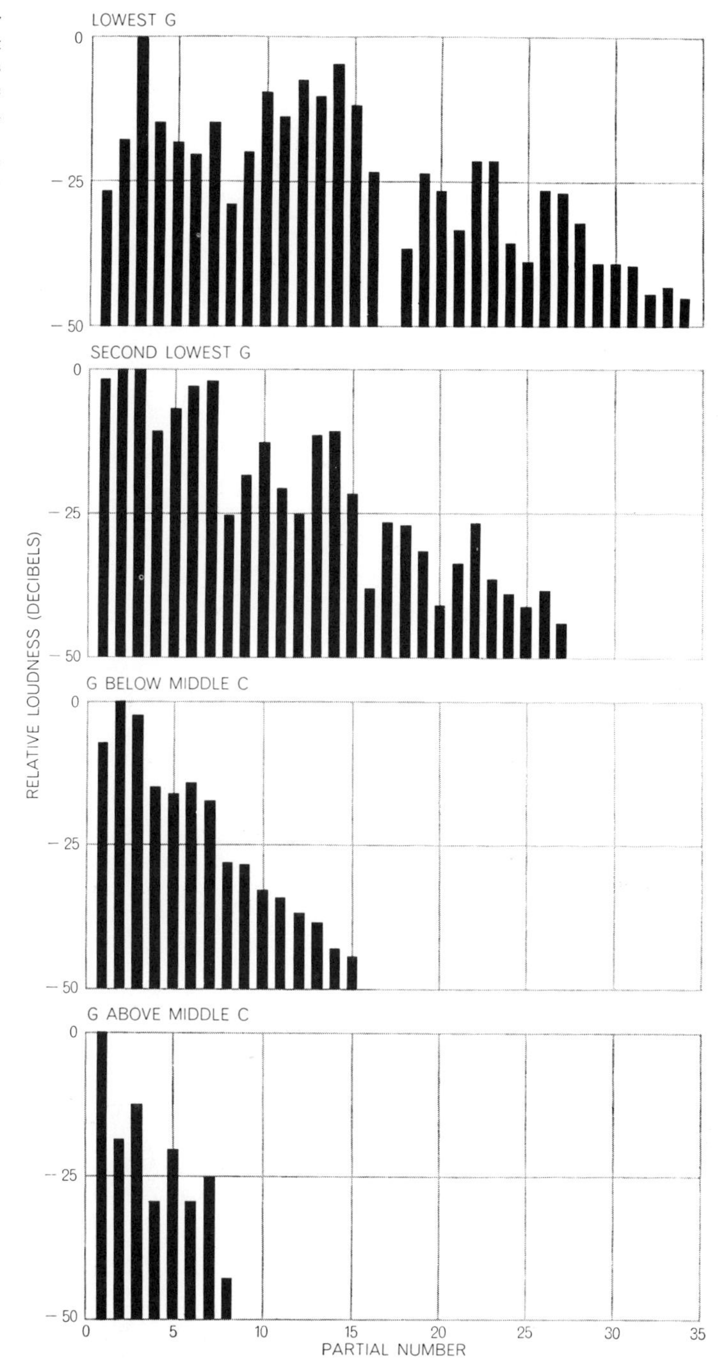


**PARTIAL STRUCTURES of the four lowest *G*'s on the piano keyboard are presented in these four bar charts. The partial structure of a musical tone is the variation in loudness of the partial tones that constitute that particular tone. The partial structures of these four notes were obtained by measuring the maximum response of each partial as it passed through an audio-frequency analyzer that was adjusted to pass only a narrow band of frequencies. The readings are given in relative decibel levels with the loudest partial of each note set at zero; the other partials can then be read as so many decibels below zero.**

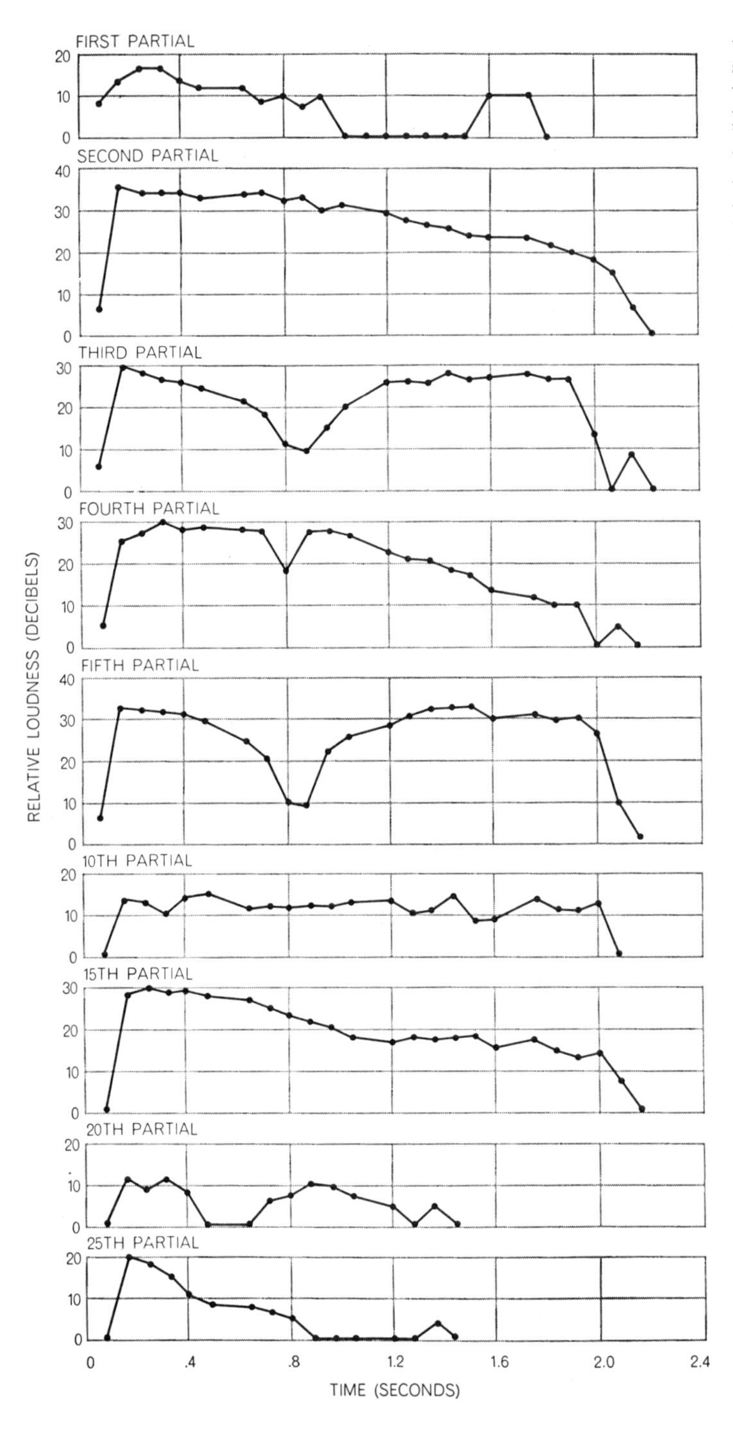


**DECAY CURVES for nine partial tones of the lowest *C* on the keyboard demonstrate that the partial tones of a piano note do not all die away from an initial maximum at the same rate. In some cases they may even increase in loudness before beginning to decay. For each curve 30 measurements were made at equal intervals of .08 second each. Obviously the partial structure of a tone at any given time is different from the structure at any other time.**

to vary the partial structure. In one test synthetic tones were built up in such a way that the loudness of each successive partial was a constant number of decibels less than that of the partial just below it in frequency. For example, if the difference was two decibels, then the second partial would be two decibels fainter than the first partial, the third partial would be four decibels fainter than the first, and so on. The limits of this "decibel difference" for obtaining a piano-like tone from the *G* above middle *C* were from five to 13 decibels per partial. In this case the acceptable range was narrower for lower notes and wider for higher notes. Tones produced when the decibel difference was below the lower limit were judged by the jury to sound "dead" or "hollow." Tones above the upper limit were described as sounding "like a harpsichord" or having "too much edge."

Synthetic tones that were built up of perfectly harmonic partials were described by the musicians and nonmusicians alike as lacking "warmth." Musicians generally use this term to suggest a certain quality of musical tone. For instance, a number of violins playing the same note at the same time produce a tone that is said to be warmer than that produced by a single violin playing alone. This quality appears to result from the fact that it is impossible for a number of musicians to play exactly in tune. When two different frequencies are sounded together, "beats" can be detected, the number of beats being equal to the difference in cycles per second between the two tones. A difference as small as two cycles per second between the fundamental frequencies of two tones can, however, produce much larger differences in the upper partials. Thus the beats that occur when two tones, each with a large number of partials, are sounded simultaneously can be quite complex. It is such beats between tones that account for the warmth produced by several violins or by a chord on the piano.

In the piano some additional warmth can be attributed to the fact that most of the hammers strike more than one string at a time. If the strings are not identically tuned, beats will occur between the high partials produced by each string. If such beats become too prominent, of course, the strings are declared to be out of tune.

The quality of a piano's tone also depends on several outside influences that

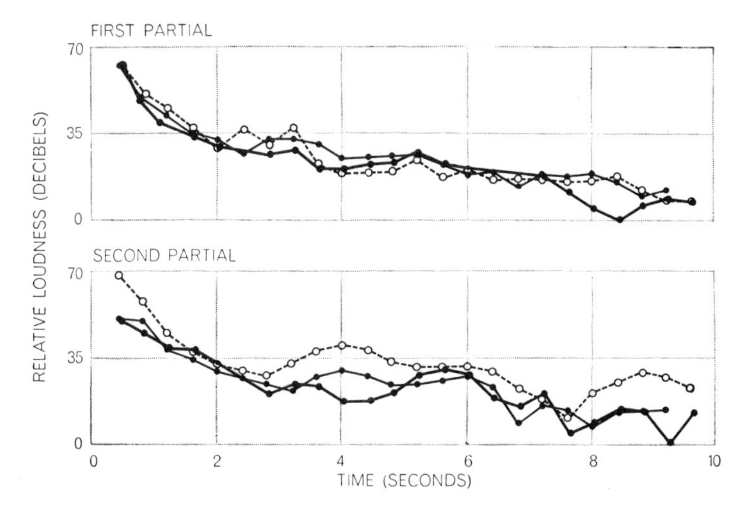


**ACOUSTICS OF ROOM in which the tones used in the decay-time analyses were recorded were shown by the author and his colleagues to have a negligible effect on the irregularities present in the decay curves of different partial tones of the same note. To obtain these curves the decay times for the first and second partials of the *G* above middle *C* were recorded in three different rooms: a normally reverberant studio (*broken black curves*), a very reverberant room (*solid black curves*) and an anechoic chamber (*solid colored curves*).**

are not usually considered intrinsic properties of a vibrating string. There is the impact noise of the hammer as it strikes the string, the mechanical noise of the damping pedals, the effect of the damper on the end of a tone, and the noise level of all the other strings, which are free to vibrate sympathetically when they are not damped. In early tests it became quite evident that our juries were using these factors as clues to distinguish the real tones from the synthetic ones.

The impact noise of the hammer is not as noticeable in the lower register as it is in the upper. For the high strings the impact noise is almost as loud as the tone itself. A similar noise had to be superposed on the synthetic tones before they could be effectively used in our tests. Preference tests were set up to see if piano tones without this noise were more acceptable musically than tones in which the noise was present. In general the individuals tested were satisfied with the quality of piano tones as it is, and any large departures from this quality were disparaged. Obviously this is the result of years of conditioning, of hearing piano tones produced by pianos. Some composers even write with this specific quality in mind. An example can be found in *Piano Concerto No. 2* of the American composer Edward MacDowell, in which certain passages are marked *martellato,* presumably to indicate that as much hammer noise as possible should be introduced into the passage.

The mechanical action of the pedals or dampers also makes a noise that has become part of the piano's tone. Moreover, there is a distinctive effect evident when the felt on the dampers is brought into contact with the string: the tone is not cut off cleanly but rather sounds as though it is being swallowed. The problems involved in trying to duplicate these "side effect" sounds can be eliminated by using piano tones that are produced by striking a key and allowing the sound to decay naturally by holding the key down. In this way all the other strings remain damped. The pedals are not used and only the damper of the struck string is disengaged by the action of the key.

Our studies have clearly shown that a complete description of the quality of the piano's tone must contain more than partial structure, attack time and decay time. Above all, the inharmonicity of the piano's tones must not be neglected. Some believe that the tone quality of the piano could be improved merely by making the tones more harmonic. Our tests have proved that synthetic tones built of harmonic partials lack the quality of warmth that is associated with the piano as it exists today.

# Editor's Comments on Papers 2 Through 6



This group of papers deals with objective characteristics of piano strings. The behavior of a vibrating string can be studied without great difficulty when it functions in isolation under carefully controlled conditions. When it functions along with many others in a typical piano, the complexity of its operation becomes much greater. It is difficult however, to establish experimental apparatus even with a monochord that provides ideal conditions. For example, boundary conditions may be such as to assume there is no vibration at the terminals of the speaking length of the vibrating string; but one may find considerably more audible sound than can be radiated from the wire alone.

Brook Taylor, an English mathematician, is credited as being the first to develop the correct formula for the frequency of a flexible vibrating string in terms of length, tension, and mass. His treatment of the vibratory motion of a stretched string, "De motu nervi tensi," *Phil. Trans. Roy. Soc., London,* **28,** 26–32 (1713) was translated by R. Bruce Lindsay as "Concerning the Motion of a Stretched String," *Acoustics: Historical and Philosophical Development,* Stroudsburg, Pa.: Dowden, Hutchinson & Ross, 1973, pp. 96–102. Dr. Lindsay also translated in the same volume (pp. 119–123) d'Alembert's "Recerches sur la courbe que forme une corde tendue mise en vibration," *Hist. Acad. Sci., Berlin,* **3,** 214–219 (1747) as "Investigation of the Curve Formed by a Vibrating String." It is believed that Jean le Rond, called d'Alembert, was the first to derive and publish the differential equation of wave propagation. He did this in connection with the vibrations of a stretched string.

In Paper 2, Kock refers to the work of others who contributed to the understanding of the struck stretched string. Still another prior contributor was R. N. Ghosh, "Elastic Impact of Pianoforte Hammer," *J. Acoust. Soc. Am.,* **7,** 254–260 (1936).

Considering the vibrating string as an electrical transmission line permits the knowledge gained regarding the characteristics of electrical circuits to be used in determining the characteristics of the piano string. Some persons skilled in the mathematics of electrical circuits will find Kock's analogy helpful. Others would prefer a different analogy, such as that presented by F. A. Firestone, "A New Analogy Between Mechanical and Electrical Systems," *J. Acoust. Soc. Am.,* **4,** 249–267 (1933). Firestone refers to the analogy where force through (dynes) ↔ emf across (volts) and velocity across (cmps) ↔ current through (amperes) as a left-handed analogy and develops an analogy where force through (dynes) ↔ current through (amperes) and velocity across (cmps) ↔ emf across (volts). This editor prefers the analogy developed by Firestone, and so did R. V. Sharman, "A Vibrating String Analogy with an Electrical Transmission Line," *J. Electronics Control,* **11**(3), 233 (1961).

As Sharman points out, analogies have some restrictions. For this reason, and others, many prefer to keep the mathematics of the vibrating string strictly in mechanical terms.

Note that Kock mentions that the partials of piano tones are "anharmonic" (p. 28) and states that this is undesirable as it impairs the tone quality. The reader should keep in mind that the proper amount of inharmonicity in piano tone partials uniformly distributed in the frequency range of the piano enhances the tones and is not undesirable.

W. E. Kock [E.E. (1932) and M.S. (physics, 1933), both University of Cincinnati; Ph.D. (physics, 1934), University of Berlin] was a Fellow at the Indian Institute of Science at Bangalore in 1936 while preparing this paper. He has served as Director of Electronic Research, Baldwin Piano Co., Director of Acoustics Research at Bell Telephone Laboratories, Director of the Bendix Research Laboratories, first Director of the National Aeronautics and Space Administration's Electronic Research Center, and most recently as Vice President and Chief Scientist of the Bendix Corporation. In 1971, he became Consultant to the corporation and a visiting Professor and Director of the Herman Schneider Research Laboratory at the University of Cincinnati. He has received many high honors and has been quite active in professional groups, as an educator, and as the author of four books.

Philip M. Morse, in *Vibration and Sound,* New York: McGraw-Hill, 1936, pp. 127–131, develops the mathematics related to the vibrations of a stiff string. (See Pages 166–170 in his second edition (1948).) He also deals with the behavior of a flexible string. His work serves as a useful background in the theoretical behavior of the piano string.

Paper 3 by Shankland and Coltman presents a study of stretched vibrating strings on a monochord. The experimental apparatus used in this paper takes into account variations in tension produced by the string's vibration. The fundamental frequency of the piano string varies during the decay of the tone and the change contributes to the "life" in the tone. The frequency of vibration decreases slightly immediately after the tone is initiated.

Robert S. Shankland (1908– ) [B.S. (1929), M.S. (1933), both in physics, Case School of Applied Science; Ph.D. (1935) University of Chicago] joined the Case faculty in 1930, was head of the Physics Department (1939–1958), and has been Ambrose Swasey Professor of Physics since 1941. He was director of the Underwater Sound Reference Laboratories at Orlando, Florida and Mountain Lakes, New Jersey, 1942–1946, and received the Presidential Certificate of Merit for this work. He served in other capacities for the U.S. Navy; has worked extensively in architectural acoustics; served for many years as a special acoustical consultant for the Cleveland Orchestra; and worked summers as physicist at the Radiation Laboratory, University of California at Berkley, and in research in neutron and reactor physics at the National Reactor Testing Station in Idaho Falls, Idaho.

Shankland has been Technical Director for the Atomic Energy Division of Phillips Petroleum Company and a physics consultant for the Standard Oil Company of Ohio. At present he is a consultant to the Idaho Nuclear Corporation. He is the author of *Atomic and Nuclear Physics* published by Macmillan.

John W. Coltman received the B.S. degree in physics (1937) at Case Institute of Technology. He did a thesis, "Vibration of Stretched Strings" (T–94) there. After receiving a Ph.D. degree (nuclear physics, 1941) at the University of Illinois, he joined the Westinghouse Electric Corporation where he now serves as Director of Research Planning for its Research Laboratories. His major research area was in electron tubes, and his invention of an image amplifier for X rays won him the Longstreth medal of the Franklin Institute and the Roentgen medal of Remscheid, Germany. He has directed research in a wide variety of areas and more recently has served to plan and coordinate central research in Westinghouse.

His interest in the flute as a player and collector led him to carry out as a hobby the acoustical research exemplified in Papers 25 and 26 in this volume.

Paper 4, "Observations on the Vibrations of Piano Strings" by Schuck and Young, covers a study of the partial frequencies and the decay characteristics of piano tone partials. Careful recording of the variation of amplitudes of partials in tones from single strings as they decayed was done. The decay characteristics of strings in unison groups will be discussed in Paper 7. The decay graphs differ greatly throughout a given piano and from one piano to another. The complex relationship of the relative magnitudes of partials as they decay contributes to the "life" and uniqueness in a piano tone.

Undulations in the magnitude of a given partial occur in some instances as the tone dies away. Note for example, the decay characteristic of the fundamental of $F_3$ string in Figure 3, p. 41. This causes an audible beat if the frequency of the undulation is slow enough. The piano tuner using the aural method of tuning will compare the frequency of this fundamental with that of an upper partial of a tone lower in the scale. He will be listening for the beat frequency produced by the two nearly coincident partials and will need to differentiate that beat from the one that may be audible when the $F_3$ string alone is sounding.

Fluctuations in the amplitude of the decay curve of a given partial can be due to one or more of several causes. The authors mention the rotation of the plane of vibration and the possible transfer of energy from one mode to another. Other possible causes include nonuniformity in stiffness, or mass, of a string (primarily found in wound strings); transfer of energy to other strings or portions of the piano; conditions at the terminals of the speaking length of a string; inadequate damping, or muting, of other strings in the unison group being checked.

The authors show what has often been referred to as the "Railsback curve" on p. 47. Because this graph represents the average tuning of 16 pianos by O. L. Railsback, some have assumed that any piano tuned accordingly would be well tuned. This is not likely to be true since pianos vary so much. Well-tuned pianos must be tuned according to the individual characteristics of each piano and not by some general formula or graph.

O. Hugo Schuck (1909–1972) [B.S. (1931), M.S. (1932), E.E. (1938), all University of Pennsylvania] was a Fellow in the Acoustical Society of America and in the Institute of Electrical Engineers, and was a member of the American Institute of Aeronautics and Astronautics.

Schuck had a varied and useful work history. He joined C. G. Conn, Ltd. in 1937 as an Acoustical Engineer. While there, he developed the Chromatic Stroboscope, invented by Railsback, into a practical frequency-measuring instrument. This device is still being manufactured under the trade name "Stoboconn" and has proven to be very useful in music education, piano tuning, industrial applications, and research. Several papers in this volume mention its use. Among his other accomplishments while with Conn he initiated the investigation of means for measuring the input acoustical impedance of wind instruments and the program to develop an electronic organ line. These projects were carried on by others when Hugo was asked to join the Harvard Underwater Sound Laboratory in 1941, where he made valuable contributions in World War II work.

He became a Staff Member of the MIT Radiation Laboratory of the Office of Scientific Research and Development when the underwater sound project was completed and then joined Minneapolis Honeywell Regulator Company as a Senior Research Engineer in 1945. While there, he became Chief of Aeronautical Research in 1946, Director of Aeronautical Research in 1954, and Director of Research of the Military Products Group in 1960. He served as Visiting Professor of Aeronautical and Astronautical Engineering, Stanford University, on special leave from Honeywell, Inc., 1966–1967.

In 1967, Schuck became Founder and Director, Office of Control Theory and Application, NASA Electronics Research Center, where he served until his death.

He was active in professional societies and advisory groups, and was awarded many honors including the Navy Certificate of Appreciation for his World War II work. He was the author of 12 technical papers and the inventor in 37 patents.

Robert W. Young (1908–      ) [B.S. (1930), physics, Ohio University (Athens); Ph.D. (1934), physics, University of Washington (Seattle)] served as Teaching Fellow, University Of Washington (1930–1934); Physicist and Head of Experimental Dept., C. G. Conn, Ltd. (1934–1941); in Chief Listening Section, University of California, Division of War Research (1946); Head, Sonar Division, System Engineering Dept., Naval Electronics Laboratory (1946–1949); Consulting Staff and Superintending Scientist, NEL (1949–1959); Acoustics Consultant and Technical Director, NEL (1959–1967); Technical Consultant to the Technical Director, San Diego Division, Naval Undersea Research and Development Center (1967–1970); Senior Scientist and Consultant, Acoustics Division and Ocean Acoustics Division, Naval Undersea Center (1970–      ).

Young has received many honors, including Phi Beta Kappa, Office of Scientific Research and Development Certificate of Merit, Commendation for Services Rendered to Submarine Force–Pacific, and Ohio

University Alumni Certificate of Merit. He has been active in many professional groups, is a Fellow in the Acoustical Society of America, and has served as its Vice President (1953–1954), President (1960–1961), and Associate Editor of its Journal since 1945. He is the author of many publications on acoustics.

In Paper 5, Harvey Fletcher carries on the study with "Normal Vibration Frequencies of a Stiff Piano String" and includes the consideration of the wrapped strings used for the bass strings of the piano where space limitations do not allow the use of plain strings.

It should be kept in mind that wound strings vary considerably in construction. The materials used, the spacing, tightness, and length of the winding may vary. The steel core wire must be malleable enough to be swaged at the winding ends in order to prevent the unwinding of the wrap. Plain strings can be made with harder wire if desired. Also, the end supports can have appreciable effect upon the inharmonicity. For these reasons, the experimental values of inharmonicity may deviate from the theoretical values.

If the length of the wound portion of a string is enough shorter than the speaking length of the string the weak partials mentioned on p. 57 can have a substantial effect upon the quality of the tone produced.

Harvey Fletcher (1884–        ), distinguished scientist and engineer, is noted for his contributions in acoustics, electrical engineering, speech, medicine, music, atomic physics, sound pictures, and education.

Born and reared in Provo, Utah, of pioneer parents, he received his early training at Brigham Young University and graduated in 1907 (B.S.). Continuing study at the University of Chicago, he, with Robert A. Millikan, measured the charge on an electron.

Upon completion of his studies at the University of Chicago, he was awarded a Ph.D. summa cum laude (1911), which was the first ever granted by the Physics Department at that University. He returned to BYU to serve as Chairman of the Physics Department for five years. He then joined the Western Electric Company in New York to do research in sound. After appointment as Director of all Physical Research at Bell Telephone Laboratories he published 51 papers, 19 patents, and two books which are accepted treatises.

He served as Professor of Electrical Engineering at Columbia University, 1949–1952; First Chairman of the Engineering Department at Brigham Young University, 1953; Dean of new College of Physical and Engineering Sciences at BYU, 1954. He supervised sound equipment for theaters in the Harris Fine Arts Center, and designed sound equipment for the Palmyra Pageant, 1961. He is still doing research in sound.

He helped found the Acoustical Society of America and became its first president. He was elected honorary member of this Society—an honor shared only by Thomas A. Edison.

Few men of American science have been so widely recognized with high honors. To name all his citations and honors would require several pages.

Paper 6, "Influence of Irregular Patterns in the Inharmonicity of Piano Tone Partials upon Tuning Practice," by the editor, was presented at the Europiano Kongress in West Berlin, Germany, May 1965. It was published in the *Congress Report* Frankfurt am Main: Fördergemeinschaft Klavier, 1966. The English version is on pages 133–136 and 143–154 and the German version on pages 137–154. A German version was included in *Junghanns Der Piano und Flügelbau,* Frankfurt am Main: Verlag Das Musikinstrument, 1971, pp. 100–110. A corrected condensation of the English version is included here. It discusses the problem tuners have with pianos having a poor scale design.

It is difficult to tune a piano properly because so much skill and good judgement are required. When the Stroboconn first became available as a tool for measuring transient frequencies accurately [see R. W. Young and Allen Loomis, "Theory of the Chromatic Stroboscope," *J. Acoust. Soc. Am.,* **10,** 112–118 (1938)], many thought it would then become possible to do better piano tuning than could be done aurally. The Stroboconn helped reveal the problem discussed in this paper and many tuners found that although a visual aid was helpful the ear is the final tool in evaluating tuning work. Therefore, compromises must be made in good tuning practice and the trained ear is vital in judgements made regarding the compromises.

Tuners who do not understand the problem discussed in this paper often attribute tuning problems to unrelated causes.

# 2

*Copyright © 1937 by the Acoustical Society of America*

Reprinted from *J. Acoust. Soc. Am.*, **8**, 227–233 (1937)

## The Vibrating String Considered as an Electrical Transmission Line

WINSTON E. KOCK*
*The Indian Institute of Science, Bangalore, India*
(Received August 12, 1936)

An analogy is drawn between the piano string and an electrical transmission line, utilizing a different correlation than is customary in usual electroacoustical analogs. The current in the line is compared with the displacement and the voltage is compared with the momentum. With this correspondence the highly developed treatment of transmission lines becomes applicable to the piano string. The various cases discussed include: Open circuited line with and without attenuation (i.e., ideal and actual string with ends rigidly fixed), terminated line (string affixed to bridge of soundboard), electrical impulse introduced (impact of piano hammer). A relation is derived giving the optimum position of striking point for a given ratio of hammer mass to string mass, and this is shown to agree with the results of George and Beckett. The appearance of the $n$th harmonic when the string is struck at $1/n$th of its length is explained, likewise the advantages of the modern practice of high string tensions. Conclusions are drawn concerning impedance matching (string to soundboard) and the velocity of propagation for different frequencies.

### 1. INTRODUCTION

THE theory of the action of the piano hammer and string was first set forth by Helmholtz and extended by Kaufman,[1] Raman and Banerji,[2] Das[3] and others.[4] In attempting to take into account as many factors as possible, the more recent extensions have become rather involved, and it was decided to attack the problem from a somewhat different angle. By making certain changes in the correspondences usually found in electroacoustical analysis, it has been possible to consider the piano string as equivalent to an electrical transmission line. Such an analogy has been known for some time[5] but it has not been developed to the fullest extent, possibly due to the required change in correlations mentioned above. In this paper the details of the analogy are set forth and various conclusions are drawn which are interpretable either in terms of the transmission line or vibrating string. The notations used are listed in Table I.

TABLE I.

| *Transmission Line* | *Piano String* |
|---|---|
| $i$ = Current | $y$ = Displacement |
| $E$ = Voltage at a point on the line. | $p$ = Momentum of unit length of string. |
| $L$ = Inductance per unit length. | $\rho$ = Mass per unit length. |
| $C$ = Capacity per unit length. | $C$ = Compliance per unit length $=1/T$. ($T$ = Total tension on the string.) |
| $L_h$ = Equivalent inductance of hammer. | $m$ = Effective mass of hammer. |
| $L_t = lL$ = Total inductance of line. | $M = \rho l$ = Total mass of string. |
| $l$ = Length of line or string. | $a$ = Distance of striking point from near bridge. |
| $v_0$ = Velocity of propagation. | |
| $\omega = 2\pi f$ = Periodicity. | $\lambda$ = Wave-length $= v_0/f$. |

### 2. DERIVATION OF THE WAVE EQUATION, IDEAL STRING

Consider a string stretched between two rigid supports and assume that there are no frictional or dissipative forces. A wave front $W$ in Fig. 1 is propagated along the string $S$ in the direction of increasing $x$ as shown by the arrow.

At $x$ the displacement is $y$, at $x+dx$ it is

$$y-(\partial y/\partial x)dx.$$

The difference in displacement along $dx$ is therefore $-(\partial y/\partial x)dx$ and is proportional to the displacing force, mass x acceleration $=\partial(mv)/\partial t$. The factor of proportionality is called the compliance $C$ and as it is per unit length, for the length $dx$ it is $Cdx$. For a thin string, considered perfectly flexible, this is simply the reciprocal of the tension $dx/T$ and we therefore have

$$-\frac{\partial y}{\partial x}dx=(Cdx)\frac{\partial(mv)}{\partial t}$$

* Of the Research Staff of the Baldwin Piano Company, Cincinnati, Ohio.

[1] W. Kaufmann, Ann. d. Physik **54**, 675 (1895).

[2] C. V. Raman and B. Banerji, Proc. Roy. Soc. **A97**, 99 (1920).

[3] P. Das, Proc. Ind. Ass. Science **1**, 13 (1921).

[4] For references see *Handbuch der Physik*, Bd. 8 Akustik, chap. 5, pp. 177 ff.

[5] For example, Pupin utilized the correspondence between a string with equally spaced loads and a telephone cable with inductances introduced at equal distances in his theory of loading in communication lines.

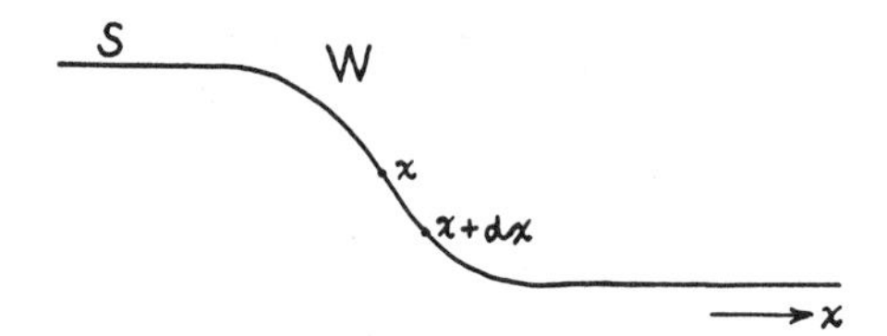


FIG. 1. Propagation of a wave front along the string.

or
$$-\frac{\partial y}{\partial x}=\frac{1}{T}\frac{\partial p}{\partial t}. \quad (1)$$

The momentum of the point $x$ is $p$ and at $x+dx$ it is

$$p-(\partial p/\partial x)dx,$$

so that for the element $dx$, the momentum is $-(\partial p/\partial x)dx$. This is equal to the mass of the element times its velocity of displacement, that is

$$-\frac{\partial p}{\partial x}dx=(\rho dx)\frac{\partial y}{\partial t}$$

or
$$-\partial p/\partial x=\rho\partial y/\partial t. \quad (2)$$

Differentiating (1) with respect to $x$ and (2) with respect to $t$ and eliminating $p$, we have

$$\partial^2 y/\partial x^2=(\rho/T)(\partial^2 y/\partial t^2), \qquad v_0=(T/\rho)^{\frac{1}{2}}. \quad (3)$$

If in the above derivation the electrical terms are substituted for their mechanical equivalents, the usual method of deriving the wave equation for the transmission line is obtained;[6] the equation for the current is then

$$\partial^2 i/\partial x^2=LC(\partial^2 i/\partial t^2), \qquad v_0=(LC)^{-\frac{1}{2}}. \quad (4)$$

It is now seen why the customary electro-acoustical correspondence displacement ↔ charge and velocity ↔ current are not applicable here. Eq. (3) is the equation of a string with ends rigidly fixed, therefore at $x=0$ and $x=l$ the displacement is zero. Similarly in an open circuited transmission line at $x=0$ and $x=l$ the current is zero, so that for the exact analog, displacement and current must be correlated. To arrive at the usual correspondence, the mechanical variables displacement and momentum in this case must be differentiated with respect to time. Then displacement ↔ current becomes velocity ↔ current and momentum ↔ voltage becomes force $((\partial/\partial t)(mv))$ ↔ voltage.

[6] See, for example, Fleming, *The Propagation of Electric Currents*, 4th edition (Constable, 1927).

### 3. Actual String with Ends Rigidly Fixed

This case corresponds to an open circuited line with attenuation and is best solved by assuming the current and voltage to be simply periodic functions of time[7] $i=I\epsilon^{j\omega t}$ and $e=E\epsilon^{j(\omega t+\theta)}$, where $j=\sqrt{-1}$ and $\theta$ is the phase angle difference.

Since any impulse (such as the hammer impact) can be analyzed into a series of pendular Fourier components, no loss in generality is suffered by this process. With attenuation present, the impedance $Z$ and admittance $Y$ will contain, in addition to the reactance introduced by $L$ and the capacitance introduced by $C$, frictional (resistance) terms, and Eq. (4) becomes $\partial^2 I/\partial x^2=\gamma^2 I$, where $\gamma=(ZY)^{\frac{1}{2}}$ is the propagation constant, and $Z$, $Y$, $I$ and $\gamma$ will in general be complex.

The real and imaginary parts of $\gamma=\alpha+j\beta$ are called the attenuation constant $\alpha$ and the wave-length constant $\beta$. The first is so called because it is a measure of the decay of energy (i.e., attentuation) as the wave moves along the line, the second because

$$2\pi/\beta=\lambda, \text{ the wave-length.}$$

Ray[8] has discussed the case of the velocity of propagation for different frequencies on a string with no dissipation. An examination of $\beta$ indicates that, for the actual string, frictional forces preclude the possibility of equal velocities at all frequencies. For when dissipation is present the velocity of propagation $v_0=\lambda f=\omega/\beta$ does not reduce to $(LC)^{-\frac{1}{2}}$ as in case (1), but remains dependent on $\omega$ due to the fact that resistance terms are present in $\beta$. The result is that the higher frequencies are propagated with greater velocity and since the wave-lengths for the successive overtones are exact integral multiples of the fundamental (i.e., the modes of vibration of the string are fixed), their frequencies are anharmonic to the fundamental.[9] This is undesirable as it impairs the tone quality.

[7] For a treatment of the transmission line, see Fleming, reference 6 and Everitt, *Communication Engineering* (McGraw-Hill, 1932), Chaps. 5 and 6.

[8] S. Ray, Phys. Rev. **28**, 229 (1926).

[9] Observed by W. Lange, Hochfreq. Technik u. Elekt. Akustik **45**, 165 (1935).

This condition is also objectionable in electrical communication,[10] and is overcome by the process of loading or by a change over from underground cable to overhead lines. The latter procedure results in an increased separation between wires which increases the inductance and decreases the capacity. This is equivalent to increasing the string tension and mass per unit length of the string and is one of the reasons for the more pleasing quality of modern pianos, made possible by the introduction of massive iron frames to permit greater string tensions and masses.

The quantity $Z_0=(Z/Y)^{\frac{1}{2}}$ is called the characteristic impedance and is that impedance with which a line must be terminated to prevent reflection, that is, it is the termination impedance giving maximum energy transfer. This quantity is seen to depend upon the constants of the line and in order to transmit the same power at lower current, it is necessary to increase this characteristic impedance, for example by decreasing the capacity. In terms of the vibrating string, this means that an increased string tension will permit the same energy transmission with lower amplitudes of displacement. Lower displacement means less deviation from linearity (anharmonic overtones) and less energy dissipated in frictional forces (corresponding to copper loss being proportional to current *squared*) and indicates another reason for the practice of high string tensions.

The input impedance of a line to a given frequency depends upon the length of line; for an open circuited dissipationless line this dependence is given by the relation

$$Z_l=Z_0\frac{\cosh j\beta l}{\sinh j\beta l}=-j\left(\frac{L}{C}\right)^{\frac{1}{2}}\cot\frac{2\pi l}{\lambda}, \qquad (5)$$

where $l$ is the length of the line and the $j$ indicates that the impedance is a pure reactance. This relation is shown graphically in Fig. 2; the negative and positive values signify capacitative and inductive reactances respectively.

For the fundamental frequency of a piano string, $l$ is $\lambda/2$ and it is observed from Fig. 2 that in this case the impedance at the center of the string is zero ($l=\lambda/4$), that is, a voltage (hammer blow) applied at that point would produce the maximum current (displacement).[11] As the position of the striking point is moved away from the center, the impedance increases so that the displacement becomes less for a given voltage and finally reaches zero at the rigid ends. For the first partial, the length of the string $l$ equals $\lambda$, so that for this frequency the center of the string presents infinite impedance and in this ideal case a hammer blow at that point would produce no vibration of that frequency.

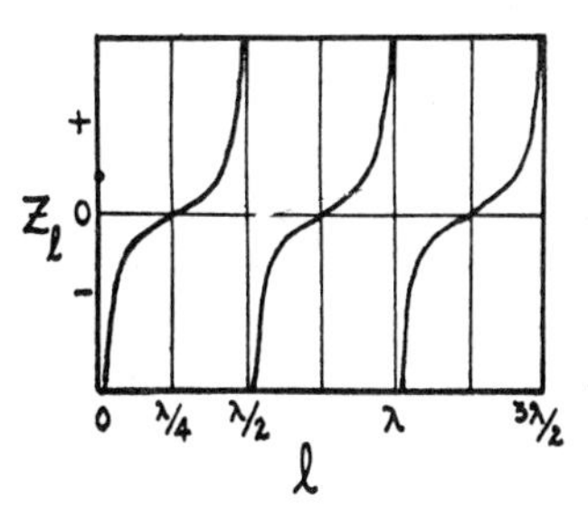


FIG. 2. Variation of impedance with length of line.

In the actual piano string, however, attenuation is present, and the formula for the magnitude of the impedance becomes

$$Z_l=Z_0\left(\frac{\sinh^2\alpha l+\cos^2\beta l}{\sinh^2\alpha l+\sin^2\beta l}\right)^{\frac{1}{2}}.$$

It is seen that only at $l=0$, i.e., at the ends of the string, is $Z_l$ infinite, for as $l$ increases, $\sinh\alpha l$ continually becomes larger so that although $\sin^2\beta l$ may continue to become zero at the nodes, the total denominator is always different from zero. Thus $Z_l$ is always finite and the actual string will accept energy of a given frequency even at the nodes of that frequency.

In practice, the hammer is placed at about 1/7th to 1/9th the length of the string for reasons which will later be observed. For an ideal string this would result in a suppression of the 7th, 8th or 9th harmonic, and Helmholtz suggested this as the reason for such a position. However, these harmonics are not objectionable, in fact they are definitely present in all good piano tones. One result of placing the striking point nearer the

[10] For example, if the velocity of propagation is dependent on frequency, the high harmonics of a square wave telegraphic signal arrive at the receiving end first and cause the pulse to drag out. This necessitates a slower sending rate and delays the transmission procedure.

[11] In part (5), where the effect of the hammer blow is treated more rigorously, it will be observed that other factors are instrumental here.

FIG. 3. Equivalent terminating impedance of a piano string.

fixed bridge is the augmentation of such overtones. This is because the free bridge corresponds to a dissipative effect and, for the wave reflected from this far bridge (the important wave as far as energy is concerned), the attenuation $\alpha$ and likewise $\sinh^2 \alpha l$ would be larger than would be the case were it reflected from the rigid bridge. The impedance of the string to these partials is therefore less and their amplitude accordingly greater.

### 4. STRING ATTACHED TO BRIDGE OF SOUNDBOARD

This case is the analog of a transmission line terminated with an impedance. For maximum transfer of energy, this terminating impedance should be equal to the characteristic impedance. For a vibrating string with negligible damping,

$$Z_0 = (L/C - \omega^2 L^2/4)^{\frac{1}{2}}.$$

When the second term is the larger, $Z_0$ is imaginary; however, the high values of string tension render this term negligible and $Z_0$ is therefore always real, i.e., $Z_0 = (L/C)^{\frac{1}{2}}$, which means that the terminating impedance should be a pure resistance.

For an acoustic radiatior such as the soundboard of a piano, the accession to inertia, which is the additional inertial mass due to the reciprocating flow of air in its neighborhood,[12] can be neglected, due to the fact that the soundboard does not vibrate as a complete unit, but acts somewhat as an acoustic baffle to its various vibrational modes. The reactive component therefore disappears and the acoustic impedance of the air reduces to a pure resistance. The remaining components of the load impedance on the string comprise the compliance, mass, and internal friction of the bridge and the soundboard. The termination is represented in Fig. 3, where $C$, $L$ and $R_i$ are the bridge and soundboard components and $R_r$ is the radiation resistance.

The bridge is made of very hard wood to minimize frictional losses in it, and due to the heavy string tension, it presents a small compliance. The mass $L$ is kept low by using light wood ribbed for strength; this has the effect of increasing the damping coefficient $R/2L$ and thereby reducing resonance effects and their accompanying undesirable tone quality caused by the presence of formant regions. Likewise $R_r$ is made high by increasing the size of the soundboard; this also increases the efficiency by making the useful component of the load resistance large in comparison with the dissipative frictional effects in the bridge and soundboard.

It is seen that the condenser $C$ discriminates against the low frequencies and this accounts for the low intensities of the fundamental in the bass section of the piano. For compactness in upright and small grand pianos, the bridges for the notes of the middle and bass registers are affixed to the soundboard in such a manner that the free vibrating area for the low tones is less than that of a concert grand. Furthermore the end sections of the deep bass strings between the bridge and hitch pins are shortened; this simultaneously shortens the distance between the bridge and the soundboard edge (where it is rigidly supported). All three of these factors reduce the freedom of vibration of that portion of the soundboard which is effective for the radiation of these low frequencies, so that the compliance $C$ is smaller and the low frequency response poorer. This is one of the reasons for the excellent bass quality of a concert grand piano, where $C$ is made as large as is practically feasible. The so-called "floating bridge"[13] is simply a device for applying the pressure of the bridge more towards the center of the soundboard in order to increase the compliance and improve the bass response.

The combination $C$, $L$ and $R$ in Fig. 3 represents an impedance possessing a broad resonance region, and the position of this region and the sharpness of resonance will vary for different notes of the scale according as the compliance, effective mass and radiation resistance of the soundboard varies for these different notes. For the treble register the effective radiative area will be less but the effective mass will not decrease in

[12] N. W. McLachlan, *Loud Speakers* (Oxford, 1934), p. 54.

[13] Glazebrook, *Dictionary of Applied Physics* (Macmillan, 1923), p. 467.

equal proportion due to the presence of the nearly constant mass of the bridge. Now the radiation resistance of a piston at these treble frequencies is approximately[14] $r=\rho_0 cA$, where $\rho_0$ is the normal density of the air, $C$ is the velocity of sound in air, and $A$ is the area. Thus for decreased $A$ the resistance will decrease and the decrement $\delta=R/2fL$ ($f$=frequency) of the circuit of Fig. 3 will decrease with frequency. Inasmuch as a filter circuit becomes more effective as the decrement decreases, the high notes of a piano should be lacking in overtones due to this filtering action, and such is found to be the case.

## 5. Analysis of the Hammer Impact

The imparting of energy to the string by means of a hammer impact is analogous to connecting across a transmission line an inductance possessing an e.m.f. between its terminals. The momentum of the hammer $mv$ corresponds to the voltage on the inductance $L_h(di/dt)$. For a resilient hammer a condenser would be in series with the inductance and a nonelastic compression of the felt on impact would be equivalent to a leak across the condenser.

As an example of the simplicity in treatment which can be introduced by means of the electrical analogy, an analysis will be given of the optimum position of impact for a given hammer mass. It will be observed that by means of a straightforward procedure, this problem, for which no satisfactory solution has previously been found, can quickly be solved to yield an equation which agrees quite well with experimental observations.

For simplicity we assume an ideal string struck by a hard hammer. The equivalent circuit is shown in Fig. 4. At the instant of impact, switch $S$ is closed and the voltage $L_h(di/dt)$ is impressed across the line. Current waves travel in both directions and are reflected from the ends with a reversal in phase. The longer the inductance is connected to the circuit, the more energy it can impart to the line, up to the point when the reflections from the ends reach it. Since the reflected waves have reversed their phase, they will tend to restore energy to the inductance;

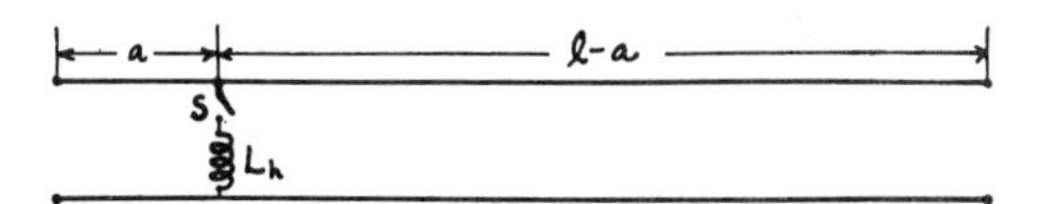


Fig. 4. Equivalent circuit for representing hammer impact.

therefore if the switch is opened just before this occurs, maximum transfer of energy is obtained. The reflected wave from the short end reaches the inductance very soon in comparison with the time of reflection from the far end, and the time of contact would be quite short if the inductance were then removed, and the energy transfer small. The desired effect is therefore obtained by allowing the reflections from the short end to reverse the voltage on the inductance (reverse the direction of motion of hammer) and to have switch $S$ open (to have the hammer quit the string) just before the reflected wave from the far end reaches it. The optimum time of contact is thus equal to twice the length $l$-$a$ divided by the velocity of propagation. That is

$$[t_c]_{\text{opt.}}=2(l-a)(LC)^{\frac{1}{2}}. \qquad (6)$$

For a given initial velocity, the time of contact of the hammer depends upon its mass, the mass of the string, and the position of impact; the heavier the hammer, the longer the duration of impact, and the further the point of contact is moved towards the near bridge, the greater the effect of the tension of the string and the shorter the contact time. These relations are implicitly contained in the expression for the impedance of the open circuited line,

$$Z_l=-jZ_0 \cot(2\pi l/\lambda). \qquad (5a)$$

From the above consideration the hammer will have left the string by the time the wave reflected from the far end reaches it, therefore the impedance which is effective in this case is that of the short end of the line,

$$Z_a=-j(L/C)^{\frac{1}{2}} \cot(\pi a/l). \qquad (\lambda=2l.)$$

Since, for $a<(l/2)$, $\cot(\pi a/l)$ is positive, the $-j$ indicates that the impedance of the short end will always be a pure condensive reactance, and the equivalent condenser $C_a$ is obtained from

$$Z_a=1/j\omega C_a=-j(L/C)^{\frac{1}{2}} \cot(\pi a/l).$$

[14] I. B. Crandall, *Vibrating Systems and Sound* (Macmillan, 1927), p. 149.

Recalling that

$$\omega = 2\pi f = 2\pi v_0/\lambda = 2\pi(1/LC)^{\frac{1}{2}}/2l = \pi/l(LC)^{\frac{1}{2}},$$

we obtain $$C_a = (lC/\pi)\tan(\pi a/l). \qquad (7)$$

We can thus replace the picture of a transmission line with its reflections by its equivalent, an inductance and a condenser connected in parallel. Then instead of many reflections there will be one surge of current which will reach a maximum and return to zero, and, if the inductance remained connected, the energy would continue to oscillate back and forth between inductance and condenser. Likewise the voltage $L_h(di/dt)$, a maximum at the instant the switch is closed, goes to zero as the hammer reverses its direction and becomes increasingly negative up to the point where the hammer leaves the string. The time of contact is thus the time of one-half cycle of the oscillatory circuit composed of $L_h$ and $C_a$. The natural frequency of this circuit is $f = 1/2\pi(L_hC_a)^{\frac{1}{2}}$, so that one-half the period is

$$t_c = \pi(L_hC_a)^{\frac{1}{2}}. \qquad (8)$$

The relation giving the position of the hammer to produce maximum energy transfer is obtained by equating $t_c$ to its optimum value as given in Eq. (6). We then have

$$2(l-a)(LC)^{\frac{1}{2}} = \pi(L_hC_a)^{\frac{1}{2}},$$

which with (7) gives

$$2(l-a)(LC)^{\frac{1}{2}} = \pi\left(\frac{L_hlC}{\pi}\tan\frac{\pi a}{l}\right)^{\frac{1}{2}}.$$

This can finally be written

$$\frac{4}{\pi}\left(1-\frac{a}{l}\right)^2 \cot\frac{\pi a}{l} = \frac{L_h}{L_l} = \frac{m}{M}, \qquad (9)$$

where $L_l = lL = M$ is the total mass of the string. This relation between $m/M$ and $a/l$ can be interpreted either as the optimum position of impact for a given ratio of hammer mass to string mass, or as the optimum hammer mass for a given striking point.

In Fig. 5 is plotted the curve of $m/M$ *versus* $a/l$ for maximum energy transfer. The smooth line is the theoretical curve and the circles are the points as found experimentally by George and

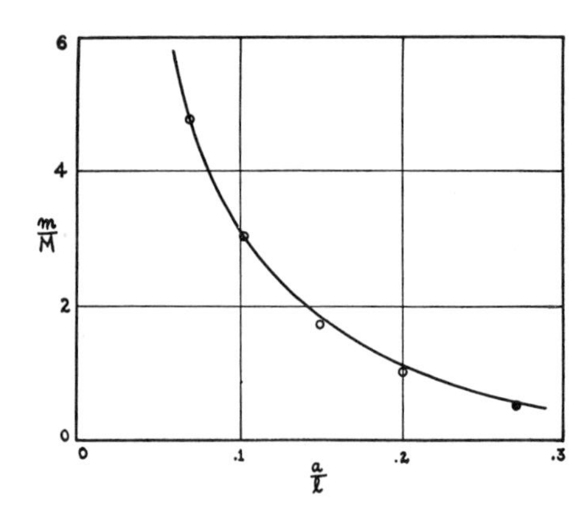


FIG. 5. Curve showing the relation between $m/M$ and $a/l$ for maximum energy transfer. The heavy line is the predicted curve and the circles are the experimental results of George and Beckett.

Beckett for various values of $m/M$;[15] since they employed in their experiments hard hammers and rigid bridges (approximating an ideal string), the conditions closely correspond to the case here analyzed and it is observed that the agreement is quite good.

From the curve it follows that, for values of $m/M$ which are used in practice, the striking point should roughly fall between one-seventh and one-ninth the length of the string, and this is actually the case.

It is interesting to note that, for small values of $a/l$, formula (9) reduces to the approximate one obtainable by considering the hammer as an additional weight attached to the string at a distance $a$ from the near bridge. Then the equation of motion is approximately

$$md^2y/dt^2 = -Ty/a, \qquad (y = \text{displacement}),$$

so that the frequency of oscillation is

$$f = (1/2\pi)(T/ma)^{\frac{1}{2}},$$

and one-half the period is

$$t_c = \pi(ma/T)^{\frac{1}{2}}.$$

Setting this equal to the optimum time of contact,

$$[t_c]_{\text{opt.}} = 2(l-a)(\rho/T)^{\frac{1}{2}} = \pi(ma/T)^{\frac{1}{2}},$$

[15] W. H. George and H. E. Beckett, Proc. Roy. Soc. **A114**, 111 (1927).

we arrive at the expression

$$\frac{m}{M}=\frac{(4/\pi)(1-(a/l))^2}{(\pi a/l)}. \quad (10)$$

This corresponds to Eq. (9) for small values of $a/l$, since in that case

$$\cot\frac{\pi a}{l}=\frac{1}{\tan(\pi a/l)}\approx\frac{1}{(\pi a/l)}.$$

For large values of $a/l$, however, formula (10) breaks down, due to the fact that in its derivation the effect of the mass of the short end of the string was not taken into account. In the more rigorous derivation, this factor entered into expression (5) from which the equivalent total capacity $C_a$ (corresponding to $a/T$ above) could then be more accurately obtained.

## 6. Summary of Results

The conclusions to be drawn from the foregoing analysis may be summarized as follows:

1. By increasing the string tension and mass per unit length, more uniform velocities of propagation of the various partials are obtained, and the distortion caused by the presence of anharmonic overtones is reduced. The increase of mass, however, is limited, due to the fact that the string eventually vibrates as a bar and again introduces anharmonic distortion. Greater string tensions also reduce attenuation and therefore permit greater resounding power; furthermore they permit the transmission of energy with less amplitude of vibration and thus again reduce nonlinearity and anharmonic distortion.
2. The $n$th harmonic can be excited by an impact at $1/n$th the length of string whenever attenuation is present in the string.
3. An increase in the compliance of the string termination (bridge and soundboard) for the lower registers results in better bass response.
4. A decrease in the effective mass or compliance of the treble register would tend towards increased brilliance.
5. For any ratio of hammer mass to string mass, the proper point of impact for maximum loudness can be calculated for the ideal case (curve of Fig. 5).

## Acknowledgment

I should like to express my appreciation for the guidance of Sir C. V. Raman in this work.

# 3

Copyright© 1939 by the Acoustical Society of America

Reprinted from *J. Acoust. Soc. Am.*, **10**(3), 161–166 (1939)

## The Departure of the Overtones of a Vibrating Wire From a True Harmonic Series

R. S. Shankland and J. W. Coltman
*Case School of Applied Science, Cleveland, Ohio*

(Received July 23, 1938)

### Introduction

THE vibration frequencies of stretched wires and strings are subject to several disturbing factors, but it has been found that in the strings of musical instruments the stiffness and amplitude of vibration produce the largest effects. These have been studied with a specially designed monochord and electrical circuits arranged for measuring the changes in frequency due to the amplitude of vibration, and due to stiffness when the wires are supported by bridges. Experiments with large amplitudes of vibration have been compared with theoretical deductions made by the method of perturbations. The comparison of theory and experiment gives a method of determining a bridge parameter which may be correlated with the several types of bridge supports used in musical instruments. Vibrations of very small amplitude may be studied with the apparatus and have been measured to determine the effects of stiffness when the string is terminated by bridges. The results show that the effects are intermediate between the two limiting cases that admit of a rigorous solution: that of a clamped end; and an end with no restoring couple. This is not in accord with the supposition advanced by Rayleigh[1] and others that a wire stretched over bridges is closely represented by the second condition. The combined influence of amplitude and stiffness on the observed departure from a true harmonic series of the overtones of stringed instruments is considered. These effects are of greatest interest in instruments such as the piano in which the vibrations are free and therefore the several allowed frequencies may exist simultaneously.

### Theoretical Considerations

The frequencies of vibration of a stretched wire string, when the amplitude of vibration is finite and the stiffness is appreciable, cannot be calculated rigorously by direct methods. The characteristics of the motion with finite amplitude and bridge supports, however, can be determined by the use of normal functions as first outlined by Rayleigh[2] for the related cases of a vibrating string with variable density, and for the lateral vibrations of bars with variable flexural rigidity. The amplitude of motion causes a variation in tension which is a function of time, distance along the string, and the nature of the bridge support. This variation in tension is treated as a perturbation affecting the ideal vibration of the

[1] Lord Rayleigh, *Theory of Sound*, Vol. I, Sec. 189.

[2] Lord Rayleigh, *Theory of Sound*, Vol. I, Sec. 141, 142, 187.

string, and its effects on frequency are computed. The amplitudes here considered are those commonly met with in musical instruments so that the usual approximation concerning curvature of the string at a point permits the motion of a string with variable tension to be expressed by the equation,

$$\frac{\partial}{\partial x}\left(T\frac{\partial y}{\partial x}\right)=\rho\frac{\partial^2 y}{\partial t^2}, \tag{1}$$

where $\rho$ is the linear density of the wire, here assumed constant, and $T$ is the tension. The solutions of Eq. (1) for the case of constant tension are linear combinations of

$$y_n{}^0=\sin\frac{n\pi x}{l}\exp\left(2\pi i\nu_n{}^0 t\right)$$

for the condition of zero displacement at the bridges. Here $l$ is the distance between bridges, $\nu_n{}^0$ is the frequency of vibration, and $n$ is the overtone number.

The solution of Eq. (1) with variable $T(x,t)$ is made by means of these zero-order solutions. Only periodic solutions giving the normal modes of vibration are considered. These may be represented by $y_n=u_n(x)\exp(2\pi i\nu_n t)$. A substitution of $y_n$ in (1) gives,

$$\frac{d}{dx}\left(T\frac{du_n}{dx}\right)+4\pi^2\rho\nu_n{}^2 u_n=0. \tag{2}$$

$\nu_n$ is the frequency of vibration when the amplitude is finite and $u_n(x)$ are the functions giving the shape of the string in this case. The functions $u_n$ can be represented between the limits $x=0$ and $x=l$ by a series of normal functions made up of the solutions for the ideal case.

$$u_n=\sum_m C_{mn}\sin\frac{m\pi x}{l}. \tag{3}$$

A substitution of (3) in (2) and simplification by means of the orthogonality condition yields the frequencies of the normal modes of vibration,

$$\nu_n=\frac{n}{2l}\left(\frac{T}{\rho}\right)^{\frac{1}{2}}\left[1-\frac{1}{\pi n T}\int_0^l \sin\frac{n\pi x}{l}\frac{dT}{\partial x}\times\cos\frac{n\pi x}{l}dx+\cdots\right]. \tag{4}$$

The value of $dT/dx$ must be known to evaluate Eq. (4).

When the amplitude of vibration is finite, the tension in the string will be a function both of $x$ and $t$ because of the constraints at the bridges on the motion of the ends of the wire, and because of the fact that in its transverse motion an element of the string moves nearly normally to the line joining the bridges. The instantaneous variation in tension at a point of the string due to the latter effect will be

$$\Delta T=\tfrac{1}{2}\pi r^2 Y(dy/dx)^2,$$

where $r$ is the radius of the wire, $Y$ is the Young's elastic modulus, and $\Delta T=0$ when the string is straight. If $T_s$ is the tension in the vibrating string when at all points $y=0$, and $T_0$ is the applied tension, then $T=T_s+\Delta T$ and $T_0=T_s+\Delta T_0$. For the $n$th overtone of the wire vibrating with amplitude $A_n$,

$$T=T_0-\tfrac{1}{2}\left[\sin^2 2\pi\nu_n t_0-\sin^2 2\pi\nu_n t\right]\times\left[\pi r^2 Y\left(\frac{n\pi A_n}{l}\right)^2\cos^2\frac{n\pi x}{l}\right].$$

Since the integration in (4) is with respect to $x$, the factors involving $t$ in the above expression may be replaced by time averages giving,

$$T=T_0-\tfrac{1}{2}C\pi r^2 Y\left(\frac{n\pi A_n}{l}\right)^2\cos^2\frac{n\pi x}{l}, \tag{5}$$

where $C=\sin^2 2\pi\nu_n t_0-\frac{1}{2}$, therefore $\frac{1}{2}\geqslant C\geqslant -\frac{1}{2}$. The value of $C=0$ would mean that $T=T_0$ throughout the cycle of the string's vibration. This would require complete freedom of motion of the wire over the bridges and also that the stretching mechanism be a perfect spring having no inertial lag. The limiting value of $C=\frac{1}{2}$ would indicate that the greatest tension is realized when the string has its maximum displacement. Negative values of $C$ will result when the tension is $T_0$ near the equilibrium line. In general the tension $T_0$ will be realized at some value short of the maximum displacement giving $C$ a positive value. A typical set of data obtained with the special monochord discussed below yields the value of $C=0.27$. When (5) is substituted in (4)

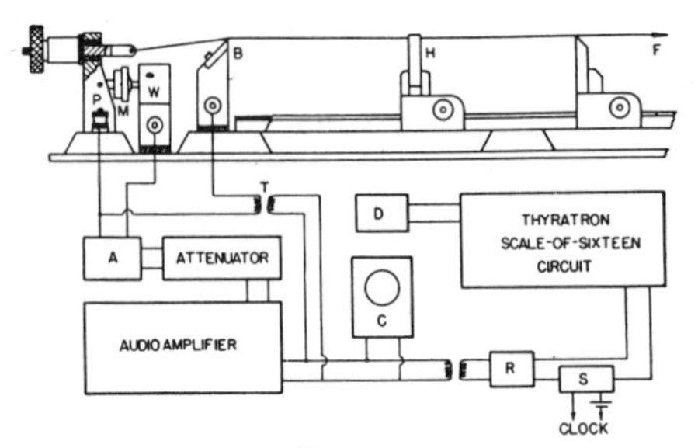


FIG. 1.

and integrated the result is,

$$\nu_n=\frac{n}{2l}\left(\frac{T}{\rho}\right)^{\frac{1}{2}}\left[1-\frac{\pi^3r^2Yn^2C}{8l^2T}A_n{}^2+\cdots\right]. \quad (6)$$

Eq. (6) shows that the frequency changes due to finite amplitude of vibration will be diminished by using small diameter, long wires under high tension, and by the use of bridge supports giving $C$ a small value.

The analysis given above is for an ideally flexible string. When a string with finite stiffness is employed, the vibrations will be still further modified. The differential equation for the string's motion must now contain a term involving the stiffness. When this is included, Eq. (2) is changed to,

$$\frac{d}{dx}\left(T\frac{du_n}{dx}\right)-\frac{\pi r^4Y}{4}\frac{d^4u_n}{dx^4}+4\pi^2\rho\nu_n{}^2u_n=0. \quad (2a)$$

There are two limiting cases. In the first, the string is clamped giving $y=0$, and $dy/dx=0$ at the ends. In the second situation the bending moment due to stiffness vanishes at the bridges giving $y=0$, and $d^2y/dx^2=0$ at the supports. Neither set of boundary conditions represents accurately the true behavior at a bridge. The solution of Eq. (2a) has been given for both sets of boundary conditions by Rayleigh.[3] The results giving the frequencies of the normal modes of vibration are: For the condition $y=0$ and $d^2y/dx^2=0$ at ends,

$$\nu_n=\frac{n}{2l}\left(\frac{T}{\rho}\right)^{\frac{1}{2}}\left[1+\frac{n^2\pi^3r^4Y}{8l^2T}+\cdots\right] \quad (7)$$

[3] Lord Rayleigh, *Theory of Sound*, Vol. I, pp. 297–301.

and

$$\nu_n=\frac{n}{2l}\left(\frac{T}{\rho}\right)^{\frac{1}{2}}\left[1+\frac{r^2}{l}\left(\frac{\pi Y}{T}\right)^{\frac{1}{2}}+\left(4+\frac{n^2\pi^2}{2}\right)\frac{\pi r^4Y}{4Tl^2}+\cdots\right] \quad (8)$$

for the end conditions that $y=0$ and $dy/dx=0$. Since the constraints introduced by the bridges are intermediate between the extremes, it is expected that the correction terms due to rigidity will be intermediate between the values given in (7) and (8). However, the ratios of the allowed frequencies for a string of constant length will be very nearly the same from either equation.

## EXPERIMENTAL METHODS

Figure 1 is a schematic diagram of the apparatus used to maintain the vibrations of the wire, and the circuits for determining its frequency both with the cathode-ray oscillograph and the thyratron scale-of-sixteen circuit used with a standard pendulum. The vibrating string communicates a small longitudinal vibration over the insulated bridge $B$ to the end post $P$, from which the string is electrically insulated. This part is rigidly attached to one side of a carbon button $M$. The other terminal of the carbon button is fixed to a large mass $W$ mounted on a soft rubber insulating support. This provides a mechanical system in which the motions of $W$ and $P$ are out of phase. The changes in resistance produced in the carbon button are of twice the frequency of the string's vibration. The characteristics of vibrations maintained by forces of double frequency have been discussed by Rayleigh.[4] The impulses are amplified and fed back into the string through a stepdown transformer $T$ of large turn ratio used to approximate a matching of impedances. A small magnet $H$ produces an intense local field and the motor action of the current in the wire causes it to vibrate. The periodic force of double frequency will aid the motion at both extremes while the impulses given while passing through the $y=0$ configuration are very small due to the large back e.m.f. and are of both signs, thus producing

[4] Lord Rayleigh, *Scientific Papers*, Vol. II, pp. 188–193; Vol. III, pp. 1–14.

no cumulative effect. This type of regenerative circuit insures that the string will vibrate with its own natural frequency. Both magnetic and nonmagnetic wires may be employed. The vibrations are free vibrations, in which the positive and negative damping are equal. These self-excited vibrations may be studied with such small amplitudes that not the slightest vibration is visible. This would be impossible if a resonance arrangement were used, since such a method

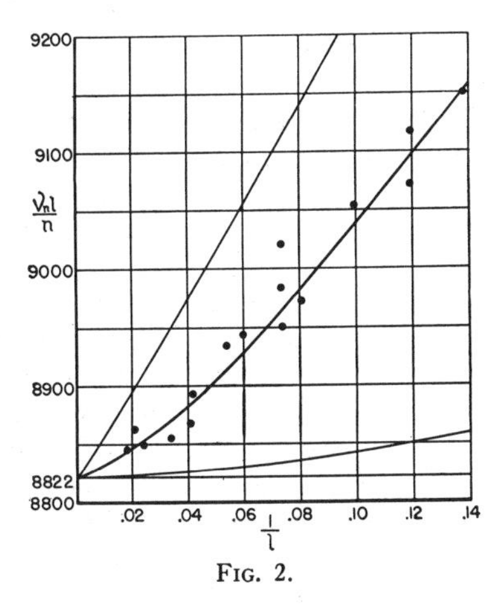


FIG. 2.

would have rather broad tuning and would require amplitudes of vibration that would make a precise determination of frequency impossible.

Any allowed frequency of vibration can be selected by adjusting the position of the magnet along the length of the wire. Several overtones can be made to vibrate simultaneously, but for the quantitative studies reported below, each normal mode of vibration was investigated separately. In some cases a filter to eliminate the overtones is found helpful in causing the fundamental alone to appear. The amplitude of vibration is regulated by the gain in the carbon-button-pick-up and by means of the attenuation network shown in Fig. 1. The attenuation box is placed in the position shown to avoid overloading the amplifier. The output of the amplifier is adequate to operate the measuring circuits even when the vibration amplitude is too small to be seen.

The absolute value of the frequency of vibration is determined by means of a thyratron scale-of-sixteen circuit which operates a Cenco impulse recorder. A rectifier $R$ in the input permits only positive impulses to reach the dividing circuit, which is necessary for its normal operation. Frequencies up to 1900 a second can be measured by this method. The circuit is switched on for sixteen-second intervals by a rotating commutator $S$ operated by a standard pendulum designed by J. G. Albright.[5] The precision of the sixteen-second interval is determined by comparison with a standard Reifler clock by means of a chronograph.

Changes in frequency due to varying amplitudes of vibration, and the relative frequencies of the fundamental and overtones for a fixed length of wire can be determined by means of a cathode-ray oscillograph used with external synchronization. Any frequency near a multiple of the synchronization frequency can be measured by observing the beat frequency of the pattern on the cathode-ray tube. The general measurement procedure is to determine certain selected frequencies with the dividing circuit, then to compare the other frequencies with these by means of the cathode-ray oscillograph. The vibration amplitude is determined by direct observation for moderately large amplitudes and the small amplitudes are extrapolated by means of the calibrated attenuation network.

## INTERPRETATION OF EXPERIMENTAL DATA

The variation of frequency with amplitude of vibration was studied with a brass wire 0.046 centimeter in diameter, supported between bridges spaced 41.65 centimeters apart and under a static tension of 4546 grams. The experimental values of the wire vibrating in its fundamental mode are given accurately by the equation $\nu_1 = \nu_1^0 - 13.5A_1^2$ of the form of Eq. (6). A comparison of the constant 13.5 with the coefficient given by the theory yields a value for the bridge parameter of $C = 0.27$ which shows that the tension passes through the value $T_0$ when the displacement is 88 percent of the amplitude of vibration. The effects due to stiffness alone are minimized in these experiments by observing vibrations that are large enough to make the perturbations due to amplitude predominate. A detailed description of the influence of bridge

[5] J. G. Albright, U. S. Patent No. 1,962,378.

supports on the vibrations of a wire can be obtained by determining $C$ for a variety of conditions—changing length, diameter, overtone, tension and material of the wire, and the smoothness of the bridges.

Further insight into the boundary conditions at the bridges can be obtained by working with amplitudes so small that the stiffness is the predominant factor in changing the frequency. When $A<0.04$ centimeter for the case just discussed, this condition will be fulfilled. Vibrations of even smaller amplitudes than this can easily be sustained by a suitable adjustment of the attenuation network. The vibrations are then not clearly visible to the eye but may be readily studied on the cathode-ray tube when the internal amplification of that instrument is employed. Under these conditions the length $l$, overtone $n$, tension $T_0$, were separately varied for several different wires. The results obtained with the brass wire described above, showing the dependence of frequency upon length, are shown in Fig. 2 for the fundamental, and in Fig. 3 for the octave. The abscissae are $1/l$ and the ordi-

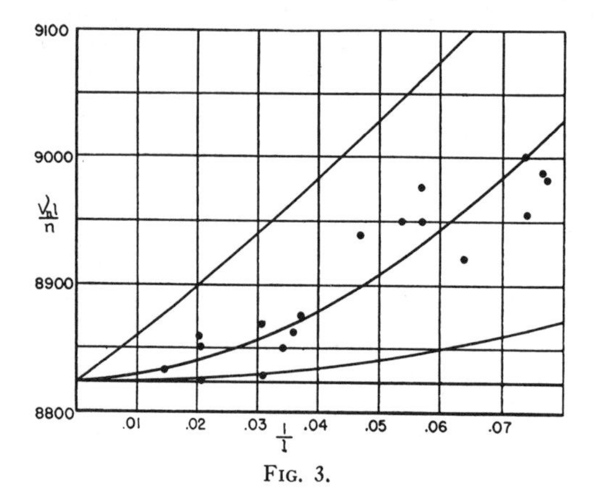


FIG. 3.

nates are $\nu_n l/n$. An ideally flexible string would vibrate with frequencies giving points lying on the horizontal line shown in both of these figures. In each figure, however, the observed points steadily depart from this straight line as the wire is shortened due to the stiffness of the wire. The lower smooth curve is computed from Eq. (7). This curve falls below the experimental points which show several times the deviation from the ideal case. The upper smooth curves in Figs. 2 and 3 are computed from Eq. (8). These curves are above the experimental points giving values for the deviation from the ideal case of more than twice those actually found. These results show that the frequencies are intermediate between those predicted by the two limiting cases. It has generally been assumed,[1] however, that the boundary conditions with bridges are nearly those leading to Eq. (7).

Data similar to those shown in Fig. 2 have been taken for several other brass and steel wires.[6] In every case the experimental points are intermediate between the values calculated from Eqs. (7) and (8), respectively. Agreement between theory and experiment can be achieved by using Eq. (8) with an empirical constant $1>B>0$ before the second term $(r^2/l)(\pi Y/T)^{\frac{1}{2}}$. The value of $B$ decreases as the length of the wire increases; it is greater for wires under higher tension; and is less for wires of small radius. For a brass wire of radius 0.0355 centimeter under a tension of 4546 grams the average value of $B$ is about 0.35; while with a tension of 8432 grams, $B$ rises to about 0.50. A steel wire 0.0519 centimeter in radius stretched with a force of 8432 grams gives $B=0.6$ or more; while a small steel wire, $r=0.0154$ centimeter with $T=4546$ grams shows $B$ only 0.1 or less. A relation $B=\text{const. } Tr/l$ is found to hold to a first approximation. The very sharp decrease in the value of $B$ for small wires is perhaps related to the variation of Young's modulus $Y$ with the diameter of the wire.[7]

The effect of the stiffness of the wire also can be shown by measuring the frequencies of the normal modes of vibration with a fixed length of wire. The ratio of the allowed frequencies for a fixed length of wire under constant tension can be obtained by manipulation of Eqs. (6), (7) and (8) giving,

$$\frac{\nu_n}{\nu_1}=n\left[1+\frac{\pi^2 r^4 Y}{8l^2 T}\left\{(n^2-1)+\frac{C}{r^2}(A_1{}^2-n^2A_n{}^2)\right\}\right]. \quad (9)$$

Fig. 4 gives the results of measurements with very small amplitudes for three lengths of the 0.046-centimeter diameter brass wire under a tension of 4546 grams. The overtones are sharp

[6] J. W. Coltman, Thesis, Case School of Applied Science, 1937.
[7] T. F. Wall, Nature **141**, 751 (1938).

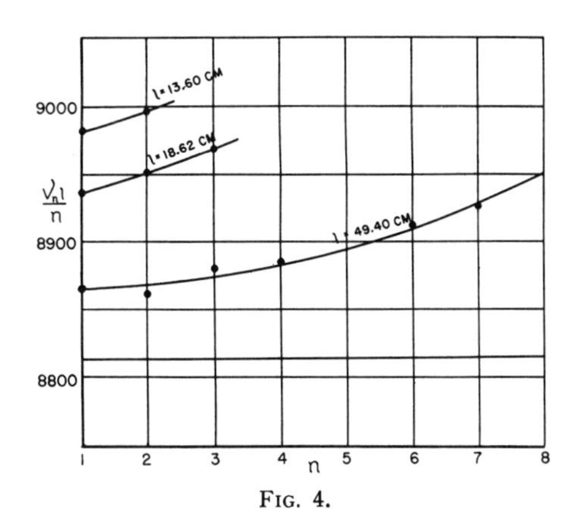


FIG. 4.

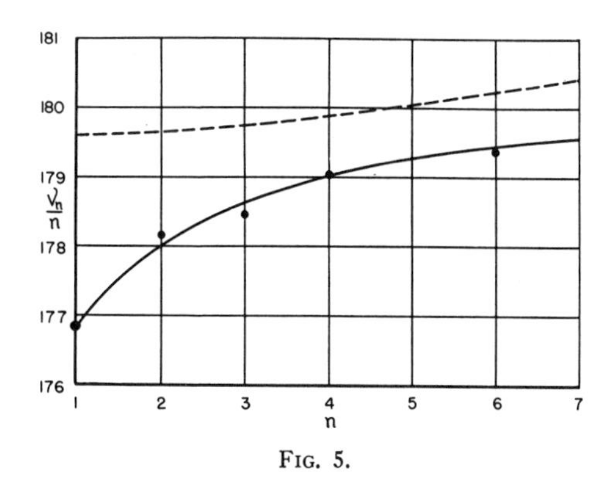


FIG. 5.

with respect to the fundamental, and the variation is that given by (9) when the vibration amplitudes are small. Fig. 5, gives the results with the same wire and tension, when the amplitudes of vibration are sufficient to give easily audible sounds. The solid curve of Fig. 5 is a plot corresponding to the vibration amplitudes: $A_1=0.55$ centimeter, $A_2=0.21$ centimeter, $A_3=0.11$ centimeter, $A_4=0.08$ centimeter and $A_6=0.01$ centimeter, respectively. The upper dashed curve is computed for negligible amplitudes.

In these experiments only one normal mode of vibration was studied at a time, but the string could also be made to vibrate with several allowed frequencies by properly placing the magnet. In such cases the incommensurate relationship between the frequencies is visible on the cathode-ray tube or by direct observation of the wire, where the beats can be clearly seen.

A vibration sustained by a single periodic driving force can have only harmonic overtones in the steady-state, but in free vibrations all the normal modes may exist simultaneously and the resulting sound may have overtones which depart from a true harmonic series. Such sounds are to be expected from the piano, harp and instruments of this kind. A study of a very complete set of phonodeik records of piano tones made by D. C. Miller[8] shows that in many cases the overtones are inharmonic in agreement with the experiments described above and also with the data on piano tuning taken by Railsback[9] and others.

The vibrations of a bowed string are classed as self-excited vibrations.[10] The action of the bow is to supply energy to the string at a constant average rate by frictional contact, which is equivalent to negative damping. There is nothing periodic in this process, and the string's frequency is governed by its tension, mass and length; so the motion is essentially a free vibration[11] and the effects due to stiffness and amplitude should be comparable with the results obtained in the present experiments. This will, of course, be strictly true when the instrument is played pizzicato. It is probable that the tone quality of instruments such as the piano, violin, harp, etc., is due not only to the relative intensities of the overtones, but to the small, constantly shifting, phase relationship which exists between them because of their departure from a true harmonic series.

---

[8] D. C. Miller, Unpublished Studies of Piano Strings.
[9] O. L. Railsback, J. Acous. Soc. Am. **10**, 86 (1938).
[10] Den Hartog, *Mechanical Vibrations*, Chap. VII, p. 288.
[11] Sir James Jeans, *Science and Music* (Cambridge, 1937), p. 100; Barton, *Text Book of Sound*, p. 347.

# 4

*Copyright © 1943 by the Acoustical Society of America*

Reprinted from *J. Acoust. Soc. Am.*, **15**(1), 1–11 (1943)

## Observations on the Vibrations of Piano Strings *

O. H. SCHUCK AND R. W. YOUNG
*C. G. Conn, Ltd., Elkhart, Indiana*

(Received May 24, 1943)

The behavior of single piano strings struck in their normal positions was investigated through measurement of the frequencies of the partials and their amplitudes as functions of time.after striking. Three-dimensional figures showing partial amplitudes *versus* time are presented. The frequencies of the partials of the tone were found to be those of the normal modes of vibration and are therefore referred to as the modal frequencies of the string. The higher modal frequencies are progressively sharp with respect to true harmonics of the fundamental; the sharpening follows approximately a square law with respect to mode number, to the extent that in one case the 15th partial had just about the frequency of a 16th harmonic. The resulting inharmonicity in piano strings is least in the two octaves below middle *C*; it rises sharply at the high end and more or less sharply at the low end, depending upon the type of piano. A correlation between inharmonicity and subjective tone quality rating is suggested. It is shown that the commonly observed "stretched" tuning (sharpening of the treble, flattening the bass) is a natural consequence of the inharmonicity.

### INTRODUCTION

INVESTIGATION of the tone and vibration of the piano string, when strung in the piano and struck by the hammer in normal fashion, is complicated by the transitory nature of the phenomenon. However, it is possible to make such studies by separating out one partial of the tone at a time with a selective filter. This partial's amplitude variation with time after striking may then be recorded with a high speed graphic level recorder and its frequency may be determined with a chromatic stroboscope. These data, taken for each of the distinguishable partials in the tone, indicate the nature of the tone quality and furnish information regarding the vibration of the string. Some observations of this kind are described below, and their significance is discussed, both in relation to tone quality and the tuning of pianos.

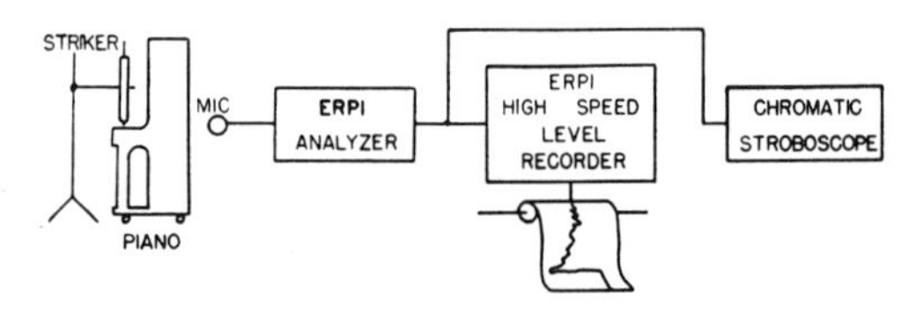


FIG. 1. Apparatus for measuring amplitudes of partials.

* Paper presented at the twenty-eighth meeting of the Acoustical Society of America, May 14–15, 1943, New York, New York.

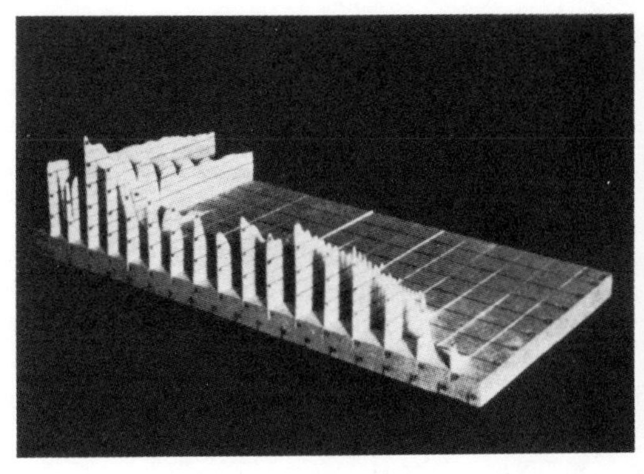

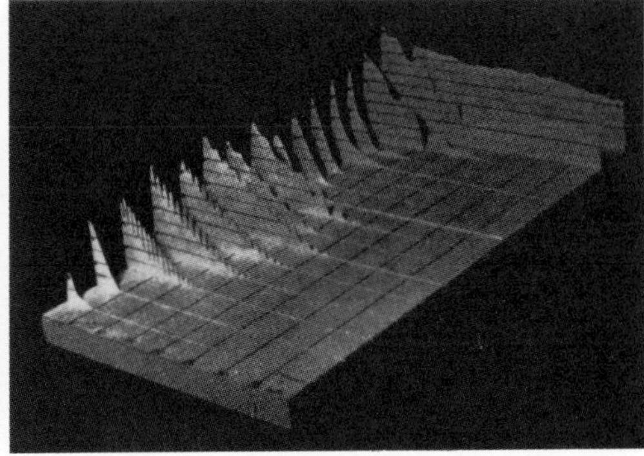

(a) (b)

FIG. 2. Amplitudes of the partials of an $F_1$ string as functions of time.

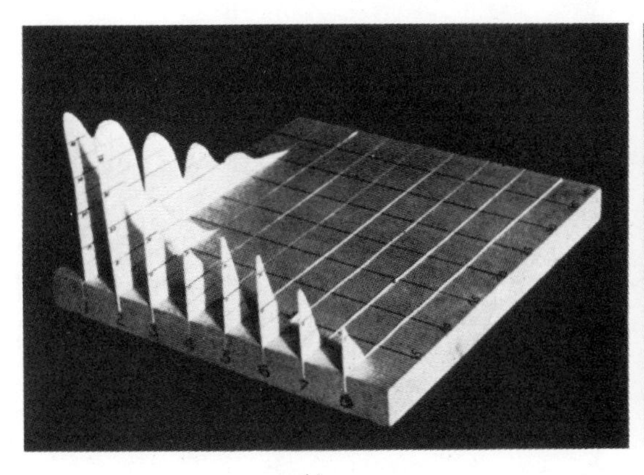

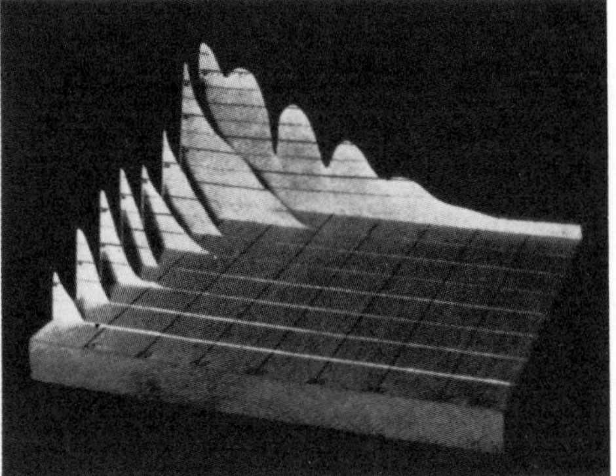

(a) (b)

FIG. 3. Amplitudes of the partials of an $F_3$ string as functions of time.

### AMPLITUDE OF PARTIALS *VERSUS* TIME

Figure 1 shows the arrangement of apparatus for measuring the variation of amplitude with time after striking, for each partial of a piano tone. The selected key is struck by a mechanical striker; when the key has two or three strings, only one is left free to vibrate. The sound is picked up by a microphone, fed through an analyzer which is tuned to one partial; the amplitude of this partial is recorded by the high speed level recorder, while its frequency is read on the chromatic stroboscope. A record is run for each of the ascending partials until they can no longer be distinguished. The records are similar in form to the examples obtained by Wolf and Sette.[1]

[1] S. K. Wolf and W. J. Sette, J. Acous. Soc. Am. **6**, 160–168 (1935).

In order to present the results in a form readily comprehended, fiber templets were cut from the level recorder records and mounted on slotted boards to form three-dimensional figures, as shown in Figs. 2 and 3. Figure 2 represents the tone from the $F_1$ string—the lowest *F*—on a small console piano. Similarly, Fig. 3 represents the tone from one string of the key $F_3$—the third *F*, the *F* below middle *C*—on the same piano. The ordinates are on a logarithmic scale.

It is seen that after the initial peak at striking,

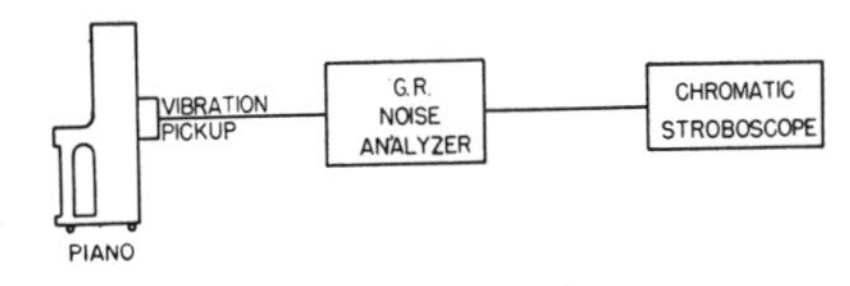


FIG. 4. Method for determining modal frequencies of piano strings.

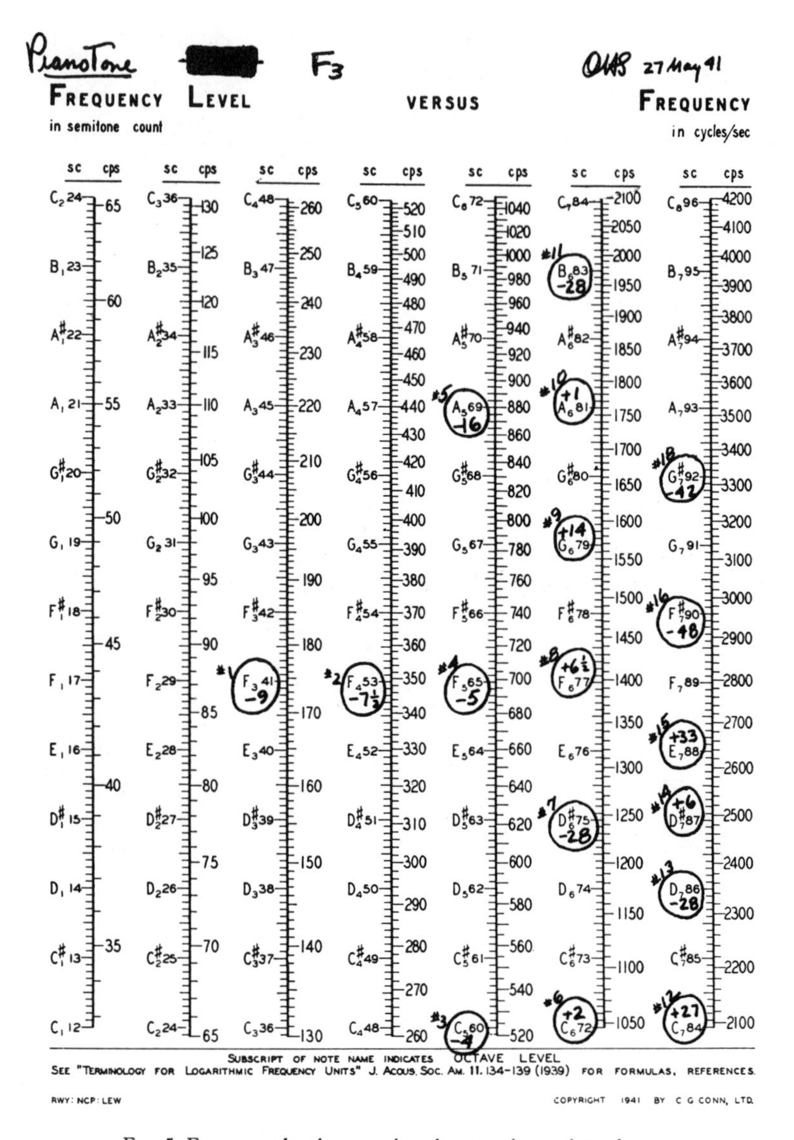


FIG. 5. Frequency level conversion chart used as a data sheet.

which is more rapid in its rise than the high speed level recorder can follow (the nominal maximum being 50 db/sec.), there is a fairly uniform rate of decrease in amplitude, the rate of decrease being more rapid the higher the number of the partial. This is to be expected from the increased air loading of the string and sounding board at the higher frequencies. The tone quality therefore changes continuously, becoming less complex as time goes on.[2] Particularly in the tone produced by the longer string (Fig. 2) the amplitudes of the partials show large fluctuations of a form suggesting half sine waves. The higher the partial, the more rapid the fluctuations. This condition may be due to rotation of the plane of vibration of the string, and there

[2] Hart, Fuller, and Lusby, J. Acous. Soc. Am. **6**, 92 (1934).

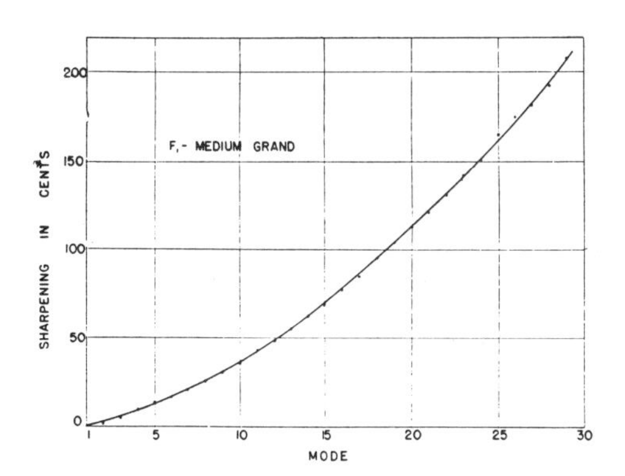


FIG. 6. Inharmonicity for the $F_1$ string of a medium grand piano.

may also be some transfer of energy from one mode to another. It is interesting to notice that the seventh partial is not particularly weak, despite the fact that the striking point is often stated to be at one-seventh of the string length to suppress this partial.

The frequency scale used in making the three-dimensional figures is linear: Harmonics would therefore appear equally spaced. The templates have been located to correspond to the measured frequencies. As is particularly evident in Fig. 2a, the frequencies of the partials are not harmonic. Along the edge of the board the number of the mode of vibration which produces each partial is indicated in the upper row of figures; in the lower row the position of each true harmonic is shown. It is seen that the partials are progressively sharpened, indeed to the extent that the 15th partial has just about the frequency of a 16th harmonic. True harmonics of the fundamental frequency could not be found. This fact indicates that the transmission system from string to air is relatively distortionless, and that the partials in the tone are indeed produced by the respective modes of vibration of the string.

It should be pointed out that these amplitude data are unquestionably influenced by the room conditions, and are only to be considered as indicating the practicability of making measurements of this kind. On the other hand, the frequencies of the partials are not influenced by the room conditions. Their measurement is relatively simple and since their influence on tone quality was considered important, all of the further work described here was concerned only with such frequency measurements.

## FREQUENCIES OF PARTIALS

The frequencies of the various partials of a struck piano string were measured by the apparatus shown in Fig. 4. (Since these frequencies are those of the normal modes of vibration they are hereafter referred to as the modal frequencies.) The output of a crystal vibration pick-up fastened to a rib of the sounding board was fed through an analyzer to a chromatic stroboscope. Only one string of the group being struck was left free to vibrate. As it was found that variations in the strength of the blow produced negligible effects on the modal frequencies, the key was struck manually.

Rapid recording of the data was facilitated by use of the frequency level *versus* frequency chart shown in Fig. 5, this being the actual work sheet of one run. The number of cents

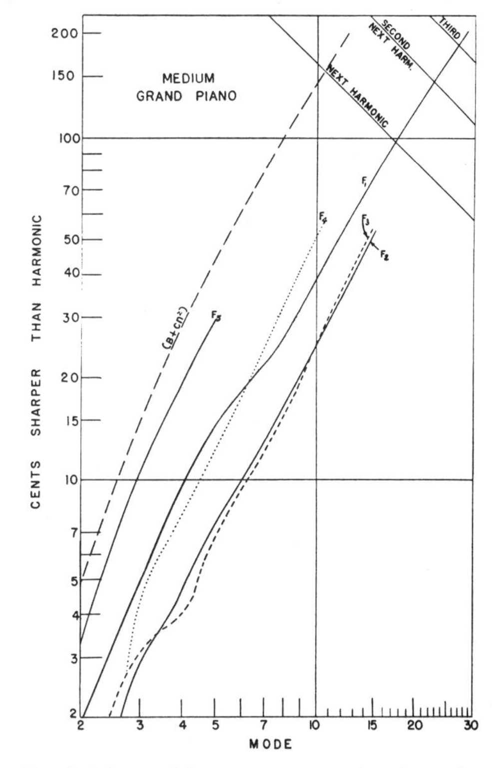


FIG. 7. Inharmonicity as some power of mode number.

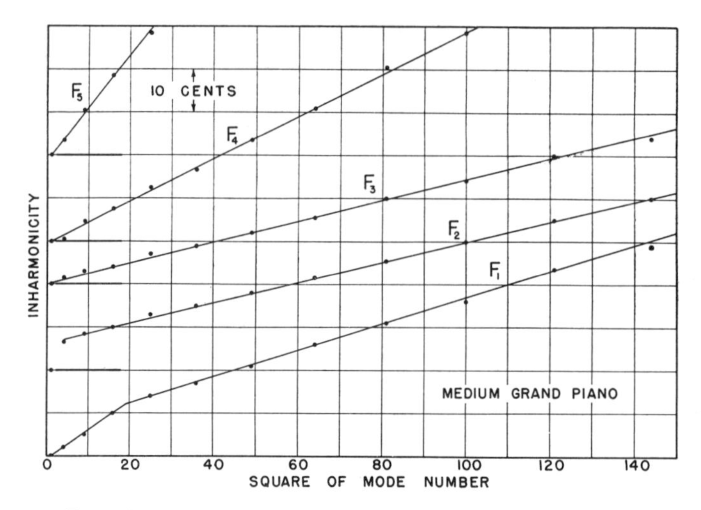


FIG. 8. Inharmonicity as a function of the square of mode number.

deviation measured with respect to a nominal value is encircled; the corresponding mode number is indicated alongside.

The readings are in terms of frequency level,[3,4] so the percentage sharpening of each partial with respect to a true harmonic is easily obtained by a subtraction procedure which is described in the Appendix. We call this percentage departure from harmonicity the "inharmonicity." More specifically it is convenient to measure and express the inharmonicity as the number of *cents* by which a particular modal frequency $\nu$ departs from its nominal value $n\nu_1$, where $\nu_1$ is the fundamental frequency and $n$ is the mode number. This departure, the inharmonicity $D$, is therefore

$$D = 1200 \log_2 (\nu / n\nu_1). \quad (1)$$

It may be recalled that the cent is one hundredth of a semitone, so there are 1200 to the octave; one cent corresponds to a percentage difference in frequency of 0.06 percent. $D$ is zero if the modal frequency is exactly harmonic.

The inharmonicities of the modal frequencies of one string in a medium grand piano are shown in Fig. 6, plotted against the number of the mode. Note that the inharmonicity follows a fairly smooth curve and is always positive. This means that the partials are always sharp with respect to true harmonics. When the inharmonicity *versus* mode number is plotted on log-log paper, as shown in Fig. 7, the observed points for a number of strings measured in the medium grand piano fall, respectively, on fairly straight lines whose slopes are close to 2. This means that approximately

$$D = 1200 \log_2 \nu / n\nu_1 \backsimeq K n^2, \quad (2)$$

where $K$ is some factor of proportionality. This is nearly equivalent to

$$\nu = n\nu_1 [1 + (K/1731) n^2], \quad (3)$$

as may be shown by substitution back in Eq. (2) and using the appropriate expansion for the logarithm.

This proportionality to $n^2$ is of the form predicted by theory for stiff strings and various boundary conditions,[5–7] provided that the terms independent of mode number are absorbed in $\nu_1$.

The line in Fig. 7 labeled "next harmonic" indicates at what point a particular mode has been sharpened to the extent that its frequency is equal to that of a true harmonic one number greater. Similarly, the intersection of the curve for $F_1$ near $n = 23$ with the line "second next

[3] H. Fletcher, J. Acous. Soc. Am. **6**, 59–69 (1934).
[4] R. W. Young, J. Acous. Soc. Am. **11**, 134–139 (1939).

[5] Lord Rayleigh, *Theory of Sound* (Macmillan, 1894), second edition, Vol. I, p. 301.
[6] R. S. Shankland and J. W. Coltman, J. Acous. Soc. Am. **10**, 161–166 (1939).
[7] P. M. Morse, *Vibration and Sound* (McGraw-Hill, 1936), p. 131.

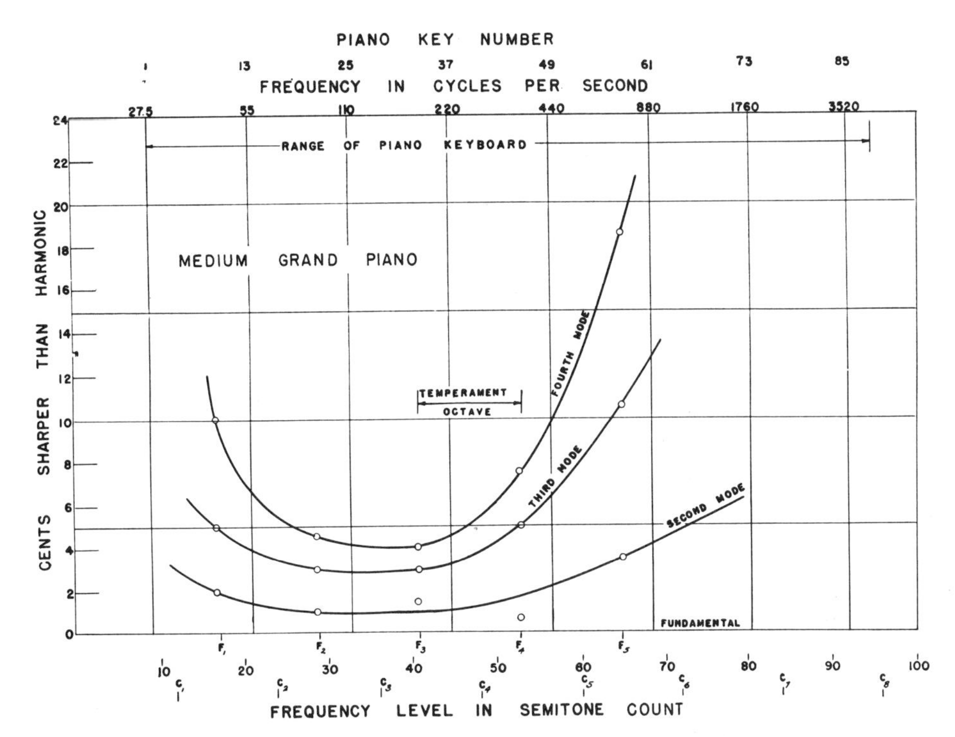


FIG. 9. Inharmonicity in relation to position of string in piano.

harmonic" means that the frequency of this mode of vibration is approximately 25 times that of the fundamental.

In order to investigate the "square" relationship in detail the inharmonicity *versus* square of mode number has been plotted in Fig. 8, again using the data on the medium grand piano. The curves have been given an arbitrary vertical displacement for clarity. The straight lines are .or convenience in visualizing the relationship; ıctually only discrete values of the inharmonicity exist corresponding to the mode numbers.

For the higher pitched strings a single straight line constitutes an excellent fit. For the lower ones a constant should be added to the second member of Eq. (2), and the exponent reduced to something less than 2. The effect of such an additive constant is illustrated by the curvature of the dashed line in Fig. 7 labeled $(B+Cn^2)$, where $B$ and $C$ have been chosen arbitrarily. Such a complication should perhaps be expected for $F_1$, in consideration of yielding of the end supports and the heavy loading.

### COMPARISON OF STRINGS

From Figs. 7 and 8 it is apparent that the inharmonicity is not the same for all strings. In Fig. 9 the inharmonicity for several of the lower modes is replotted against frequency level and position on the piano keyboard. The sharpening is least in the two octaves below middle $C$ and increases rapidly below and above this region. In fact, it shows signs of reaching quite surprising values at the top end of the keyboard. This is quite plausible for the top strings are so short and stiff as to be really more like bars than strings.

One would surmise that, since all pianos have about the same string dimensions in the middle and upper registers, there would be little variation here in the inharmonicity among different pianos. On the other hand, the lengths of the bass strings vary with the size of the piano, and one would accordingly expect variations in the inharmonicity in the low register. These expectations were corroborated by measurements on different sizes of pianos.

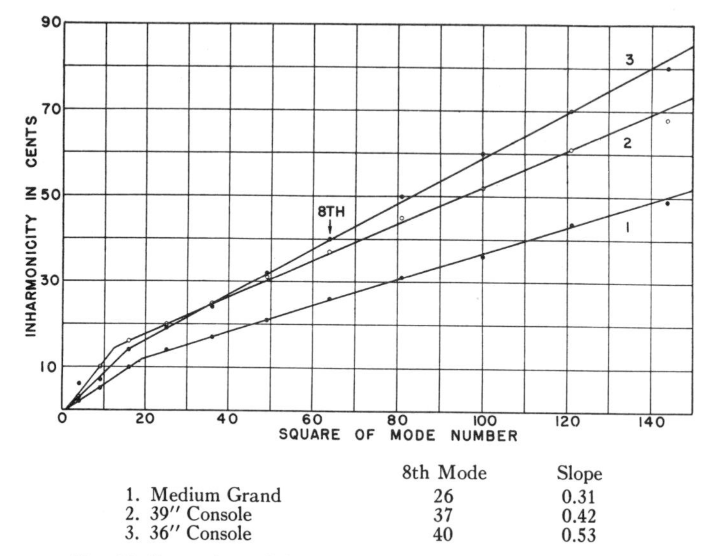


| | 8th Mode | Slope |
|---|---|---|
| 1. Medium Grand | 26 | 0.31 |
| 2. 39″ Console | 37 | 0.42 |
| 3. 36″ Console | 40 | 0.53 |

FIG. 10. Comparison of the inharmonicity of $F_1$ for various pianos.

Figure 10 gives a comparison of the inharmonicity of the $F_1$ strings of several pianos, again plotted against the square of the mode number for convenience. The inharmonicity is less for the larger piano. The eighth modes, for example, were respectively 26, 37, and 40 cents sharper than the corresponding harmonic values. This observation is in line with the widely held opinion that the piano with longer bass strings has a "rounder, fuller, richer tone." Let us consider this point philosophically for a moment.

It is generally agreed that a tone is round, full, and rich if it consists of a fundamental and a long series of harmonic overtones of gradually decreasing amplitudes. Nevertheless, if the fundamental is missing or weak, as it often is in the lower tones of a piano, the listener will still imagine he hears a fundamental in the series and be pleased with the tone. This subjective fundamental is derived from the differences between the successive partials. When they are harmonically related as when produced, for example, by a horn, the frequency differences between successive partials are constant, and the derived fundamentals all have the same frequency, which is that of the actual fundamental. However, if the partials are not harmonically related, as in the piano tone, the various derived fundamentals do not have the same frequency, there is confusion in the ear, and the tone is not considered pleasing.

The inharmonicity of some arbitrarily selected mode therefore constitutes a simple criterion of excellence of a string. However, particularly for bass strings, the fundamental is often almost lacking, so the accurate determination of the interval from the fundamental to the eighth mode, say, is not always easy. Moreover, the manner in which the inharmonicity changes with mode number may vary among different pianos. On the hypothesis suggested above it is the differences between successive partials which are significant, so that the rate of increase of inharmonicity with mode number is pertinent. The caption with Fig. 10 shows also this method of rating, the slope relative to $n^2$ having been used for simplicity. Observe that although pianos 2 and 3 had nearly the same inharmonicity of the eighth mode, the greater slope of the curve 3 indicates a greater spread of differences between successive partials. This criterion of slope relative to $n^2$ may be determined experimentally with accuracy in a straightforward manner. On the other hand, there may be needed some power of mode number other than two, and the criterion does not recognize that the subjective fundamental created within the ear will depend upon the actual frequencies and

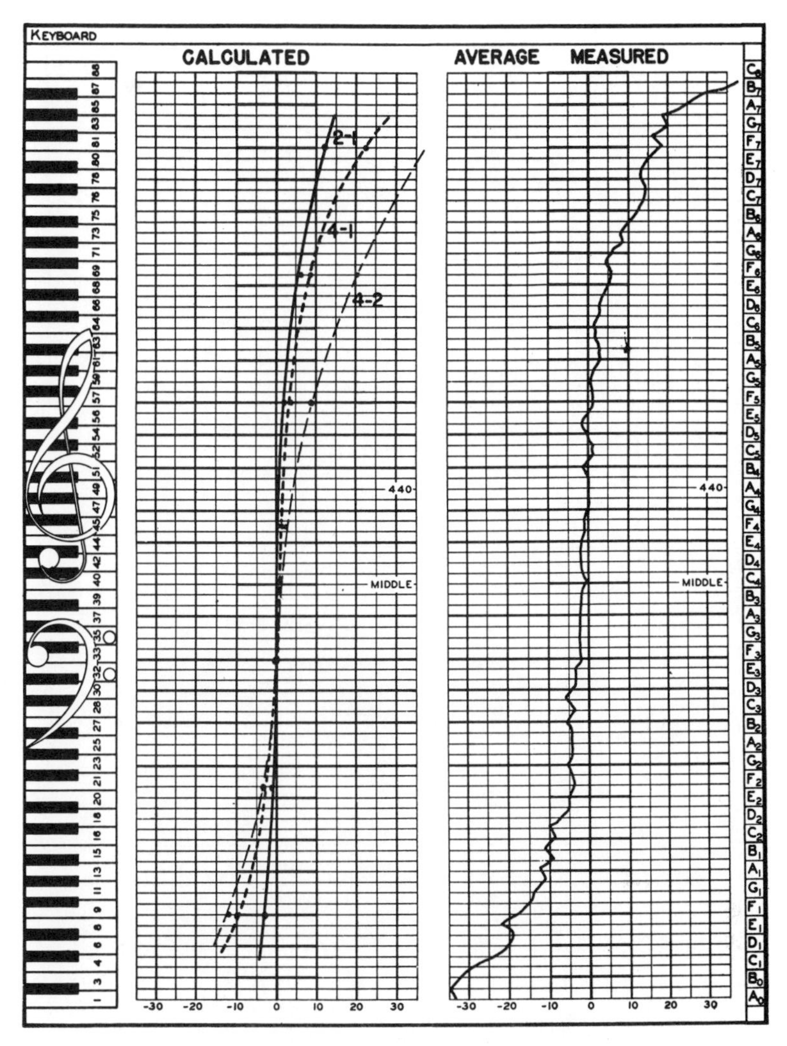


FIG. 11. (a) Left: Calculated tunings, showing deviations in cents.
(b) Right: Average of 16 pianos tested by Railsback.

relative amplitudes of the various partials involved.

That the longer string is desirable for its better tone quality is appreciated by the piano designer,[8] who takes considerable pains to make the bass strings as long as the dimensions of the case will allow.

### EFFECT OF INHARMONICITY ON TUNING

There is another effect of interest produced by the inharmonicity of the partials. Measurements by Railsback[9] show that piano tuners usually tune progressively sharp in the middle and high registers, progressively flat in the low. The process of piano tuning[10,11] is carried out by "laying the temperament" in an octave in the middle of the keyboard—usually the octave from $F_3$ to $F_4$—and then tuning up and down by octaves. To tune upward by an octave, one

[8] W. B. White, J. Acous. Soc. Am. **12**, 409–411 (1941).

[9] O. L. Railsback, J. Acous. Soc. Am. **9**, 274 (1938); **10**, 86 (1938).

[10] G. F. H. Harker, J. Acous. Soc. Am. **8**, 243–256 (1937).

[11] W. B. White, J. Acous. Soc. Am. **9**, 47–50 (1938).

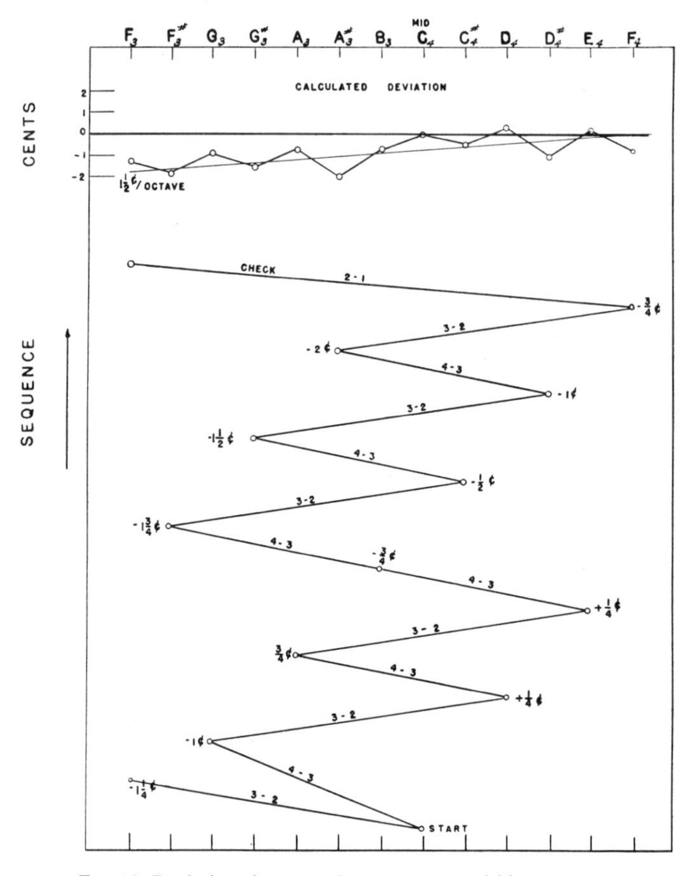


FIG. 12. Deviations from equal temperament within an octave resulting from inharmonicity.

adjusts the tension of the upper string until its fundamental has the same frequency as the second mode of the lower string, as indicated by the absence of beats. If the second mode of the lower string is sharper than a true second harmonic of the fundamental, then the upper string's fundamental will be tuned sharp. The next octave jump will increase the sharpening still further, particularly since the inharmonicity increases toward the high end, as shown in Fig. 9. From the curve there given for the second mode one can derive the expected tuning curve for this particular piano as given by (2–1) in Fig. 11, in which deviations from nominal equal temperament are given in cents. It is seen to be very similar in shape to the average tuning curve found by Railsback (right-hand curve), although its deviations are not as great as he shows.

If the fundamental is missing or weak, as is often the case in the lower register, it may be that rather than beating first and second, the tuner is actually adjusting the second partial of the upper tone to have the same frequency as the fourth partial of the lower tone. When this is the case the tuning curve marked (4–2) in Fig. 11 should be obtained. It has the same shape as (2–1), but its deviations are much greater, even greater than those of Railsback's average curve in the upper register. However, it is quite comparable in the lower register where this method of tuning is more likely to be used.

A tuner often checks his tuning by double octaves, that is, beating the fourth partial of the lower tone against the fundamental of the upper tone. If this were done as a tuning procedure, the resulting tuning curve would be that labeled

(4–1) in Fig. 11, which is seen to fall between the curves. Which of these methods of tuning is actually used, and in which section of the keyboard, appears to depend upon the individual tuner and the particular piano he is tuning.

In laying the temperament initially the tuning is also affected somewhat by the sharpening of the partials. The tuner adjusts the fundamental of one string to his tuning fork, then adjusts another string to the first by listening for beats between partials of the same approximate frequency. He adjusts the beats to be in accordance with a table calculated on the assumption that the partials are truly harmonic. In Fig. 12 is illustrated the sequence used by one tuner. Starting at the bottom with $C_4$ (middle $C$), the lines indicate the intervals being adjusted, each being labeled with the partials which are beating. Taking the corresponding inharmonicities from Fig. 9 and subtracting gives the amounts in cents by which the intervals are long. The resulting tuning is plotted at the top of the figure and is seen to be somewhat irregular, but the general rise is quite similar to that often found throughout the middle register of the piano.

The measurements described here indicate that the "stretched"[11] tuning is a natural result of the inharmonicity of the partials of the piano tone and is perhaps necessary if the piano is to sound in tune with itself. Whether or not stretching is desirable may therefore depend upon the size and construction of the piano and whether it is to be used alone or with other instruments.

TABLE I. Semitones corresponding to numbers to 50. Semitones $=\log_{2^{1/12}} N = 12\times\log_2 N$. 100 cents = 1 semitone.

| $N$ | Interval | Semitones | Cents | $N$ | Interval | Semitones | Cents |
|---|---|---|---|---|---|---|---|
| 1 | | 0.00 | 0.00 | 26 | | 56.41 | 5640.53 |
| | 12.00 | | | | 0.65 | | |
| 2 | | 12.00 | 1200.00 | 27 | | 57.06 | 5705.87 |
| | 7.02 | | | | .63 | | |
| 3 | | 19.02 | 1901.95 | 28 | | 57.69 | 5768.82 |
| | 4.98 | | | | .61 | | |
| 4 | | 24.00 | 2400.00 | 29 | | 58.30 | 5829.58 |
| | 3.86 | | | | .59 | | |
| 5 | | 27.86 | 2786.31 | 30 | | 58.88 | 5888.27 |
| | 3.16 | | | | .57 | | |
| 6 | | 31.02 | 3101.95 | 31 | | 59.45 | 5945.04 |
| | 2.67 | | | | .55 | | |
| 7 | | 33.69 | 3368.82 | 32 | | 60.00 | 6000.00 |
| | 2.31 | | | | .53 | | |
| 8 | | 36.00 | 3600.00 | 33 | | 60.53 | 6053.27 |
| | 2.04 | | | | .52 | | |
| 9 | | 38.04 | 3803.91 | 34 | | 61.05 | 6104.95 |
| | 1.82 | | | | .50 | | |
| 10 | | 39.86 | 3986.31 | 35 | | 61.55 | 6155.14 |
| | 1.65 | | | | .49 | | |
| 11 | | 41.51 | 4151.32 | 36 | | 62.04 | 6203.91 |
| | 1.51 | | | | .47 | | |
| 12 | | 43.02 | 4301.95 | 37 | | 62.51 | 6251.34 |
| | 1.39 | | | | .46 | | |
| 13 | | 44.41 | 4440.53 | 38 | | 62.98 | 6297.51 |
| | 1.28 | | | | .45 | | |
| 14 | | 45.69 | 4568.82 | 39 | | 63.42 | 6342.48 |
| | 1.19 | | | | .44 | | |
| 15 | | 46.88 | 4688.27 | 40 | | 63.86 | 6386.31 |
| | 1.12 | | | | .43 | | |
| 16 | | 48.00 | 4800.00 | 41 | | 64.29 | 6429.06 |
| | 1.05 | | | | .42 | | |
| 17 | | 49.05 | 4904.95 | 42 | | 64.71 | 6470.78 |
| | 0.99 | | | | .41 | | |
| 18 | | 50.04 | 5003.91 | 43 | | 65.12 | 6511.51 |
| | 0.94 | | | | .40 | | |
| 19 | | 50.98 | 5097.51 | 44 | | 65.51 | 6551.32 |
| | 0.89 | | | | .39 | | |
| 20 | | 51.86 | 5186.31 | 45 | | 65.90 | 6590.22 |
| | 0.84 | | | | .38 | | |
| 21 | | 52.71 | 5270.78 | 46 | | 66.28 | 6628.27 |
| | 0.81 | | | | .37 | | |
| 22 | | 53.51 | 5351.32 | 47 | | 66.66 | 6665.51 |
| | 0.77 | | | | .36 | | |
| 23 | | 54.28 | 5428.27 | 48 | | 67.02 | 6701.95 |
| | 0.74 | | | | .36 | | |
| 24 | | 55.02 | 5501.95 | 49 | | 67.38 | 6737.65 |
| | 0.71 | | | | .35 | | |
| 25 | | 55.73 | 5572.63 | 50 | | 67.73 | 6772.63 |
| | 0.68 | | | | | | |

TABLE II.

| 1<br>$n$ | 2<br>sc | 3<br>sem | 4<br>sc | 5<br>cents |
|---|---|---|---|---|
| 1 | 40.91 | 0.00 | 40.91 | |
| 2 | 52.92 | 12.00 | 40.92 | 1 |
| 3 | 59.96 | 19.02 | 40.94 | 3 |
| 4 | 64.95 | 24.00 | 40.95 | 4 |
| 5 | 68.84 | 27.86 | 40.98 | 7 |
| 6 | 72.02 | 31.02 | 41.00 | 9 |
| 7 | 74.72 | 33.69 | 41.03 | 12 |
| 8 | 77.06 | 36.00 | 41.06 | 15 |

Column headings: 1. Mode number; 2. Frequency level; 3. Nominal harmonic interval; 4. Frequency level of "reduced" fundamental; 5. Inharmonicity.

## CONCLUSION

The observations described above, while admittedly preliminary, show definitely that the actual strings used in the piano do not behave like idealized strings. Their modal frequencies do not follow exactly the harmonic series, but are progressively sharp with respect to true harmonics. At least within certain limits the inharmonicity is approximately proportional to the square of the mode number, and increases considerably toward the upper and lower ends of the keyboard. It seems to be about the same in the middle and upper registers of different pianos, but to be less in the lower registers of pianos with longer bass strings. These observations lead to a plausible explanation of the better tone quality generally ascribed to pianos with longer bass strings.

A consideration of piano tuning procedure indicates that the effect of the inharmonicity is to produce just the sort of deviations in tuning that have actually been observed. Much work remains to be done to add to the data here presented, to study in detail the effects of bridge forms, braces, and string construction, and to investigate further the influence on tuning.

The authors are indebted to O. M. Salati and O. H. Kraushaar for their cooperation in making the measurements.

## APPENDIX

### Routine for Establishing Inharmonicity

The basis of this method is the comparison of the logarithms of the ratios of the modal frequencies with the logarithms of the nominal ratios. Furthermore, by choosing as the base of logarithms $2^{1/12}$, the ratios are measured directly in semitones (or cents), and are thus capable of convenient interpretation in terms of the musical intervals.

Table I gives these logarithms for integers to 50. This represents an expansion of a similar table published by Wead[12] and a few corrections have been made. The table shows, for example, that a true seventh harmonic is 33.69 semitones above the fundamental, and that the interval between the seventh and eighth harmonics is 2.31 semitones.

Table II illustrates the subtraction process, based on the data given in Fig. 5. The eighth mode, for example, was found to have a frequency level of 77.06 sc (semitones counted from a reference frequency of 16.35 cycles/sec.). Upon subtracting 36.00 from this value we obtain the frequency level of the fundamental, had this mode been harmonic. Then by subtracting the frequency level of the measured fundamental we arrive at the number of semitones (rather with the decimal point moved over for cents) by which each mode exceeds its harmonic value. The last step is unnecessary in constructing curves as in Fig. 10, since the frequency level of the "reduced fundamentals" may be plotted directly. This is a convenience when an accurate measurement of the fundamental frequency is not available.

The position at which to match the nominal intervals is found by inspection. If the differences in column 4 of Table II are not approximately constant a poor choice of the starting point has been made.

[12] C. K. Wead, Report of the National Museum for 1900, U. S. Government Printing Office (1902), pp. 417–462.

# 5

Copyright © 1964 by the Acoustical Society of America

Reprinted from *J. Acoust. Soc. Am.*, **36**(1), 203–209 (1964)

# Normal Vibration Frequencies of a Stiff Piano String

HARVEY FLETCHER

*Brigham Young University, Provo, Utah*

(Received 5 August 1963)

This paper deals with the normal modes of vibration of a stiff piano string. The equations that govern the vibration of a solid string are developed along traditional lines. They are modified to apply to strings having a solid-steel core upon which are wrapped one or two copper windings. The bass strings of most pianos are made this way. Two boundary conditions are considered: namely, (1) pinned by sharp knife edges at both ends and (2) clamped at both ends. Formulas for the partial frequencies for both of these conditions are developed. The partial frequencies that are calculated by these formulas are compared to the experimental values obtained on an upright Hamilton piano. The experimental values appear to agree somewhat better with the pinned boundary condition rather than the clamped boundary condition, although the differences are not much greater than the observational error. It was found that the formula $f_n = nf_1[(1+Bn^2)/(1+B)]^{\frac{1}{2}}$ gives values of the partial frequencies that agree with the experimental ones where $n$ is the number of the partial, $f$ the fundamental frequency, and $B$ a constant that can be calculated from the dimensions of the wire.

USUALLY, the frequencies of the partials of a piano tone are considered to be harmonic, that is, integer multiples of the fundamental frequency. Many college courses in physics still treat piano strings as having no stiffness, and this leads to the conclusion that the partials are harmonic.

For nearly one hundred years, this has been known to be only approximately true and a poor approximation for the bass strings. For some of these strings, the 40th or 50th partial may depart from the corresponding harmonic by as much as two full-tones sharp. This paper reviews the theoretical aspects of the problem of solid strings and modifies the equations so that they will apply to the wrapped strings in the bass section.

Lord Rayleigh,[1] Seebeck, and Donkin[2] worked on this problem seventy-five or eighty years ago. More recently, Morse,[3] Shankland,[4] Schuck,[5] Young[6,7] and others[8–11] have made contributions, but there seems to be no complete coverage of both the theoretical and experimental aspects of this problem in a single publication. This paper tries to do this, and adds some additional material on wrapped strings.

When a piano string is displaced a distance $y$ at the position $x$, the restoring force due to the tension $T$ is known to be

$$T(\delta^2 y/\delta x^2).$$

It is not so well-known, although it was given by Lord Rayleigh[1] more than eighty-five years ago, that the restoring force due to the elastic stiffness is

$$-QSK^2(\delta^4 y/\delta x^4),$$

where $Q$ is Young's modulus of elasticity, $S$ the area of cross section of the wire, and $K$ its radius of gyration.

Let $\sigma$ be the linear density and $t$ the time. Then, the equation governing the motion of the piano string is

$$-QSK^2(\delta^4 y/\delta x^4)+T(\delta^2 y/\delta x^2)=\sigma(\delta^2 y/\delta x^2). \quad (1)$$

This is the form of the equation originally set up by Lord Rayleigh.

A frictional term of the form

$$R(\delta y/\delta t),$$

should be introduced on the left-hand side of this equation. However, for the piano strings as they are now made and used, this term produces only a very small effect upon the values of the partial frequencies. As its introduction makes the solution of Eq. (1) much more

[1] Lord Rayleigh, *The Theory of Sound* (MacMillan and Co. Ltd., London, 1894), Vol. 1, pp. 298–301.
[2] W. F. Donkin, *Acoustics* (Clarendon Press, Oxford, England, 1884), 2nd ed., p. 187.
[3] P. M. Morse, *Vibration and Sound* (McGraw-Hill Book Co., Inc., New York, 1948), 2nd ed., pp. 127–131.
[4] R. S. Shankland and J. W. Coltman, J. Acoust. Soc. Am. **10**, 161–166 (1939).
[5] O. H. Schuck and R. W. Young, J. Acoust. Soc. Am. **15**, 1–11 (1943).
[6] R. W. Young, J. Acoust. Soc. Am. **24**, 267–273 (1952).
[7] R. W. Young, Acustica **4**, 259–262 (1954).
[8] W. E. Kock, J. Acoust. Soc. Am. **8**, 227–233 (1937).
[9] Franklin Miller, Jr., J. Acoust. Soc. Am. **21**, 318–322 (1949).
[10] Otto Schaefer, Ann. Phys. **62**, 156–164 (1920).
[11] G. E. Allan, Phil. Mag. **4**, 1324–1337 (1937).

complicated, it is not considered here. But it must be remembered that it is the principal term that measures the decay of the vibration of the string after it has been struck.

Let $l$ be the length of the string between its supports and $d$ its diameter. It is convenient to make the following substitutions:

$$B=(\pi^3 QSK^2/Tl^2), \quad (2)$$

$$f_0=(1/2l)(T/\sigma)^{\frac{1}{2}}. \quad (3)$$

For a string that has no stiffness and negligible frictional retarding force, the value of $f_0$ is the fundamental vibration of such a string. As we shall see, it is a close approximation to the fundamental vibration of actual piano strings. If the string is driven by an external periodic force, then $f_0$ is exactly the resonance frequency for a string having no stiffness.

To solve Eq. (1), one assumes $y$ is a sum of terms of the form

$$y=Ce^{2\pi kx}e^{-2\pi jft}, \quad (4)$$

where $C$, $k$, and $f$ are constants to be determined from Eq. (1) and the boundary and initial conditions. If the value of $y$ from (4) is substituted in (1), the following equation results:

$$k^4-(1/4Bl^2)k^2-(f^2/16Bl^4f_0^2)=0. \quad (5)$$

This shows that for any possible frequency $f$ there are four possible values of $k$ as follows:

$$k=\pm k_1 \quad \text{where} \quad k_1^2=\frac{1}{8Bl^2}\left[\left(1+\frac{4Bf^2}{f_0^2}\right)^{\frac{1}{2}}+1\right], \quad (6)$$

and

$$k=\pm jk_2 \quad \text{where} \quad k_2^2=\frac{1}{8Bl^2}\left[\left(1+\frac{4Bf^2}{f_0^2}\right)^{\frac{1}{2}}-1\right]. \quad (7)$$

It will be noted that $k_1$ and $k_2$ are related as follows:

$$k_1^2-k_2^2=(1/4Bl^2). \quad (8)$$

The general solution of Eq. (1) is then

$$y=e^{-j2\pi ft}(K_1\cosh 2\pi k_1x+K_2\cos 2\pi k_2x$$
$$+K_3\sin 2\pi k_1x+K_4\sin 2\pi k_2x). \quad (9)$$

All these relations are independent of the boundary conditions. So, for every possible value of $k_1$, there is a corresponding $k_2$ obtained from Eq. (8) and a corresponding value of $f$ obtained from Eq. (5). If we choose the origin of the $x$ axis at the center of the piano string, then one end will be at $l/2$ and the other at $-l/2$, and the boundary conditions will be symmetrical. Then, the even functions are built from the first two terms of Eq. (9) and the odd functions from the last two terms. For both of these, if the boundary conditions fit at $l/2$ they will also fit at $-l/2$.

### PINNED BOUNDARY CONDITION

If both ends are pinned by knife edges, then $y=\partial^2y/\partial x^2=0$ at $x=l/2$ and $-l/2$. If we use only the even functions, that is, take $K_3$ and $K_4$ equal to zero, these boundary conditions will fit if $K_1=0$ and $\cos\pi kl=0$; that is,

$$k=n/2l, \quad (10)$$

where $n$ can be 1, 3, 5, 7, or any odd integer.

For each of these values of $k$, there is a corresponding frequency $f$ of the odd partials obtained from Eq. (5) as

$$f_n=nf_0(1+Bn^2)^{\frac{1}{2}}. \quad (11)$$

For these frequencies,

$$y=K_2\cos(\pi nx/l)\cos 2\pi f_nt, \quad (12)$$

where $K_2$ takes on a different value for each odd partial and is determined by the amplitude of that partial.

If we use only the odd functions, then $K_1$, $K_2$, and $K_3$ are zero and $\sin\pi kl=0$, or

$$k=(n/2l), \quad (10A)$$

where $n=2$, 4, 6, or any even integer.

The frequencies corresponding to these values of $k$ are also given by Eq. (11), and the values of $y$ are

$$y=K_4\sin(\pi nx/l)\cos 2\pi f_nt, \quad (13)$$

where $K_4$ takes a different value for each even partial and is determined by the amplitude of that partial.

### CLAMPED BOUNDARY CONDITIONS

For the case when the two ends are clamped, the solution is more complicated. The boundary conditions at $x=l/2$ are $y=0=\partial y/\partial x$. Applying these two conditions to the even functions gives

$$K_1\cosh(\pi k_1l)=-K_2\cos(\pi k_2l)$$

and

$$K_1k_1\sinh(\pi k_1l)=K_2k_2\sin(\pi k_2l).$$

Dividing one equation by the other gives, for the condition for determining the values of $k_2$ from the even functions,

$$-\tanh(\pi k_1l)=(k_2/k_1)\tan(\pi k_2l). \quad (14)$$

Similarly, applying the boundary conditions to the odd functions,

$$\tanh(\pi k_1l)=(k_1/k_2)\tan(\pi k_2l). \quad (15)$$

If the value of $k_1$ from Eq. (8) is substituted in Eqs. (14) and (15), the allowed values of $k_2$ for both the odd and the even functions can be obtained by numerical solution. These allowed values of $k_2$ can then be sub-substituted in Eq. (6) to obtain the values of the normal frequencies $f_n$ as

$$f_n=2k_2lf_0(1+4B^2k_2^2)^{\frac{1}{2}}. \quad (16)$$

An approximate formula for $k_2$ in terms of the constants of the string can be obtained as follows. From the previous analysis, one should expect that the value of $k_2$ would be close to $n/2l$. So

$$k_2 = n/2l(1+\epsilon), \quad (17)$$

where $\epsilon$ is a small quantity as compared to unity. The equations for determining $\epsilon$ are now derived. Since $k_2$ is approximately equal to $n/2l$, the quantity $k_1 l_1$ is approximately equal to $\pi/2[n^2+(1/B)]^{\frac{1}{2}}$. The smallest value of this quantity will be when $n=1$ and $B$ is the largest value found in piano strings. The largest experimental value of $B$ was found to be 0.024 for the highest note on the piano. This gives for $\pi k_1 l$ a value of 10. Therefore, the quantity $\tanh(\pi k_1 l)$ can always be taken as unity. Then, Eq. (14) reduces to

$$-\tan \pi k_2 l = -\tan\left(\frac{\pi n\epsilon}{2}+\frac{\pi n}{2}\right)$$

$$= \cot\frac{\pi n\epsilon}{2} = \frac{[k_2^2+(1/4B^2)]^{\frac{1}{2}}}{k_2}. \quad (18)$$

If $n/2l(1+\epsilon)$ is substituted for $k_2$ and $1/\pi n\epsilon$ for $\cot \pi n\epsilon/2$, the following equation in $\epsilon$ is obtained:

$$[(\pi n\epsilon)^2/2]\{[(\pi n\epsilon)^2/2]Bn^2(1+\epsilon)^2\} = Bn^2(1+\epsilon)^2. \quad (19)$$

If higher powers of $\epsilon$ greater than $\epsilon^2$ are neglected, the solution of (19) is

$$\epsilon = (2/\pi)B^{\frac{1}{2}} + (4/\pi^2)B. \quad (20)$$

If this value of $\epsilon$ is substituted in Eq. (16) and terms containing $B$ to powers greater than unity are neglected, then

$$f_n = nf_0[1+(2/\pi)B^{\frac{1}{2}}+(4/\pi^2)B](1+Bn^2)^{\frac{1}{2}}. \quad (21)$$

This shows that clamping the ends, instead of pinning them, increases the partial frequencies by the factor

$$[1+(2/\pi)B^{\frac{1}{2}}+(4/\pi^2)B].$$

Equation (21) can be written

$$f_n = nf_0\{1+(4/\pi)B^{\frac{1}{2}}+[(12/\pi^2)+n^2]B\}^{\frac{1}{2}}, \quad (22)$$

which is the formula first deduced by Seebeck.[2]

If we start with Eq. (21) and retain only the square-root expansion, then this equation reduces to

$$f_n = nf_0\{1+(2/\pi)B^{\frac{1}{2}}+[(4/\pi^2)+(n^2/2)]B\}. \quad (23)$$

This is the formula given by Morse[3] in his book.

This was deduced for the even functions where $n=1$, 3, 5, 7, etc. For the odd functions $n=2$, 4, 6, 8, etc., Eq. (15) reduces to

$$\tan(\pi k_2 l) = k_2/k_1).$$

Again, let $k_2 = (n/2l)(1+\epsilon)$. Then,

$$\tan(\pi k_2 l) = \tan(\pi n\epsilon/2) = k_2/k_1,$$

when $n$ is an even integer. This equation is the same as Eq. (18). Therefore, the above equations hold for $n$ being any integer, either even or odd.

An examination of the supports for the wires in a piano shows that the boundary condition lies somewhere between the two conditions treated above. In general, for either boundary conditions, one sees that

$$f_n = nF(1+Bn^2)^{\frac{1}{2}}, \quad (24)$$

where $F$ and $B$ are two constants that can be obtained from an accurate measurement of the frequencies of any two partials. The frequency of all the other partials can be obtained from Eq. (24).

If $f_n$ is the frequency of the $n$th partial and $f_m$ the frequency of the $m$th partial, then it follows from Eq. (24) that

$$F^2 = \frac{[(m/n)f_n]^2 - [(n/m)f_m]^2}{m^2 - n^2}, \quad (25)$$

$$B = \frac{(rm/n)^2 - 1}{n^2 - (rm/n)^2 m^2}, \quad (26)$$

where $r$ is the ratio of the frequency of the $n$th partial to the frequency of the $m$th partial.

The value of $f_0$ is between the value of $F$ and $F$ divided by

$$1+(2/\pi)B^{\frac{1}{2}}+(4/\pi^2)B.$$

Since $B$ depends upon $f_0$, there will be two calculated values of $B$ corresponding to the two boundary conditions.

## COMPARISON OF CALCULATED AND EXPERIMENTAL VALUES FOR $B$ FOR SOLID PIANO WIRES

It will be seen from Eqs. (2) and (3) that the calculated value of $B$ is given by

$$B = \pi^2 QSK^2/4l^4\sigma f_0^2. \quad (27)$$

Solid piano strings are round and made of steel. If we use cgs units for all numerical work, then the volume density of steel is 7.7, the value of $Q = 19.5\times10^{11}$,

$$S = \pi d^2/4, \; K = d/4, \text{ and } \sigma = 7.7S.$$

Therefore,

$$B = 3.95\times10^{10}(d^2/l^4 f_0^2). \quad (27a)$$

The values of $d$ and $l$ can be measured directly on an installed piano string, but the value of $f_0$ must be obtained from the fundamental frequency $f_1$ of the string. The relationship between $f_1$ and $f_0$ is different for the two boundary conditions considered. The value of $f_1$ is the same under each of the boundary conditions.

Let $f_p$ represent $f_0$, calculated from $f_1$ with pinned boundary conditions, and $f_c$ the corresponding value for the clamped condition. Also, let $B_p$ and $B_c$ be the corresponding calculated values of $B$ from Eq. (27a).

For the fundamental frequency, $n=1$ so

$$f_1=f_p(1+B_p)^{\frac{1}{2}}, \tag{28}$$

and

$$f_1=f_c[1+(2/\pi)B_c^{\frac{1}{2}}+(4/\pi)B_c^{2}](1+B_c)^{\frac{1}{2}}. \tag{28a}$$

All of the quantities in Eq. (28), except $f_0$, are the same for both boundary conditions. Therefore,

$$B_c/B_p=(f_p/f_c)^2$$
$$=[1+(4/\pi)B_c^{\frac{1}{2}}+(12/\pi^2)B_c][(1+B_c)/(1+B_p)]. \tag{28b}$$

Since the values of $B_c$ and $B_p$ range from 0.01 to 0.0001 and are never far apart, it is safe to put the last factor equal to unity. Also, the third term is usually negligible. For example, for notes below high C, the value of $B$ is less than 0.01, and so the last term is always 500 or more times the second term. Therefore,

$$B_c=[1+(4/\pi)B_c^{\frac{1}{2}}]B_p. \tag{28c}$$

The values of $f_1$ can be obtained arbitrarily from a table or calculated from the equation

$$f_1=27.5\times 2^{(N-1)/12}, \tag{29}$$

where $N$ is the number of the key starting with the first key on the left side of the keyboard as number 1 and the last key on the right as number 88.

The piano used for this comparison was a Hamilton upright with key system 763. The dimensions of the wires are given in Table I for the solid strings, starting with key No. 31. The values of $B$ calculated from Eq. (28b) are given by the solid points in Fig. 1. The sudden breaks in the curve are due to sudden changes in the gauge of the piano wire as shown by underlines in Table I. The one exception to this is from key No. 58 to No. 59. The jump in the value of $B$ at this point is due to a change in the frame that supports the wires, thus producing a sudden large change in the length of the wire.

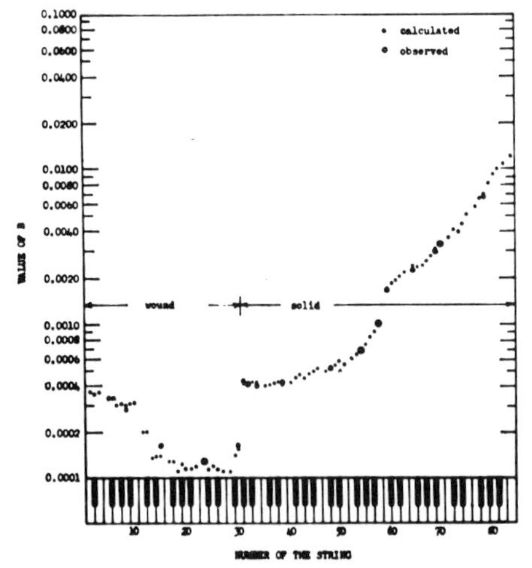


Fig. 1. Values of $B$ in Hamilton upright piano (new model).

To find experimentally the values of $B$ of this piano, one must find the frequencies of the partial tones. A method of doing this was described in **our** paper, "The Quality of Piano Tones."[12] This method was refined by obtaining a better analyzer with a passband only 4 cps wide. Another change was to pluck the string instead of hitting the key in the usual manner. This intensified the higher partials and, therefore, made it possible to obtain a greater accuracy in the measurement of their frequencies. The three strings corresponding to a single key in the upper register of the piano were not exactly in tune. In Table II are given the three frequencies as measured by a Stroboconn. For example, the frequency of the tenth partial of one of the G′ wires is more than twenty-three cps above one of the others. For this reason, it was difficult to identify the partial unless only one string was vibrating.

Table I. Dimensions of solid strings in Hamilton upright piano (new model).

| Key No. | $d$ (cm) | $l$ (cm) | Key No. | $d$ (cm) | $l$ (cm) | Key No. | $d$ (cm) | $l$ (cm) |
|---|---|---|---|---|---|---|---|---|
| 31 | 0.119 | 86.1 | 51 | 0.094 | 40.0 | 71 | 0.085 | 13.65 |
| 32 | 0.119 | 83.6 | 52 | 0.094 | 38.1 | 72 | 0.085 | 12.95 |
| 33 | 0.119 | 81.1 | 53 | 0.094 | 36.4 | 73 | 0.084 | 12.25 |
| 34 | 0.119 | 78.5 | 54 | 0.094 | 34.6 | 74 | 0.084 | 11.55 |
| 35 | 0.114 | 76.0 | 55 | 0.094 | 33.0 | 75 | 0.084 | 10.88 |
| 36 | 0.114 | 73.4 | 56 | 0.094 | 31.4 | 76 | 0.084 | 10.24 |
| 37 | 0.114 | 70.8 | 57 | 0.094 | 29.8 | 77 | 0.084 | 9.63 |
| 38 | 0.114 | 68.4 | 58 | 0.094 | 28.3 | 78 | 0.084 | 9.15 |
| 39 | 0.109 | 65.3 | 59 | 0.094 | 23.8 | 79 | 0.084 | 8.60 |
| 40 | 0.109 | 63.2 | 60 | 0.094 | 22.8 | 80 | 0.084 | 8.08 |
| 41 | 0.109 | 60.7 | 61 | 0.094 | 21.9 | 81 | 0.079 | 7.59 |
| 42 | 0.109 | 58.2 | 62 | 0.094 | 21.0 | 82 | 0.079 | 7.13 |
| 43 | 0.104 | 55.8 | 63 | 0.094 | 20.1 | 83 | 0.079 | 6.77 |
| 44 | 0.104 | 53.5 | 64 | 0.094 | 19.1 | 84 | 0.079 | 6.36 |
| 45 | 0.104 | 51.4 | 65 | 0.085 | 18.3 | 85 | 0.079 | 5.97 |
| 46 | 0.104 | 49.4 | 66 | 0.085 | 17.5 | 86 | 0.079 | 5.60 |
| 47 | 0.099 | 47.4 | 67 | 0.085 | 16.7 | 67 | 0.079 | 5.25 |
| 48 | 0.099 | 45.3 | 68 | 0.085 | 15.9 | 88 | 0.079 | 4.90 |
| 49 | 0.099 | 43.6 | 69 | 0.085 | 15.05 | | | |
| 50 | 0.099 | 41.7 | 70 | 0.085 | 14.35 | | | |

A third method, which gave a greater accuracy than either of the two mentioned above, is now described. An alternating magnetic driving force was produced by a small magnetic driving coil. When the frequency of the driving force was equal to one of the partial frequencies, a maximum sound was produced by the string vibrating in the mode corresponding to this frequency. A small microphone was placed near the string, which picked

[12] H. Fletcher, E. D. Blackham, and R. Stratton, "Quality of Piano Tones," J. Acoust. Soc. Am. 34, 749 (1962).

T ~ 2×10⁸

up the sound. The corresponding electrical current was sent to a voltmeter. The frequency was varied until the voltmeter read a maximum. This frequency was then measured either on the Stroboconn or an electronic counter. The former was used for the low frequencies and the latter for the high frequencies.

Typical results obtained by this last method are shown in Tables III and IV. The method of making the calculations of $F$ and $B$ from these data is also indicated in these tables. For all solid strings in this piano, the values of $Bn^2$ are always so small that Eq. (24) can be written

$$f_n - nF = BFn^3/2. \tag{24a}$$

If we designate $f_n - nF$ as $\Delta f$, then it is seen that

$$B = (2/F)(\Delta f/n^3). \tag{26b}$$

For calculating $F$ and $B$ from such data as those in Tables III and IV, it is convenient to choose the two partials such that $m=2n$, in which case Eqs. (25) and (26) reduce to

$$F = (8f_n - f_{2n})/6n, \tag{25a}$$

$$B = (2/n^2)[(r-2)/(8-r)]. \tag{26a}$$

These equations make the calculations more simple. For example, in Table III, the number $n$ of the partial is given in Column 1, and the corresponding observed frequency in column 2. In column 3, the values of $\Delta f/n^3$ are given. It is seen that these values are very nearly the same for partials from 4 to 17. For the lower partials, an observational error of 0.2 or 0.3 cps will account for the variation. For the partials higher than 16, the intensity level is so low that the ability to pick up the partial in the background noise becomes much more difficult and, hence, a large observational error results. So only values corresponding to $n=4$ to $n=16$ were used in the average values shown. The data in Table IV were similarly treated.

In this way, the experimental values of $B$ were obtained, which are shown by the circles in Fig. 1. It is seen that they agree very well with the calculated values. These calculations are for the pinned boundary condition. The difference between $B_p$ and $B_c$ is not much greater than the observational error, being 10% for the highest key No. 78 and less than 4% for the

TABLE II. Frequencies of the three strings associated with one key.

| | | | |
|---|---|---|---|
| A# | 477.9 | 474.3 | 474.9 |
| G | 403.5 | 402.1 | 401.2 |
| D | 570.6 | 570.6 | 566.0 |
| F# | 717.3 | 713.1 | 712.7 |
| G | 765.2 | 765.6 | 763.2 |
| C | 1018.5 | 1020.8 | 1019.1 |
| F | 1350.1 | 1343.1 | 1334.6 |
| D | 2251.0 | 2253.6 | 2245.8 |

TABLE III. Observations and calculations for key No. 31.

| $n$ | obs $f_n$ | $\Delta f/n^3$ |
|---|---|---|
| 1 | 152.6 | ... |
| 2 | 305.8 | 0.025 |
| 3 | 459.2 | 0.030 |
| 4 | 613.0 | 0.0281 |
| 5 | 767.9 | 0.0312 |
| 6 | 924.3 | 0.0346 |
| 7 | 1080.9 | 0.0328 |
| 8 | 1240.2 | 0.0346 |
| 9 | 1399.7 | 0.0335 |
| 10 | 1561.7 | 0.0337 |
| 11 | 1725.8 | 0.0338 |
| 12 | 1891.8 | 0.0337 |
| 13 | 2060.0 | 0.0335 |
| 14 | 2230.3 | 0.0332 |
| 15 | 2405.0 | 0.0334 |
| 16 | 2574.0 | 0.0318 |
| 17 | 2744.0 | 0.0297 |
| 20 | 3317.0 | 0.0327 |

Calculation of $F$ and $B$

| $n$ | $F$ | $B$ |
|---|---|---|
| 1 and 2 | 152.50 | 0.0013 |
| 2 and 4 | 152.62 | 0.00082 |
| 3 and 6 | 152.74 | 0.00058 |
| 4 and 8 | 152.66 | 0.00048 |
| 5 and 10 | 152.77 | 0.00045 |
| 6 and 12 | 152.85 | 0.00043 |
| 7 and 14 | 152.78 | 0.00043 |
| 8 and 16 | 153.07 | 0.00045 |
| 10 and 20 | 152.94 | 0.00053 |
| Average | 152.8 | 0.000448 |

Average $\Delta f/n^3 = 0.0337$
Corresponding $B = 0.000441$
Final $B = 0.000444$

TABLE IV. Observations and calculations for key No. 59.

| $n$ | obs. $f_n$ | $\Delta f/n^3$ |
|---|---|---|
| 1 | 777.2 | 0.50 |
| 2 | 1558.1 | 0.59 |
| 3 | 2348.0 | 0.66 |
| 4 | 3148.7 | 0.66 |
| 5 | 3966.0 | 0.66 |
| 6 | 4800.0 | 0.65 |
| 7 | 5647.0 | 0.61 |
| 8 | 6544.0 | 0.65 |
| 9 | 7451.0 | 0.64 |

Calculation of $F$ and $B$

| $n$ | $F$ | $B$ |
|---|---|---|
| 1 and 2 | 776.6 | 0.00160 |
| 2 and 4 | 776.4 | 0.00175 |
| 3 and 6 | 776.9 | 0.00166 |
| 4 and 8 | 776.9 | 0.00166 |
| Average | 776.7 | 0.00167 |

Average $\Delta f/n^3 = 0.650$
Corresponding $B = 0.000167$
Final $B = 0.000167$

keys below No. 58. The data seem to indicate that the pinned condition is the one that governs, although the evidence is not conclusive. It also shows that Eq. (28b), with the numerical constant shown, will give accurate values of $B$ for the piano wires used on this piano. It is our understanding that these same wires are used generally for pianos.

Having the values of $B$, one can calculate all the partial frequencies from the equation

$$f_n = \left[ f_1 \Big/ \left(1+\frac{B}{2}\right)\right]\left(n+\frac{B}{2}n^3\right), \qquad (24b)$$

where $f_1$ is the fundamental frequency.

## PIANO STRINGS WITH STEEL CORE WOUND WITH COPPER WIRE

The first 30 keys are associated with wound wires, some with one and some with two copper windings. Therefore, the above equations cannot be applied without modification. If these cases, the elastic-restoring torque is due almost entirely to the steel core, but the linear density is due to the core and the windings. Let us first consider the linear density.

### Determination of the Linear Density

Let $d$ be the diameter of the steel core and $D$ the diameter of the string including the winding. If the copper winding were a sheaf, its cross-sectional area would be

$$(\pi D^2/4) - (\pi d^2/4).$$

If it were a round wire, its cross section would be reduced by $\pi/4$ of this value. By use of the volume density of steel as 7.7 and of copper as 8.8, the value of the linear density of the wound string (in cgs units) is then

$$\sigma = 5.43D^2 - 0.62d^2. \qquad (30)$$

It must be remembered that this is the linear density of only the part of the string that is fully covered.

There are two windings on the core of some of these strings so that the copper may be packed somewhat tighter than for a single winding; but the above formula agrees with direct measurements of $\sigma$.

A section of the A'''' string was cut and weighed and $\sigma$ was found to be 2.086. For this string, the outer diameter is 0.617 cm and the core diameter is 0.141 cm. Equation (30) then gives $\sigma = 2.083$.

Similarly, for the G''' string, the value of $\sigma$ was measured to be 0.860. The values of $D$ and $d$ were measured to 0.395 cm and 0.125 cm, so Eq. (30) gives the value of 0.860. This close agreement indicates that Eq. (30) should give fairly accurate values for the linear density.

### Experimental Determination of $QSK^2$

It is known that a rod of length $l$ clamped tightly at one end has a period of vibration of $T$ sec, such that

$$QSK^2 = 3.19(l^4\sigma/T^2). \qquad (31)$$

It is also known that such a bar will be deflected a distance $y$ by a weight $w$ that is hung $l$ centimeters from the support if

$$QSK^2 = \tfrac{1}{3}(980wl^3/y). \qquad (32)$$

For the A'''' string, the first bass string on the piano, $\sigma = 2.08$ gm/cm. Vibration tests gave the following results:

$l = 34.5$ cm, $T = 0.477$ sec, so, $QSK^2 = 4.1\times10^7$;
$l = 43.0$ cm, $T = 0.755$ sec, so, $QSK^2 = 4.0\times10^7$.

Deflection tests gave the following results:

$l = 10.85$ cm, $y/w = 0.01035$, so, $QSK^2 = 4.0\times10^7$;
$l = 11.9$ cm, $y/w = 0.0135$, so, $QSK^2 = 4.1\times10^7$.

Deflection measurements upon the core alone gave the value $QSK = 3.84\times10^7$. A value calculated for a steel wire of diameter 0.141 cm from Eq. (28) is $3.80\times10^7$. This indicates that the measured value of $QSK^2$ only about 7% higher than that for the core alone. A solid steel wire of the same size would have a value 38 times larger than the one given above.

Similar deflection measurements that were made on the G''' string gave a value of $QSK^2 = 2.4\times10^7$. For the core alone, such measurements gave a value of $2.30\times10^7$, which may be compared to a value calculated for $d = 0.124$ cm of $2.27\times10^7$. This indicates that the G''' string has a value of $QSK^2$ that is only about 5% higher than its core. Similar deflection measurements of the G'' string yielded $QSK^2 = 0.99\times10^7$ and for the core alone a value of $0.96\times10^7$.

### Calculation of $B$ for Wrapped Strings

If we assume that the restoring elastic torque is all due to the steel core, then $Q = 19.5\times10^{11}$, $S = \pi d^2/4$, and $K = d/4$, where all of these quantities refer to the steel core. If $D$ is the outer diameter, then the linear density $\sigma$ is given approximately by $\sigma = 5.5D^2$. If it is assumed that the windings extend the entire length $l$ of the core, and that the torque is 7% greater than that produced by the core, then Eq. (28) becomes

$$B = 4.6\times10^{10}(d^4/D^2 f_0^2 l^4). \qquad (28c)$$

Since the windings do not cover the entire length of the core, there are two lengths $l$ and $l_1$ for those wires having one winding, and three lengths $l$, $l_1$, and $l_2$ for those having two windings. There must be a reflection of the wave on the wire at the places where each winding stops. Consequently, we would expect three fundamental modes with the corresponding frequencies close together. Measurement of the partials of these strings show that there are many weak partials besides those accounted for by Eq. (24b). In this paper, no attempt is made to account for all these partials, but only the most prominent ones. These can be calculated approximately by Eq. (28c) if $l$ is taken as the distance between where the outside winding starts and where it ends.

The dimensions of the bass strings in this piano are given in Table V. The value of $l$ is taken as the value of $l_2$ for the first ten strings and as the value of $l_1$ in the other bass strings. Then the calculated values of $B$ from Eq. (28c) are shown by the curve in Fig. 1. It is seen that there is fair agreement between the observed $B$ and that calculated by (28c).

TABLE V. Dimensions of wound strings in Hamilton upright piano (new model).

| Key No. | $f_1$ | $d$ | $D$ | $l$ | $l_1$ | $l_2$ |
|---|---|---|---|---|---|---|
| 1 | 27.5 | 0.140 | 0.600 | 121.6 | 118.1 | 115.4 |
| 2 | 29.1 | 0.140 | 0.585 | 120.6 | 117.1 | 114.3 |
| 3 | 30.9 | 0.140 | 0.550 | 119.6 | 115.8 | 113.5 |
| 4 | 32.7 | 0.135 | 0.521 | 118.6 | 114.8 | 112.3 |
| 5 | 34.6 | 0.135 | 0.500 | 117.6 | 113.8 | 111.3 |
| 6 | 36.7 | 0.130 | 0.470 | 116.6 | 112.8 | 110.3 |
| 7 | 38.9 | 0.130 | 0.449 | 115.6 | 111.8 | 109.3 |
| 8 | 41.2 | 0.130 | 0.432 | 114.6 | 110.8 | 108.5 |
| 9 | 43.7 | 0.130 | 0.413 | 113.3 | 109.7 | 107.2 |
| 10 | 46.3 | 0.130 | 0.397 | 112.5 | 108.7 | 106.0 |
| 11 | 49.0 | 0.114 | 0.345 | 111.5 | 107.7 | ... |
| 12 | 51.9 | 0.114 | 0.332 | 110.5 | 106.7 | ... |
| 13 | 55.0 | 0.104 | 0.318 | 109.5 | 105.7 | ... |
| 14 | 58.3 | 0.104 | 0.305 | 108.5 | 104.7 | ... |
| 15 | 61.7 | 0.104 | 0.295 | 107.5 | 103.7 | ... |
| 16 | 65.4 | 0.102 | 0.285 | 106.5 | 102.7 | ... |
| 17 | 69.3 | 0.102 | 0.271 | 105.4 | 101.6 | ... |
| 18 | 73.4 | 0.102 | 0.261 | 104.4 | 100.6 | ... |
| 19 | 77.8 | 0.102 | 0.256 | 103.4 | 99.6 | ... |
| 20 | 82.4 | 0.099 | 0.247 | 102.4 | 98.6 | ... |
| 21 | 87.3 | 0.099 | 0.236 | 101.4 | 97.6 | ... |
| 22 | 92.5 | 0.099 | 0.223 | 100.4 | 96.6 | ... |
| 23 | 98.0 | 0.099 | 0.207 | 99.3 | 95.5 | ... |
| 24 | 103.8 | 0.094 | 0.191 | 98.3 | 94.5 | ... |
| 25 | 110.0 | 0.094 | 0.179 | 97.3 | 93.5 | ... |
| 26 | 116.5 | 0.094 | 0.174 | 96.3 | 92.5 | ... |
| 27 | 123.5 | 0.094 | 0.171 | 95.3 | 91.5 | ... |
| 28 | 130.8 | 0.094 | 0.166 | 94.3 | 90.5 | ... |
| 29 | 138.6 | 0.094 | 0.156 | 91.6 | 86.2 | ... |
| 30 | 146.8 | 0.094 | 0.150 | 88.6 | 82.6 | ... |

TABLE VI. Comparison of calculated and observed values of partial frequencies.

| | String No. 23 | | String No. 54 | |
|---|---|---|---|---|
| $n$ | Calc | Obs | Calc | Obs |
| 1 | 97.3 | ... | 581.5 | ... |
| 2 | 194.6 | ... | 1163.3 | ... |
| 3 | 292.1 | ... | 1449.5 | ... |
| 4 | 389.6 | 388.5 | 2338.5 | 2338.5 |
| 5 | 487.2 | 487.9 | 2932.0 | 2932.0 |
| 6 | 584.1 | 583.6 | 3532.0 | 3532.0 |
| 7 | 683.1 | ... | 4139.0 | 4138.0 |
| 8 | 781.4 | 780.0 | 4755.0 | 4755.0 |
| 9 | 880.0 | 879.5 | 5381.0 | 5377.0 |
| 10 | 978.8 | 976.4 | 6013.0 | 6010.0 |
| 11 | 1078.0 | 1076.0 | 6661.0 | 6654.0 |
| 12 | 1178.0 | 1176.0 | | |
| 13 | 1277.0 | 1276.0 | | |
| 14 | 1378.0 | 1377.0 | | |
| 15 | 1479.0 | 1478.0 | | |
| 16 | 1591.0 | 1581.0 | | |
| 17 | 1683.0 | 1682.0 | | |
| 18 | 1686.0 | 1682.0 | | |
| 19 | 1786.0 | 1782.0 | | |
| 20 | 1889.0 | 1889.0 | | |

To show how close the calculated values of the frequencies agree with those observed using the values of $B$ in Fig. 1, a table of observed and calculated values is given in Table VI for string No. 23 and No. 54.

It is concluded that for the usual piano strings, such as are used in the Hamilton piano, Eq. (28) gives an accurate value of $B$ for solid strings, and that the frequencies of the partials can be calculated from Eq. (24b). For the wound strings, Eq. (28c) gives a good approximation for $B$ and also Eq. (24b) gives the partial frequencies. As indicated in our paper,[12] the excellence of the tone from a piano can not be said to be greater or less as the value of $B$ becomes greater or less. There must be an optimum value of $B$ for each string and this value has not yet been found. It is certainly not $B=0$, which would mean that all the partials should be harmonic.

## ACKNOWLEDGMENTS

I wish to acknowledge the valuable assistance of Donnell Blackham and Norman Geertsen on the experimental part of this research work. This work was sponsored financially by the National Science Foundation.

# 6

*Copyright © 1966 by Fördergemeinschaft Klavier e.V.*

# INFLUENCE OF IRREGULAR PATTERNS IN THE INHARMONICITY OF PIANO TONE PARTIALS UPON TUNING PRACTICE

**Earle L. Kent**

*C. G. Conn, Ltd., Elkhart, Indiana (USA)*

*This corrected translation was prepared expressly for this Benchmark volume by Earle L. Kent, from "Influence of Irregular Patterns in the Inharmonicity of Piano Tone Partials Upon Tuning Practice," from* Dokumentation Europiano Kongress Berlin, 1965. *Illus: Copyright© 1966 by Fördergemeinschaft Klavier e.V. Reprinted from* Dokumentation Europiano Kongress Berlin, 1965

It has been shown that inharmonicity of the partials in piano-string tones influences the tuning of the piano.[1] The term "inharmonicity" is used here to denote that partials do not have the whole-number relationship to each other that harmonics have. The partials usually are at frequencies higher than those that would be harmonic. They play an important part in the tuning process and in judging the results from the tuned piano. The fact that the upper partials are not harmonically related to the fundamental frequencies produces a scale that deviates from the equally tempered scale. Measurements made by Railsback, and published in the article by Schuck and Young [see Paper 4], showed that piano tuners usually tune progressively sharp with respect to equal temperament in the middle and treble registers and progressively flat in the bass. In addition to the general trend of stretching the octaves, they showed that the typical tuner does not tune on a uniformly or smoothly stretched scale but that slightly irregular deviations from a smooth scale result. This may be partly due to tuning instability, partly due to the judgment of the tuner, and partly due to the fact that the string-to-string pattern of partial inharmonicity is not smooth. Schuck and Young showed how one tuner deviated up to 2 cents from the equally tempered scale in tuning the octave $F_3$ to $F_4$ which often is used by the piano tuner for laying the foundation bearings from which the rest of the piano is tuned.

An examination of conditions that exist in some pianos indicates that the string-to-string patterns of partial inharmonicity can be irregular enough to cause a problem for the conscientious tuner. This paper deals with this problem and the practical implications for the tuner and the musician.

A number of factors influence the frequencies of the partials in the tone produced by a piano string.[2] The stiffness of the wire, its uniformity, and its boundary conditions are the principle factors. It is normally expected that these factors will cause the partials to be at frequencies slightly higher than the frequency of the harmonics and that they will depart from the harmonic frequency progressively more as the mode number of the partial increases. In some instances, there are exceptions, however. Some piano strings have partials that are found to be harmonic or at a lower frequency than harmonic. Some strings are found to have a partial that is not as inharmonic as a lower-mode partial.

The frequencies of partials were carefully measured for the $F_3$ to $F_4$ octave in several upright pianos. The Stroboconn was used for all measurements. A Hewlett Packard Model 302A wave analyzer or a General Radio sound analyzer Type 760A was used as a filter during the measurements to facilitate the reading of the stroboscopic patterns on the Stroboconn. The results of the measurements of the first eight partials in this octave on a 42-inch piano are shown in Figure 1. Note the sharp jump in inharmonicity between $F_3$ and $F\sharp_3$. This was a transition from wound strings for $F_3$ and plain strings.

Many piano technicians tune this octave first and use it as the foundation from which the piano is tuned. Therefore, it is especially important that this octave be tuned as well as possible in order that inaccuracies not be carried into other octaves and perhaps compounded in the process.

The usual goal in tuning a piano, at least in its mid-range, is to tune it in such a way that the beats per second produced by the nearly coincident partials when playing two tones in a musical interval will be the correct number. Producing precisely a theoretically correct number of beats for a given interval is not considered as important as having the beat rate increase uniformly as the interval moves up the scale. Without an instrument to measure the beats per second, or the frequencies of the partials, the tuner must estimate the beat rate. A well-trained ear becomes quite expert at this, but even an untrained ear can hear large jumps in the beat rate as the interval progresses up the scale. In order for a chord to sound the same regardless of the key in which it is played, the progression of beat rates should be uniform.

If the fundamentals are tuned to the equally tempered scale and the higher partials are harmonic, the aural tests often used by piano tuners produce beats as shown by the broken lines in Figure 2. Tuning the fundamentals of the strings given in the example in Figure 1 to the equally tempered scale produces uneven progressions of beat rates as shown by solid lines in Figure 2.

A common method of tuning the temperament octave is to tune the intervals of the fourths and fifths to given numbers of beats per second in a uniformly increasing progression as the intervals proceed up the scale.[3] If this method were used on the piano in this example, the fundamentals would be tuned as shown in Figure 3. When the major and minor thirds tests and sixth tests are applied, the resulting beats are shown in Figure 4.

Neither of these tuning methods produces smooth progressions in the beat-rate tests. Some smoothing can be obtained by compromises, but helping one test is usually accomplished at the expense of another test.

At the transition from wrapped to plain strings, or from a two-string unison to a three-string unison, there is apt to be a jump in the inharmonicity pattern, if proper care in the scale is not taken.

FIGURE 1

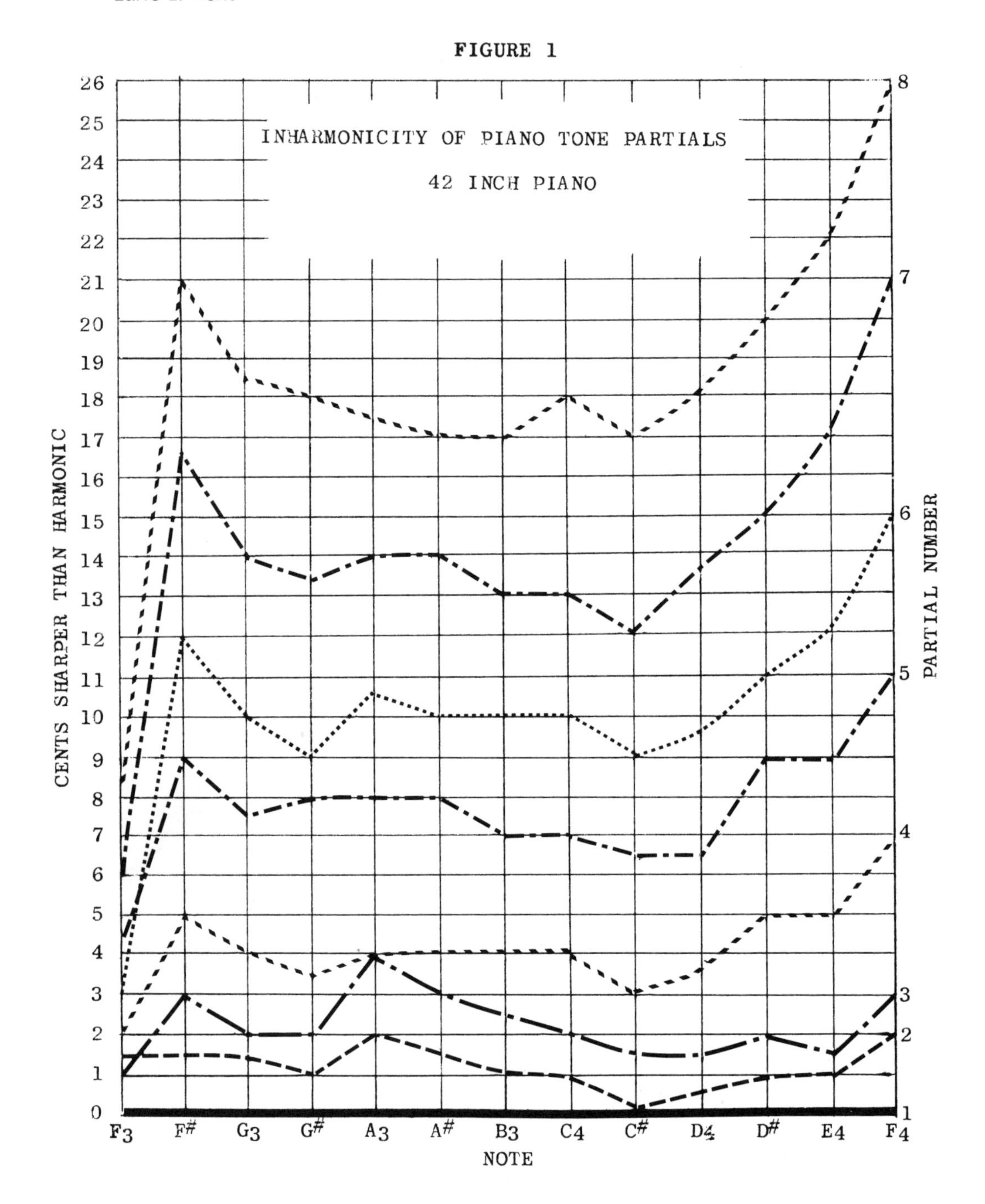

INHARMONICITY OF PIANO TONE PARTIALS
42 INCH PIANO
CENTS SHARPER THAN HARMONIC
PARTIAL NUMBER
NOTE
0
1
2
3
4
5
6
7
8
9
10
11
12
13
14
15
16
17
18
19
20
21
22
23
24
25
26
F3
F#
G3
G#
A3
A#
B3
C4
C#
D4
D#
E4
F4

FIGURE 2

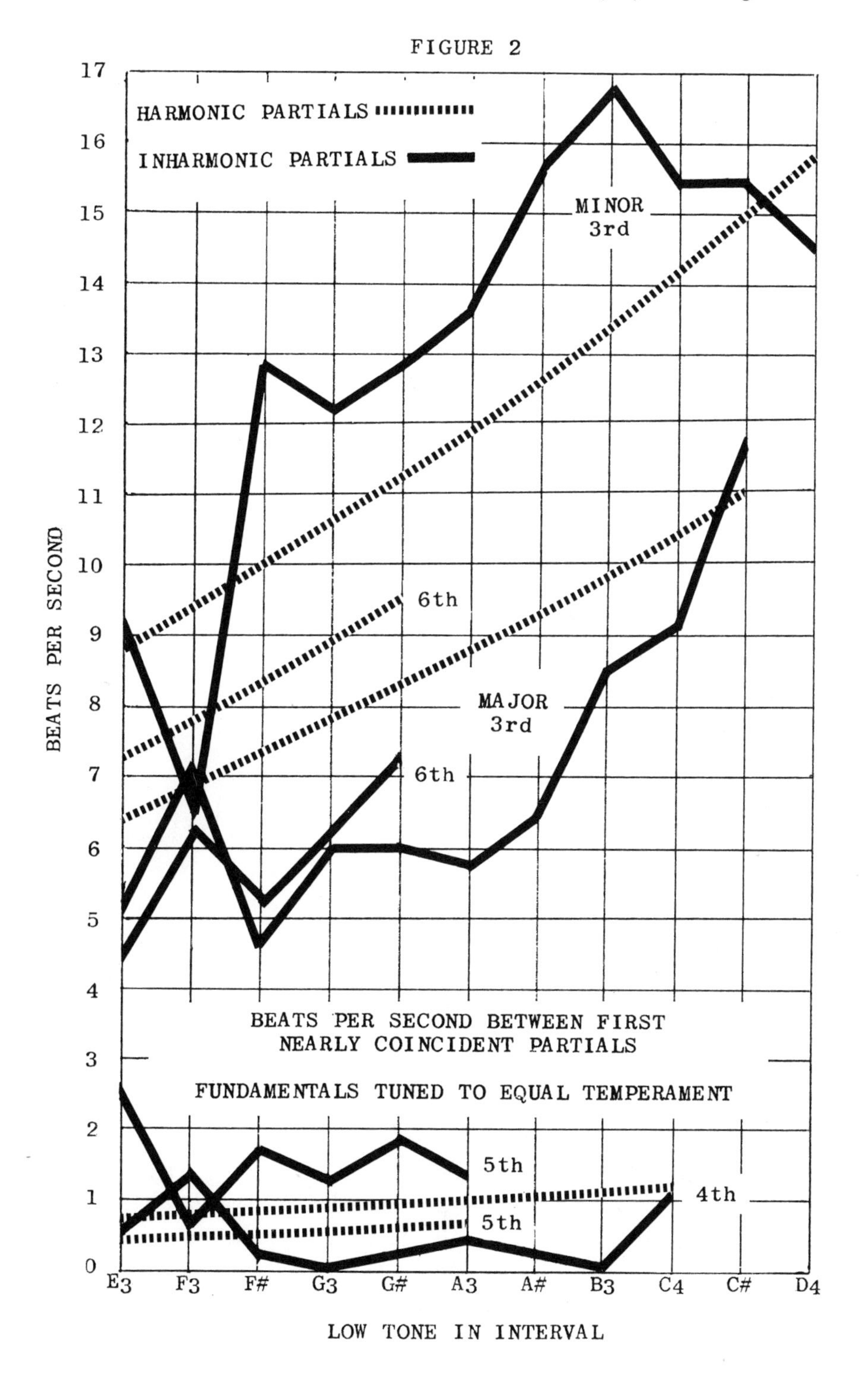
HARMONIC PARTIALS
INHARMONIC PARTIALS
MINOR 3rd
6th
MAJOR 3rd
6th
BEATS PER SECOND BETWEEN FIRST NEARLY COINCIDENT PARTIALS
FUNDAMENTALS TUNED TO EQUAL TEMPERAMENT
5th
4th
5th
BEATS PER SECOND
LOW TONE IN INTERVAL
E3 F3 F# G3 G# A3 A# B3 C4 C# D4
0 1 2 3 4 5 6 7 8 9 10 11 12 13 14 15 16 17

FIGURE 3

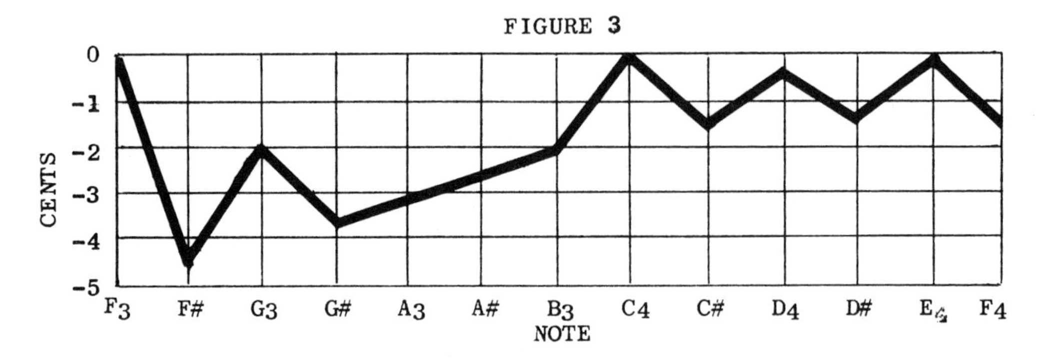


Resulting Tuning of Fundamentals When Fourths And Fifths are Tuned for "Theoretical" Beat Rates.

In order to note the effect of inharmonicity on the tuning process when the inharmonicity pattern from string-to-string is uniform, a hypothetical case is examined. The inharmonicity relationships for the hypothetical case are shown in Figure 5. The beat rates for the aural tests in this hypothetical case are compared to what they would be if the upper partials were harmonic in Figure 6. The fundamentals are tuned to equal temperament in both cases. A smooth

FIGURE 4

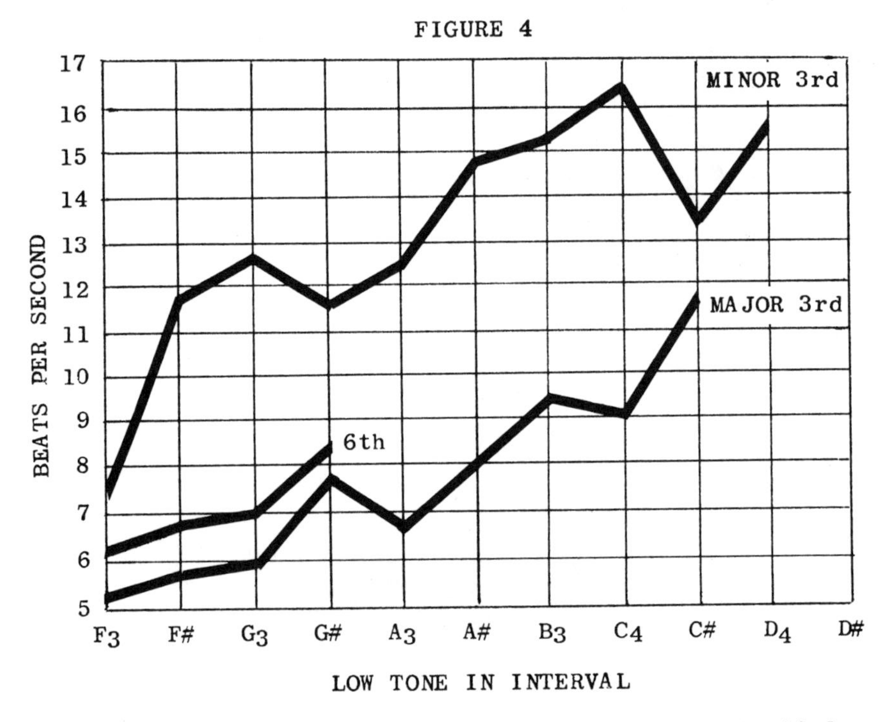


Beats Per Second Between First Nearly Coincident Partials. Fourths and Fifths Are Tuned For "Theoretical" Beat Rates.

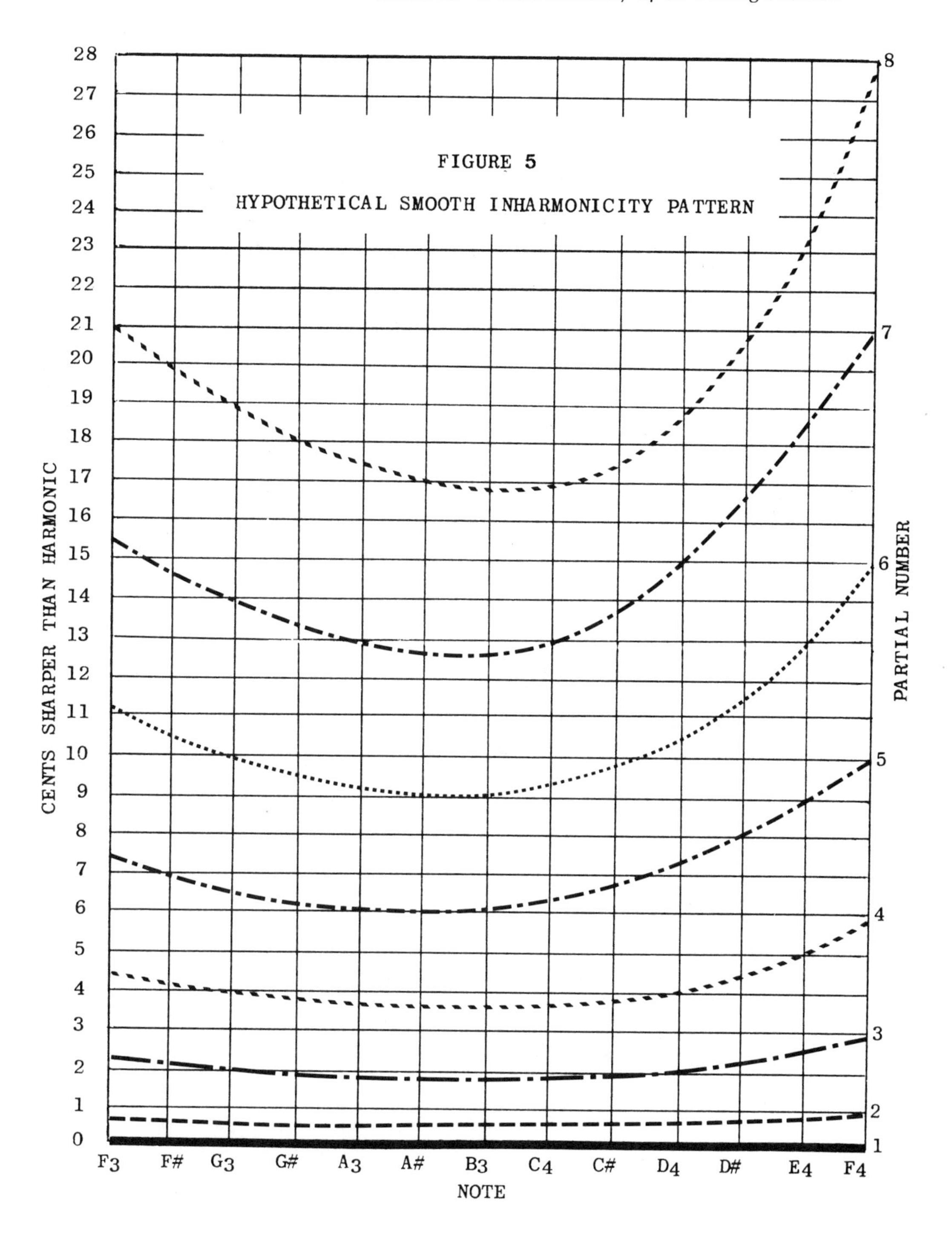
FIGURE 5
HYPOTHETICAL SMOOTH INHARMONICITY PATTERN
CENTS SHARPER THAN HARMONIC
28
27
26
25
24
23
22
21
20
19
18
17
16
15
14
13
12
11
10
9
8
7
6
5
4
3
2
1
0
PARTIAL NUMBER
8
7
6
5
4
3
2
1
F3
F#
G3
G#
A3
A#
B3
C4
C#
D4
D#
E4
F4
NOTE

FIGURE 6

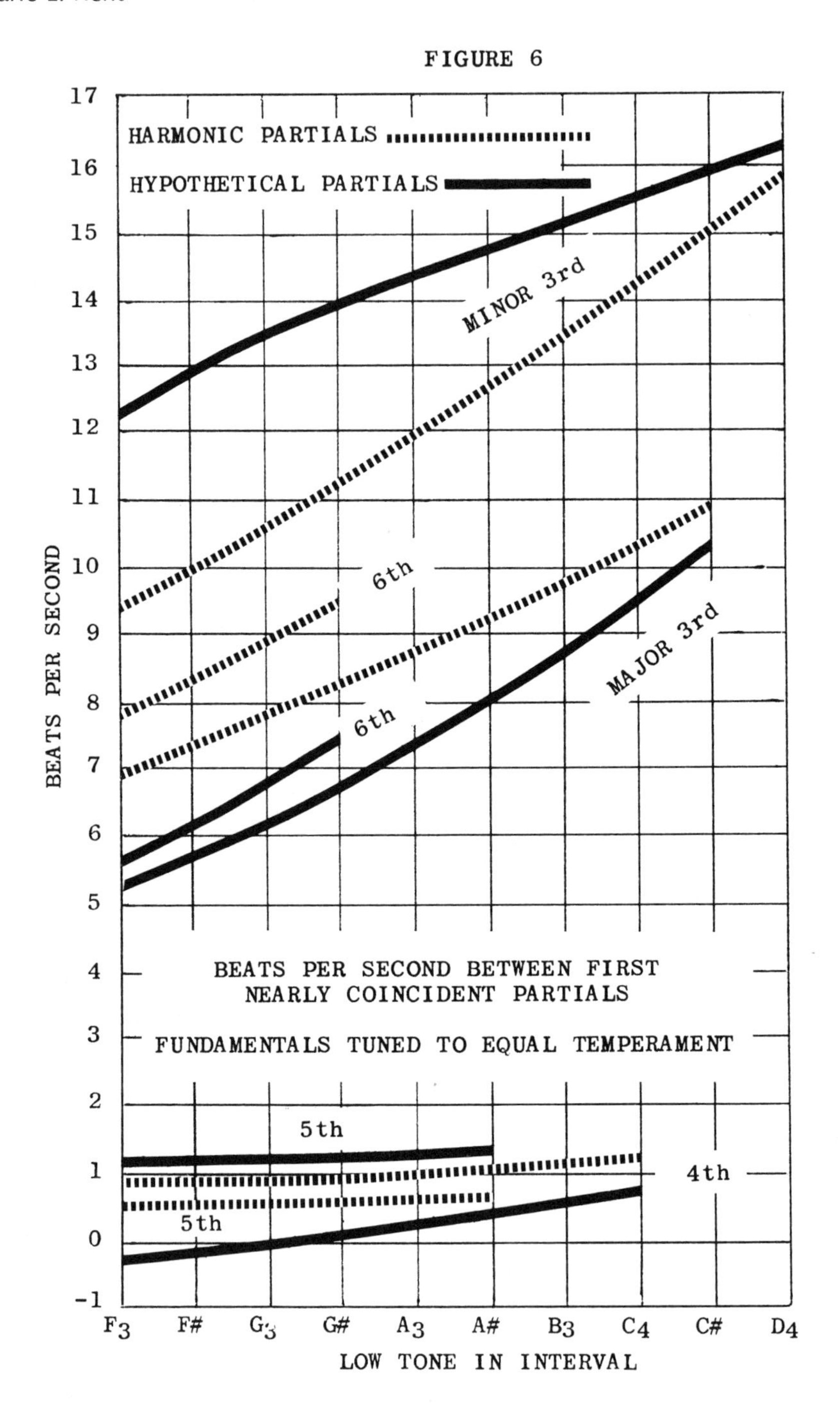
HARMONIC PARTIALS
HYPOTHETICAL PARTIALS
MINOR 3rd
6th
6th
MAJOR 3rd
BEATS PER SECOND BETWEEN FIRST NEARLY COINCIDENT PARTIALS
FUNDAMENTALS TUNED TO EQUAL TEMPERAMENT
5th
5th
4th
BEATS PER SECOND
17
16
15
14
13
12
11
10
9
8
7
6
5
4
3
2
1
0
-1
F3
F#
G3
G#
A3
A#
B3
C4
C#
D4
LOW TONE IN INTERVAL

increase in the beat rates as the interval test moves up the scale is achieved in this hypothetical case—except for the fourth-interval test. The beat rates are not the same in the hypothetical case as they would be when the partials are harmonic. The beat rates for the minor third and fourth test are faster in the hypothetical example. The beat rates for the major third, fourth, and sixth tests are slower. The effect of inharmonicity on the fourth test is special here. The beat rate starts at 0.28 beats per second at the low end. It slows toward zero as the interval test moves up the scale and then increases in its rate. Changes like this actually happen in some pianos during the tests of the fourths or the fifths. Since the beat rates are all slow for the fourth tests in this hypothetical case, it may not be serious, musically, to not have the beat rates increase uniformly as the interval test moves up the scale. But it can cause some confusion for the tuner, if he is using the tests of the interval of the fourth as a guide in the tuning process. Normally one would expect the beat rate to increase in the fourth test if the tension in the top string of the interval were raised. That is not always true. Using the interval of the fourth to raise the frequency of the three higher-pitched strings during the first three tests at the low end of the octave will slow the beats instead of increase them. The rest of the tests behave in the normally expected manner. This phenomenon is indicated in Figure 6 by negative numbers even though negative beats do not exist.

The inharmonicity patterns measured in two other pianos in the $F_3$ *to* $F_4$ octave are given in Figure 7 and Figure 8.

The influence of irregular patterns in the inharmonicity of piano tone partials extends beyond the temperament octave since these partials are used to check other intervals such as tenths, twelfths, octaves, double octaves, and others.

The upper treble piano tones are of such short duration that beats between nearly coincident partials may no longer serve as a guide in tuning. The tuner's judgment regarding pitch of tones and the sound of intervals, such as octaves and double octaves, becomes the sole guide for the aural tuner.

Irregular inharmonicity patterns in the lower bass strings of small pianos are accompanied by a related problem which further handicaps the conscientious piano tuner. The fundamentals are usually very weak and do not contribute much, if any, to the pitch of the tone. The difference frequency between any two consecutive partials is not a constant and this leads to a diffuse pitch in the subjective difference tone. Poor pitch definition in short bass strings results more in a nonmusical clang than a musical tone having definite pitch.

The criterion of a well-tuned piano is how it sounds. Musical taste, musical knowledge, and prejudice can influence subjective judgments as to whether or not a piano is well tuned. In much of the range of the piano, the upper partials of the tones have an important bearing upon tuning techniques and upon the musical appraisal of how well the piano is tuned. It is obvious that smooth tuning results cannot come from irregular string-to-string patterns in inharmonicity of the partials used as guides in tuning. Since each piano usually presents somewhat different inharmonicity patterns, it is not likely that simple rules or procedures can be followed and result in the best possible tuning for a particular piano. There is no substitute for experience, understanding, skill, and conscientious workmanship in fine piano tuning.

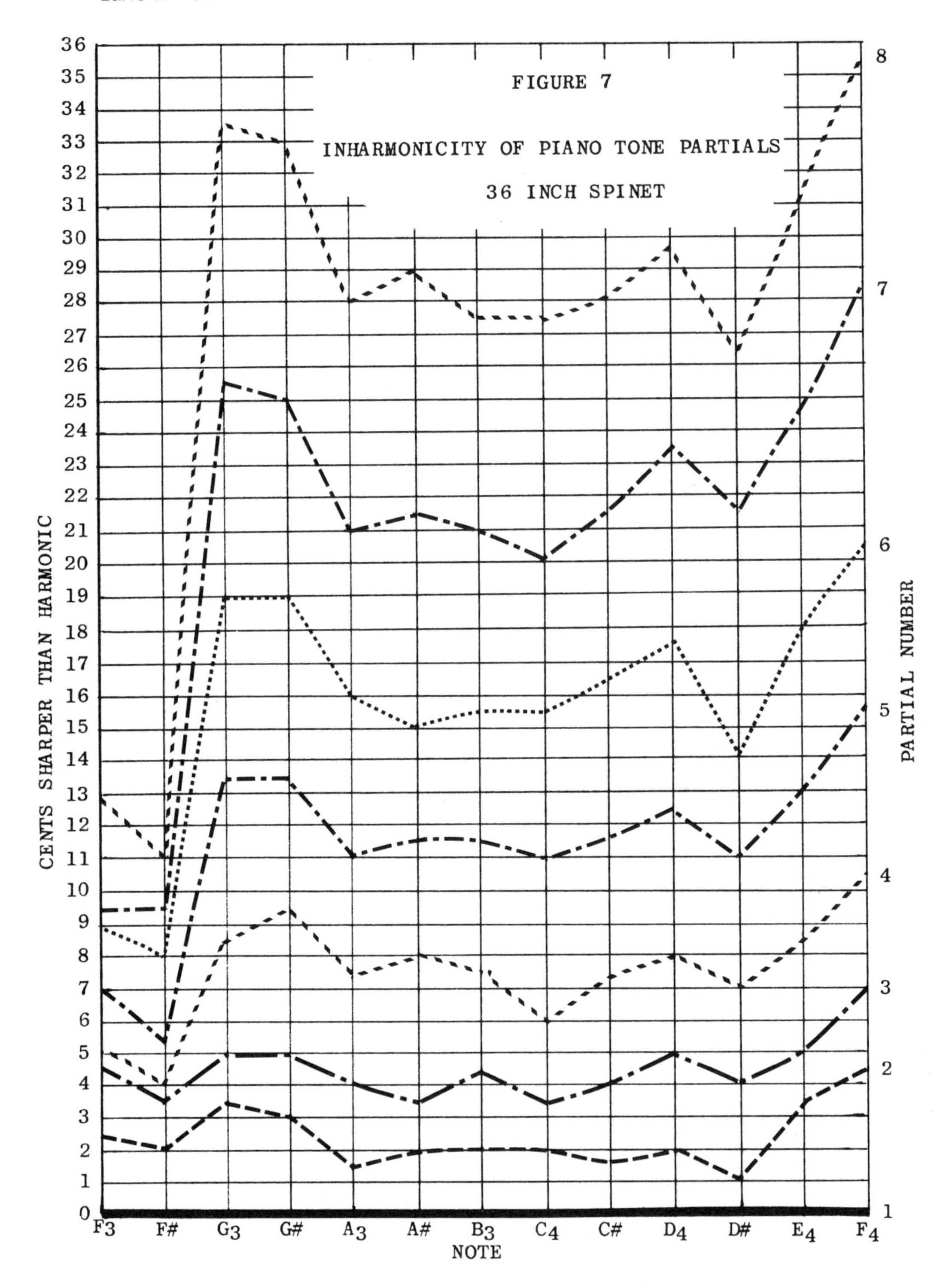
FIGURE 7
INHARMONICITY OF PIANO TONE PARTIALS
36 INCH SPINET
CENTS SHARPER THAN HARMONIC
PARTIAL NUMBER
NOTE
F3
F#
G3
G#
A3
A#
B3
C4
C#
D4
D#
E4
F4
0
1
2
3
4
5
6
7
8
9
10
11
12
13
14
15
16
17
18
19
20
21
22
23
24
25
26
27
28
29
30
31
32
33
34
35
36

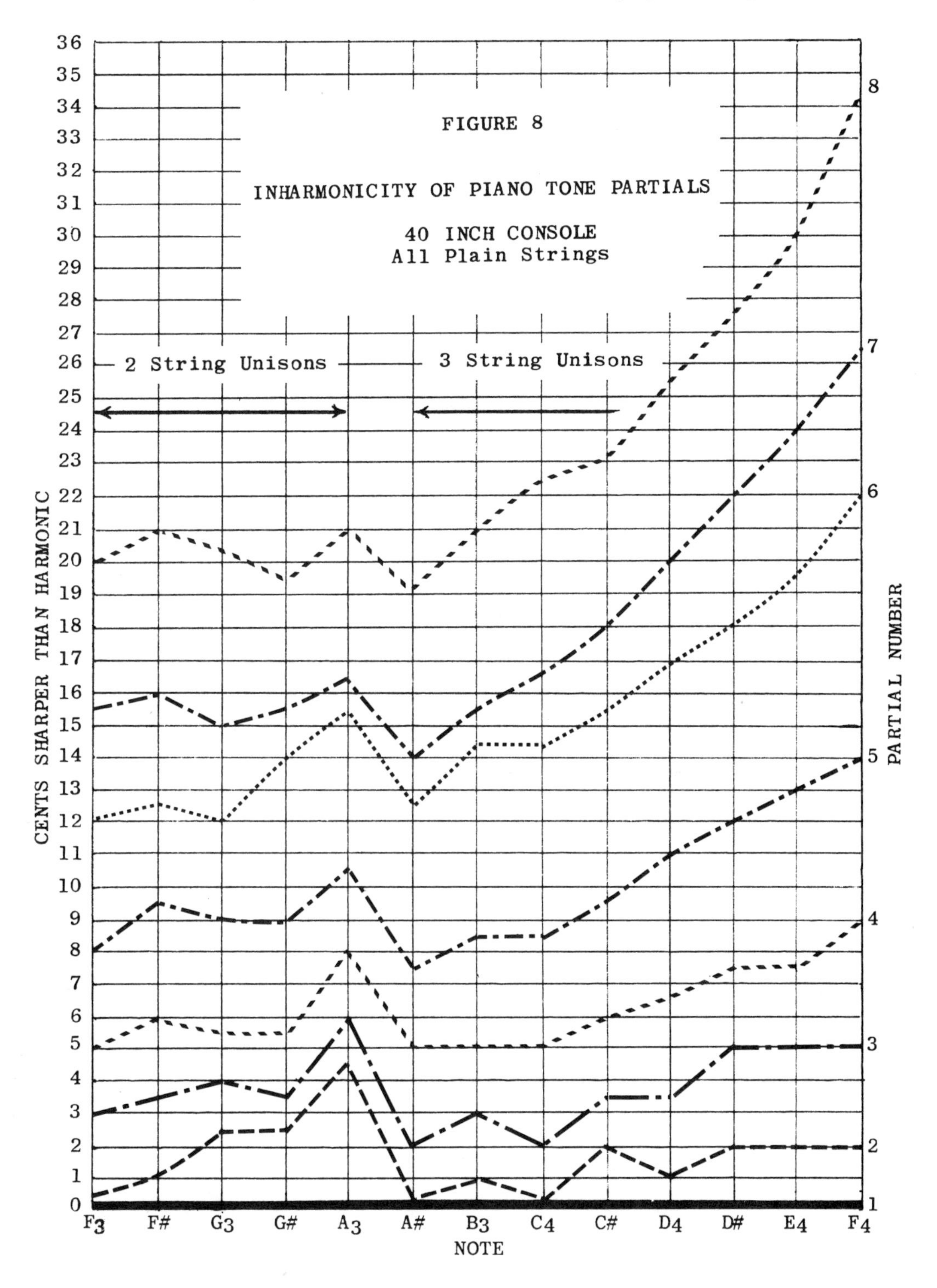
FIGURE 8
INHARMONICITY OF PIANO TONE PARTIALS
40 INCH CONSOLE
All Plain Strings
2 String Unisons
3 String Unisons
CENTS SHARPER THAN HARMONIC
PARTIAL NUMBER
NOTE
F3 F# G3 G# A3 A# B3 C4 C# D4 D# E4 F4

The author is indebted to Mr. James W. Coleman, Sr., who measured the frequencies of the partial in the examples used and who made me more aware of the piano tuner's problems. Discussions with Mr. Douglas Strong and other members of the Piano Technicians Guild have been helpful also.

## REFERENCES

1. O. H. Schuck and R. W. Young, "Observations on the Vibrations of Piano Strings," *J. Acoust. Soc. Am.,* **15** (1), 1–11 (1943). (See Paper 4.)
2. P. M. Morse, *Vibration and Sound,* 2nd ed., New York: McGraw-Hill, pp. 166–170 (1948).
3. W. B. White, *Piano Tuning and Allied Arts,* 4th ed., Boston: Tuners Supply Co., pp. 58–89 (1943).

# Editor's Comments on Papers 7 Through 10



This group of papers considers subjective evaluations of piano tones along with the objective studies.

In Paper 7, Martin deals with the decay characteristics of tones produced by conventional pianos and introduces some matters to consider when electronic amplification is used with piano tones.

The decay characteristics of piano tones depend upon the energy in the string, how efficiently the energy is utilized to produce sound, and how rapidly the energy is dissipated. In order for a conventional piano to be able to produce the sound power meeting modern requirements in music, the strings must be as heavy as practicable. Plain strings in the treble portion of the piano are stiff and rod-like. This results in large inharmonicity values in the strings for the top treble tones. Space limits the string length in the bass portion of the piano and wound strings are used to obtain string mass and keep stiffness as low as practicable. The piano is an inefficient radiator of low frequencies and this adds to the problem of low-sound power at the lower frequencies. If required sound power can be obtained by electronic amplification, that burden on the string can be relieved.

Maximum transfer of string energy to radiated sound will occur when the impedance match between string and air is maximum. If a perfect match could be attained, the piano would not produce a musical sound; the energy would be radiated as a step function of short duration. Resonance can take place in the string, and the decay rate increases as the impedance match decreases.

The use of electrical energy in and with musical instruments has become quite common. Some instruments, such as electronic organs, can not produce music without electrical input. Other instruments use electricity for amplification and/or timbre modification of tones. It seems likely that electricity can be a useful parameter in piano design. Amplified string tones have been used in some pianos no longer in production; other pianos are currently using electronic amplification. This paper indicates recognition of the importance of public opinion when significant changes in a musical instrument are contemplated.

Martin points out cases in which two different decay times exist in a sustained tone. In these cases, the initial part of the decay characteristic decays at a faster rate than that of the latter part. When two or three strings in a unison group are struck, it can be seen that well-tuned unisons will be vibrating in phase and imparting energy accordingly. If they are not tuned to exactly the same frequency, as is usually true, or if other small differences exist in the strings or their terminations, the strings will eventually depart from the in-phase condition and the rate of energy transfer to the soundboard will change also. This condition will not apply when only one string is struck. Generally, the lowest frequency tones of the piano are produced by single strings. Martin shows two decay rates for the lowest frequencies in Figures 3 and 5 (pp. 76, 77). If the hammer dwells too long on a string after striking it, or if the hammer should return to touch the string again shortly after striking it, the damping effect can cause a rapid decay rate at the initial part of the tone. It appears, however, that Martin has, in some instances—as in Figure 2 (p. 75)—taken the slope of the decay curve immediately after the start of the tone as the ${}_{A}T_{60}$ time when it is just a part of the undulations in the decay curve. He points out that the double slope effect is clearly audible (p. 77) but one might question if it can be heard when strings function singly. The double-slope effect contributes to the complexity of the piano tone and becomes a part of its "life" and uniqueness.

Daniel W. Martin (1918–      ) [A.B. (physics, mathematics, 1937) Georgetown College; M.S. (physics, 1939) and Ph.D. (physics, 1941), both from University of Illinois], a Fellow of the Acoustical Society of America, Institute of Electrical & Electronic Engineers, and Audio Engineering Society, was employed by Radio Corporation of America (1941–1949) as an acoustical engineer and has been Director of Research for the Baldwin Piano & Organ Co. since 1949. He has taught part time at the University of Illinois (physics and acoustics), Purdue University at Indianapolis, (mathematics), and since 1964 at the University of Cincinnati (musical acoustics).

Martin has served as President of Audio Engineering Society, IEEE Audio Group, and the Engineering Society of Cincinnati. He is the author of numerous papers on musical acoustics, musical instruments, music education systems, speech communication devices and systems, and architectural acoustics. He is also the patentee of many patents related to these subjects.

Paper 8 places special emphasis upon the care that must be taken in the subjective evaluation of musical tones if reasonably valid results are to be obtained. It is difficult to arrive at meaningful evaluations of tones sounded in isolation, or even in short musical passages. Perception and evaluation of tones are influenced by the listener's expectation which, in turn, is influenced by the listener's past experience or training.

Kirk states in the second paragraph of his paper that artist tuners deliberately do not tune the unison groups in exact unison. But, although tuners do not make a practice of tuning unisons with the aid of a level recorder, many of the tuners this editor has consulted on the subject claim they do try to tune the unisons exactly. They state that they do not stay exact very long after the piano is tuned. Playing the piano, and changes in temperature or humidity, can cause slight changes in the tuning of the unisons. It is fortunate that this is musically desirable. Tuners have stated that it would promote carelessness in tuning to advocate deliberately leaving the unisons mistuned.

When a fundamental is tuned to $E_3$ (164.181 hertz), a one-cent deviation is 0.10 Hz. If the tenth partial were harmonic, the deviation there would cause just one beat per second. At $G_5$ (739.99 Hz), a one-cent deviation of the fundamental is 0.45 Hz. The tenth partial of this tone usually is weak enough so that beats produced by mistuning unisons probably would not be a problem.

Kirk states that the unison groups in the top two-and-a-half octaves of the piano were not included in the investigation and that the zero-beat tuning condition there is very transitory.

Roger E. Kirk received his B.S. and M.A. degrees in music and his Ph.D. degree in Experimental Psychology from the Ohio State University. Following his graduation he worked for the Baldwin Piano Company, Cincinnati, Ohio, as a psychoacoustic engineer and was engaged in basic and applied research in the areas of musical acoustics and speech communication. He is currently professor of psychology and director of behavioral statistics training at Baylor University, Waco, Texas. In addition to writing numerous articles on music acoustics, human engineering, and statistics, he is the author of *Experimental Design: Procedures with Behavioral Sciences* and *Statistical Issues*. He is also consulting editor in statistics for Brooks/Cole Publishing Company, a division of Wadsworth Publishing Company, and associate editor of the *Journal of Educational Statistics.*

Paper 9 presents a useful study of some of the objective qualities of piano tones and subjective evaluations of comparisons made between actual piano tones and various synthetic tones.

The authors show that the sounds produced by pianos are complex and that some noise components are included. Pianos, like some other musical instruments, produce tones that are not uniform in content throughout their range and also contain components which may seem to detract from the musical value of the tones. The question often arises as to the desirability of producing tones without such "aberrations." The onset of tones sounded by some organ pipes produces a transient noise known as "chiff." Electronic organs can produce tones of similar tone quality but without the "chiff." Many people do not consider "chiff" to be undesirable. The number of people who believe it to be a necessary ingredient in a good organ tone is sufficient for some electronic organ manufacturers to make "chiff" available at an added expense. In this paper, another example is found. As pointed out earlier in these comments, a tone having inharmonic partials may be considered by some to have a musically undesirable defect. The authors show this not to be the case.

Variations in construction of the piano make a variety of tone qualities possible, and this paper gives some guide lines of listener preferences that can be helpful in piano design. Musical tastes vary considerably and many factors can be involved when purchasers are selecting a piano.

It may be noted that some of the strings used for data in this paper did not have their fundamentals tuned to the equally tempered scale (A = 440). The frequencies did not deviate from equal temperament as one might expect in the usually "stretched" tuning due to the inharmonicity of partials. For example, in Table IV (p. 94), the given observed fundamental frequency of 193.0 Hz is 26.7 cents flat with respect to the G = 196.00 Hz in the equally tempered scale. This string is in the octave that normally deviates very little, if any, from equal temperament if properly tuned. This tuning could have some influence upon the resulting inharmonicity. In Table V (p. 94), the observed fundamental frequency of 393.0 Hz is 4.4 cents sharp with respect to G = 392.00 Hz. In Table VI, (p. 95) the observed fundamental frequency of 779.0 Hz is 11 cents flat with respect to G = 783.99 Hz (cents = $3986.313714 \log_{10} R$, $R$ = frequency ratio).

Some biographical information regarding Harvey Fletcher is given with comments on Paper 5. E. Donnell Blackham is the author of Paper 1.

Richard B. Stratton [B.E.S. and M.S., Brigham Young University] joined the Sandia Systems Studies Department of Sandia Laboratories in Albuquerque, New Mexico in 1969 after receiving his Ph.D. from Michigan State University.

He is a member of various honorary and professional groups including Phi Kappa Phi, Sigma Xi, Tau Beta Pi, and IEEE.

Paper 10 describes some measurements to show the effects of soundboard structure and mountings upon tone quality. The soundboard, with its bridges and ribs, cooperates with the vibrating strings to radiate sound. The bridge pins; the shape, location, and material in the bridge; the downbearing of the strings upon the bridge; the cupping, if any, of the soundboard; and the dimensions, material, and support of the soundboard, all influence the tone quality of the piano. Evaluating the effect of any one of these variables, while holding all others constant, is a difficult task.

Since so much wood is used in the conventional construction of pianos and since dimensions and some vibration characteristics of wood are subject to change depending upon the age, moisture content, temperature, and kind of wood, it becomes even more difficult to make quantitative studies regarding the subject of this paper. Bilhuber effectively points out the general principles involved in the function of the soundboard and in arriving at an optimum response. The impedance relationship between the string and the bridge–soundboard influences the transfer of energy from the string to the soundboard and is influenced by all of the variables listed above.

Paul H. Bilhuber (1889–       ) [C.E. Columbia University] is a Fellow in the Acoustical Society of America. He began his piano work in 1909 as an Apprentice Journeyman with Steinway & Sons, N.Y., and has served that company as Foreman, Asst. Factory Supt., Asst. Factory Manager, Manager of their London factory, Chief Engineer, Director, and Senior Vice President. During World War I, he served in the 311th Infantry, AEF as Layout and Building Supt. of the CG4A glider for the Army. He has been granted eleven U.S. and eight foreign patents on piano improvements and methods. He resides at Stonehenge, Box 108, Buck Hill Falls, Pennsylvania 18323, and still has great interest in piano technology.

# 7

*Copyright © 1947 by Acoustical Society of America*

Reprinted from *J. Acoust. Soc. Am.*, **19**(4), 535–541 (1947)

## Decay Rates of Piano Tones*

DANIEL W. MARTIN
*RCA Victor Division, Camden, New Jersey*

(Received May 22, 1947)

Decay curves were recorded for an upright piano, a baby grand, and an electronic spinet. For some tones the partials were recorded separately. Decay rates for the electronic piano were measured at different levels of piano amplification. Analysis of the data reveals the degree of control exerted by the sounding board upon decay rate, particularly in the initial stage of decay. The significance of this control by the sounding board is discussed, in relation to the problem of electrical amplification of piano tones.

### INTRODUCTION

IT has been established on a scientific basis that action of the vibrating system of a piano is determined by the velocity of the felt hammer, and that no subsequent control exists for the performer except damping means applied suddenly by the release of the key.[1,2] More attention appears to have been given to the degree of control possible through "touch" than to study of the tone itself. This paper presents data on the decay characteristics of the tones of conventional upright and baby grand pianos and an electronic piano model. Some decay measurements have been reported several times previously, but in each case they were incidental to the main purpose of the investigators.[3–5]

Removal of the sounding board from conventional pianos, in order to convert to electronic performance, has been recognized as a factor tending to decrease the decay rate of the tones.[6] In this investigation a secondary purpose was to compare decay rates for electronic and conventional pianos. Some degree of control over decay rate is possible electronically, and it is desirable to know in advance to what extent such control may be useful. Public reaction to the somewhat longer decay time of electronic pianos has been varied, ranging from the comment by the writer's voice instructor, "it's one of those pianos that sustain," to that of his secretary, "that's nice—it keeps."

### MEASUREMENT OF DECAY CHARACTERISTICS

The total sound level was recorded with a Sound Apparatus Company high speed level recorder (model PL) for all eighty-eight notes of each of the three pianos. The measurements were made in a room having a reverberation time of approximately 0.5 second. The recorder was used in its normal condition, with no electrical damping added. The noise level in the room was 50 db below the maximum signal from the piano. The sustaining pedal was not used.

Figure 1 shows three typical decay curves for the upright piano.[7] Figure 2 is for the electronic piano. In some cases beat effects are apparent, resulting from slight detuning of the several strings (two or three, as the case may be) associated with the same tone. In the low and middle ranges of the conventional piano, it is common for the decay characteristic to have a more rapid slope trend initially than later. Initial and terminal slopes were measured for curves having both. The initial slope, effective for the first few seconds of the tone, is probably of greater importance because a majority of the notes in a musical composition are of less than five seconds duration. However, the terminal slope is important in sustained passages, affecting the

---

* Paper delivered at the meeting of the Acoustical Society of America, May 8, 1947, New York, New York.

[1] W. B. White, "Human element in piano tone production," J. Acous. Soc. Am. **1**, 357 (1930).

[2] Hart, Fuller, Lusby, "Precision study of piano touch and tone," J. Acous. Soc. Am. **6**, 80 (1934).

[3] S. K. Wolf and W. J. Sette, "Some application of modern acoustic apparatus," J. Acous. Soc. Am. **6**, 160 (1935).

[4] P. H. Bilhuber and C. H. Johnson, "The influence of soundboard on piano tone quality," J. Acous. Soc. Am. **11**, 311 (1939).

[5] O. H. Schuck and R. W. Young, "Observations on the vibrations of piano strings," J. Acous. Soc. Am. **15**, 1 (1943).

[6] B. F. Miessner, "Design considerations for a simple and versatile electronic music instrument," J. Acous. Soc. Am. **6**, 181 (1935).

[7] The notation follows R. W. Young, "Terminology for logarithmic frequency units," J. Acous. Soc. Am. **11**, 134 (1939).

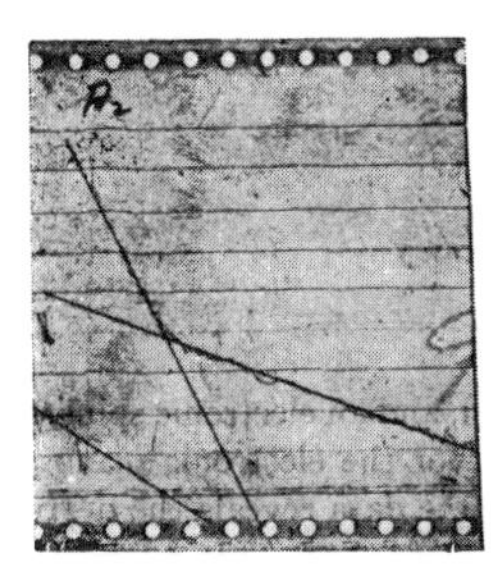

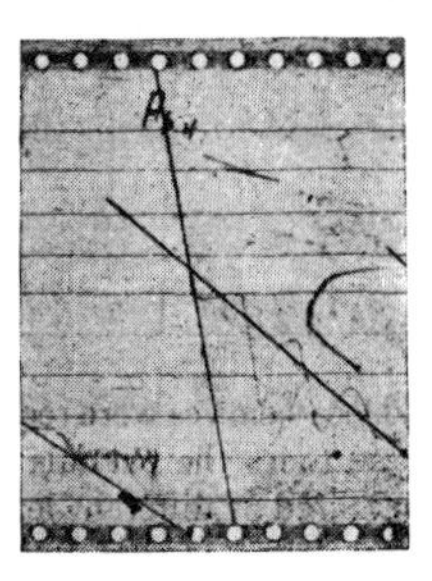

FIG. 1. Typical decay curves—upright piano.

"after-sound" and matters of technique such as the use of the sustaining pedal. Because of the familiarity of acoustical engineers with the sixty-db decay time used in describing reverberation, and the availability of a suitable scale[8] for the measurement, all decay data have been plotted in units of time defined as follows: ${}_AT_{60}$ is the time in seconds required for the sound level to decay 60 db at the average rate determined by the initial part of the decay characteristic; ${}_BT_{60}$ is the same for the latter part of the decay characteristic. When a single slope adequately describes the trend of the characteristic, it has been designated arbitrarily as ${}_BT_{60}$. In all of the subsequent graphs, dots are used for ${}_BT_{60}$ and crosses for ${}_AT_{60}$, except in Fig. 7 where the legend is given. In some tones a very slow beat produced a ${}_AT_{60}$ which would have been eliminated by exact tuning of the multiple strings. This is apparent in one of the curves for the electronic spinet piano. Correction of this condition was not considered necessary, although a more uniform appearance would have been given to the data, because exact tuning is not encountered in practice.

Figures 3–6, 8–9, and 11 are graphs plotted with a vertical logarithmic time scale and a horizontal logarithmic scale of fundamental frequency. However, superposed on the fundamental frequency scale is a piano keyboard which identifies the data musically. At the top of each

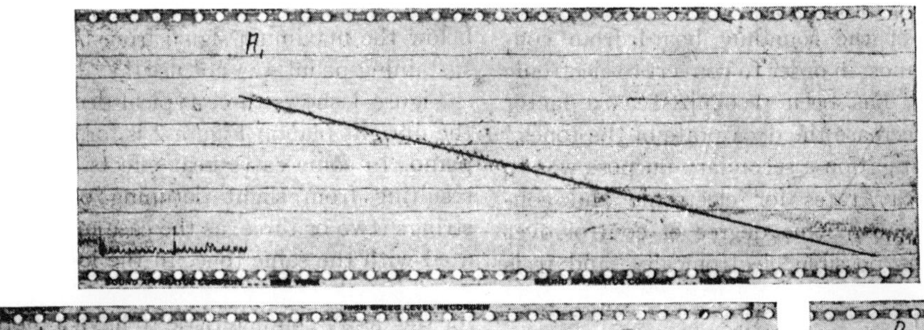

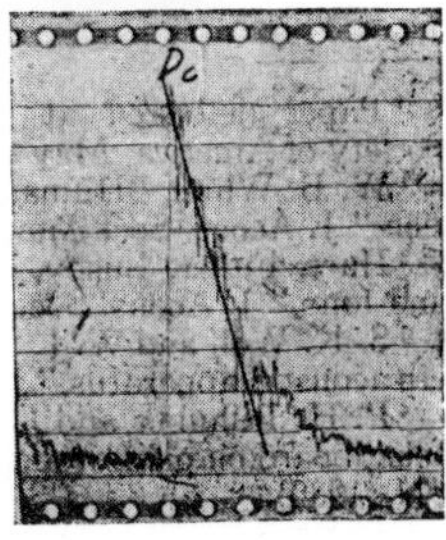

FIG. 2. Typical decay curves—electronic piano model.

[8] K. C. Morrical, "Reverberation-time scale for high speed level recorders," J. Acous. Soc. Am. **10**, 300 (1939).

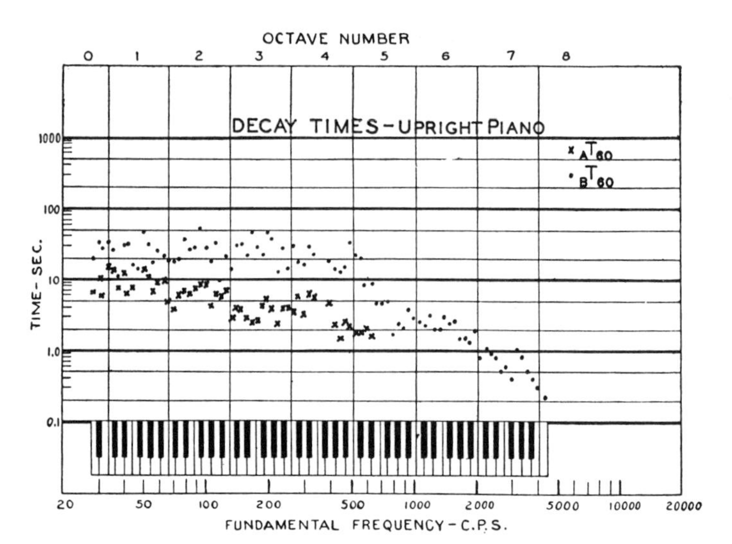


FIG. 3. Decay times—upright piano.

graph is an octave number scale, based upon the subscript numbers used in the musical notation. The vertical lines separate the octaves between the notes $B$ and $C$.

### DECAY RATES FOR CONVENTIONAL PIANOS

Figure 3 contains the data for the upright piano. In Fig. 4 are shown the average data for each of the seven complete octaves, omitting data for $A_0$, $A\#_0$, $B_0$, and $C_8$. It is observed that nearly all of the tones up to $D\#_5$ have both types of decay rate. $_BT_{60}$ varies from a maximum of 53 to a minimum of 0.2 second. The points are scattered rather widely with rates of adjacent tones having a ratio as high as 3 to 1 in exceptional cases. The initial slope in the first four octaves averages almost five times the terminal slope. One point of interest in connection with this particular piano is that the decay rate for notes of moderate duration is greater in the third and fourth octaves than it is in the fifth. This is a result of the change-over from $A$ to $B$ decay rates. Figures 5 and 6 are for a baby grand piano. The total range of variation of $_BT_{60}$ is very similar to that for the upright piano, i.e., 46 to 0.3 second. The octave averages of $_AT_{60}$ are similar to

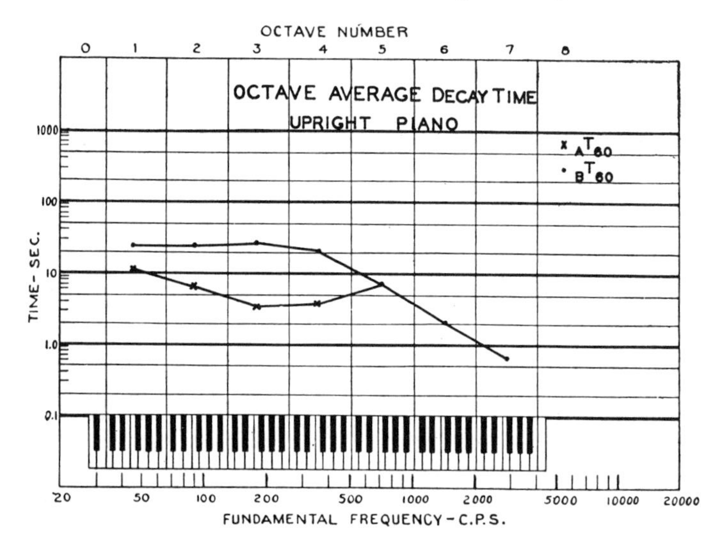


FIG. 4. Octave average decay times—upright piano.

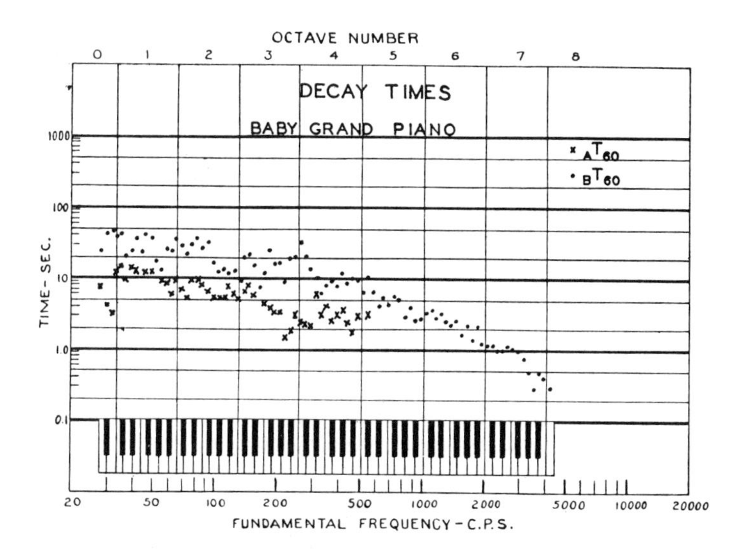


FIG. 5. Decay time—baby grand piano.

the upright piano, but in the lower octaves $_BT_{60}$ is somewhat less, making the average ratio of initial to terminal slope only 3.3, as compared to 5.0 for the upright piano.

When one listens to the decay of an individual piano tone, the double-slope effect is clearly audible, and a quality change as well as a slope change can be heard. Some of the change in quality can be explained on the basis of the equal loudness contours of the ear. This accounts for the rapid disappearance of the lowest partials. However, the quality change is more complex. In an effort to explain this audible change and also the double rate measured, decay characteristics were recorded for separate partials of three tones of the upright piano. The tones were chosen for the smoothness of the decay of the total sound and the sharpness of the break in slope, because it was believed that these properties might turn up some singular cases. Apparently the smoothness of decay was a coincidence, because decay characteristics of separate partials displayed irregularities of the same order as observed in the decay of the total sound of other tones. Figure 7 presents the data of these tests. A General Radio type 760A sound analyzer was used to separate

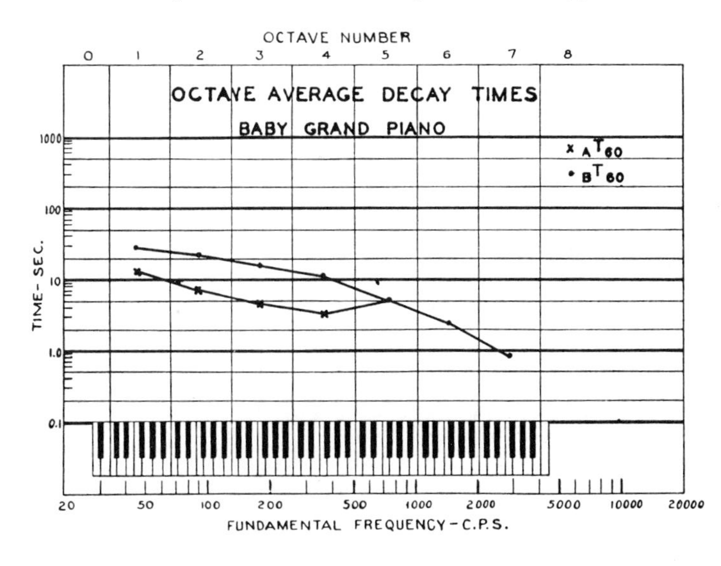


FIG. 6. Octave average decay times—baby grand piano.

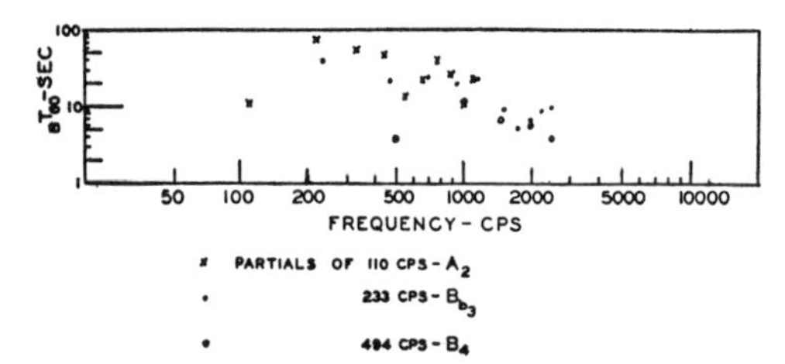


FIG. 7. Decay times—separate partials of upright piano tones.

the partial under test. Its selectivity is on the basis of constant percentage band width, and therefore measurements beyond the tenth partial were not significant. Neglecting the fundamental component in two of the three cases, it can be concluded that the high frequency partials decay much more rapidly than those in the mid-frequency range. Schuck and Young[5] have shown decay characteristics for two tones which also exhibited a more rapid decay for the higher partials. This accounts for the audible change in quality as the tone decays. Comparison of Figs. 6 and 7 also indicates that a high frequency partial of a tone having a low fundamental will decay much less rapidly than a tone having a correspondingly high fundamental frequency.

### DECAY RATES FOR ELECTRONIC PIANO

It was considered likely that the decay rates for the tones of an electronic piano would be dependent upon the degree of amplification. Therefore, the first tests on the electronic piano were made with the volume control set to match the loudness of a conventional piano. The data of Figs. 8 and 9 were obtained for this condition. The trend of the $_BT_{60}$ points is smoother for the electronic piano than for the conventional pianos. The $_AT_{60}$ points occur less frequently, and a number of them are a result of a slow beat, with no indication of a real break in the slope trend. On the average $_AT_{60}$ and $_BT_{60}$ are more nearly alike for the electronic piano, their ratio averaging 2.1 in the first four octaves.

A special study was made of decay rate as a function of the amplification of the electronic piano. Output-level measurements were made on the conventional pianos and the electronic spinet with the power turned off. Because of the omission of the sounding board in the latter, the output level was reduced 14 db on the average, the reduction being somewhat larger at the extreme ends of the keyboard than in the central part. With the particular amplification system used, maximum gain was 10 db greater than the setting for conventional piano loudness. Decay times were measured for gain settings 5 and 10 db above and below the normal loudness condition. Octave average values of $_BT_{60}$ are plotted in Fig. 10. $_AT_{60}$ data were omitted in order to avoid complicating the graph. Their presence would not have altered the conclusion that, within the range of amplification tested, the decay rate is es-

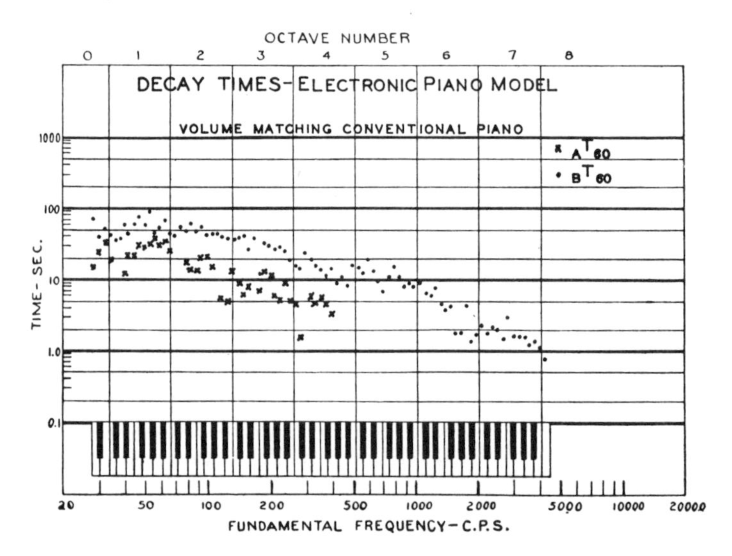


FIG. 8. Decay times—electronic piano model.

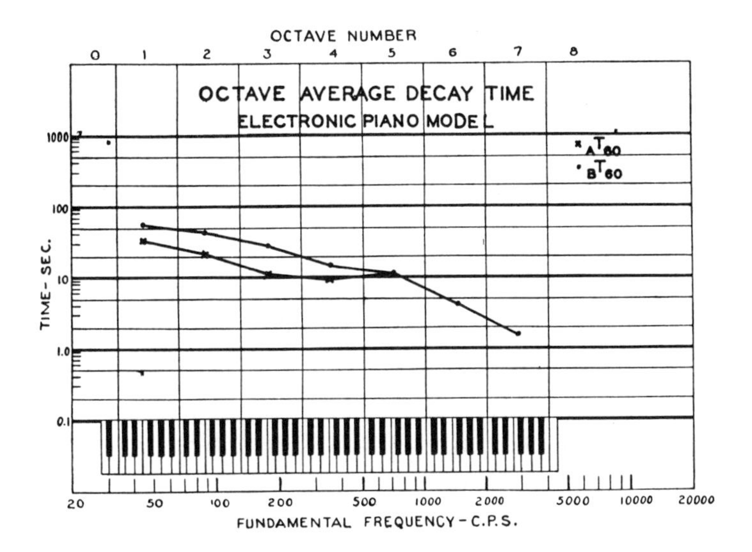


FIG. 9. Octave average decay time—electronic piano model.

sentially constant, except possibly in the first and second octaves. Here an increase of approximately 40 percent in decay time is observed for 20-db rise in output level. Longer decay rates for electronic pianos can be attributed to the removal of the mechanical damping provided by the sounding board, rather than to a tendency for feedback to occur in the amplification system.

### COMPARISON OF DECAY RATES

In Fig. 11 are compared the effective octave-average decay times for the three pianos. By effective is meant that the short time $_AT_{60}$ is used in the lower octaves, where there is a choice, and $_BT_{60}$ elsewhere. In all cases the electronic piano, with sounding board removed, has a longer decay time. The ratio between the decay time for the

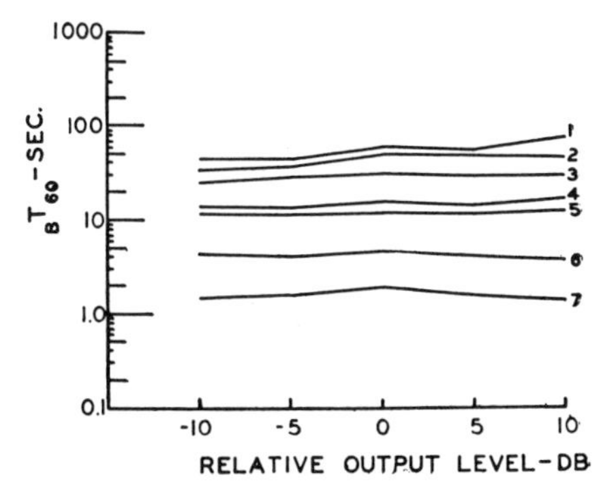


FIG. 10. Octave average decay time *vs.* output level of electronic piano model.

electronic piano and the average of the decay times for the two conventional pianos does not vary greatly from one octave to another. Values of this ratio are shown in Table I. The average

TABLE I. Ratio of decay rates for electronic and conventional pianos.

| Octave No. | $_AT_{60}$ | $_BT_{60}$ |
|---|---|---|
| 1 | 2.47 | 2.06 |
| 2 | 3.20 | 1.75 |
| 3 | 2.51 | 1.29 |
| 4 | 2.58 | 0.90 |
| 5 | | 1.97 |
| 6 | | 1.72 |
| 7 | | 2.10 |
| | | Average = 2.36 |

value of 2.36 can be interpreted in terms of db/sec. decay as follows: a typical tone played in the central part of the keyboard on an electronic piano has an initial decay rate of the order of 5 db per second. A typical tone on a conventional piano with sounding board has an initial rate approximately 2.4 times as great or 12 db/sec. The slower decay rate of the electronic piano is such that an amplitude-modulation type of vibrato of the order of plus and minus four db makes the decay hardly apparent to the average observer, producing an organ-like effect. Several points of interest are noted concerning the relative efficiency of the sounding board and the remainder of the piano structure. The omission of

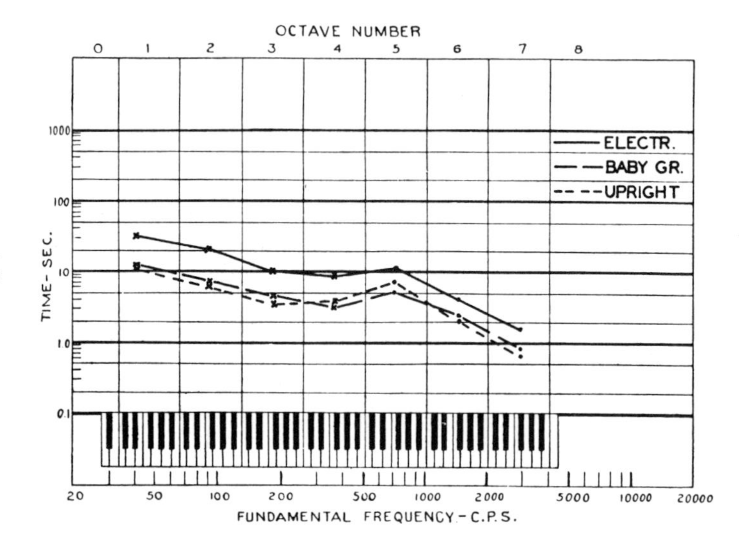


FIG. 11. Octave average decay time—comparison of three pianos.

the sounding board by no means eliminates the acoustical output of a piano. However, if the efficiency of conversion of mechanical energy into acoustical energy were the same for the sounding board as for the rest of the structure, one could assume from a comparison of the decay rates, with and without sounding board, that removal of the sounding board would lower the sound level by only four db. The 14-db average reduction measured confirms that the sounding board has a much higher efficiency than the remainder of the piano structure.

## CONCLUSIONS

1. Initial decay rates for conventional piano tones vary from approximately $4\frac{1}{2}$ to 80 db/sec., depending upon the frequency level of the tone played.

2. In the first four octaves of conventional pianos it is common for the decay characteristic to have an initial slope several times the terminal slope.

3. Removal of the sounding board approximately halves the rate of decay of piano tones. The effect is somewhat greater on low tones than on high ones.

4. The output level of an electronic piano less sounding board can be raised at least 10 db above conventional piano output level without substantial dependence of decay rate upon gain setting.

# 8

Copyright © 1959 by the Acoustical Society of America

Reprinted from *J. Acoust. Soc. Am.*, **31**(12), 1644–1648 (1959)

## Tuning Preferences for Piano Unison Groups*

Roger E. Kirk†
*The Baldwin Piano Company, Cincinnati 2, Ohio*

(Received July 9, 1959)

Unison strings of a concert grand piano were tuned to five "unison" conditions. The conditions were "zero-beat" tuning and the upper string of three string unison groups tuned sharp and the lower string tuned flat by ½, 1, 2, and 3 cents relative to the center string. Magnetic tape recordings were made of the piano tuned under these conditions. These recordings in the form of a paired comparison preference test were presented to musically trained and untrained subjects. The most preferred tuning conditions for three string unison groups as recorded and reproduced from magnetic tape, are 1 and 2 cents maximum deviation among strings. Musically trained subjects prefer less deviation in tuning among unison strings than do untrained subjects. Close agreement was found between the subject's tuning preferences and the way artist tuners actually tune piano unison strings.

### INTRODUCTION

THIS investigation was designed to determine the most preferred tuning condition for piano three string unison groups. Although much information has been obtained regarding the relative merits of different tuning methods and preferences for temperament,[1] little has been written concerning tuning preferences for unison groups. The dearth of literature on piano unison tuning is a logical outgrowth of assuming that piano unison groups are, as their name would imply, tuned to a *unison* condition. In the process of tuning a piano, tuners set the temperament in the octave from $F_3$ (175 cps) to $F_4$ (349 cps) and then successively tune by octaves the middle string of three string unison groups to this temperament. One of the last steps in the tuning process is the tuning of the two outer strings of a three string group to unison with the middle string. Measurements made with a Conn Chromatic Stroboscope on pianos immediately after tuning by artist tuners indicate that three string unison groups are rarely tuned to an exact unison condition. In the case of concert grand pianos, the average maximum difference among strings of a three string unison group measured at the fundamental frequency of the string is approximately 1½ cents.[2,3]

It appears from the measurements cited in the foregoing as well as from discussions with artist tuners that unison groups are deliberately not tuned to exact unison. According to piano tuners, unison groups which are tuned too closely lack interest and diminish too rapidly. A preference of musically trained subjects for some detuning of three string unison groups has been reported previously.[4] Hundley, Martin, and Benioff[5] have shown that the characteristic multiple diminution of piano tone envelope is due primarily to small differences in fundamental frequency of the unison strings. They attribute the decrease in diminution rate of the tone envelope as a function of time to two related factors: interference between strings which are almost exactly in tune, and change in rate of energy transfer from the multiple string source, before and after transition from an initial in-phase condition to a later out-of-phase condition.

It is apparent from the above considerations that some detuning of piano unison strings is desirable. The question which this research was designed to answer is how much detuning of unison strings is desirable.

### PROCEDURE

In order to establish experimentally a hierarchy of preferences for unison string tuning, preliminary experiments were conducted to determine the maximum tuning difference among unison strings which would be acceptable to musically trained subjects. This difference was found to be of the order of 6–8 cents. On the basis of these preliminary experiments, five tuning conditions were selected for inclusion in a tuning preference test. The five conditions were 0, 1, 2, 4, and 6 cents difference in tuning between outside strings of unison groups. The center string of three string unison groups was tuned midway between the outside strings. It should be pointed out that in actual practice, artist tuners do not attempt to tune three string unison groups so that the center string is midway between the two outside strings. Preliminary listening tests indicated that judgments of "goodness of tuning" are related to the maximum frequency difference among the three strings rather than to the frequency spacings among the strings. The tuning procedure used in this investigation of equal frequency spacing among the strings was adopted because it provided an additional check on accuracy during the tuning process.

#### Tuning Method

A Baldwin grand piano style M was used in the investigation. The piano was placed in a nonreverberant

* Presented at the fifty-eighth meeting of the Acoustical Society of America, Cleveland, Ohio (October 22, 1959).

† Now at Baylor University, Waco, Texas.

[1] See R. W. Young, J. Acoust. Soc. Am. **26**, 955–959 (1954).

[2] The difference in cents between two frequencies is 1200 times $\log_2$ of their frequency ratio.

[3] Unpublished data by the writer and staff of the Acoustical Laboratory of The Baldwin Piano Company.

[4] D. W. Martin and W. D. Ward, J. Acoust. Soc. Am. **26**, 932 (1954).

[5] Hundley, Martin, and Benioff, *Proceedings of the Second International Congress on Acoustics* (American Institute of Physics, New York, 1957), paper FD4, p. 159.

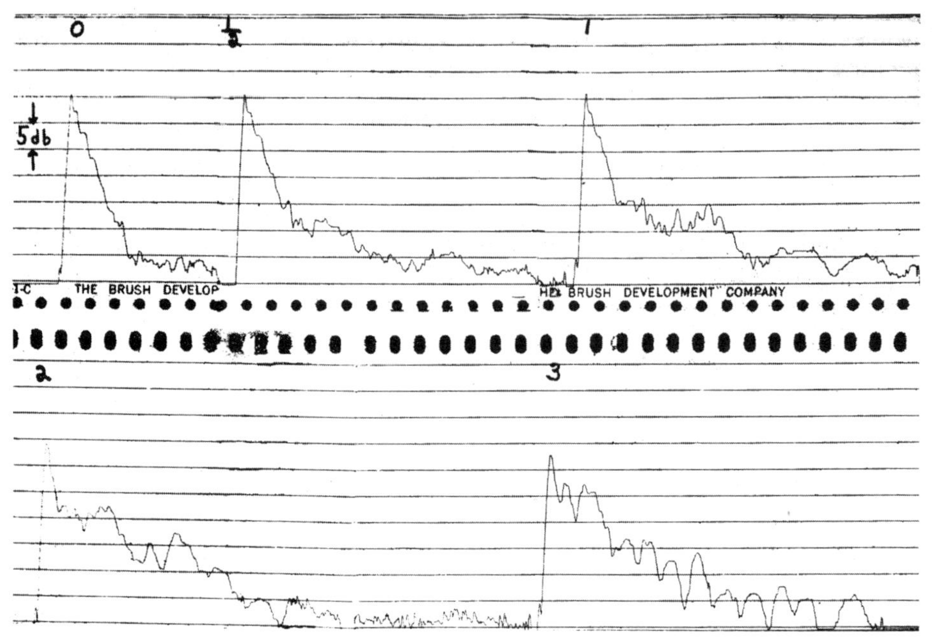


Fig. 1. Level *vs* time recordings of piano tone $B_3$ (247 cps). The number above the recordings refers to the tuning difference in cents between the center string and the outside strings of the unison group. These tone envelopes are representative of the envelopes produced by each of the five tuning conditions used in the preference test.

room and tuned prior to the experiment by an artist tuner. The center strings of three string unison-groups, corresponding to tones $E_3$ (165 cps) through $G_5$ (784 cps), were then checked with a Conn Chromatic Stroboscope to verify their agreement with the equally tempered scale.[6]

In order to achieve the "0 cent" tuning condition, the three string unison-groups were first tuned as close as possible to a zero-beat condition by the conventional aural method. A 640-AA Western Electric microphone was positioned 2-ft above the piano strings. Its output was amplified and led to a Brüel and Kjaer high speed level recorder. Final adjustments in the tensions of the outside strings were made while monitoring the results with the level recorder. The criterion for the zero-beat condition was the absence of amplitude fluctuations in the level recordings for two seconds after onset of the tone and for a level decrease of 30 db relative to the initial peak level of the tone.[7] Unison groups in the top $2\frac{1}{3}$ octaves of the piano were not included in this investigation. The zero-beat tuning condition there is very transitory. Attempts to achieve and maintain this condition in the upper $2\frac{1}{3}$ octaves of the piano long enough to record the tones on magnetic tape were not successful.

The 1-, 2-, 4-, and 6-cent differences between outside strings of three string unison groups were obtained with the aid of a Conn Chromatic Stroboscope. The upper string of three string unison-groups was tuned sharp and the lower string tuned flat by $\frac{1}{2}$, 1, 2, and 3 cents relative to the center string. The differences in tuning between outside strings were thus 1, 2, 4, and 6 cents, respectively.

High speed level recordings of the five "unison" conditions for the tone $B_3$ are shown in Fig. 1. This figure illustrates the absence of a dual diminution slope and the short duration of tones tuned to a zero-beat condition. A dual diminution slope is characteristic of piano tone.[8]

### Preference Test Program Material

Three types of recorded program material were used in determining tuning preferences for piano unison groups. The three types were: individual tones $E_3$, $B_3$, $F_4$, $C_5$, and $G_5$, an authentic cadence chord progression in the key of F and four measures of the melody line from Schubert's Unfinished Symphony No. 8 in B Minor. The program material was recorded on magnetic

[6] In these octaves of the piano, strings are tuned approximately to the equally tempered scale. Departure from the equally tempered scale increases above and below this range according to O. H. Schuck and R. W. Young, J. Acoust. Soc. Am. **15**, 1–11 (1943).

[7] Several unison-groups could not be tuned to meet these criteria and were not included in the investigation.

[8] D. W. Martin, J. Acoust. Soc. Am. **19**, 535–541, (1947).

tape. The recording system consisted of a Western Electric 640-AA condenser microphone, Western Electroacoustic amplifier and an Ampex 300 tape recorder. The recordings were made in a nonreverberant room. The piano keys for the individual tones and melody were struck by an automatic key actuating device which was controlled from an adjoining room. The chord progressions were played by the experimenter.

The recorded tape was prepared for presentation in an A-B preference test. Each of the five tuning conditions was paired with every other tuning condition, making a total of ten paired comparison judgments for each of the five individual tones, the melody and the chord progression. Each subject thus made a total of seventy judgments, ten for each of the five individual tones, ten for melody and ten for the chord progression. The order in which the tuning conditions were presented was determined from a table of random numbers.

### Subjects

One hundred and twenty-three subjects served in the experiment. One hundred and two of the subjects were students in introductory psychology classes at the University of Kentucky Northern Center. The remaining twenty-one subjects included music students from the Cincinnati College Conservatory of Music and Baldwin engineering and research personnel.

### Preference Test Administration

The recorded tuning preference test was given to the subjects in groups of from seven to thirty over a period of a year and a half. All of the test administrations were made in the same room under controlled environmental conditions. The floor area of the room was 40×30 ft with a total volume of 15 600 cu ft. The acoustic treatment of the room consisted of six 36 sq ft absorptive panels suspended from the ceiling. The reverberation time of the room was approximately 1.3 sec. An Altec 800 theater loudspeaker system, an Ampex 300 tape recorder, and a Fisher 50 w power amplifier were used in the play back system for the recorded preference test. The loudspeaker system was located on a stage $1\frac{1}{2}$ ft high behind an acoustically transparent screen. The first row of subjects sat approximately 15 ft in front of the loudspeaker system. The Ampex 300 tape recorder was located in an adjoining room to minimize extraneous noise.

The level for presenting the preference test material was determined by comparison with the loudness of the same material performed with maximum effort on a grand piano. The loudness of the test material at a distance of four feet in front of the speaker system was approximately equal to the loudness observed by a performer seated in front of a grand piano playing the same test material.

The subjects were told that they were participating in a tone quality preference test. Their task was to indicate on an answer sheet which tone quality they preferred. A one-second interval of silence separated the end of the first stimulus of a pair from the onset of the second stimulus. A silent period of five seconds after termination of the second stimulus of a pair was provided during which the subjects recorded their preference.

### RESULTS AND DISCUSSION

The data for the 123 subjects were pooled in determining the most preferred tuning condition for piano three string unison groups. A technique has been described by Kendall[9] for estimating the true ranking of $m$ sets of $n$ rankings. This technique was used to assign a rank order to the tuning conditions. The results of this analysis are shown in Table I. A statistical test described by Kendall was used to determine the significance of the rank orders in Table I. This statistic is given by

$$\left\{\left[\sum(\gamma^2)-m\sum(\gamma)+\binom{m}{2}\binom{n}{2}\right]-\frac{1}{2}\binom{n}{2}\binom{m}{2}\frac{m-3}{n-2}\right\}\frac{4}{m-2} \quad (1)$$

and is distributed as chi-square with

$$v=\frac{\binom{n}{2}m(m-1)}{(m-2)^2} \quad (2)$$

degrees of freedom. In the first formula, $\gamma$ refers to the summation of scores either above or below the diagonal of an $n$ by $n$ table. It is evident from Table I that the most preferred tuning conditions for piano unison groups are 1 and 2 cents maximum deviation between outside strings. The 6 cent tuning condition was consistently ranked last. It will be recalled that in earlier preliminary investigations, this was the maximum tuning difference among strings which was acceptable to musically trained subjects.

TABLE I. Tuning preferences for piano three string unison groups.

| Tuning condition | $E_3$ | $B_3$ | $F_4$ | $C_5$ | $G_5$ | Chordal passage | Melodic passage |
|---|---|---|---|---|---|---|---|
| 0 | 2[a] | 4[b] | 4[c] | 3[c] | 3[c] | 4[a] | 2[c] |
| 1 | 1 | 2 | 3 | 2 | 1 | 3 | 1 |
| 2 | 3 | 1 | 1 | 1 | 2 | 1 | 3 |
| 4 | 4 | 3 | 2 | 4 | 4 | 2 | 4 |
| 6 | 5 | 5 | 5 | 5 | 5 | 5 | 5 |

[a] significant at 10% level.
[b] significant at 2% level.
[c] significant at 1% level.

[9] M. G. Kendall, *The Advanced Theory of Statistics* (Charles Griffin and Company, London, England, 1943), Vol. I, pp. 421–433.

It would seem on *a priori* grounds that musical training and experience would influence a subject's tuning preferences for piano three string unison groups. In order to test this hypothesis, brief musical autobiographies written by the subjects at the completion of the preference test were analyzed. The subjects were assigned to one of three categories on the basis of their musical background. The first category (A) consisted of 45 subjects who had regularly engaged in the performance of music either individually or in ensembles for a minimum of five years. The second category (B) consisted of 35 subjects with less than five years of individual or ensemble performance of music but more than one year of such experience. This category consisted primarily of subjects who had participated in high school music organizations but who had discontinued their music activities after high school. The third category (C) consisted of 27 subjects with less than one year of music performance. Sixteen of the subjects were not classified because of insufficient autobiographical information. The foregoing criteria used in categorizing the subjects are admittedly arbitrary. For purposes of this investigation, however, they appear to possess face validity although they fail to take into account the subjects' attitudes toward music or their music listening habits. Pragmatic considerations dictated the use of musical background information in classifying the subjects.

The median tuning preference of subjects in the three categories is shown in Fig. 2. There is a tendency evident in Fig. 2 for subjects whose autobiographies revealed the longest history of music study and performance to prefer the least detuning of piano three string unison groups. The statistical significance of the tuning preference differences among categories A, B, and C was evaluated by a Kruskal-Wallis one-way analysis of variance test. The differences among the categories failed to reach the 5% level of significance. The dispersion of tuning preference judgments was greatest for subjects in category C and smallest for subjects in category A. The difference in dispersion of preference judgments was significant at the 1% level. This difference in dispersion of judgments among the groups probably resulted from the operation of two factors. First, the subjects in category A may have been more interested in the recorded sounds because of their prior musical experience. This difference in interest among the three categories of subjects would manifest itself in greater alertness and ability to sustain attention for subjects in category A. The experimental design of the preference test was such that lapses in attention always resulted in greater variability in the subjects' responses. Thus, part of the difference in tuning preference variance may be error variance attributable to the experimental procedure. It seems unlikely that this is the sole explanation for the observed differences in variability. A second factor is that in many types of skills, training decreases intragroup

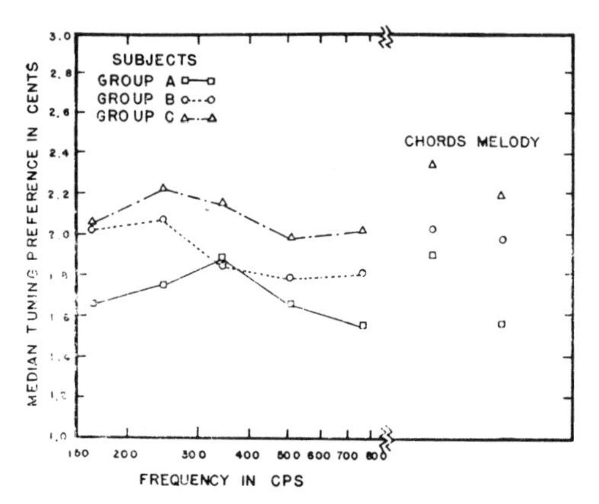


Fig. 2. Median tuning preference of subjects for individual tones, chordal passage and melodic passage. The subjects were assigned to groups A, B, and C according to their musical background. Subjects in category A had the most musical training while subjects in category C had the least musical training.

differences. It seems likely that the smaller variability of subjects in category A is in part real and not just an artifact of the experimental design.

In order to determine the discriminability of the five tuning conditions, the preference test was readministered to 32 subjects in category B. The purpose of this phase of the investigation was to determine the ability of the subjects to detect a difference between the tuning conditions presented in the paired comparison test. Since a forced choice method was used in obtaining the preference judgments, it is necessary that each of the tuning conditions in comparison with the other conditions be equally discriminable. Failure to satisfy this conditions leads to ambiguity in interpretating the data. The measure of discriminability for the five tuning conditions was the subjects' ability to indicate which tone of a stimulus pair sounded smoother to them. The subjects' judgments of "smoother" were then compared with physical measurements of the tone envelopes. The percentage of judgments in which the five tuning conditions were correctly identified by the subjects as being smoother are as follows: 0 cent condition = 73%, 1 cent condition = 68%, 2 cent condition = 74%, 4 cent condition = 77%, and 6 cent condition = 87%. According to a chi-square test, the differences in correct identification associated with the five tuning conditions are not statistically significant.

It was noted earlier that piano tuners seldom tune three string unison-groups to exact unison. The mean maximum difference in fundamental frequency among strings of concert grand pianos measured immediately after tuning was 1.6 cents. The most preferred tuning condition of the subjects in category A was a mean maximum difference among unison strings of 1.7 cents. In an investigation by Corso and Lewis[10] of the pre-

[10] J. F. Corso and D. Lewis, J. Appl. Psychol. **34**, 206–211 (1950).

ferred rate and extent of frequency vibrato of a complex tone, close agreement was found between the preferred extent of vibrato and the vibrato actually used by professional violinists. In their investigation, musicians preferred a narrower extent of frequency vibrato than did nonmusicians.

The results of Corso and Lewis' experiment and the present investigation raise a question concerning the role of the subjects' past experience in determining their listening preferences. We must assume that the subjects' preference judgments are determined not only by the stimulus configuration present during the test but also by the sum total of the subjects' relevant past experiences. Within this framework, the probability of evoking a listening "set" is positively correlated with the number of stimulus elements between the test situation and the subjects' previous experience which are perceived as similar at some level of awareness. It is further assumed that the level of awareness necessary for the evocation of a listening set varies from subject to subject. It has been demonstrated previously that listening to electroacoustically reproduced music with either a restricted frequency range (180–3000 cps) or an unrestricted frequency range (30–15 000 cps) results in the establishment of sets to prefer these frequency ranges.[11] This effect was greatest for musical selections similar to the selections played during the training trials and for preference tests conducted in the same environment as that used for the training trials. The importance of environmental cues in eliciting appropriate response sets has also been observed by Dulsky[12] and Abernethy.[13]

In order to determine whether the close agreement between the way pianos are tuned and listener preferences for tuning could be interpreted in terms of a set hypothesis, the preference test was readministered to 31 of the subjects in category A. The subjects were asked to indicate which tones sounded most like a piano. The mean of the distribution of judgments was 1.7 cents. It will be recalled that the mean of the distribution of preference scores for category A was also 1.7 cents. If tuning preferences are influenced by previous experience, one would predict a positive correlation between each subject's tuning preferences and his judgment of the way unison-groups are tuned in actual practice. In addition, one would predict that the correlation would be highest for subjects in category A and lowest for subjects in category C. Spearman rank-difference correlation coefficients were computed to determine the degree of relationship between tuning preferences and judgments of the way pianos are tuned. A correlation of 0.38 was obtained for 31 subjects in category A and a correlation of 0.29 for 18 subjects in category C. These correlations, while not high, are in the predicted direction and are interpreted as supporting the above set hypothesis.

[11] R. E. Kirk, J. Acoust. Soc. Am. **28**, 1113–1116 (1956).
[12] S. G. Dulsky, J. Exptl. Psychol. **18**, 725–740 (1935).
[13] E. M. Abernethy, J. Psychol. **10**, 293–301 (1940).

## SUMMARY AND CONCLUSIONS

The most preferred tuning condition for piano three string unison groups was determined by means of a paired comparison preference test. Five tuning conditions were used: zero-beat tuning and the upper string of three string unison groups tuned sharp and the lower string tuned flat by ½, 1, 2, and 3 cents relative to the center string. The preference test, recorded on magnetic tape, was given to both musically trained and untrained subjects.

An analysis of the results indicates the following:

(1) The most preferred tuning conditions for three string unison groups are 1 and 2 cents maximum deviation among strings.

(2) Subjects with the longest history of musical performance prefer the least detuning of unison groups. The intragroup variability of these subjects with respect to tuning preferences is less than the variability of subjects having little or no musical training.

(3) There is a close agreement between the average tuning preference of the subjects and the way artist tuners actually tune piano unison groups.

(4) The subjects' tuning preferences are positively correlated with the way they believe pianos sound.

(5) The findings of this investigation are interpreted as supporting a set or learning hypothesis concerning the origin of preferences for piano unison tuning.

## ACKNOWLEDGMENTS

The support and stimulating suggestions of Dr. D. W. Martin, and the assistance of the writer's colleagues especially Mr. R. K. Duncan and Mr. T. C. Hundley, are gratefully acknowledged. The co-operation of Mr. T. Hankins, the faculty and student body of the University of Kentucky Northern Center is appreciated.

# 9

Copyright © 1962 by the Acoustical Society of America

Reprinted from *J. Acoust. Soc. Am.*, **34**(6), 749–761 (1962)

## Quality of Piano Tones

Harvey Fletcher, E. Donnell Blackham, and Richard Stratton
*Brigham Young University, Provo, Utah*

(Received November 27, 1961)

A synthesizer was constructed to produce simultaneously 100 pure tones with means for controlling the intensity and frequency of each one of them. The piano tones were analyzed by conventional apparatus and methods and the analysis set into the synthesizer. The analysis was considered correct only when a jury of eight listeners could not tell which were real and which were synthetic tones. Various kinds of synthetic tones were presented to the jury for comparison with real tones. A number of these were judged to have better quality than the real tones. According to these tests synthesized piano-like tones were produced when the attack time was less than 0.01 sec. The decay can be as long as 20 sec for the lower notes and be less than 1 sec for the very high ones. The best quality is produced when the partials decrease in level at the rate of 2 db per 100-cps increase in the frequency of the partial. The partials below middle C must be inharmonic in frequency to be piano-like.

### INTRODUCTION

THIS paper is a report of our efforts to find an objective description of the quality of piano tones as understood by musicians, and also to try to find synthetic tones which are considered by them to be better than real-piano tones.

The usual statement found in text books is that the pitch of a tone is determined by the frequency of vibration, the loudness by the intensity of the vibration, and the quality by the waveform. This picture is far too simple for any of these three subjective aspects of a tone. Pitch and loudness have received very extensive study. In this paper an attempt has been made to throw some additional light upon the quality of a piano tone.

It is true that the quality depends upon the waveform. But it also depends upon the pitch, the loudness, the decay and attack time, the variation with time of the intensity of the partials, the impact noise of the hammer, the noise of the damping pedal, and also the characteristic ending of the tone by the damping felt, etc.

In order to study the relative importance of these various factors, the following laboratory equipment and room facilities have been developed, namely, (1) anechoic chamber, (2) loudspeaker system, (3) tone synthesizer, and (4) the frequency changer. To these facilities have been added, a sonograph, an analyzer, a single-track tape recorder, a 5-track tape recorder, and other apparatus usually available in electronic research laboratories. A block diagram of the arrangement is shown in Fig. 1.

### EQUIPMENT

#### 1. Anechoic Chamber

An anechoic chamber was constructed for use as a listening room. It was built according to the architect's drawings loaned to us by the Bell Telephone Laboratories. Therefore, it is a copy of the one at those laboratories.

It consists of a rectangular block of cement with inside dimensions of 40×30×30 ft. The block rests on sand and gravel, and is completely separate from the rest of the Eyring Science Center building. The room was treated with 6-ft acoustical wedges on each side, thus reducing the size 12 ft in each direction. A wire-mesh floor was constructed by stretching steel wires across the steel I-beams on the sides. These wires were separated by 2 in., and there were two sets at right angles to each other. This resulted in meshes 2 in. square. The floor is 10 ft below the ceiling edge of the

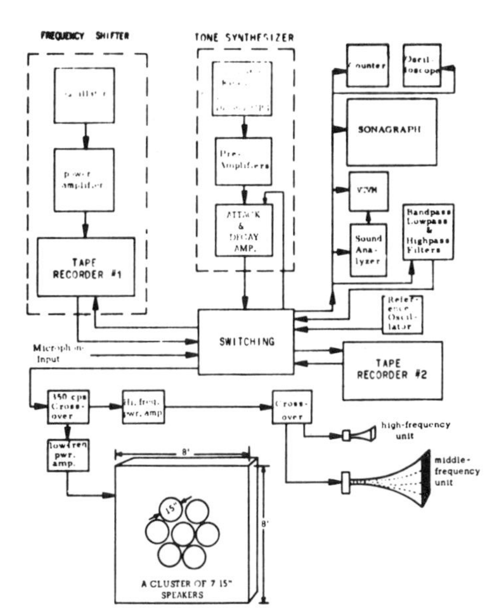


FIG. 1. Block diagram of equipment.

acoustical wedges and 8 ft above the lower set of wedges. It will support considerable weight but has little or no reflection for any of the sounds in the audible range. Chairs were supported on this wire floor at one end of the chamber for the jury of listeners. The loudspeaker system was installed at the opposite end.

## 2. Loudspeaker System

This consists of a three-channel system, each channel transmitting, respectively, the bands of frequency 20 to 400 cps, 400 to 4000 cps, and 4000 to 16 000 cps. The low-frequency channel consists of seven Altec 803 B drivers mounted close together in a circular arrangement as shown in Fig. 1, with a baffle which was 8 ft square. This baffle was mounted so it could turn about a horizontal axis. At certain angles from the vertical, a more uniform response for the very low frequencies was obtained.

As indicated in Fig. 1, the medium-range loudspeaker was a sectional-type horn, and the high-frequency loudspeaker was of a tweeter type. The response of this system is given in Fig. 2.

## 3. Tone Synthesizer

The tone synthesizer used to produce the synthetic tones consisted of five major parts, namely, a power supply, audio-frequency oscillators, a white noise source and filter set, attenuators and preamplifiers, and an attack and decay amplifier. A block diagram is shown in Fig. 3.

### *Power Supply*

The requirements placed upon the power supply consisted of (a) supplying adequate power at the appropriate voltages and (b) maintenance of a low level of noise and hum. The second of the two requirements was the most difficult to satisfy, and was especially difficult in this case because of the surges of power involved in the operation of the attack and decay amplifier. To obtain this low noise level, a 6-v dc battery was used for the attack and decay amplifier vacuum-tube grid and filament supplies, and for the transistor oscillators' power requirements. The use of this simple battery eliminates the inherent problems posed by alternating current supplies. To obtain the required plate voltage for the attack and decay amplifier, a General Radio high-voltage supply was used in conjunction with specially designed filters. These filters consisted of *R-C* filter sections and voltage regulator tubes; it produced a constant voltage output with a noise or "ripple" level 80 db below the output signal level.

### *Audio-Frequency Oscillators*

Since 100 oscillators were required it was necessary to select a design which was compact and which gave a stable oscillation. This was accomplished by using transistors with printed circuits. The circuit elements were mounted on a panel board 5 in. long and 1½ in. wide. The inductance element can be varied by turning a key which can be inserted in a small hole through the face of the panel. In this way each oscillator can be turned to any desired frequency within about 1-octave range. The 100 oscillators can be tuned to cover a range from 50 to 15 000 cps. These 100 small panels supporting the oscillators were stacked together into three large panels. Two of these large panels are shown at the bottom half of Fig. 4. The other panel is on the opposite side of the portable table carrying the synthesizer.

### *Attenuators and Preamplifiers*

The output of each oscillator is sent through an attenuator and then to its preamplifier. The 100 attenuators were arranged in a compact form at the back of a black panel board. White knobs (100 of them) which were projecting through the black panel board and which were connected to the sliding contact of the attenuator could be moved up and down in vertical slots to control the amount of attenuation introduced into each oscillating circuit. Each attenuator covered a range of 50 db. They were constructed so that the downward movement of the knob produced an attenuation

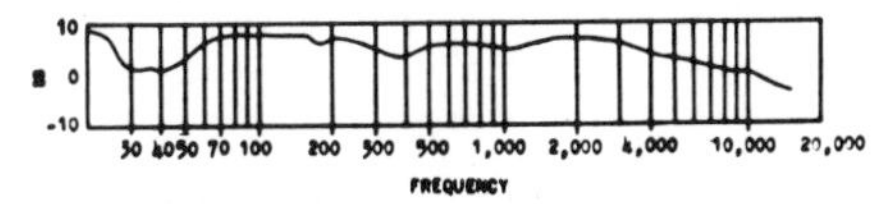


FIG. 2. Relative response of loudspeaker system.

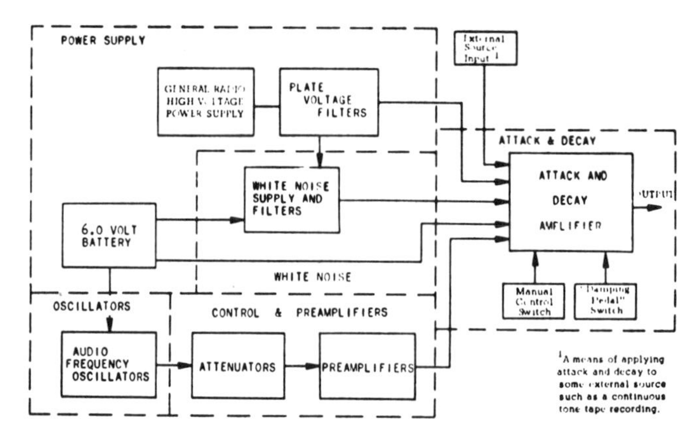


FIG. 3. Block diagram for tone synthesizer.

in db which was proportional to the distance it was moved. A db scale was engraved on the face of this panel. It is thus seen that the relative positions of these white knobs in vertical level give the relative levels in db of the current going from the oscillators to the preamplifiers and shows graphically the structure of the partials of the tone being synthesized.

In the upper part of Fig. 4 this panel is shown. The knobs in the picture are set to produce the synthetic piano tone A'''', the lowest note on the piano.

### *Attack and Decay Amplifier*

The attack and decay amplifier[1] functions just as the name implies—it gives a beginning and an ending or attack and decay to any constant-level input. The specific requirements placed upon the amplifier, are listed as follows: (a) Frequency response: ±2 db from 50 to 15 000 cps. (b) Noise and switching transients: 50 db below the signal level. (c) Intermodulation distortion: 5%. (d) Harmonic distortion: 2%. (e) Time rate of attack and decay continuously variable from 4,000–6 db/sec and very nearly exponential. (f) The attack and decay amplifier must operate over a range of 70 db (from maximum to minimum output signal). Considerable developmental work was necessary before a circuit was obtained which would fulfill these requirements, particularly the last one. The circuit which was finally used is given in Fig. 5. The concept involved is that of a two-stage push-pull amplifier in which the grids of both stages (4 vacuum tubes) are biased in accordance with the attack and decay required. The grid bias voltage comes from a resistance–capacitance–battery network which will thus provide an exponentially increasing or decreasing voltage depending upon whether the capacitor is charging or discharging. The function (attack or decay) of the amplifier is determined by connecting the battery voltage through a resistor and capacitor series circuit or shorting through the same capacitor but different resistors. This function is controlled by a push-button switch called the manual control switch. The output signal will increase when the button is pushed, build up to its maximum value, and remain at that point until the button is released. Upon release, the decay circuit is in use and the decaying rate is applied to the signal. The rate of attack and decay is determined by the adjustment of the resistance used in the *R-C* circuits. See Fig. 5.

Another control used is the "damping pedal" control which places a resistor in parallel with (by means of a pushbutton) the decay resistor. Thus the rate of decay can be changed to a more rapid one during the decay time and thus simulate the action of the damping pedal on the piano.

One serious limitation of the synthesizer is that the decay rate is constant and the same for all frequencies. This means that a curve showing level in db vs the time in seconds will be a straight line. The time in seconds to decay 20 db will be called the decay time. This is the time for the current in the attack and decay amplifier to decrease to 0.1 of its maximum value. Likewise, the

FIG. 4. Photograph of synthesizer.

[1] R. N. Christensen, "An Attack and Decay Amplifier Suitable for use in a Tone Synthesizer," thesis (unpublished), Brigham Young University, Provo, Utah (1959).

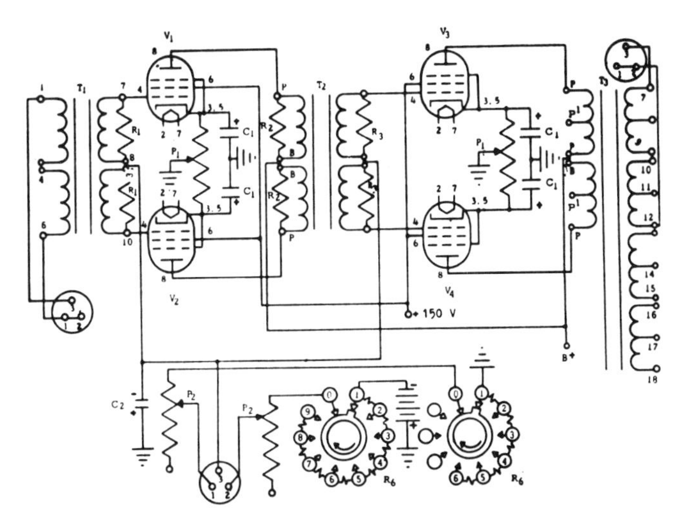


Fig. 5. Attack and decay amplifier circuit.

attack time is the time in seconds for the current to reach 0.9 of its maximum value.

### 4. Frequency Shifter

The frequency shifter consisted of a tape recorder with a synchronous motor which was driven by a combination of an oscillator and a power amplifier. By varying the frequency of the oscillator, the speed of the tape recorder could be increased to $\frac{4}{3}$ normal speed and decreased to $\frac{1}{4}$ normal speed or to any speed within these limits. This made it possible to set up any partial structure on the synthesizer, record it on the frequency shifter, and then shift to any desired fundamental frequency.

## Method of Analyzing the Piano Tone

During the first part of our analysis work a sonograph was used. This instrument has been described in the literature and is in common use. The tone to be analyzed is recorded on a rotating cylinder. The sectioner is switched on and then the instrument draws horizontal lines whose lengths are proportional to the relative levels of the partials. The position of a peg on the top of the rotating cylinder determines the time during the duration of tone that corresponds to the partial structure being measured. By moving the peg on the rotating drum the chosen time can be changed in 0.04-sec intervals. The sonograph will record only sounds having a duration less than 2.4 sec. Thus the partial structure can be measured at 60 different times during the duration of such a tone. The approximate frequency can be read from this graph.

In the later part of our work a conventional analyzer was used which passed only a narrow band of frequency (approximately 4 cps). The output was read directly in db on a level meter. This procedure would be straightforward if the tone were steady. But a piano tone is continually varying so the piano tone was recorded on a continuous loop so that the tone could be continually repeated. The analyzer was set to give a maximum response for each partial near the beginning of the tone. Then a pure tone from an oscillator was sent through the analyzer with this setting and the frequency adjusted to give maximum response. The frequency of this pure tone was then measured on the electronic counter which will measure frequency with an accuracy of about 0.1%. In this way the frequencies and the relative levels of the partials at the beginning of the tone were determined. The variation of the partials with time can be inferred from the sonograph measurements.

In a third method of obtaining the partial structure and its variation with time, a level recorder was used. The complex tone from the loop was sent through the analyzer to the recorder. All of these methods have their advantages and disadvantages, and one method serves to check the others. In our general study of musical sounds all of these methods have been used. The general arrangement of these and other standard instruments is shown in Fig. 1.

As shown in Fig. 1, the current from the oscillators goes into the preamplifiers and then into the attack and decay amplifier. From here it may be switched to the loudspeaker system or to any of the other instruments shown.

With this instrumentation we can record the tones from the piano. From this recorded tone we are able to find the partial structure and how it varies with time. Also the attack and decay times can be measured. This analysis is then used to produce a synthetic tone, which may be compared to the real tone by judgment tests. Also new tones having any partial structure and any attack and decay times can be created for judgment uses.

## EXPERIMENTAL

It is known that in a real-piano tone the partial structure is varying; that is, the decay curves of the partial tones will not be straight lines. It is also known[2] that the partials coming from a struck string are not strictly harmonic. At the impact of the hammer, a sound like that of hitting a board is superimposed on the tone from the string. This sound is particularly noticeable in the upper three octaves of the piano. When the piano tone is damped with the pedal it stops first the low tones and finally the higher ones giving a characteristic ending of the tone. The pedal itself produces a noise which is readily recognized as due to its movement. If one wanted to reproduce all these complicated sounds, one would make a tape recording of the actual piano tone. But we are interested in knowing the relative importance of these various factors.

This paper describes experiments which were designed to increase our understanding of these and other factors which govern the quality of piano tones. To begin the investigation, tones from a Baldwin grand piano were recorded. The piano was in a studio room of about the usual characteristics.

The tones recorded were designated thus:

| | |
|---|---|
| C‴ | Three octaves below middle C. |
| C″ | Two octaves below middle C. |
| C′ | One octave below middle C. |
| C | Middle C, frequency 261.6 cps. |
| $C_1$ | One octave above middle C. |
| $C_2$ | Two octaves above middle C. |
| $C_3$ | Three octaves above middle C. |

The same designations were used on the G-pitched, or any other tones, using middle G as the G a fifth above middle C.

About 2 sec after the key was struck, the damping pedal was used to dampen the tone. These tones were analyzed by use of the sonograph; three or four samples being taken at different times. The average of these four samples was taken as the partial structure. The results of these measurements are given in Fig. 6.

A careful measurement of the spacing on the frequency scale of the tracings made on the sonograph indicated that, within the observational error, the partials were approximately harmonic except for those of C‴ and C″. The frequencies of the partials of these two low-pitched tones were found to be definitely higher than the harmonic frequencies. For example, for C‴ the 30th partial frequency was found to be 1105 cps which is 134 cps greater than the harmonic frequency. It will be seen later that the partials of any piano tone are inharmonic and can be calculated by the formula given by Young[2] and others.

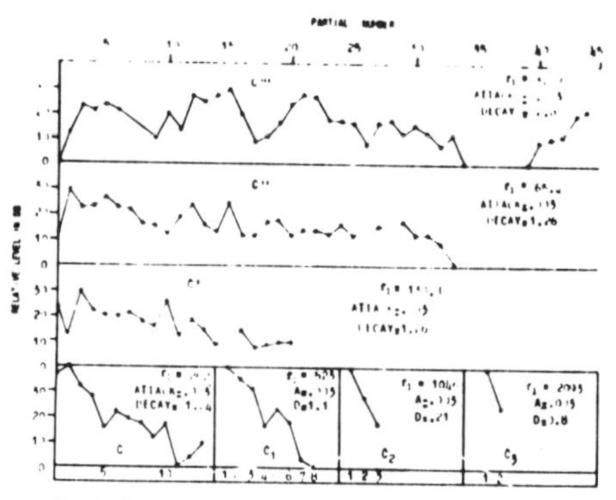

Fig. 6. Average partial structure of the studio piano.

### Preliminary Judgments Tests

To obtain a first approximation of the relative importance of the various factors influencing the quality of the piano tone the following identification test was made. Synthetic tones were created having partial structures in accordance with those shown in Fig. 6. From these synthetic and the original piano tones, the following program was recorded. [The letter in the parentheses (R) indicates it was a real tone. Similarly the letter (S) indicates it was a synthetic tone.]

Test (1) C(S)—C(S)—C(R)—C(S)—C(R).

Test (2) C′(R)—C′(R)—C′(S)—C′(S)—C′(S).

Test (3) C″(S)—C″(S)—C″(S)—C″(S)—C″(R).

Test (4) C‴(R)—C‴(S)—C‴(S)—C‴(R).

Test (5) $C_1$(S)—$C_1$(R)—$C_1$(S)—$C_1$(S)—$C_1$(R).

Test (6) $C_2$(S)—$C_2$(S)—$C_2$(R)—$C_2$(R)—$C_2$(R).

Test (7) $C_3$(S)—$C_3$(S)—$C_3$(S)—$C_3$(R)—$C_3$(S).

Test (8) C″(S)—C′(R)—C″(R)—C(R)—C‴(S)—C(R)—$C_1$(S)—$C_2$(S)—$C_3$(R).

A jury of four musicians was asked to check which they considered were the real-piano tones. A second jury of laymen also took the test. The musicians identified 90% correctly and the laymen 86%. Both teams scored less than 75% on these tests for identifying middle C as a real-piano tone, showing the synthetic C tone was a better match for this than for the others.

From listening to the above program of tests and talking to members of these two juries, it was obvious that there were a number of clues for identifying the real-piano tones. Some of these are (1) the noise of the piano hammer striking the string, (2) the noise of the pedal dampening the tone, (3) higher background noise for the piano tones, (4) reverberation effects of the room

[2] R. W. Young, J. Acoust. Soc. Am. 24, 267-273 (1952).

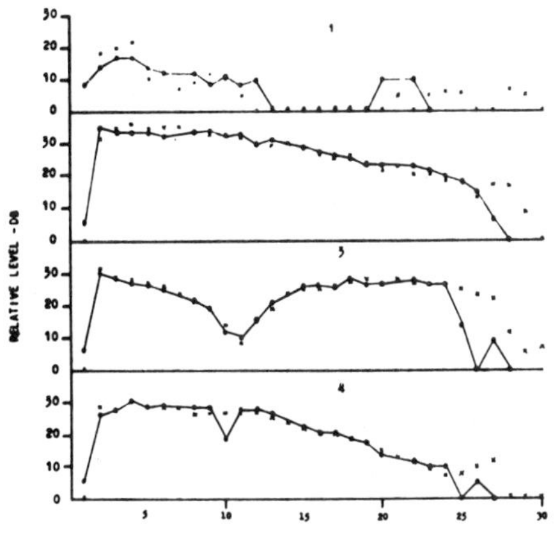


FIG. 7. Curves showing the changing level vs time for the partials 1, 2, 3, and 4 of the tone C‴.

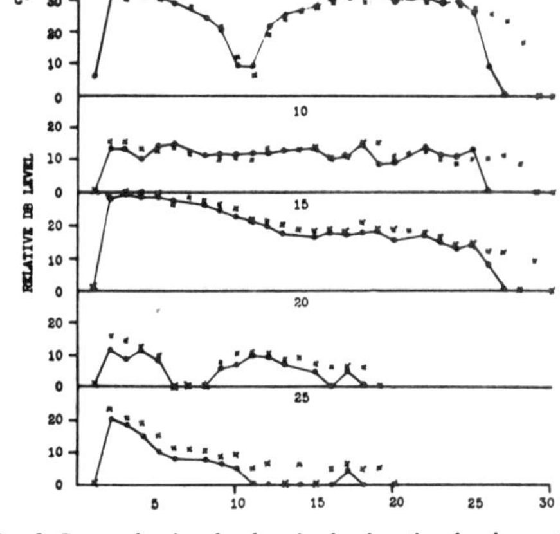


FIG. 8. Curves showing the changing level vs time for the partials 5, 10, 15, 20, and 25 of the tone C‴.

for the real-piano tones which were absent for the synthetic tones.

The electrical circuit was arranged so that the original beginning and ending of the tones were eliminated. This removed the clues associated with the starting and stopping of the tones. Then the musicians correctly identified 74% of the tones and the laymen 75%. In Test 8, where the tones are arranged haphazardly as to frequency, the scores were much lower, namely 63% correct. It will be remembered that a 50% score means that the observer is guessing. It should also be remembered that in these tests the frequency of each partial in the synthetic tone was an exact multiple of the fundamental and the rate of decay was constant and the same for all partials.

### Partial Level vs Time

The preliminary tests showed more clearly how to proceed to match real-piano tones with synthetic tones. Before improving the synthetic tones, it was decided to make a more careful study of real-piano tones. So the C″ was chosen for a more critical study to see how the various partials change with time. By means of the sonograph, at a time interval of 0.08 sec, 30 observations were made on each of the 30 measurable components. Samples of these results are shown in Figs. 7 and 8. In Fig. 7 the decay curves for the first 4 partials are given and in Fig. 8 the curves for partials numbered 5, 10, 15, 20, and 25 are given.

These results are rather surprising although somewhat similar results have been observed before. To be sure there was no artifact, the key for C‴ was struck a second time and a separate analysis made. The two sets of points in the figures represent the two sets of data. It is seen that there is good agreement. The discrepancy at the end of the tones means simply that one tone was damped quicker than the other.

It will be seen that some of these curves exhibit a fairly uniform rate of decay such as for partial 2, 4, and 15. However, most of the others show very irregular decay time characteristics. It is obvious from these curves that the partial structure is continually changing as the tone dies away. In Fig. 9, similar data on the piano tone C is given for the first six partials. It is obvious from these data that the partials of the piano tone do not even approximately decay at the same rate. They sometimes increase in intensity rather than decrease. Thus to give the decay rate as Xdb per sec,

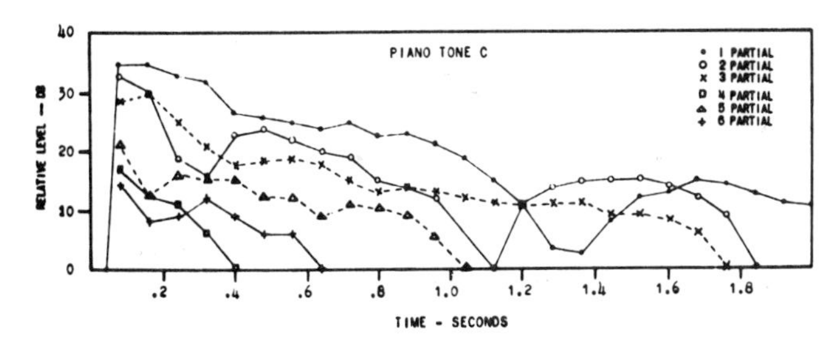


FIG. 9. Relative level vs time for the first six partials of the tone C.

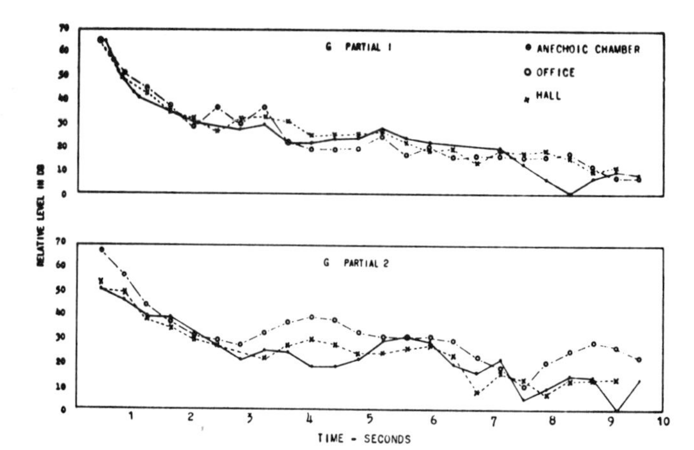


FIG. 10. Room effect on the level vs time curves for the partials 1 and 2 of the tone G.

as some authors still do, gives a rather erroneous picture.

Since these tones were recorded in a live music studio, it was decided to bring a piano into our anechoic chamber to see if these irregular variations with time were due to the room or were characteristic of the piano.

A Hamilton upright piano was taken into our laboratory where there were three rooms of different reverberation characteristics available in which the piano could be played. Room O had a reverberation time for speech of 0.6 sec (studio type). In Room H the reverberation time was 2.2 sec, that is, very reverberant. Room A was the anechoic chamber and the reverberation time was very close to zero. It could not be measured with the instruments available.

The same piano selection was recorded in each of the three rooms. Judgment tests were made first by a jury of 8 musicians and then by a jury of 12 laymen to determine which room was preferable for listening to the music. The musicians voted 1 for Room O (studio), 1 for Room H (reverberant), and 6 for Room A (anechoic). The laymen voted 1 for Room O, 5 for Room H, and 6 for Room A. Thus the anechoic chamber was definitely considered best for listening. This confirmed the conclusion reached some time ago that musicians prefer to listen to music in a nonreverberant room. However the player always prefers to play in a reverberant room.

While the piano was in each of these rooms, the tones produced by playing the white keys on the piano were also recorded on the tape recorder. The result of tests taken with the sonograph on the piano tone G played in these three rooms are given in Figs. 10 and 11. It is seen that the irregularities in the decay pattern exist in all three rooms. In the acoustically live room (hall) they are no greater than in the acoustically dead room.

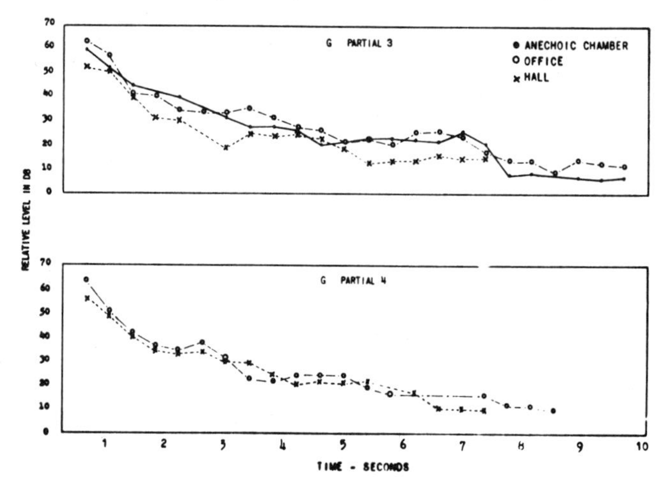


FIG. 11. Same as Fig. 10 but for partials 3 and 4 of the tone G.

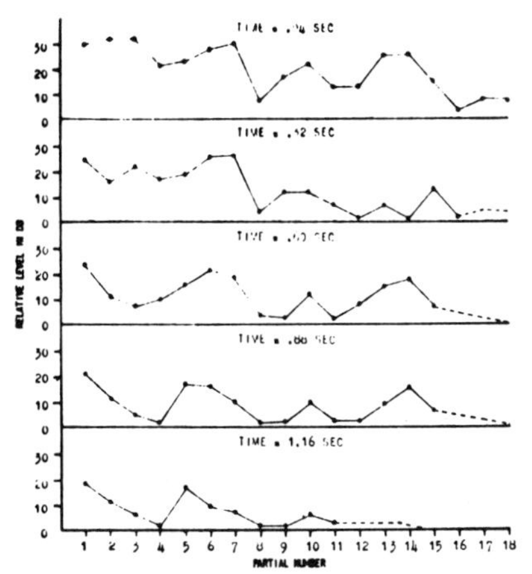


FIG. 12. Partial structures at different times for the tone G″.

It can also be noted that the decay rate is faster at the beginning and becomes slower after the first two sec. If the decay rate at the beginning persisted, the tone would go below hearing threshold in about 3 sec, but actually the tone can be heard for about 20 sec.

Measurements on $G_1$ and $G_2$ gave similar results. The curves in Fig. 12 show how the partial structure of the piano tone G″ changes with time. It is obvious that to match these real-piano tones with synthetic tones is a very complicated process. Of course the easiest way to do this is to make a tape recording of the tone. Then all these variations are preserved and can be reproduced.

TABLE I. Observed frequencies of the partials of piano tone A'''', as well as the frequencies calculated for $B=0.00053$.

| $n$ | $27.5n$ | obs $f_n$ | calc $f_n$ | db | $n$ | $27.5n$ | obs $f_n$ | calc $f_n$ | db |
|---|---|---|---|---|---|---|---|---|---|
| 1 | 27.5 | 27.5 | 27.51 | −23 | 26 | 715 | 835 | 833 | −17 |
| 2 | 55 | 55 | 55.06 | −29 | 27 | 742.5 | 876 | 874 | −16 |
| 3 | 82.5 | 83 | 82.2 | −9 | 28 | 770 | 917 | 916 | −7 |
| 4 | 110 | 111 | 110.5 | −19 | 29 | 797.5 | 959 | 959 | −9 |
| 5 | 137.5 | 138 | 138.4 | 0 | 30 | 825 | 1003 | 1003 | −18 |
| 6 | 165 | 166 | 166.5 | −3 | 31 | 852.5 | 1049 | 1047 | −23 |
| 7 | 192.5 | 193 | 195 | −15 | 32 | 880 | 1094 | 1093 | −25 |
| 8 | 220 | 222 | 224 | −28 | 33 | 907.5 | 1144 | 1140 | −33 |
| 9 | 247.5 | 251 | 253 | −22 | 34 | 935 | 1189 | 1187 | −16 |
| 10 | 275 | 281 | 282 | −12 | 35 | 962 | 1237 | 1236 | −11 |
| 11 | 302.5 | 311 | 312 | −13 | 36 | 990 | 1287 | 1286 | −17 |
| 12 | 330 | 340 | 342 | −3 | 37 | 1017.5 | 1336 | 1337 | −26 |
| 13 | 357.5 | 371 | 373 | −3 | 38 | 1045 | 1386 | 1388 | −28 |
| 14 | 385 | 402 | 404 | −7 | 39 | 1072.5 | 1440 | 1441 | −31 |
| 15 | 412.5 | 435 | 436 | −11 | 40 | 1100 | 1495 | 1495 | −33 |
| 16 | 440 | 467 | 469 | −15 | 41 | 1127.5 | 1550 | 1550 | −27 |
| 17 | 467.5 | 501 | 502 | −8 | 42 | 1155 | 1602 | 1607 | −34 |
| 18 | 495 | 534 | 535 | −4 | 43 | 1182.5 | 1659 | 1664 | −29 |
| 19 | 522.5 | 569 | 570 | 0 | 44 | 1210 | 1716 | 1722 | −31 |
| 20 | 550 | 605 | 605 | +4 | 45 | 1237.5 | 1776 | 1782 | −36 |
| 21 | 577.5 | 641 | 641 | 0 | 46 | 1265 | 1834 | 1842 | −38 |
| 22 | 605 | 677 | 678 | −1 | 47 | 1292.5 | 1884 | 1904 | −33 |
| 23 | 623.5 | 715 | 716 | −6 | 48 | 1320 | 1940 | 1967 | ··· |
| 24 | 660 | 753 | 754 | −21 | 49 | 1347.5 | 1997 | 2031 | −37 |
| 25 | 687.5 | 793 | 793 | −25 | | | | | |

But are these variations necessary for a good quality tone or are they just accidental?

To help answer this question, it is necessary to determine if a tone having a constant harmonic content and a constant decay rate would be indistinguishable by most observers from the piano tone if the duration of the tone was about 1 sec, corresponding to the time for a half or whole note depending on the tempo. It will be seen from the figures that during this time the decay curve is almost a straight line, corresponding to a logarithmic decay.

For matching the harmonic content with the synthesizer, we were not sure that the sonograph was sufficiently reliable for the higher partials, particularly for the low pitched tones. So the analyzer was used for obtaining the harmonic content at the beginning of the tone.

## Warmth as a Factor in Piano Quality

Synthetic tones were constructed with partial structures thus determined. For the tones below middle C, there was still something lacking in the quality of the tone. The musicians said the tones lacked live-ness, or warmth. The warmth is probably due to rapid variation of the partial structure. We will use this term "warmth" for indicating this factor of the quality of a musical tone. To imitate exactly the varying intensity among the partials would require a rather complicated control mechanism. It probably could be built. However, it would give only a tone similar to one recorded directly from the piano.

Is it possible to warm the tone by some simple process rather than trying to follow the variations of 30 or 40 partials? A method for doing this was suggested by the comment of musicians that four or five violins playing in unison produces a much warmer tone than that from a single violin. One way of implementing this suggestion is as follows. Set up the desired partial structure on the synthesizer. With these settings create a continuous

TABLE II. Frequencies of partials of piano tone G‴ for $B=0.00028$.

| $n$ | $48.6n$ | obs $f_n$ | calc $f_n$ | db | $n$ | $48.6n$ | obs $f_n$ | calc $f_n$ | db |
|---|---|---|---|---|---|---|---|---|---|
| 1 | 48.6 | 49 | 48.6 | −26 | 18 | 874.8 | 912 | 914 | −36 |
| 2 | 97.2 | 97 | 97.3 | −17 | 19 | 923.4 | 967 | 969 | −23 |
| 3 | 145.8 | 145 | 146 | 0 | 20 | 972 | 1024 | 1026 | −26 |
| 4 | 194.4 | 194 | 195 | −15 | 21 | 1020.6 | 1082 | 1083 | −33 |
| 5 | 243 | 244 | 244 | −18 | 22 | 1069.2 | 1140 | 1139 | −21 |
| 6 | 291.6 | 292 | 293 | −20 | 23 | 1117.8 | 1198 | 1197 | −21 |
| 7 | 340.2 | 340 | 342 | −14 | 24 | 1166.4 | 1249 | 1257 | −36 |
| 8 | 388.8 | 391 | 392 | −29 | 25 | 1214 | 1318 | 1315 | −40 |
| 9 | 437.4 | 440 | 442 | −20 | 26 | 1263.6 | 1379 | 1378 | −26 |
| 10 | 486 | 491 | 492 | −9 | 27 | 1312.2 | 1441 | 1441 | −26 |
| 11 | 534.6 | 542 | 544 | −13 | 28 | 1360.8 | 1504 | 1504 | −32 |
| 12 | 583.2 | 593 | 595 | −7 | 29 | 1409.4 | 1569 | 1565 | −39 |
| 13 | 631.8 | 644 | 647 | −10 | 30 | 1458.0 | 1634 | 1632 | −39 |
| 14 | 680.4 | 698 | 699 | −4 | 31 | 1506.6 | 1701 | 1697 | −39 |
| 15 | 729 | 750 | 752 | −12 | 32 | 1552.2 | 1763 | 1767 | −45 |
| 16 | 777.6 | 798 | 804 | −23 | 33 | 1603.8 | 1832 | 1832 | −43 |
| 17 | 826.2 | ··· | 856 | ··· | 34 | 1652.4 | 1902 | 1905 | −45 |

tone and record on the frequency shifter. The tone from this is then recorded on the tape recorder. The speed of reproducing on the frequency shifter is then slightly changed and a second tone from it recorded on top of the first one. In the same way a third tone is superimposed. When these superimposed tones were reproduced from the tape recorder (2) it was found that the continuous tone was much warmer than a single tone. This warm continuous tone was sent through the attack and decay amplifier to give the synthetic tone the desired attack and decay times.

Later in this work a five channel tape recorder was added to the other instruments shown in Fig. 1. This made possible a second method. The tone from the synthesizer was recorded on the five channels, the frequency on each channel being slightly different. An attenuator in each channel made it possible to reproduce the five tones with any desired relative level. In this way a large range of warmth values was obtained.

A third method of warming the tone was used particularly for tones above middle C. Two adjacent oscillators were adjusted to nearly the same frequency as that of the partial in order that beats would occur. The loudness of the beats which depends upon the relative level of these three tones, could be controlled by raising and lowering the knobs on the synthesizer. This method is similar to that used sometimes in tuning the piano where three strings are provided for each note. The strings are not tuned to vibrate exactly in unison but to slightly different frequencies.

Tones warmed in this way were used in identification tests. The judgment tests indicated that the jury of musicians made three times as many errors in identifying real piano tones when warm tones were used instead of unwarmed ones. Similarly the jury of nonmusicians made twice as many errors with such tones.

## Accurate Determination of the Frequency and Level of the Partials of Piano Tones

At this point it was surmised that perhaps the inharmonicity of the partials particularly for the lower

TABLE III. Frequencies of partials of piano tone G″ for $B=0.00015$.

| $n$ | $98n$ | obs $f_n$ | calc $f_n$ | db | $n$ | $98n$ | obs $f_n$ | calc $f_n$ | db |
|---|---|---|---|---|---|---|---|---|---|
| 1 | 98 | 98 | 98.01 | −1 | 15 | 1470 | 1494 | 1494 | −21 |
| 2 | 196 | 196 | 196.06 | 0 | 16 | 1568 | 1599 | 1598 | −38 |
| 3 | 294 | 294 | 294.2 | 0 | 17 | 1666 | 1701 | 1701 | −26 |
| 4 | 392 | 392 | 392.4 | −10 | 18 | 1764 | 1805 | 1807 | −27 |
| 5 | 490 | 492 | 490.9 | −6 | 19 | 1862 | 1913 | 1912 | −31 |
| 6 | 588 | 590 | 589.6 | −2 | 20 | 1960 | 2019 | 2019 | −41 |
| 7 | 686 | 689 | 688.5 | −1 | 21 | 2058 | 2128 | 2126 | −33 |
| 8 | 784 | 788 | 787.4 | −25 | 22 | 2156 | 2334 | 2234 | −26 |
| 9 | 882 | 889 | 887.4 | −18 | 23 | 2252 | 2344 | 2344 | −36 |
| 10 | 980 | 989 | 987.3 | −12 | 24 | 2352 | 2453 | 2453 | −39 |
| 11 | 1078 | 1087 | 1087 | −20 | 25 | 2450 | 2571 | 2565 | −41 |
| 12 | 1176 | 1189 | 1189 | −25 | 26 | 2548 | 2669 | 2675 | −38 |
| 13 | 1274 | 1291 | 1290 | −11 | 27 | 2646 | 2778 | 2684 | −44 |
| 14 | 1372 | 1392 | 1392 | −10 | | | | | |

TABLE IV. Frequencies of partials of piano tone G′ for $B=0.00005$.

| $n$ | $193.5n$ | obs $f_n$ | calc $f_n$ | db | $n$ | $193.5n$ | obs $f_n$ | calc $f_n$ | db |
|---|---|---|---|---|---|---|---|---|---|
| 1 | 193.5 | 193 | 194 | −7 | 8 | 1552 | 1553 | 1553 | −28 |
| 2 | 387 | 388 | 388 | 0 | 9 | 1731.5 | 1748 | 1748 | −28 |
| 3 | 580.5 | 583 | 582 | −2 | 10 | 1935 | 1942 | 1942 | −33 |
| 4 | 774 | 776 | 776.1 | −15 | 11 | 2182.5 | 2137 | 2137 | −34 |
| 5 | 967.5 | 970 | 970.2 | −16 | 12 | 2322 | 2328 | 2331 | −37 |
| 6 | 1163 | 1167 | 1164.4 | −14 | 13 | 2515.5 | 2525 | 2526 | −38 |
| 7 | 1354.5 | 1362 | 1358.7 | −17 | 14 | 2709 | 2720 | 2721 | −43 |
| | | | | | 15 | 2902.5 | 2917 | 2917 | −44 |

range of pitches might be the cause of the warmth and be one of the factors for good quality rather than the reverse. So a very careful measurement of both the frequency and also the level of each of the partials in the tones A⁗, G‴, G″, G′, G, $G_1$, and $G_2$ were made. These tones were produced on a good upright piano which was placed in the anechoic chamber. The analyzer was used to determine the partial structure at the beginning of the decay of the tone by the method described earlier in this paper.

The data are given in Tables I–VII. It is seen that the inharmonicity is very large especially for the strings in the lower frequency range. Young[2] and others found that this inharmonicity could be explained by Lord Rayleigh's equation for strings having stiffness. The magnitude of this effect depends upon the relative amount of the two factors contributing to the restoring force of a displaced piano string, namely, that due to the tension compared to that due to the stiffness. In free solid rods this latter effect produces the entire restoring force and produces partials which are nonharmonic. In strings without stiffness the restoring force is entirely due to the tension and the partials are harmonics if the ends are fixed rigidly. Such an analysis gives the following equations.

$$fn=nf_0(1+Bn^2)^{\frac{1}{2}}, \quad (1)$$

$$B=\pi^3 Qd^4/64\, l^2 T. \quad (2)$$

$Q$ is Young's modulus, $d$ is the diameter of the piano wire, $l$ its length, and $T$ its tension. The inharmonicity constant $b$ as defined by Young[2] is related to $B$ by

$$b=865B. \quad (3)$$

For A⁗ and G‴ the hammer strikes a single string, which is a large gauge piano wire which has a smaller gauge wire wrapped around it. The G″ strings are con-

TABLE V. Frequencies of partials of piano tone G for $B=0.0004$.

| $n$ | $393n$ | obs $f_n$ | calc $f_n$ | db | $n$ | $393n$ | obs $f_n$ | calc $f_n$ | db |
|---|---|---|---|---|---|---|---|---|---|
| 1 | 393 | 393 | 393 | 0 | 5 | 1965 | 1976 | 1976 | −21 |
| 2 | 786 | 785 | 786.7 | −19 | 6 | 2358 | 2380 | 2376 | −30 |
| 3 | 1179 | 1180 | 1181 | −13 | 7 | 2751 | 2798 | 2780 | −26 |
| 4 | 1572 | 1577 | 1577 | −30 | 8 | 3144 | 3174 | 3187 | −44 |

TABLE VI. Frequencies of partials of piano tone $G_1$ for $B=0.0002$.

| $n$ | $779n$ | obs $f_n$ | calc $f_n$ | db | $n$ | $779n$ | obs $f_n$ | calc $f_n$ | db |
|---|---|---|---|---|---|---|---|---|---|
| 1 | 779 | 779 | 779.1 | 0 | 4 | 3116 | 3123 | 3121 | −36 |
| 2 | 1558 | 1562 | 1558.6 | −22 | 5 | 3895 | 3897 | 3905 | −31 |
| 3 | 2337 | 2337 | 2339 | −24 | | | | | |

TABLE VII. Frequencies of partials of piano tone $G_2$ for $B=0.0002$.

| $n$ | $1568n$ | obs $f_n$ | calc $f_n$ | db |
|---|---|---|---|---|
| 1 | 1568 | 1568 | 1568.2 | 0 |
| 2 | 3136 | 3134 | 3137 | −38 |
| 3 | 4704 | 4707 | 4709 | −28 |

structed similarly but the hammer strikes two strings. Although Eq. (1) was developed for a single bare piano wire it was found that it would fit the data for the entire range of the piano provided the single constant B was obtained from the observed data rather than from $Q$, $d$, $l$, and $T$.

The value of $B$ is given at the top of each table. The number of the partial $n$ is given in the first column. In the second, third, fourth, and fifth columns are given, respectively, the harmonic frequency $nf_0$, the observed frequency $f_n$, the frequency $f_n$ calculated from Eq. (1), and the relative level in db of the partial.

It will be seen that the calculated frequencies are in good agreement with the observed ones. Consider the data for A'''' in Table I. It is the first note on the piano. It can be observed that the 16th partial tone is a semitone sharp from the harmonic series. The 23rd partial is more than a whole tone sharp, the 33rd partial more than two tones sharp, and the 49th partial is 7.3 semitones sharper than the corresponding 49th harmonic. Similarly the 30th partial for G''' is two semitones sharper and the 27th partial for G'' is a semitone sharper than the corresponding harmonic series. For the tone G' and for the tones of higher frequency, Eq. (1) explains the departures from the harmonic series within the observational error of measuring these partial frequencies. However, the partial number is small and so the departures from the harmonic series are small. It was found that for these tones a good quality match could be made with a harmonic series of frequencies.

The partial structure as given in Table I was set up on the synthesizer. The various oscillators were tuned to the observed frequencies and the levels set according to those given in this table. The result was a very good match for the piano tone. No warming was necessary. It is obvious that the warmth is due to the inharmonicity of the partials. This warmth gives the piano tone its distinctive piano quality. With these facts in mind new identification tests were made using synthetic tones with partial structures corresponding to the observed ones in Tables I–VII. The oscillators in the synthesizer were tuned to these frequencies.

### Final Judgment Tests

Synthetic tones made in this way were arranged with real tones according to the program shown in Table VIII. The members of the jury were asked to judge which were real and which were synthetic. Under M the percent of correct judgments by the musicians jury are given and under NM the percent of correct judgments by the nonmusicians. The letter S or R in parentheses after the notation of the note, indicates whether synthetic or real.

Before discussing the data in Table VIII, the A-B preference tests will be presented so that these tests and the identification tests can be discussed together. It will be remembered that in the preference A-B test, a tone designated A is produced and then a tone designated B of the same frequency but of different quality is produced. The observer is asked to decide which he prefers. These A-B judgment tests used the following synthetic tones. For Tone A'''', seven different qualities were considered.

(0) The tone was taken directly from a tape recording of the piano.
(1) This was a synthetic tone with partials having the same frequencies and levels as found for the piano and given in Table I.
(2) The partial levels were the same as 1, but the frequencies were made harmonic.
(3) This tone was the same as 1 except the fundamental was raised 38 db, that is, 15 db higher level than partial 5.
(4) The partial frequencies were the same as 1 but the levels were adjusted so that as the partial frequency changed 100 cps the level decreased 2 db.

These same notations were also used for the quality of the tones at other frequencies used in this test.

(5) The same partial frequencies as in 1 were used but the levels were adjusted as follows:

| Number of partial | 1 | 2 | 3 | 4 | 5 | 6 | 7 | 8 | 9 | 35 | 80. |
|---|---|---|---|---|---|---|---|---|---|---|---|
| Relative level, db | 10 | 7 | 4 | 1 | 0 | 3 | 6 | 9 | 10 | 10. | |

From partial 9 to 35, the levels were at −10 db, and from 35 to 80 they decreased 2 db per 100 cps change in partial structure.
(6) The same partial frequencies were used as in 1. The levels were adjusted as follows. The first five partial levels were −18, −14, −10, −6, and −2. The levels of the partials from 6 to 35 were all at zero level. The partial levels above 35 were the same as 5.
(7) The same partial frequencies as 1 were used. The partial levels started at −12 db for number 1, then rose to 0 for number 6, then dropped to −18 at number 14, rose to 0 at number 22, dropped

again to −26 for number 33, rose again to −10 at number 40, and finally dropped again to −34 at number 48.

For the tone G‴, the qualities 1, 2, 3, and 4 have the same significance as for the similar qualities for A⁗ except the fundamental was at 3 db above the level of third partial instead of 15 db above it. Qualities 5 and 6 were special, as follows:

(5) For this quality of G‴, the levels of the components were:

Number of partial 1 2 3 4 5 6 7 etc.
Level, db −14 −7 0 −1 −2 −3 −4.

Above the fourth partial, the level dropped 1 db per partial.

(6) For this quality, the partial structure was as follows:

Number of partial
1 2 3 4 5 6 7 8 9 10.
Level, db
−18 −15 −12 −9 −16 −3 0 −1 −2 −3.

Above the eighth partial, the level dropped 1 db per partial.

For the tone G″, the qualities described for A⁗ were used except for quality 5 where $f_1$ was +4 db. A fifth quality was used with partial structure as follows:

Number of partial
1 2 3 4 5 6 7 8 9 10.
Level, db
−10 −8 −6 −4 −2 0 −2 −4 −6 −8.

Above the eighth partial, the levels decreased 2 db per component.

TABLE VIII. Synthetic and real tones used in identification tests and percent of correct judgments.

| Tone no. | Note | Percent correct M | Percent correct NM | Tone no. | Note | Percent correct M | Percent correct NM |
|---|---|---|---|---|---|---|---|
| 1 | A⁗(S) | 50 | 23 | 19 | $G_1$(S) | 63 | 92 |
| 2 | G′(R) | 75 | 92 | 20 | G′(R) | 100 | 85 |
| 3 | A⁗(R) | 88 | 92 | 21 | G(S) | 88 | 77 |
| 4 | G(R) | 50 | 54 | 22 | G″(R) | 100 | 85 |
| 5 | $G_1$(R) | 100 | 69 | 23 | G′(S) | 63 | 69 |
| 6 | G″(R) | 100 | 85 | 24 | A⁗(R) | 88 | 100 |
| 7 | G′(R) | 63 | 69 | 25 | $G_1$(R) | 100 | 69 |
| 8 | G‴(S) | 37 | 77 | 26 | G‴(R) | 50 | 46 |
| 9 | G″(S) | 50 | 67 | 27 | $G_1$(S) | 75 | 85 |
| 10 | G′(S) | 25 | 54 | 28 | G″(S) | 88 | 62 |
| 11 | G(S) | 75 | 92 | 29 | $G_1$(R) | 75 | 85 |
| 12 | A⁗(S) | 75 | 31 | 30 | G‴(R) | 63 | 92 |
| 13 | G(R) | 63 | 69 | 31 | A⁗(S) | 100 | 77 |
| 14 | G″(S) | 63 | 67 | 32 | G‴(S) | 30 | 54 |
| 15 | G(S) | 88 | 67 | 33 | $G_1$(S) | 100 | 85 |
| 16 | A⁗(R) | 88 | 92 | 34 | G′(S) | 88 | 54 |
| 17 | G‴(S) | 63 | 54 | 35 | G″(R) | 88 | 85 |
| 18 | G(R) | 75 | 77 | 36 | G‴(R) | 50 | 77 |

For the tone G′, the four qualities described for A⁗ were used.

For tones $G_2$ and $G_3$, only qualities 1 and 4 were used, but the noise of the striking hammer was not considered part of the piano tone and was not in the synthetic tones.

### Program for Real vs Synthetic Tones

The program of the A-B test was recorded as indicated in Table IX. Let us consider these data from the identification tests in Table VIII and A-B tests in Table IX. First consider the judgment data for A⁗, the first note on the piano. To a layman, the sound of this note is very much like a noise without any pitch. So it was thought that two improvements might be made. The first was to make the frequencies of the partials have harmonic ratios rather than those with inharmonic ratios.

None of the synthetic qualities was preferred to the piano quality. Qualities 1 and 3 were considered nearly equal to the piano quality. The identification tests (shown in Table VIII, tests 1, 12, and 31) also confirm

TABLE IX. Preference test on piano tones.

| | Test No. | Quality A | vs B | Preference A | Preference B |
|---|---|---|---|---|---|
| A⁗ | 1 | 0 | 1 | 16 | 5 |
| | 2 | 2 | 0 | 2 | 19 |
| | 3 | 3 | 0 | 7 | 14 |
| | 4 | 0 | 4 | 18 | 3 |
| | 5 | 1 | 2 | 20 | 1 |
| | 6 | 3 | 1 | 6 | 15 |
| | 7 | 4 | 1 | 3 | 18 |
| | 8 | 3 | 2 | 10 | 11 |
| | 9 | 2 | 4 | 16 | 5 |
| | 10 | 4 | 3 | 5 | 16 |
| | 11 | 5 | 1 | 5 | 16 |
| | 12 | 1 | 6 | 18 | 3 |
| | 13 | 1 | 7 | 16 | 6 |
| G‴ | 14 | 1 | 0 | 12 | 9 |
| | 15 | 0 | 2 | 13 | 8 |
| | 16 | 0 | 3 | 15 | 6 |
| | 17 | 4 | 0 | 7 | 14 |
| | 18 | 2 | 1 | 9 | 12 |
| | 19 | 1 | 3 | 13 | 8 |
| | 20 | 4 | 1 | 7 | 14 |
| | 21 | 2 | 3 | 9 | 12 |
| | 22 | 4 | 2 | 9 | 12 |
| | 23 | 4 | 3 | 9 | 12 |
| | 24 | 1 | 5 | 15 | 6 |
| | 25 | 1 | 6 | 19 | 2 |
| G″ | 26 | 1 | 0 | 9 | 12 |
| | 27 | 0 | 2 | 13 | 8 |
| | 28 | 3 | 0 | 10 | 11 |
| | 29 | 0 | 4 | 14 | 7 |
| | 30 | 1 | 2 | 11 | 10 |
| | 31 | 1 | 3 | 7 | 14 |
| | 32 | 4 | 1 | 5 | 16 |
| | 33 | 2 | 3 | 5 | 16 |
| | 34 | 4 | 2 | 9 | 12 |
| | 35 | 3 | 4 | 15 | 6 |
| | 36 | 1 | 5 | 20 | 1 |
| G′ | 37 | 1 | 0 | 17 | 4 |
| | 38 | 0 | 2 | 14 | 7 |
| | 39 | 3 | 0 | 13 | 8 |
| | 40 | 4 | 0 | 14 | 7 |
| | 41 | 2 | 1 | 13 | 8 |
| | 42 | 1 | 3 | 8 | 13 |
| | 43 | 1 | 4 | 10 | 11 |
| | 44 | 3 | 2 | 12 | 9 |
| | 45 | 2 | 4 | 7 | 14 |
| | 46 | 3 | 4 | 10 | 11 |
| G | 47 | 1 | 0 | 16 | 5 |
| | 48 | 0 | 2 | 6 | 15 |
| | 49 | 0 | 4 | 6 | 15 |
| | 50 | 1 | 2 | 17 | 4 |
| | 51 | 4 | 1 | 12 | 9 |
| | 52 | 2 | 4 | 12 | 9 |
| $G_1$ | 53 | 0 | 1 | 13 | 8 |
| | 54 | 2 | 0 | 4 | 17 |
| | 55 | 4 | 0 | 4 | 17 |
| | 56 | 1 | 2 | 16 | 5 |
| | 57 | 4 | 1 | 11 | 10 |
| | 58 | 2 | 4 | 6 | 15 |
| $G_2$ | 59 | 0 | 4 | 15 | 6 |
| | 60 | 0 | 4 | 14 | 7 |
| | 61 | 0 | 5 | 16 | 5 |
| | 62 | 5 | 4 | 12 | 9 |
| $G_3$ | 63 | 0 | 4-5 db | 14 | 7 |
| | 64 | 0 | 4-10 db | 14 | 7 |
| | 65 | 0 | 5-10 db | 13 | 8 |

this conclusion as the synthetic tone of quality 1 was mistaken for the real tone about half of the time.

The A-B on G‴ (see Table IX) indicated that no synthetic tone was definitely preferred over the real piano tone. However, quality 1 and possibly quality 2 were considered to be about equal in quality. The tests also show that quality 1 was preferred above any of the other qualities.

The identification tests (Table VIII, tests 8, 17, 26, 30, 32, and 36) show that the synthetic quality 1 of G‴ could not be distinguished from the real piano tone. These two sets of preference tests (for A⁗ and G‴) seem to indicate that any quality that departs much from real piano quality is discriminated against by either jury.

Consider now G″ and we will see that qualities 1 and 3 were about equal to the real piano tone (Table VIII). Also this synthetic tone of quality 1 could not be identified from the real piano tone as indicated in the data in Table VIII. Although quality 1 was preferred about equally with the piano, quality 3 was judged to be somewhat better (see Table VIII, tests 26, 28, and 31.)

Next, consider G′. Here, where we would least expect it, there was a preference for qualities 1, 3, and 4 over the real piano tone. Of these, 3 and 4 were preferred over 1 and also over 2. In the identification tests (Table VIII, tests 10, 23, and 34) the synthetic tone could not be identified from the real tone.

For middle G the qualities 1, 2, and 4 were preferred to the real piano tone. The other results of the A-B tests were inconclusive. For instance, test 50 (Table IX) indicates that 1 is better than 2, but tests 51 and 52 indicate the opposite. Thus it would be safe to say that qualities 1, 2, and 4 are nearly equally preferred and all are preferred over the piano. However, the identification tests (Table VIII) 11, 15, and 21 clearly show that the synthetic tone of quality 1 could be identified from the real piano tone.

For $G_1$ no synthetic tone was preferred to a real piano tone but quality 1 was close. It was preferred above the other two qualities tried. Due to the absence of the hammer noise in the synthetic tone, it was identified correctly 85% of the time. Nevertheless, in the identification tests the jury missed the real piano tone 74% of the time. To our great surprise the jury preferred the real piano tones with the high-impact noise for $G_2$ and $G_3$ rather than any synthetic tones without the impact noise.

These seem to indicate that most persons are satisfied with the quality of piano tones and that any large departures from this quality seem to be disliked. Comments indicated that some of these tones would be interesting if they were to come from a musical instrument different from the piano, but not as a piano tone.

We will now try to describe in an objective way what is meant when one says the tone sounds "piano-like."

## RANGE OF ATTACK AND DECAY FOR PIANO-LIKE TONES

Judgments of the attack time were made from synthesized G″, G, and $G_2$ tones. A decay time was given each tone somewhat near the decay time of the piano tones having the same pitch. The attack time was then varied.

The attack for G″ tones must be between the limits of 0 to 0.09 sec to be piano-like, 0.09 to 0.14 sec to be questionable. Any tones with an attack time which is greater than this makes the tone no longer piano-like.

The attack time for G tones had similar limits which were 0 to 0.05 sec, 0.05 to 0.12 sec, and greater than 0.12 sec. For the higher pitched tones, the attack time was about 25% smaller than those given above.

A determination of decay time was made by giving a piano-like attack to the synthesized G″, G, and $G_2$ tones, and then varying the decay time. The following limits produced undampened piano tones: 5–9 sec for G″, 2–5.5 sec for G, 1–4 sec for $G_2$. Decay times slower than these sounded like sustained-tone instruments. Faster decay times produced an unnatural decay. To sound like a damped piano tone, the decay time can be between 0.8 and 7 sec, and must be damped by the damping button (a control on the attack and decay amplifier which produces a change in the decay rate during actual decay. This change can be made large, thus adjusting the decay to a very fast rate, and for simulating the damping pedal on the piano).

## EFFECT OF HARMONIC CONTENT ON THE PIANO QUALITY OF MUSICAL TONES

Since there are an infinite number of arrangements for the harmonics of a tone of given frequency, it is difficult to circumscribe those that are piano-like. An attempt to do this was made in the following way. The partials were set up on the synthesizer so that the level of each successive partial was a constant number of decibels less than that of the partial just below it in frequency. As an example of this treatment applied to G″ (when the difference is 2 db), this harmonic content was produced.

| Partial number | 1 | 2 | 3 | 4 | 5 | 6 | 7 | etc. |
|---|---|---|---|---|---|---|---|---|
| Relative level, db | 0 | −2 | −4 | −6 | −8 | −10 | −12 | etc. |

Judgment tests, made with such tones, indicated the following. Tests were for the most part centered around G″, G, and $G_2$ with attack and decay approximating those of the piano.

### Tone G″

(1) The limits for a piano-like quality extended from 2.5 to 1.5 db per partial.
(2) When the level difference between components was large, that is when essentially only the fundamental was present, the piano-like quality was gone and the tone tended toward that of a kettledrum.

(3) From this point until the difference approached 2.5 db, the quality approached that of a piano but would be referred to by musicians as dead, hollow, or having no edge.
(4) A difference of 1 db per partial produced a tone that had too much edge. This quality of tone approached that of a harpsichord rather than a piano.
(5) Differences less than this produced tones that were entirely too edgy.
(6) The first five or six components could be changed around in any position and the tone was still piano-like provided the remaining components conformed to the limits given above.

### Tone G

(1) Limits for a piano-like quality were from 13.0 to 5.0 db per partial.
(2) When a single partial, namely the fundamental, was used, the tone could not be called piano-like.
(3) Differences greater than 13.0 db resulted in dead or dull tones.
(4) Differences less than 5.0 db produced tones with too much edge.
(5) The first 2 or 3 components could be changed and the tone was still piano-like provided requirement (1) was fulfilled.

### Tone $G_2$

(1) Piano-like quality had limits from 40 to 7.5 db per partial.
(2) The fundamental alone has a piano-like quality. However, adding the next partial in the above limits, improves the tone quality.
(3) Less than 7.5 db per partial produces a tone which is too edgy.

The midpoints on the limits of G″, G, and $G_2$ are, respectively, 2, 8, and 32 db per partial, each being four times that of the preceding tone. A single partial above the fifth or sixth could be eliminated without producing any noticeable effect. However, if it were raised 4 or 5 db from its position in the series, it was distinctly noticeable and the resulting tone was less pleasing.

These conclusions above were based on synthetic tones whose components were harmonic. When the components had inharmonic frequencies equal to those in the piano, results obtained were approximately the same as those stated above with one very important exception. The lack of being harmonic gives rise to the peculiar quality known as piano quality, namely, the live-ness or warmth. This is very important for the first three octaves on the piano.

# 10

*Copyright © 1940 by the Acoustical Society of America*

Reprinted from *J. Acoust. Soc. Am.*, **11**(3), 311–320 (1940)

## The Influence of the Soundboard on Piano Tone Quality

PAUL H. BILHUBER
*Steinway & Sons, New York, New York*

AND

C. A. JOHNSON
*E. E. Free Laboratories, New York, New York*

(Received October 11, 1939)

THE main purpose of the soundboard in a piano is to amplify the tones produced by the strings. It is desirable to make this amplification as great as possible, but it is also necessary to get at least an approximately uniform response over as much of the frequency range of the scale as possible. The actual gain obtained depends upon the size of piano and type of soundboard.

Piano makers are well aware of the importance of the soundboard in determining tone quality. In fact the difference between a good and bad piano may be simply a difference of soundboard material or structure. The material used for a soundboard has been standardized for a number of years and is now more or less the same for most pianos. There is, however, some variation in the structure and method of mounting employed by different manufacturers.

It is the purpose of this paper to describe some measurements devised to show the effects of soundboard structure and mounting on tone quality. The term "tone quality" in this case is used to describe general piano performance rather than merely to indicate the harmonic content of the tones.

### History of Soundboard Development

Considerable difficulty has been experienced in attempting to design a single structure that will respond uniformly to the full frequency range of the piano scale; since it covers the range from 27.5 cycles up to 4186. Almost any type of board will tend to discriminate against the tones of higher frequency. Furthermore, the string tones in the treble region are much weaker in energy and shorter in duration.

As a result of this inherent difficulty, a great deal of experimentation has been resorted to by piano makers in an effort to discover some ideal solution to the problem. This experimentation has involved a rather complete investigation of materials and of possible variations in structure. No material of any promise has been overlooked. In addition to the suitable varieties of woods, an attempt has been made to use such widely differing materials as metals, parchment and plywood, both individually and in various combinations. The various structures have included double soundboards, separate soundboards for the treble part of the scale, cylindrical and box-like resonators, leverage devices, and auxiliary boards. Piano patent literature is replete with examples of this soundboard evolution. There are discernible style cycles or periods during which a succession of patents of a similar nature were persisted in. The net result was that none of these radical designs contributed any important improvements in piano tone quality, and eventually all were abandoned in favor of the general type of board in use at present.

For the past 25 years or so all manufacturers have standardized upon the main structural features of the soundboard. The shape of the board is made to conform generally to the shape of the piano case which, in turn, is determined by the size of the piano and the length of the strings. The board is made of quarter-sawed spruce. Spruce has proved to be the most satisfactory wood for this purpose, probably because it has a high ratio of elasticity to mass. The spruce strips are edge-glued together in such a way that the longitudinal grain of the wood runs from the treble to the bass corner of the piano. Ribs are glued to the underside of the board at right angles to the direction of the grain. Gluing is done in a hollowed form with the board in an inverted position; so that the top of the completed board has a slightly convex shape.

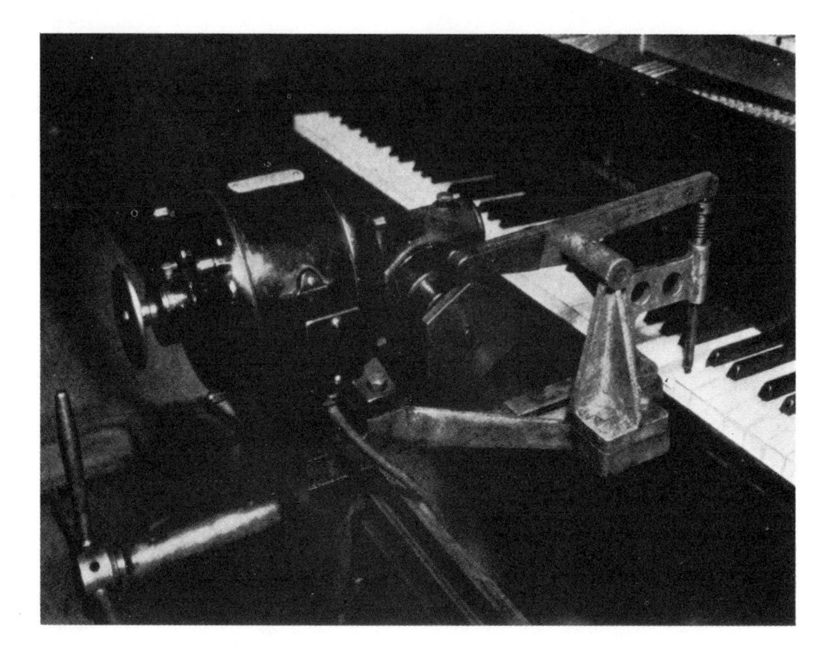

FIG. 1. A motor-driven striker used for producing a continuous succession of strikes of equal intensity.

The completed board is mounted in the piano by securely gluing the edges to the case, the gluing surface generally being in a plane. Some manufacturers taper the board toward the rear edge in an attempt to compensate for the added stiffness produced by the presence of the two bridges in this area. Another manufacturer has introduced the refinement of extending this taper for a distance around the treble edge of the board.

The point of contact between the soundboard and strings consists of a bridge which is glued to the convex surface of the board in proper position for the speaking length of the string scale. Two bridges are provided; one for the middle and treble part of the scale and one for the longer bass strings. The side of the bridge making contact with the strings lies in a slightly higher plane than the ends of the strings so that they are raised slightly in passing over the bridge. This introduces a downward compressive force on the soundboard. The amount of compression can be varied for different sections of the bridge by raising or lowering the iron frame to which the ends of the strings are anchored.

## PRELIMINARY STUDIES OF SOUNDBOARD BEHAVIOR

When our experimental work was started several years ago we were in search of some method for measuring the vibrational behavior of the soundboard when energized by various strings of the piano scale. We were in hopes that such measurements would help to explain why pianos of similar construction sometimes differed in tone quality.

After some preliminary tests, it was decided that the vibrational behavior of the board could be determined, at least to some extent, by means of a suitable type of vibration pick-up applied to the upper surface of the board. All the accessible area of the board was marked off in two-inch squares and a mounting was provided for the pick-up so that its probe could be placed in contact with the board at the approximate center of each square. The output of the pick-up was coupled to a standard sound-meter system so that the relative level of vibration could be measured for all accessible squares on the board.

The soundboard was energized by striking any

desired key with the motor-driven striker shown in Fig. 1. The speed and intensity of strike could be controlled by using different sizes and shapes of cams on the motor shaft. Easy selection of any key was made possible by mounting the motor and striker on a rack-and-pinion carriage.

Our first set of measurements was made on a 5-foot 7-inch grand piano having a very acceptable tone quality ás judged by musical experts. When these measurements were completed the compression on the board was deliberately mal-adjusted so that the tone quality was definitely

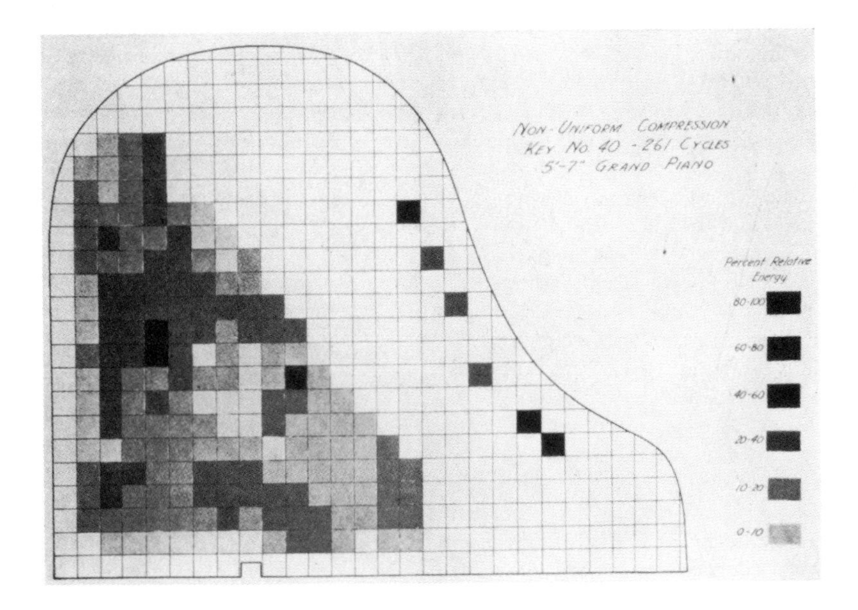


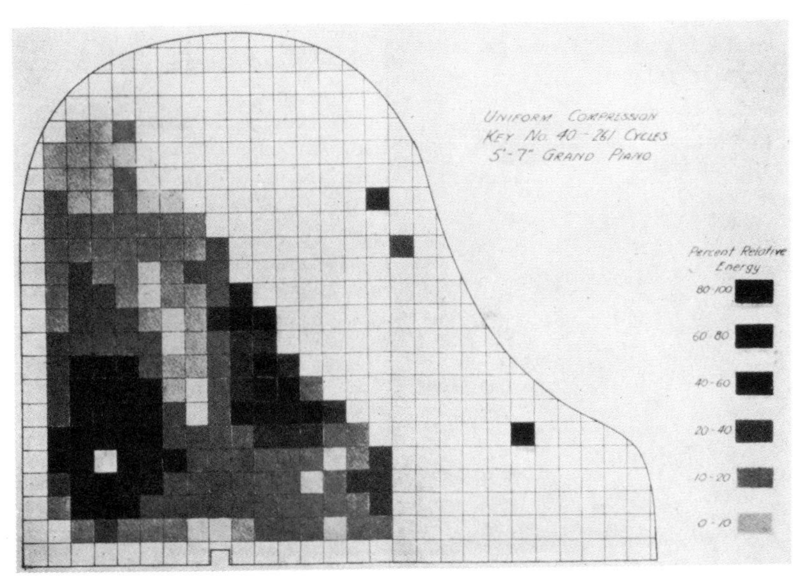


FIG. 2. Maps showing distribution of vibrational energy in soundboard of 5-ft. 7-in. grand piano for different adjustments of compression.

impaired. This non-uniform adjustment of compression produced an audible change both in intensity and duration of tone for certain sections of the scale. A second set of vibration-pick-up measurements was made with the piano in this condition.

The data for each condition was tabulated in terms of percent of the maximum vibrational energy observed, and these percentage values were indicated by shaded squares on a map of the soundboard. The two maps obtained for middle C, Key No. 40, are shown in Fig. 2. The non-uniform compression refers to the maladjusted condition. The different shades represent percent relative vibrational energy in terms of the maximum observed for each condition of compression. The darkest shade shows the regions from 80 to 100 percent, the next 60 to 80 percent, and so on down to 20 percent. The two lightest shades represent 10 to 20 percent and 0 to 10 percent, respectively.

A comparison of these two charts indicates that a greater area of soundboard is active for the condition of uniform compression. Moreover, the numerical data showed that the average level for the uniform case was 4 decibels higher than for the non-uniform condition. In the latter case some points had been reduced by as much as 14 decibels, when the compression was maladjusted, whereas a few had been raised two or three decibels. The two charts shown typify the results

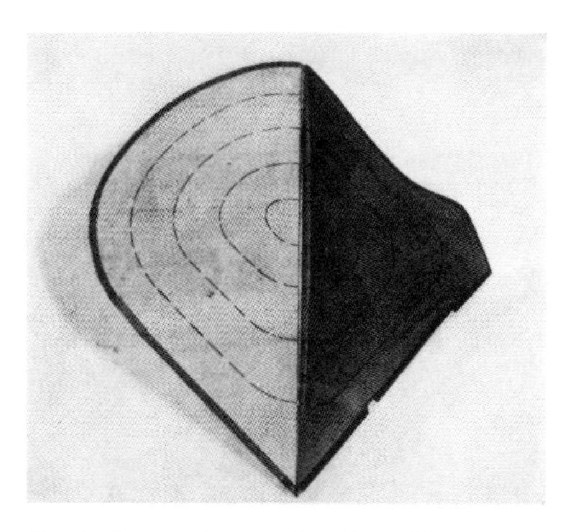

FIG. 3. Photograph of soundboard sawed in two to show decrease in thickness toward edges. The contour lines represent regions of equal thickness.

obtained for several other keys distributed over the piano scale.

From this data we concluded that the maladjusted compression had introduced buckling strains in the soundboard; thereby tending to stiffen certain portions. This added stiffness apparently interfered with the tendency of the board to vibrate like a diaphragm when energized by the strings. The response of the board under uniform compression was not only greater, but also more nearly like a diaphragm. Therefore these preliminary results seemed to indicate that anything that could be done to encourage the diaphragmatic response of the board would result in better tone.

## Changes in Soundboard Design

The results summarized in the preceding section indicated that the tone quality and general performance of the piano could be improved by any change that would increase the responsiveness of the board. Such improvement is desirable at least for the treble part of the scale of any piano. For the smaller pianos that have been built in recent years, it was absolutely necessary to increase the response per unit area of soundboard in order to maintain the desirable standard of quality. This is true because of the inherent limitations of shorter string lengths and reduced soundboard area in these smaller instruments.

Accordingly a study of soundboard construction was undertaken with the following objectives in view: (1) Reduction of mass and stiffness of the soundboard; (2) elimination of any cross or buckling strains in the soundboard structure and its mounting.

The minimum mass and stiffness that can be realized in a soundboard structure is fixed by the requirements for mechanical strength and resistance to compression. An inspection of the standard type of board indicated that it should be possible to make the board thinner at the edges and still fulfill these requirements. Accordingly in order to compensate for the greater thickness adjacent to the anchorage around the edge, the soundboard was tapered in a parabolic curve from the center of area toward all the edges as indicated in Fig. 3. The contour lines shown

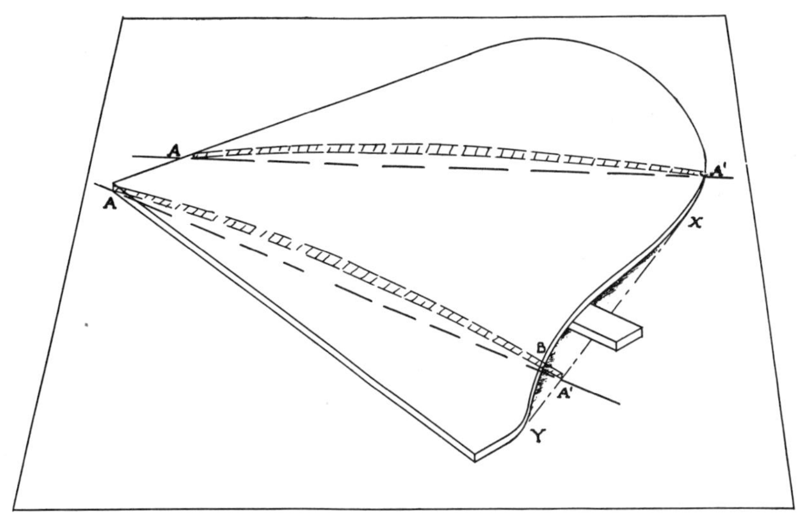


FIG. 4. Drawing illustrating how edge of indented portion of soundboard between $X$ and $Y$ lies in a plane slightly higher than the other edges. The lines $AA'$ also show curvature of board and taper toward edges.

in the figure are drawn through regions of equal thickness, showing that the rate of taper is less for the regions farthest from the center of the board. This tapering reduced the weight of the board approximately 7 percent, and static loads applied to the center of the board showed that the stiffness had been reduced 20 percent. This reduction appeared to be the maximum practicable from the standpoint of mechanical strength.

A study of the method of mounting the board in the piano case revealed at least one source of buckling strains that could be eliminated. The sketch in Fig. 4 shows the general shape of the grand-piano soundboard. Since the upper surface is slightly convex, the portion of the edge that is indented lies in a slightly higher plane than the other edges. However, when the board was mounted in the piano case, the standard practice had been to press all edges down to gluing surfaces in the same plane. This procedure introduced a buckling strain in the portion of the board between the points indicated by $X$ and $Y$ in the figure. In order to eliminate this strain, the gluing surface in this region was raised to meet the raised edge of the board.

We have already noted how undesirable strains might be set up in various sections of the board by improper adjustment of the compression of the strings on the bridge. In order to minimize such strains, a method was devised for measuring the vertical component of force on the bridge for each string. The method for doing this is illustrated in Fig. 5. A special type of slope level or inclinometer was constructed for measuring the angle made by each string as it crosses the bridge. Then, from a knowledge of the tension in the string, it was a simple matter to calculate the downward component of force on the bridge. The possibility of measuring this force made it possible to adjust the compression on each piano in terms of a predetermined optimum.

FIG. 5. This illustrates how the slope level is used in measuring the angle that the strings make with the horizontal plane at the point where they cross the bridge.

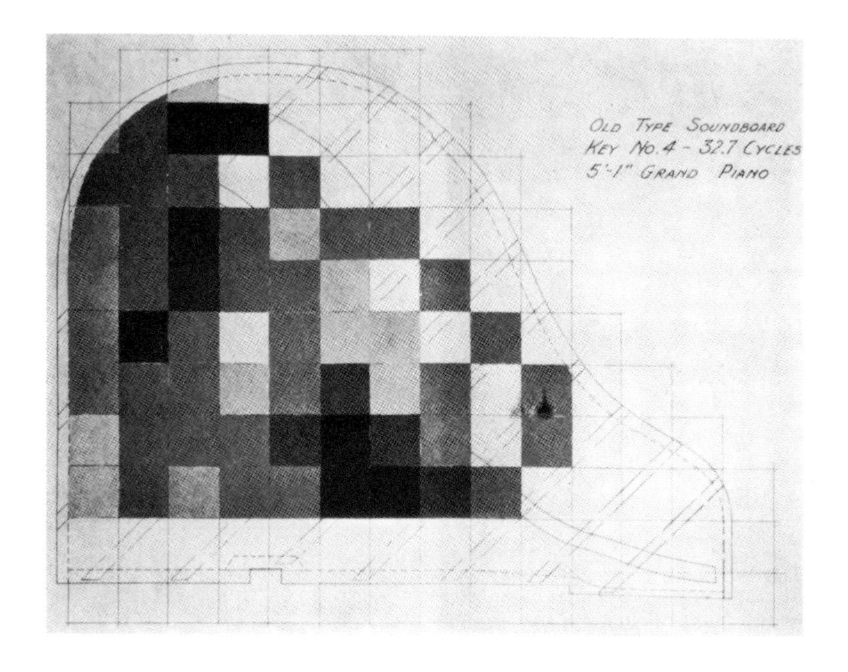


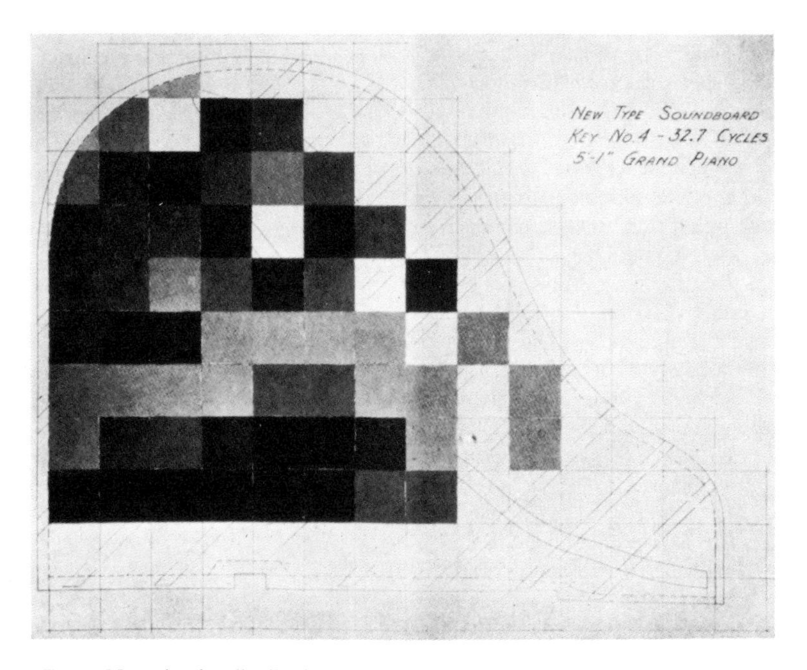


FIG. 6. Maps showing distribution of vibrational energy in old and new type of soundboard of 5-ft. 1-in. grand piano when driven with Key No. 4. The shaded areas represent percent relative energy as in Fig. 2.

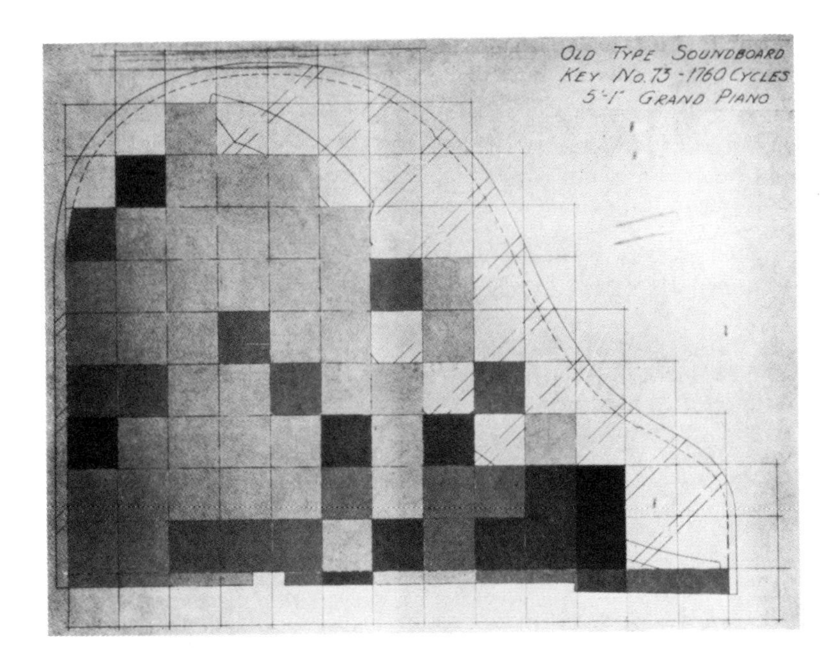

FIG. 7. Maps showing distribution of vibrational energy in old and new type of soundboard of 5-ft. 1-in. grand piano when driven with Key No. 73. The shaded areas represent percent relative energy as in Fig. 2.

Hence our program of revision of soundboard structure and mounting involved three definite changes, as follows:

1. Reduction of mass and stiffness by tapering.
2. Elimination of buckling strains in mounting by raising the plane of the gluing surface along the treble edge.
3. Minimizing adverse strains due to non-uniform compression by measuring downward force of strings and equalizing compression for different sections of bridge.

### Measurements on Pianos with Revised Soundboard

After these changes had been worked out, the new type of board was adapted to a 5-foot 1-inch grand piano. A piano of the same size was fitted with a soundboard of the old type. Great care was taken to make every other detail of construction exactly alike in both cases. In order to eliminate differences in hammers, provision was made for using the same hammers and action in both pianos. The only differences, then, between the two pianos were the strings and the soundboards. With modern methods of string manufacture, the performance of strings can be duplicated to very close tolerance in successive instruments. Hence any audible difference between these two pianos should be due to the changes in soundboard design and mounting.

The first comparisons between the two instruments were made by listening tests. There was a clearly audible difference in the sound produced by each. Pianists and musical experts showed a decided preference for the one with the new type of board. The general reason given for this choice was that this piano had a more "lively" response. Apparently, therefore, the changes in the soundboard had given the musicians something they wanted. Our problem now was to express this improvement in terms of some kind of practicable measurement on the performance of the piano.

Our first attempt in this direction consisted of a set of vibration-pick-up surveys similar to those described above. Instead of marking off the squares on the board, a removable grille was built to fit over the top of either piano case. This grille consisted of 4-inch squares covering the entire soundboard area. Vibration-pick-up measurements were made at the approximate center of each square for all the accessible area of each board. Surveys of this type were made for about two dozen keys distributed over the scale. Typical results are shown in Figs. 6 and 7. Fig. 6 is a comparison between the old and new type of board for Key No. 4 having a frequency of about 32.7 cycles, and Fig. 7 is a similar comparison for Key No. 73 with a frequency of 1760 cycles. The different shades have the same meaning as in Fig. 2. These charts are typical of the patterns obtained for the lower and upper sections of the scale.

Our general conclusion from these surveys was that the changes in the soundboard had made a definite difference in its performance. Apparently the new design permitted more of the string energy to get into the board and this energy also appeared to be more evenly distributed. The average increase in vibrational energy for the new type of board was about 2.5 decibels.

We next made a series of measurements of vibrational energy at the center of the board for the complete scale. Concurrent with these measurements, we measured intensity level of the air-borne sound in a plane 2 feet above the board and at a radius 10 feet from the center. The summary of these results is shown in Table I.

The average gain per octave in the case of the new type of board is shown in the table both for vibrational energy and air-borne sound. Note that there is a reasonably close agreement between these two quantities in the three treble octaves. A somewhat greater gain is shown for the vibrational energy in the bass. These gains are not very great but even small increases are

Table I. *Summary of gain per octave in 5′ – 1″ grand piano.*

| Octave | Average gain in decibels for new Type of Soundboard: Vibrational Energy measured at center | Air-borne energy measured at a radius of 10 feet from center |
|---|---|---|
| 1 | 4.8 | 2.3 |
| 2 | 1.8 | 0.8 |
| 3 | 4.6 | 1.2 |
| 4 | 1.8 | 1.1 |
| 5 | 2.3 | 2.0 |
| 6 | 2. | 2.1 |
| 7 | 1. | 1.2 |
| Average | 2.5 | 1.6 |

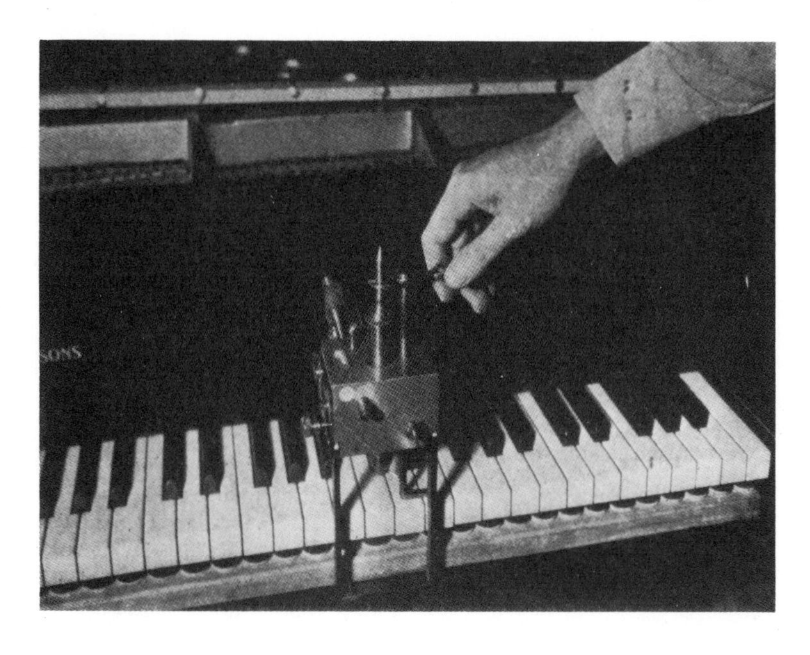

FIG. 8. Photographs illustrating the use of a gravity-operated striker for tone-decay measurements. The height of the plunger may be adjusted for a predetermined intensity of strike. When the clamping jaws are released the plunger falls and produces a single strike on the key.

welcome in the treble part of the scale, which is inherently weaker.

Our measurements thus far showed that the new type of soundboard vibrated more freely than the old type and that the radiated sound was slightly greater for the same intensity of strike. We were not certain, however, that this difference in energy output accounted for all of the difference in "liveliness" observed by the musicians. Accordingly we decided also to compare the duration of tone for the two instruments.

For this measurement each key was actuated with a single-action gravity-operated striker illustrated in Fig. 8. A tone-decay meter was arranged so that it started a timer when the tone was struck. The circuit was adjusted so that the timer was stopped when the intensity of the initial tone had decreased 30 decibels. These measurements were confined to the upper part of the piano scale; since it was in this region that the differences were most audible. The results are summarized in Table II.

The data in Table II shows that the new type of board increases the average time of tone duration about 30 percent, for the part of the piano scale above the fourth octave. Fig. 9 is a graph of the time required for a 30-decibel decay of the individual tones above the fifth octave. It is interesting to note that the decay period is longer for the new type of board for almost all of the tones in this part of the scale. It seems, therefore, that the new board has accomplished an important change in the time of tone duration.

TABLE II. *Summary of decay periods for treble tones in 5′−1″ grand piano*

| Octave | Average Time in Seconds for 30 db Decay of mf Tone | | | |
|---|---|---|---|---|
| | Old Type Soundboard | New Type Soundboard | Increase for New Type Soundboard | % Increase |
| 5 | 1.66 | 2.11 | 0.45 | 27 |
| 6 | 1.26 | 1.74 | 0.48 | 38 |
| 7 | 0.85 | 1.10 | 0.25 | 29 |
| 8 | 0.65 | 0.89 | 0.24 | 37 |
| Average | 1.10 | 1.46 | 0.36 | 32 |

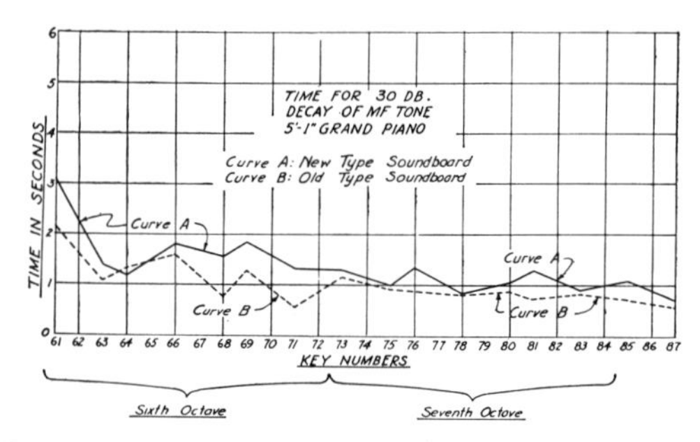


FIG. 9. Graphs showing times for 30-decibel decay of tones for old and new type of soundboard.

## General Conclusions

Our general conclusions on this experimental work are as follows:

1. The changes in structure of the soundboard and its mounting have increased its tendency to vibrate like a diaphragm with the maximum amplitude near the center of the board.

2. A systematic method of adjusting the downward pressure of the strings permits an optimum equalization of this pressure for different sections of the bridge. Such equalization also aids the board in its diaphragmatic response.

3. The increased response of the board has resulted in a small increase in intensity level of the air-borne sound. The pianist can produce slightly louder tones with the same amount of playing effort.

4. The increased response of the board has definitely increased the duration of tone for a given intensity of strike. This is a major factor in increasing what the musician calls the "liveliness" of the piano.

## Acknowledgments

While this work has been in progress we have received many helpful suggestions both from members of the musical profession and from those interested in this phase of acoustical research. In particular we wish to thank Professor D. C. Miller for originally suggesting an investigation along this line and Professor L. B. Ham for his valuable assistance in the earlier part of our experimental work.

Part II

# ACOUSTICS OF BRASS INSTRUMENTS

# Editor's Comments on Papers 11 Through 20

**11 BENADE**
*The Physics of Brasses*

**12 EISNER**
*Complete Solutions of the "Webster" Horn Equation*

**13 BENADE and GANS**
*Sound Production in Wind Instruments*

**14 MARTIN**
*Lip Vibrations in a Cornet Mouthpiece*

**15 WEBSTER**
*An Electrical Method of Measuring the Intonation of Cup-Mouthpiece Instruments*

**16A LONG**
*The Performance of Cup-Mouthpiece Instruments*

**16B YOUNG**
*On the Performance of Cup-Mouthpiece Instruments*

**16C LONG**
*On the Performance of Cup-Mouthpiece Instruments*

**17 KENT**
*Wind Instrument of the Cup-Mouthpiece Type*

**18 CARDWELL**
*Cup-Mouthpiece Wind Instruments*

**19A BENADE and JANSSON**
*On Plane and Spherical Waves in Horns with Nonuniform Flare. I: Theory of Radiation, Resonance Frequencies, and Mode Conversion*

**19B JANSSON and BENADE**
*On Plane and Spherical Waves in Horns with Nonuniform Flare. II: Prediction and Measurements of Resonance Frequencies and Radiation Losses*

**20 PYLE**
*Effective Length of Horns*

In Paper 11, Benade presents a general overview of the history of acoustical study of the cup-mouthpiece instruments often referred to as brass instruments. He also introduces information regarding the construction and the functioning of these instruments along with some techniques used in studies of their acoustical properties. This article was intended for general readership but it serves well as an introduction to the acoustics of brass instruments and adds coherence to the papers that follow.

Benade uses the terms "mouthpipe" and "leaderpipe" interchangeably since both are used by musicians and instrument manufacturers. He uses the term "conical" in the manner that is common among musicians, but he makes it clear that while some portions of the bore are called conical they are not necessarily cone shaped.

In addition to the cylindrical and the tapered sections there are step discontinuities in brass instruments. They usually occur at the end of the mouthpiece as it joins the mouthpipe and at the ends of the tuning slides. They may be present in the valves also. The location and the size of the discontinuities influence the acoustical behavior of the instruments.

Arthur H. Benade [A.B. (1948), Ph.D. (1952), Washington University, St. Louis, Mo.] was born in Chicago, Ill. and grew up in Lahore, India (now Pakistan), where his father taught physics at Punjab University. He joined the Physics Department of Case Institute of Technology in Cleveland (now Case Western Reserve University) as an Instructor in 1952, and has been full Professor since 1969.

Benade's original fields of research were in cosmic rays and nuclear physics, but a long-term interest in musical instruments and their physics led him to devote full time to this subject in 1963. He has served as Vice President of the Acoustical Society of America and as Chairman of its Technical Committee on Musical Acoustics. He is a member of the Galpin Society, which is devoted to a study of old instrument; is Past President of the Catgut Acoustical Society; and is a Fellow in the Acoustical Society of America. He is the author of *Horns, Strings, and Harmony,* New York: Anchor-Doubleday, 1960, which has been translated into six foreign languages, including Japanese, and has sold over 100,000 copies. His second book, *Fundamentals of Musical Acoustics,* was published in 1976 (New York: Oxford University Press). In addition, he has written numerous technical articles and several for general readership. He provided the article on wind instruments for the new edition of Grove's *Dictionary of Music and Musicians,* 5th ed., New York: St. Martin's Press, 1954.

Instruments of all sorts are brought to Benade by leading players in both America and Europe for modification and adjustment. He has also contributed to the design of several instruments on the commercial market.

Paper 12, by Edward Eisner, is an excellent source of technical and historical information related to musical acoustics. It provides a good perspective of mathematics related to both vibrating strings and wind instruments and includes an extensive bibliography.

The "Webster" equation appears in some form in most studies of sound waves in wind instruments. The original paper by A. G. Webster, "Acoustical Impedance and the Theory of Horns and of the Phonograph," is reprinted in *Physical Acoustics* R. Bruce Lindsay (ed.), Stroudsburg, Pa.: Dowden, Hutchinson & Ross, 1974; pp. 58–65.

Edward Eisner (1929– ) [B.A. (physics, 1950, Ph.D. (physics of surfaces, 1950), Cambridge University, England] was born in Hungary. His family came to England as refugees from the Nazis in 1938. He worked in Safety in Mines Research Establishment (Civil Service), Sheffield, England, 1954–1960; Bell Telephone Laboratories, Research Departments, New Jersey, 1960–1968, Research on Acoustic Waves in Solids and in Astronomy (Project Telstar).

Eisner joined the University of Strathclyde, Glasgow, Scotland, in 1968; he became Professor and first Head of Department of Applied Physics. He developed a new undergraduate course in Applied Physics, emphasizing application of physics to solutions of "real-world" problems outside physics, and physics as a basis for general education. He established research in physical methods for the study of macrobiological problems, especially the experimental determination of cause–effect relations in ecology.

He was elected Fellow in the Institute of Physics (U.K.), and in the Acoustical Society of America in 1969.

When one can quantify the many facets of a musical instrument, it is possible to deal with them more intelligently. Some measurements can be made without great difficulty. The static and dynamic characteristics of the keys on a reed instrument or the valve pistons of a cup-mouthpiece instrument can be measured rather easily. The metallurgical qualities of materials used in instruments can be determined. The exterior dimensions of instruments can be learned readily. The interior dimensions are more difficult to measure accurately in cup-mouthpiece instruments, due to the bends in the bore and discontinuities in the valves, but still possible. The analysis of tones produced by different wind instruments by different players can be made. However, it is difficult to measure the acoustic response of a wind instrument in order to learn exactly what the sensitive musician feels when he plays it. This goal can be approached, but probably not reached completely at present.

Prior to World War II, efforts were being made by Conn researchers to measure the input impedance of wind instruments. The work was carried out primarily by the late O. H. Schuck and by Robert W. Young. Several methods were tried but the one that seemed to show the most promise introduced sound from a loudspeaker to the mouthpiece through a decoupling capillary tube. Sound pressure was measured in the mouthpiece or at the bell of the instrument and plotted against frequency.

World War II caused all work on Conn musical instruments to stop while all activity was devoted to other products required by the U.S. government. After the war, musical activities were resumed. The acoustic response measurements made by feeding the input sound to a mouthpiece through a capillary tube were found to be helpful, but good correlation between such measurements and what a player felt could not be made. It was speculated that part of the reason for this might be due to the low magnitude of the sound pressure at the output of the capillary. In order to get greater undistorted sound pressure to the mouthpiece, a tube filled with fine wires was used for decoupling the input instead of the single capillary tube. Although this change gave more meaningful measurements, the interpretation of wind instruments as linear regenerative stationary-wave systems did not appear to be adequate. The consulting services of Dr. Arthur H. Benade were retained to help the Conn research department gain a better understanding of the acoustics involved. In his February 1958 progress report, Benade developed the mathematics to support his proposals regarding the nature of the nonlinear interactions in wind instruments. His report a month later presented interesting experimental evidence to support his nonlinear formulation and made possible unambiguous specifications of what musicians meant by the terms "hard blowing" and "easy blowing." (This was a forerunner of paper 13 by Benade and Gans.) Acoustic response measurements could then be more closely correlated with the subjective evaluation of a player. An example of the acoustic response of an experimental cornet is shown in Figure 1. This shows the relative sound pressure measured in the mouthpiece over the frequency range 130.81 to 1568.0 hertz and reveals much about the acoustics of the instrument. The numbers across the top of the figure denote the resonance mode numbers of the tones produced without the use of

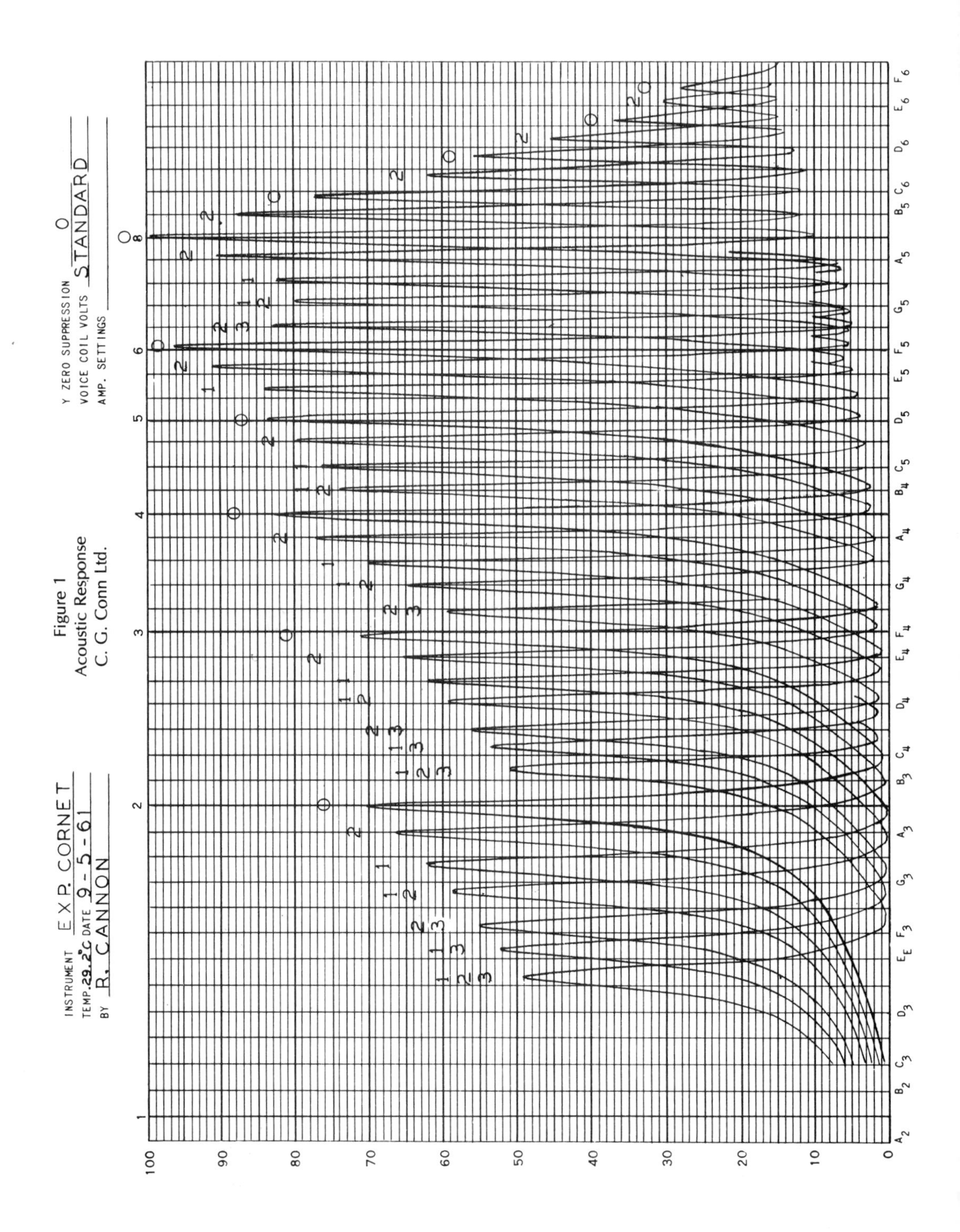


Figure 1
Acoustic Response
C. G. Conn Ltd.

valves—the "open" tones. The first and seventh modes are not normally used. The numbers just above the peaks of the curves indicate which vales, if any, were used. It can be seen that extra tubing introduced by the use of valves lowered the resonance frequencies and increased acoustical loss in the bore.

When these records were being recorded, the technician read the frequencies at the peaks of the response curves using a Stroboconn. The results of these readings, expressed in the notation of the equally tempered scale and deviation from that scale in cents, were as follows:

$E_3-66$, $F_3-66.5$, $F\sharp-62$, $G_3-38$, $G\sharp-25$, $A_3+1.5$, $A\sharp+6.5$, $B_3+42$, $C_4+24.5$, $C\sharp+12$, $D_4+12$, $D\sharp+1.5$, $E_4+15$, $F_4-7$, $F\sharp-12.5$, $G_4-10$, $G\sharp-15$, $A_4-0$, $A\sharp-0$, $B_4-7$, $C_5-5$, $C\sharp+13.5$, $D_5+18$, $D\sharp+25$,$E_5+31$, $F_5+18.5$, $F\sharp+5$, $G_5+7$, $G\sharp+5$, $A_5+18$, $A\sharp+8$, $B_5+2.5$, $C_6-13.5$, $C\sharp-18$, $D_6-60.5$, $D\sharp-49$.

Acoustic response curves, such as the ones shown here, reveal much about the acoustics of the instrument. Consider, for example, the resonance peaks involved when $A\sharp_3$ (233.08 Hz) is played. The peak for $A\sharp_3$ is 6.5 cents sharp (233.96 Hz). The second harmonic of that tone finds the peak for $A\sharp_4$ in tune. The third harmonic finds its peak at $F_5+18.5$ cents (705.96 Hz), 16.5 cents sharper than the third harmonic of $A\sharp_3$ (233.08 Hz). The fourth harmonic (932.32 Hz) finds its peak at $A\sharp_5+8$ cents (936.65 Hz). The peaks for the third and fourth harmonics will have a considerable influence upon the intonation of $A\sharp_3$, so the data indicates that tone will tend to be played sharp. The magnitudes of the peaks should reduce in a uniform manner, in accordance with the general format of the instrument, as extra tubing is introduced by the valves. This will not be the case if a leak or bore discontinuity is introduced by a valve.

Input measurements, such as given in this example, can give useful information when evaluating existing instruments, experimental models, mouthpieces, or mutes. These kinds of data can be helpful in improving wind instruments or creating new ones, if taken in the light of the theory and mathematics included in this volume.

Paper 13 by Benade and Gans presents basic insights regarding sound production in wind instruments and supplements the two previous papers as an introduction to wind-instrument acoustics. Many details not reported in Paper 13 are supplied in papers that follow it.

The Tacet Horn described in this paper is one of many means that Benade has used to demonstrate the accuracy of the theories he develops.

A biographical sketch regarding Benade was given on page 111.

Daniel J. Gans (1939–    ) B.S. (physics, 1960) Case Institute of

Technology (now part of Case Western Reserve University); M.S. (mathematics, 1962) University of Illinois] served as Instructor and Head of Statistical Consulting in the Department of Statistics, Purdue University (1967–1970); and Instructor in Mathematics Department, Wabash College, Crawfordsville, Indiana (1970–1971). He then joined the Department of Clinical Research, Pfizer Central Research, Inc., Groton, Connecticut, where he is a statistician.

Paper 14 reports an early study of the vibrating lips as the sound energizer in the cornet. The study was made in connection with Martin's Doctoral thesis, "A Physical Investigation of the Performance of Brass Musical Instruments," at the University of Illinois (1941), where it is reported in more detail.

In working with musical instruments, it is natural to think of their resonance frequencies in terms of length. One lowers the resonance frequency of a valve instrument by adding length with tubing. Pulling the mouthpiece of a reed instrument increases its length and lowers its resonance frequencies. John Webster uses the term "effective length," in Paper 15, as that length of acoustic-transmission line that would be required to account for the observed transit time of sound waves if the waves were transmitted with an assumed velocity of 13,650 inches per second (p. 176). Robert Pyle, Jr., deals with effective length in Paper 20. He points out the confusion that has resulted in the use of the term and gives a definition he believes avoids that confusion (p. 252). It is the same definition given by Long in Paper 16A (p. 185).

Paper 15 reports an early attempt to deal with resonance frequencies of brass instruments in terms of effective length. Companion paper 16A uses that means also. The term was used frequently by members of the Conn research staff and sometimes in an awkward fashion. One indication of the confusion caused by terminology can be seen in the letter to the editor by R. W. Young following Long's paper and Long's reply to Young's letter. These letters are reprinted following paper 16A.

Better measuring equipment, better measuring techniques, and better understanding of the acoustics of cup-mouthpiece instruments were developed by Conn researchers and others, following these early papers by Webster and by Long.

John C. Webster [B.A (1941); M.A. (1943); Ph.D. (speech and audiology, 1953), State University of Iowa] served as Instructor, AAF Communication Cadet School, Yale University (1943–1944); Acoustic Research Engineer, C. G. Conn, Ltd. (1945–1946); Research Psychologist, Naval Electronics Laboratory Center (1947– ); NSF Senior Post Doctoral Fellow (1959–1960) and Exchange Scientist (1966–1967), Applied Psychology Research Unit, Cambridge, England. He is a member of Phi Beta Kappa and Sigma Xi and a Fellow of the Acoustical Society of America, American Psychological Association, American Speech and Hearing Association, and AAAS. Also, he is a charter member of American Association of Phonetic Sciences.

Webster is author or coauthor of over 100 professional papers and government reports in the fields of hearing, speech, and noise. He has been, and still is, quite active in a number of professional groups.

Thomas H. Long (1905–1949) [B.S.E.E. (Senior Honors 1927), Kansas State College] was a member of Phi Kappa Phi. He worked as Development and Design Engineer with Westinghouse Electric Company (1927–1933); operated his own electrical repair shop in Wakeeny, Kansas (1934–1941); and joined C. G. Conn, Ltd. in 1942 where he served until his death. As Research and Development Engineer at Conn, Long made major contributions, as inventor, researcher, and designer, toward military instruments used in World War II, magnetic recording projects, and work regarding electronic organs and wind instruments. He was the author of several papers published in the Transactions of A.I.E.E., and was listed in the Sixth Edition of *Who's Who in Engineering* (1948).

Paper 17, a patent granted the editor, reports an effort made toward achieving a mathematical model for brass instruments. It involves the piecewise approach mentioned by Benade in Paper 11 (p. 131). In that paper, Benade states, "At first it would seem that the computer is ideally suited to be one of these tools and that it could immediately be put to work designing the perfect instrument. As a practical matter one finds that although we have a reasonable understanding of the goals to be achieved, the complexity of the problem is such that it is very difficult to specify the problem for the computer in sufficient detail" (p. 132). Concrete evidence of the truth of his comment was provided when an instrument was designed and built using this mathematical model. Traditional shapes were deliberately disregarded to make the test more valid. The resulting instrument produced resonance frequencies so close to those predicted by the mathematics, it was considered a major breakthrough by the research personnel. But the top management of the company did not share their enthusiasm, because the instrument had no practical value as a product that could be sold. The mouthpiece cup was too small for the instrument and a player could not deal with it adequately; in addition, the sound produced by the instrument did not seem to fit a musical need even though it could easily be played in tune with the equally tempered scale.

Wind instrument design is complex, but each step taken toward a better understanding of wind instrument acoustics, including the physical and the psychological needs of the musician, can lead to improved instruments and to additional types of musical instruments. The computer is a valuable tool in this effort if wisely used.

Paper 18, a patent by W. T. Cardwell, Jr., continues the pursuit of a mathematical means for dealing with the intonation characteristics of brass instruments. The information given in this patent contributes to better understanding of the acoustics of cup-mouthpiece instruments and provides another approach to musical instrument design—an approach that Cardwell has proven to be practical. He has designed and built trumpets in F using the method in this patent and has made improvement in existing trumpets in *B*♭.

Cardwell gave a paper at the 86th meeting of the Acoustical Society of America building upon the method reported in this patent and making it more convenient to use. He has called attention in a private communication that an error was printed in the abstract of his paper, *J. Acoust. Soc. Am.*, **55**, 457 (1974). The first omega in the numerator of the formula should be squared. The patent and the papers presented by Cardwell indicate a good practical and theoretical understanding of cup-mouthpiece acoustics.

William T. Cardwell, Jr. (1917–      ) [B.S. (1938), M.S. (1939), California Institute of Technology] joined Standard Oil Co. of California in 1939 as Assistant Chemist, became Petroleum Engineer in 1941 and Senior Research Engineer in 1947; he is now Senior Research Associate with Chevron Research Co., a subsidiary of Standard Oil Co. of California.

Cardwell is a member of Society of Petroleum Engineers of AIME, American Chemical Society, Acoustical Society of America, Audio Engineering Society, Sigma Xi, and Tau Beta Pi. Most of his patents and technical publications are related to his work with petroleum drilling, production methods, and devices, but as this patent indicates, he has considerable interest in musical acoustics.

Papers 19A and 19B by Benade and Jansson deal with the behavior of sound waves in horns, as in the bells of cup-mouthpiece instruments. The acoustics of such horns is quite complex. The bell of a brass instrument has an important role in the intonation of the instrument, the timbre of the tone produced, and how the instrument "feels" and responds to the musician. These papers makes a major contribution to an understanding of the acoustics of brass instrument bells.

The authors report agreement between theory and experiment to be generally within 0.05 percent. This is good agreement and particularly so considering the subject and the bells used in the experiments. Deviation in the tuning of musical instruments is often expressed in cents (a cent is one hundredth of a half step). One-half of 1 percent is 8.6 cents.

At A = 440 Hz this would be close to a 2-Hz deviation. If all elements that contribute to the intonation of wind instruments could be constructed to respond within 0.05 percent of the desired values it would be remarkable. Variations among musicians would generally be found to exceed that amount. It should be kept in mind that skilled musicians do not always want to play the equally tempered scale. They want the instrument to be flexible enough to be under the control of the player for best musical results.

Erik V. Jansson (1941– ) [M.S.EE. (1966), Doctor of Science (1973), Royal Institute of Technology (KTH), Stockholm] worked with Dr. Arthur H. Benade at Case Western Reserve University in 1967 on wave propagation in bells of brass wind instruments. He joined the musical acoustics group in the Department of Speech Communications at KTH in 1968 where he worked on the development of the STL-Ionophone until 1971. He then began, and is presently, working with the acoustics of string instruments employing holographic methods to investigate the plate vibrations in cooperation with the Institute of Optical Research KTH.

Most of Dr. Jansson's many published papers and reports have been related to violin acoustics. His doctoral thesis was "Investigations of Acoustical Phenomena as Revealed by Properties of Musical Instruments."

In Paper 20 R. W. Pyle, Jr. makes important contributions to the understanding of brass instrument acoustics. This paper was written with both theory and practice well in mind. The author points out, for example, that in normal playing, the player's lips protrude into the mouthpiece cup, somewhat reducing the cup volume, (p. 259). Experimenters need to take this into account when making acoustical measurements involving mouthpieces. Pyle also mentions that the bell of a French horn is normally partially closed by the player's right hand and this influences the behavior of the sound waves in the instrument. Actually, due to reflected sound, the effective length of a brass instrument is influenced by the environment in which it is played. This is more pronounced in an instrument having a large bell, such as a Sousaphone. Normally, the air in the mouthpiece and mouthpipe of a brass instrument will be warmer than the air in the bell, and this will influence the speed of sound and the effective length accordingly.

Robert W. Pyle, Jr. (1936– ) [A.B. (1957), A.M. (1958), Ph.D. (1963) Harvard University] joined the staff of Bolt Beranek and Newman, Inc., in 1965, after two years as a research fellow in acoustics at the Harvard Acoustics Research Laboratory. As Senior Scientist in the Instrument Systems Division he has worked on a variety of programs in architectural acoustics, underwater acoustics, industrial noise control, ship silencing, digital signal processing, airport noise monitoring, and related topics.

In his spare time, Pyle plays the French horn and does occasional work on the acoustics of musical instruments.

11

*Copyright © 1973 by Scientific American, Inc. All rights reserved.*

Reprinted with permission from *Sci. Am.*, 24–35 (July 1973)

# THE PHYSICS OF BRASSES

by Arthur H. Benade

[*Editor's Note:* Illustrations were rendered in color in original publication.]

It is easy to grasp why stringed instruments make the sounds they do. When the strings are struck or plucked, they vibrate at different natural frequencies in accordance with their tension and their diameter. The energy of vibration is then transferred to the air by way of a vibrating plate of wood and a resonating air chamber, with the sound eventually dying away. The musician can vary the pitch, or frequency, of individual strings by changing their vibrating length with the pressure of his fingers on the frets or the fingerboard.

The principles underlying the acoustics of bowed-string instruments such as the violin or wind instruments such as the oboe are a good deal less obvious. Here a vibration is maintained by a feedback mechanism that converts a steady motion of the bow, or a steady application of blowing pressure, into an oscillatory acoustical disturbance that we can hear. On the violin and in the oboe different tones are produced by altering the effective length of the string or the air column.

Like the oboe and other woodwinds, the brass instruments can produce sustained tones. The question arises, however, of how a bugle, which is hardly more than a loop of brass tubing with a mouthpiece at one end and a flaring bell at the other, can produce a dozen or more distinct notes. Horns were fashioned and played for centuries before physicists were able to work out good explanations of how they worked, even though scientific attention has been directed to these questions from the earliest days. For centuries the skilled craftsman has usually been able to identify what is wrong with faulty instruments and to fix them without recourse to sophisticated knowledge of horn acoustics.

All brass instruments consist of a mouthpiece (which has a cup and a tapered back bore), a mouthpipe (which also has a carefully controlled taper), a main bore (which is either cylindrical or conical) and a flaring bell that forms the exit from the interior of the horn into the space around the instrument. Brass instruments are of two main types. Those in one family, which includes the trumpet, the trombone and the French horn, have a considerable length of cylindrical tubing in the middle section and an abruptly flaring bell. Those in the other family, called conical, include the flügelhorn, the alto horn, the baritone horn and the tuba. The generic term conical refers to the fact that much of the tubing increases in diameter from the mouthpiece to the bell and the flare of the bell is itself less pronounced than it is in the first family. Actually all the horns called conical incorporate a certain amount of cylindrical tubing in their midsection. Here I shall deal primarily with the properties of instruments in the trumpet and trombone family. The properties of the conical instruments are very similar except for being somewhat simpler acoustically because overall they have much less flare.

The acoustical study of waves in an air column whose cross section varies along its length (a "horn") goes back to the middle of the 18th century. Daniel Bernoulli, Leonhard Euler and Joseph Louis Lagrange were the first to discuss the equations for waves in such horns during the decade following 1760. Their activity was a part of the immensely rapid blossoming of theoretical physics that took place in the years after the laws of motion had been formulated by Newton and Leibniz. Theoretical investigations of fluid dynamics, acoustics, heat flow and the mechanics of solid objects took their inspiration from the workaday world outside the laboratory and the mathematician's study. The work of Bernoulli, Euler and Lagrange on horns (and their similar researches on strings) did not have much influence in the long run on the science of acoustics or the art of music. It was nonetheless a part of the initial blooming of the theory of partial differential equations underlying nearly all physics.

The "horn equation," as we call it today, was neglected until 1838, when George Green rediscovered it while investigating the erosion caused by waves in the new canal systems of England. Then the equation was buried again until 1876, when a German mathematician, L. Pochhammer, independently derived it for waves in a column of air and learned the properties of its most important solutions. Neither Pochhammer nor his equation was long remembered. Finally in 1919 an American physicist, A. G. Webster, published a report on the horn equation, with the result that the equation is commonly named for him.

Since Webster's time interest in loudspeakers on the part of the phonograph and radio industries, to say nothing of military demands for sonar gear to detect submarines, has kept the subject of horn acoustics in a lively state. A loudspeaker horn must be designed to radiate sound efficiently out into the air over a broad range of frequencies from a small source. A horn designed to serve as a musical instrument has quite different requirements. In a musical horn the flare of the bell must be designed to trap energy inside the horn, giving strongly marked standing waves at precisely defined frequencies.

It is obvious that as a wave travels into the enlarging part of a horn its pressure will decrease systematically, simply because the sound energy is being spread over an ever wider front. If one extracts this intuitively obvious part of the behavior of a wave in a horn from the mathematics of the horn equation, one is left with a much simpler equation that is identical in form with the celebrated Schrödinger equation of quantum mechanics. The Schrödinger equation shows that a particle of energy $E$ has associated with it a de Broglie wavelength lambda ($\lambda$) that depends on the square root of the difference between the energy and the potential energy function $V$ at any point in space. The "reduced," or simplified, form of the horn equation shows similarly that at any point in the horn the acoustic wavelength depends on the square root of the difference between the squared frequency and a "horn function" $U$ that depends in a rather simple way on the nature of the horn flare [*see top illustration on next page*].

It is not difficult to show from the horn equation that sounds propagate with dif-

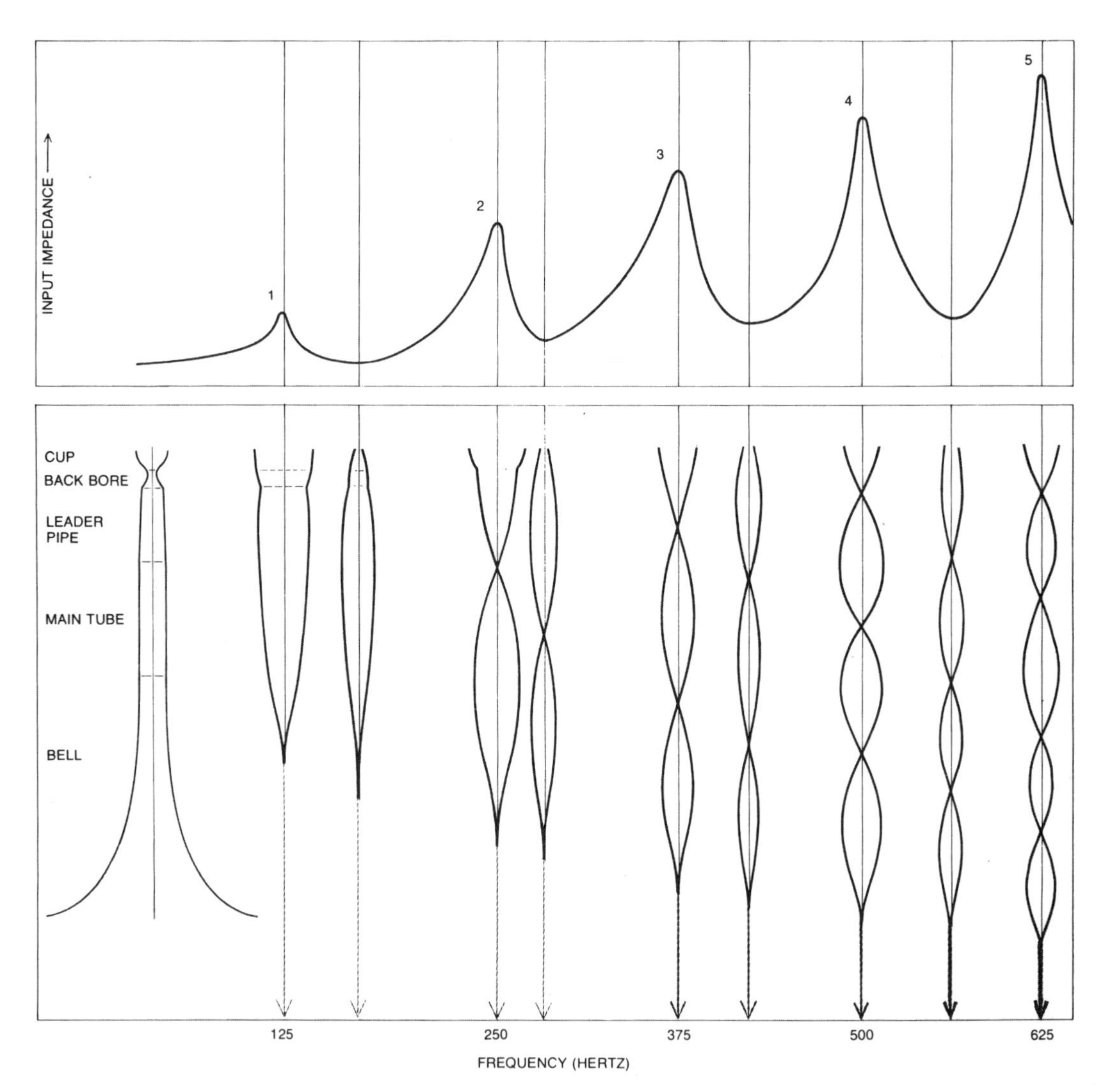


**RESONANCE PEAKS OF A TRUMPETLIKE INSTRUMENT can be plotted (*top*) in terms of the impedance measured at the mouthpiece. Impedance is defined as the ratio of the pressure set up in the mouthpiece to the excitatory flow that gives rise to it. The impedance depends on whether the sound wave reflected from the bell of the horn returns in step or out of step with the oscillatory pressure wave produced in the mouthpiece. The shape of the air column in the trumpetlike instrument is shown at the extreme left of the bottom part of the diagram. The curves at the right are the standing-wave patterns that exist in the air column of the instrument at frequencies that produce the maxima and minima in the impedance curve. The first maximum is at about 100 hertz (cycles per second), when the reflected wave is precisely in step with the entering wave. The small irregularities in the standing-wave pattern are produced by the abrupt changes in the cross section of the instrument. The first minimum comes just above 125 hertz, where the returning wave and the incoming wave are exactly out of step with each other in the mouthpiece of the instrument. The subsequent maxima and minima are similarly explained. The number of nodes in the standing-wave pattern increases by one at each impedance peak.**

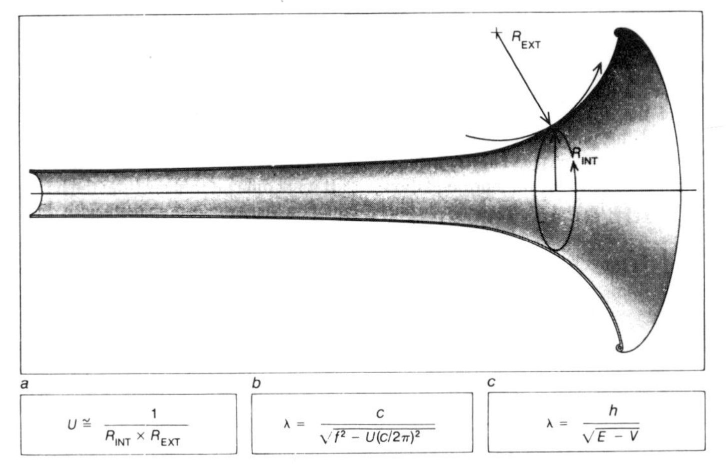


**GEOMETRY OF HORN FLARE** largely governs the pitch and timbre of sounds produced by horns of the trumpet and trombone family. As a sound wave travels into the flaring bell of the horn its pressure falls steadily as the cross section of the instrument increases. A "horn function," $U$, determines how much of the acoustic energy leaves the horn and how much is reflected back into the horn to produce standing waves inside the instrument. The horn function (*equation "a"*) is approximately equal to 1 over the product of the internal radius ($R_{int}$) of the horn and the external radius ($R_{ext}$) at any given point. The simplified form of the horn equation (*equation "b"*) gives the acoustic wavelength ($\lambda$) at any point in the horn, where $f$ is the sound frequency and $c$ is the velocity of sound. This velocity varies with $U$ and $f$. The horn equation has the same form as the celebrated Schrödinger equation ($c$), which shows how the de Broglie wavelength ($\lambda$) of a particle of energy $E$ is related to Planck's constant ($h$) and the potential energy function $V$ at any point in space.

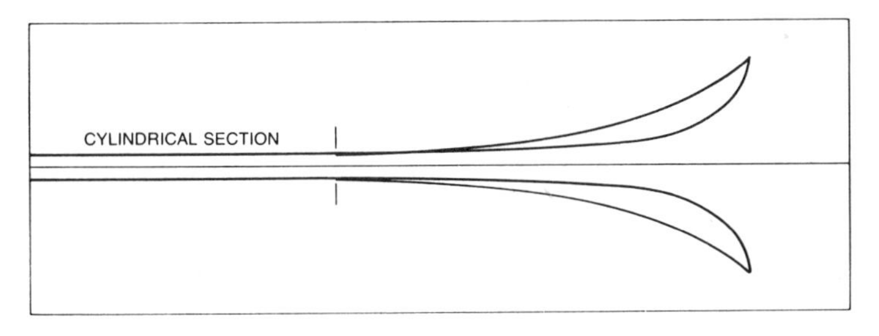


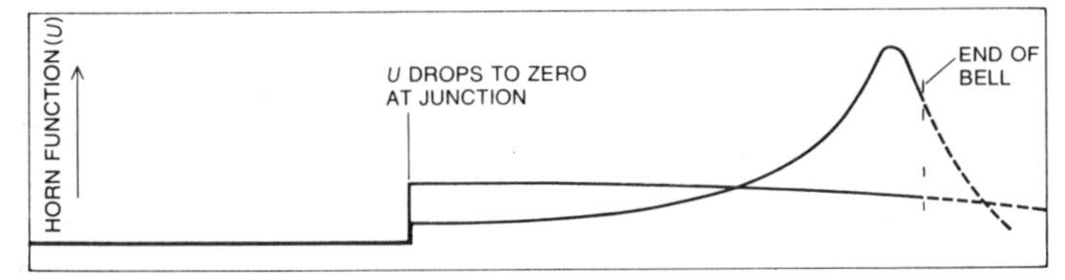


**TROMBONE BELL AND LOUDSPEAKER HORN** are markedly different in geometry and acoustic properties. The catenoidal shape (*black curve at top*) of the loudspeaker horn favors the efficient radiation of sound into the air. The flaring shape (*colored curve at top*) of the trombone bell is designed to save energy inside the horn, thus generating strongly marked standing waves at closely defined frequencies. Both the trombone bell and the loudspeaker horn are shown attached to a short section of cylindrical pipe. The two curves at the bottom show the horn function, $U$, for each horn. The catenoidal horn has a horn function (*colored curve*) that is low and nearly constant except for a slight falling off at the large end, where the sound wave fronts begin to bulge appreciably. The horn function (*black curve*) of the trombone bell rises steeply and falls. The higher the value of the function $U$, the higher the barrier to sounds of low frequency. Sounds of higher frequency are able to progress farther before they are reflected back by the barrier. In both cases above a certain frequency most of the sound energy radiates over the top of the barrier, so that the bell of the trombone loses its musically useful character and behaves like a loudspeaker horn.

ferent speeds as they travel through regions of differing horn function $U$. The speed of propagation also depends on the frequency. Another similarity between horn acoustics and quantum mechanics is that for frequencies below a certain critical value determined by the magnitude of $U$, the wavelength becomes mathematically imaginary, or, to put it in more physical terms, the wave changes its character and becomes strongly attenuated. In other words, regions where the horn function $U$ is large can form a barrier to the transmission of waves and can therefore reduce the escape of energy from within a horn to the outside. The leaking of sound from the horn through the horn-function barrier is an exact analogue to the leaking of quantum-mechanical waves (and therefore particles) through the nuclear potential barrier in the radioactive decay of the atomic nucleus.

Let us look more closely at the difference between a musical horn and a loudspeaker horn. A simple example of a musical horn can be constructed by joining a trombone bell to a piece of cylindrical pipe. To a similar pipe one can join a typical loudspeaker bell, whose figure is described as catenoid. Even if the bells are matched to have the same radii at both ends, we find that their horn functions are quite different [*see bottom illustration at left*]. The catenoidal bell has a horn function that is approximately constant from one end to the other, whereas the acoustical properties of the horn function for the musical horn vary from point to point.

Five years ago Erik V. Jansson of the Speech Transmission Laboratory of the Royal Institute of Technology in Stockholm worked with me at Case Western Reserve University on a detailed study of air columns similar to those found in musical horns. In this work, which was both theoretical and experimental, we studied bells of the type found on trumpets, trombones and French horns. We unearthed a number of subtle relations between our experiments and calculations that we did not have time to clarify immediately. It is only recently that we have had an opportunity to prepare complete reports on our results. In what follows I shall lean heavily on information gained in our work five years ago and its later development, and on the earlier observations of many people concerned with acoustics or making musical horns.

In a brass musical instrument the small end of the horn is connected to the

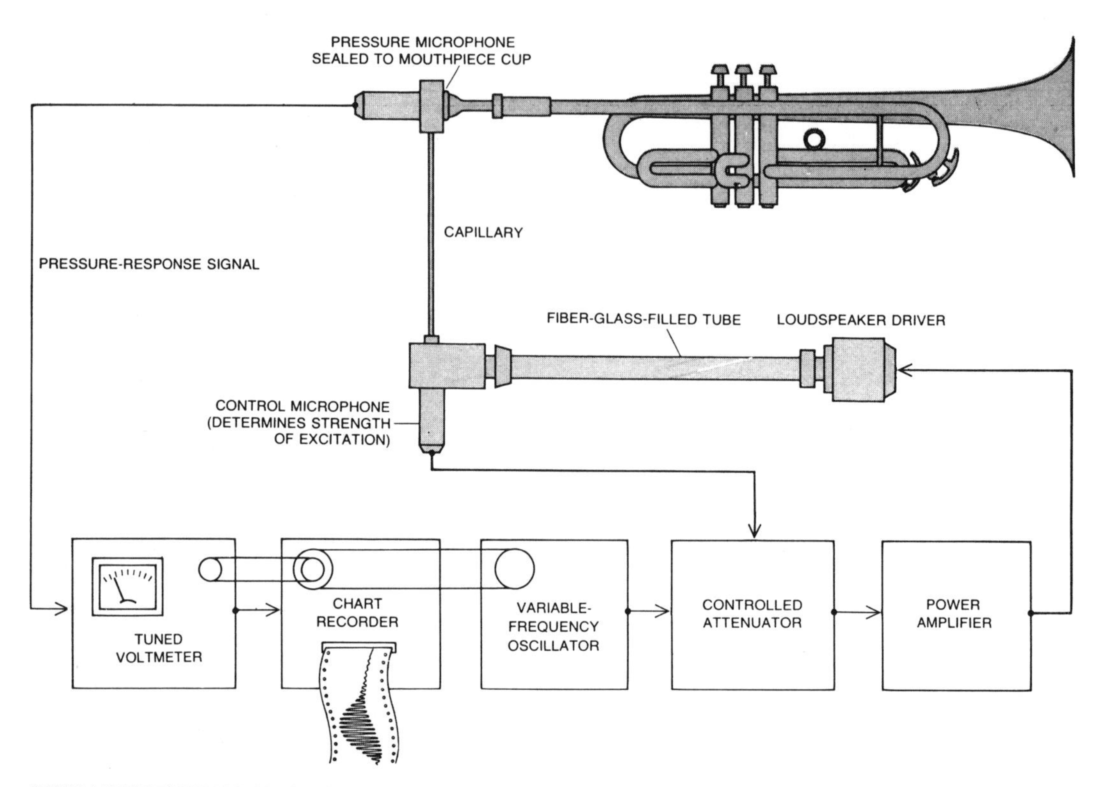


**IMPEDANCE-MEASURING APPARATUS uses the driver from a horn loudspeaker as a pump to feed a flow stimulus through a capillary into the mouthpiece cup of the instrument under study. A control microphone sends signals to an attenuator to ensure that the acoustic stimulus entering the capillary remains constant. The pressure response of the instrument, and thus its input impedance, is detected by a second microphone that forms the closure of the mouthpiece cup. The signal from the microphone goes to a frequency-selective voltmeter coupled by a chain drive to oscillator. A chart recorder coupled to the voltmeter plots the resonance curves.**

player through his lips, which constitute a kind of automatically controlled valve for admitting air from the player's lungs to the horn. The opening and closing of the valve is controlled chiefly by the pressure fluctuations within the mouthpiece as they act on the lips in concert with the steady pressure from the lungs. Therefore an initial objective is to find the relations between the flow of air into the horn and the acoustical pressure set up at the input end.

Let us begin by imagining a laboratory experiment in which the horn is excited not by air from the player's lips and lungs but rather by a small oscillatory flow of air being pumped in and out of the mouthpiece through a fine capillary by a high-speed pump. This small oscillatory flow disturbance in the mouthpiece gives rise to a pressure wave that ultimately reaches the flaring part of the horn. As the wave travels down the length of the bore of the horn some of its energy is dissipated by friction and the transfer of heat to the walls of the instrument. In the flaring part of the bell a substantial fraction of the acoustic wave is reflected back toward the mouthpiece while the remainder penetrates the horn-function barrier and is radiated out into the surrounding space. The wave that is reflected back down the bore of the horn combines with newly injected waves to produce a standing wave.

If the round-trip time that the wave takes to go from the mouthpiece to the bell and back to the mouthpiece is equal to half the repetition time of the original stimulus or to any odd multiple of the repetition time, a standing wave of considerable pressure can build up and result in a large disturbance in the mouthpiece. At intermediate frequencies of excitation the return wave tends to cancel the influence of the injected wave. In other words, depending on the precise interaction between the injected wave and the reflected wave, the pressure disturbance inside the mouthpiece can be large or small. For purposes of describing such disturbances in the mouthpiece under conditions of constant flow excitation in a laboratory apparatus, engineers define a quantity termed input impedance: the ratio between the pressure amplitude set up in the mouthpiece and the excitatory flow that gives rise to it [*see illustration on page 25*].

The shape of the horn controls the natural frequencies associated with the various impedance maxima and minima by determining the penetration of the standing waves into the bell. The shape also controls the amount of wave energy that leaks out of the horn into the surrounding space. Furthermore, the kinks in the standing wave that arise from discontinuities in cross section and taper along an air column produce significant changes in both the resonance and the radiation properties of the bell. The interaction of the kinks and the primary shape of the air column can spell the difference between success and failure in the design of an instrument.

There are several ways one might measure the input impedance, or response, of the air column. Conceptually the simplest method would be to pump air in and out of the mouthpiece through a capillary tube at some frequency and measure the amplitude of the resulting pressure fluctuations in the mouthpiece by means of a probe microphone. It is more practical, however, to use the driver of a commercial horn loudspeaker as a pump. The motion of the driver is controlled electronically by an auxiliary monitor microphone that maintains a constant strength of oscillatory flow through the capillary as one sweeps automatically through the appropriate range of frequencies. Between 1945 and 1965 Earle L. Kent and his co-workers at C. G. Conn Ltd. in Elkhart, Ind., developed this basic technique to a high degree of dependability. We often employ a modification of their technique in our work [*see illustration on preceding page*].

In Cleveland we make use of two additional methods that have special advantages for certain purposes. The first method, based on a device described in 1968 by Josef Merhaut of Prague, can be applied in measurements not only on the smaller brasses but also on bassoons and clarinets [*see illustration below*]. In Merhaut's device a thin diaphragm forms a closure at the end of the mouthpiece cup and itself serves as the pump piston. The diaphragm is driven acoustically through a pipe that connects it to an enclosed loudspeaker. The diaphragm motion is monitored for automatic control by the electrode of a condenser microphone mounted directly behind it. The second method is based on a device that was used by John W. Coltman of the Westinghouse Research Laboratories in investigating the sounding mechanism of the flute. In Coltman's device the excitatory diaphragm is driven directly by a loudspeaker coil whose motion is monitored by means of a second pickup coil that is moving in an auxiliary magnetic field [*see illustration on opposite page*].

If one attaches to any one of these excitation systems a cylindrical section about 140 centimeters long from a trumpet, one discovers dozens of input impedance peaks evenly spaced at odd multiples of about 63 hertz (cycles per second) [*see curve "a" in top illustration on page 30*]. The peaks correspond exactly to what elementary physics textbooks describe as the "natural frequencies of a cylindrical pipe stopped at one end." Because frictional and thermal losses inside the tube walls increase with frequency, the resonance peaks become smaller at higher frequencies. The energy radiated from the open end of such a pipe is only a tiny fraction of 1 percent of the wall losses.

If one now adds a trumpet bell to the same cylindrical pipe, the impedance response curve is substantially altered [*see curve "b" in bottom illustration on*

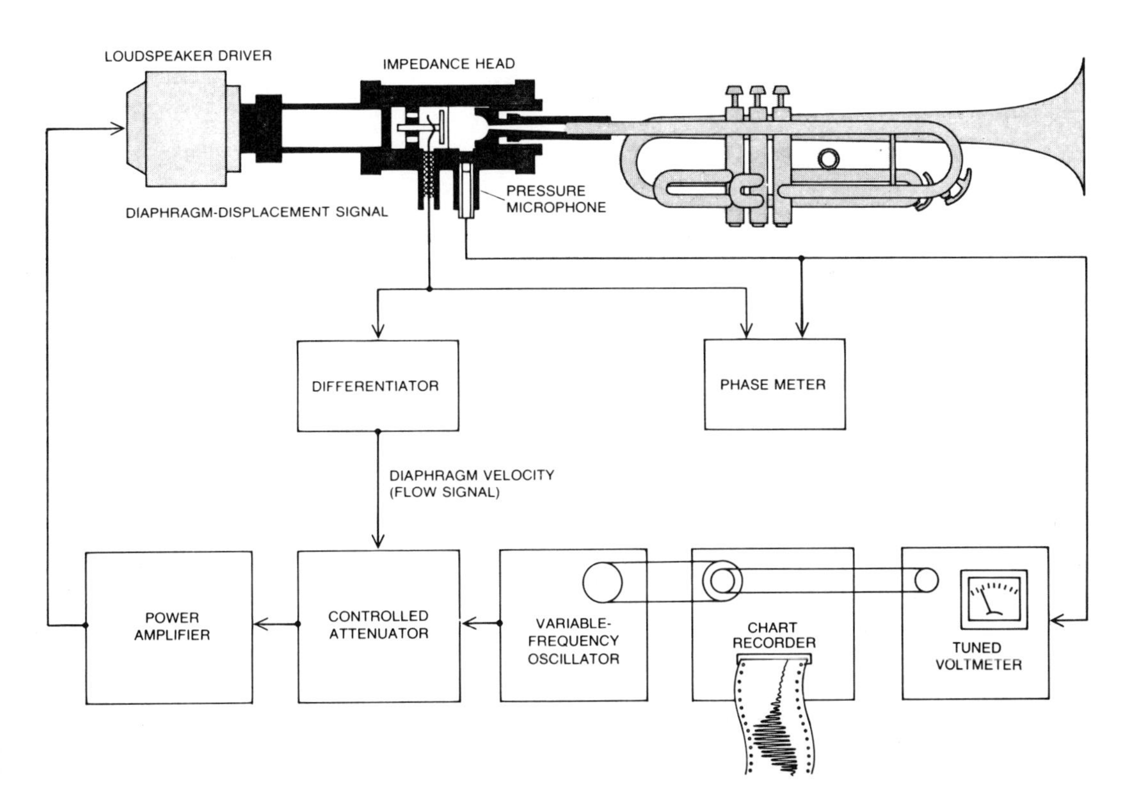


**SECOND TYPE OF IMPEDANCE-MEASURING DEVICE was developed by Josef Merhaut. It differs from the apparatus illustrated on the preceding page only in the way that the flow stimulus into the mouthpiece is controlled. Here the acoustic stimulus produced by a loudspeaker moves an aluminized Mylar diaphragm that in turn pumps air into the mouthpiece. The diaphragm also acts as one electrode of a condenser microphone to produce a signal proportional to the diaphragm's velocity and thus proportional to the oscillatory flow of air at the mouthpiece cup. The velocity signal adjusts the attenuator in order to maintain constant excitation at a particular frequency. The pressure response of the instrument is monitored by a microphone on the cup side of the diaphragm. A phase meter shows the relation between the phase of the input stimulus and the phase of the pressure response of the instrument.**

*next page*]. The first peak is hardly shifted at all by adding the bell, but the frequencies of the other resonances are lowered in a smooth progression because the injected waves penetrate ever more deeply into the bell before being reflected. In addition the peaks at higher frequencies are markedly reduced in height because a growing fraction of the energy supply leaks through the bell "barrier" as the frequency is increased. In sum, the return wave in the pipe-plus-bell system is weakened not only by wall losses but also by radiation losses, particularly at high frequencies. Above about 1,500 hertz essentially no energy returns from the flaring part of the bell. The small wiggles in the impedance curve at high frequencies are due chiefly to small reflections produced at the discontinuity where the bell joins the cylindrical tubing.

By comparing these curves for incomplete instruments with the impedance curve for a complete cornet [*see illustration on page 31*] one can see at a glance that the presence of a mouthpipe and mouthpiece has a considerable effect on the overall nature of the input impedance. The resonance peaks of the cornet grow taller up to around 800 hertz, then fall away much more abruptly than the curve produced by the pipe-plus-bell system.

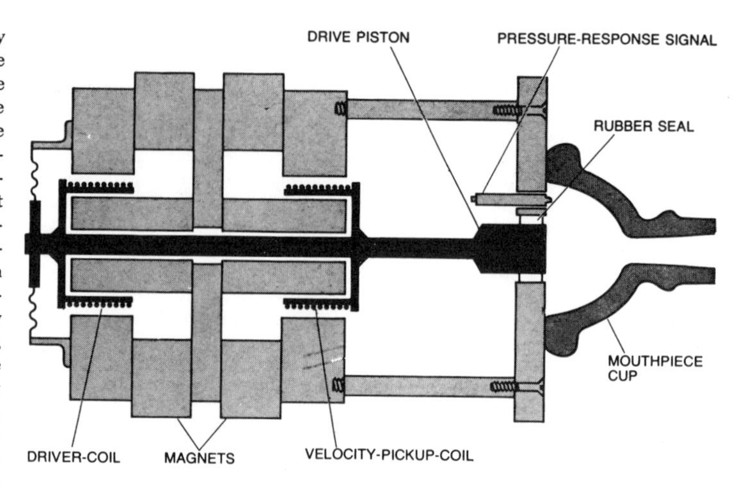


**ELECTROMAGNETIC SOURCE for projecting acoustic waves into a test instrument was devised by John W. Coltman. The excitatory piston is directly coupled to the voice coil of a loudspeaker. The coil in turn drives the piston with an amplitude that is ultimately determined by a voltage induced in a pickup coil that is mounted on the same shaft. The mechanism is used in an overall system similar to that used with the Merhaut impedance head. The pressure response in the mouthpiece cup is detected by a miniature microphone.**

Let us now consider how the player's lips control the flow of air from his lungs into the instrument. As the player blows harder and harder, the flow increases both because of the increased pressure across the aperture formed by his lips and because his lips are forced farther apart by the rising pressure inside his mouth. Equally important is the variation imposed on the flow by pressure variations inside the mouthpiece, which tend to increase or decrease the flow by their own ability to affect the size of the lip aperture. It is this pressure-operated flow control by the lips under the influence of the mouthpiece pressure that ultimately leads to the possibility of self-sustained oscillation. Let us abstract from this rather complicated situation only the relevant part of it: the alteration in net flow that is produced by acoustical pressure variations within the cup of the mouthpiece. As long ago as the middle of the 19th century it was clearly understood that it is the flow alteration due to mouthpiece pressure that can maintain an oscillation.

In 1830 Wilhelm Weber described experiments on the action of organ reeds that led him to a correct theory for the effect of a compliant structure (the reed or, in our case, the player's lips) on the input impedance of a column of air. This effect of the yielding closure of the mouthpiece cup provided by the lips is quite separate from the lips' functioning as a valve. Hermann von Helmholtz provided the next advance. In 1877 he added an appendix to the fourth German edition of his classic work *Sensations of Tone* that gives a brief but complete analysis of the basic mechanisms by which a pressure-controlled reed valve collaborates with a single impedance maximum. He found that for a given pressure-control sensitivity (what an engineer today calls the transconductance) a certain minimum impedance value is required. Oscillating systems of the type analyzed by Helmholtz are found around us everywhere. The pendulum clock is possibly the oldest and most familiar. The wristwatch, electronic or otherwise, falls into this category. Every radio and television set has one such oscillator or more.

Engineers have studied oscillating systems intensively and have learned that even if the alteration in flow (of whatever kind) that results from a given pressure is not exactly proportional to the pressure (as Helmholtz assumed for simplicity in his pioneering investigation) but varies in some more arbitrary fashion, the properties of the system are not drastically altered. The presence of such nonlinearity in the control characteristics gives rise to additional frequencies at double, triple and quadruple the frequency of the basic oscillation. The net generation of oscillatory energy from the player's steady muscular effort, however, is still almost exclusively at the frequency of the impedance maximum; energy diverted in the process to other frequencies is dissipated in various ways to the outside world.

We must now try to explain how oscillations in a wind instrument can take place at not just the tallest impedance maximum but at any one of several maxima belonging to an actual air column. According to the Helmholtz theory, a wind instrument should show a strong preference for oscillations that take place at the tallest of the impedance maxima. Thus the question arises of how the bugle player finds it possible to play the notes based on lesser impedance maxima. Furthermore, one must ask how the bugler is able to select one or another of these peaks in accordance with his musical requirements.

It is not in fact difficult to deal with the problem of how the player selects one note or another. His lips are so massive compared with the mass of the air in his instrument that the influence of the air column on the lips is relatively small. The player adjusts the tension of his lips in such a way that their own natural tendency of vibration favors oscillation at the desired note, so that the

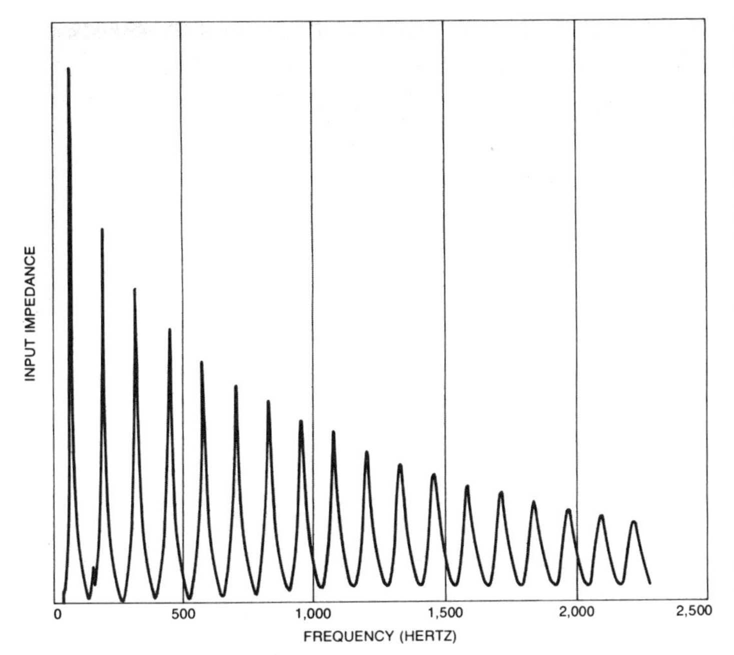


**IMPEDANCE PATTERN OF SIMPLE CYLINDRICAL PIPE** 140 centimeters long shows peaks evenly spaced at odd multiples of 63 hertz. The higher the frequency, the greater the loss of wave energy to the walls of the pipe through friction, hence the steady decline in the height of the peaks. Less than 1 percent of the input energy is radiated into the room.

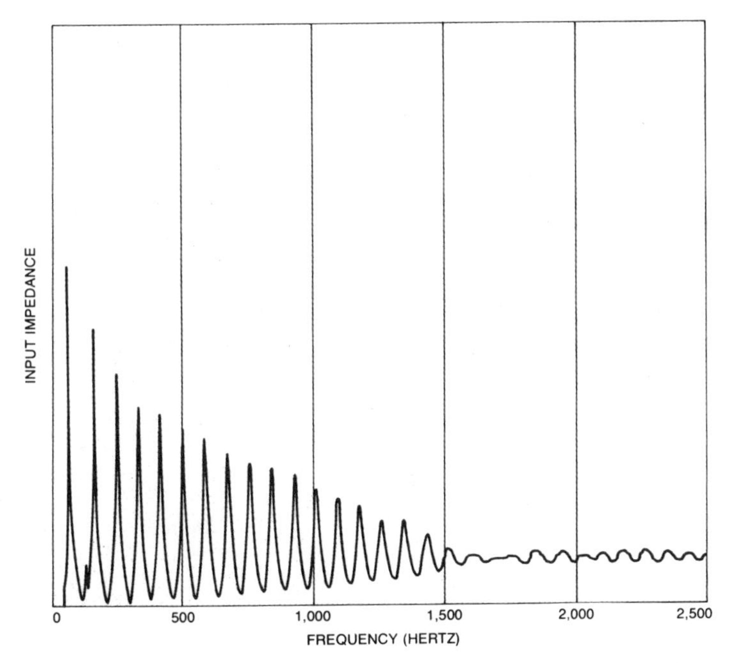


**ADDITION OF TRUMPET BELL TO PIPE** lowers the overall height of the impedance peaks and squeezes them together. Whereas the pipe alone produces 16 peaks in a span of 2,000 hertz, the pipe-plus-bell system compresses the first 16 peaks into a span of 1,400 hertz. Beyond 1,500 hertz more and more of the acoustic energy leaks through the bell barrier.

air column and the lips collaborate in producing the desired frequency.

So far we have not said anything that could not have been understood in terms of 19th-century acoustics. The best account of the Weber-Helmholtz analysis and its musical consequences was made by a French physicist, Henri Bouasse, in his book *Instruments à Vent,* the two volumes of which appeared in 1929 and 1930. These volumes contain what still constitutes one of the most thorough accounts of the acoustics of wind instruments, encompassing the flute and reed organ pipes, the orchestral woodwinds and the brasses. Bouasse has left us with a gold mine of mathematical analysis, along with an account of careful experiments done by himself in collaboration with M. Fouché or selected from the writings of earlier investigators.

Bouasse was quite aware of the inadequacy of a theory of oscillation assuming that all the energy production is at the basic frequency of oscillation. He described many phenomena observed among the reed organ pipes and the orchestral woodwinds and brasses that underscore the limitations of this general viewpoint and that imply cooperation among several air-column resonances. Bouasse's interest in these matters was to serve both as a strong incentive and as an invaluable guide when I later undertook a close study of the subject. The first fruits of this study were described in a series of technical reports written in 1958 for C. G. Conn Ltd.

By 1964 I found it possible to deal well enough with the interaction between a reed valve and an air column having several impedance maxima that I could design and build a nonplaying "tacet horn." This "instrument" has several input impedance maxima chosen in such a way as to make them unable to maintain any oscillation in cooperation with a reed, even though the Weber-Helmholtz theory would predict the possibility of oscillation. In 1968 Daniel Gans and I published an account of this theory of cooperative oscillations. That report, based on Gans's undergraduate thesis at Case Western Reserve, included a description of the tacet horn and explanations of various phenomena discussed by Bouasse. Since that time the work has been carried much further in our laboratory, particularly by Walter Worman, who wrote his doctoral dissertation on the theory of self-sustained oscillations of this multiple type in 1971. Although his work was focused on clarinetlike systems, his results apply broadly to all the wind instruments, including the brasses. These studies were aided by counsel from many people, in particular Bruce Schantz, Kent, Robert W. Pyle, Jr., and John H. Schelleng.

It is now time to see how the Weber-Helmholtz form of the theory had to be modified, using the trumpet as our example. When the musician sounds one of the tones of a trumpet, the air column and his lips are functioning in what we shall formally call a regime of oscillation: a state of oscillation in which several impedance maxima of the air column collaborate with the lip-valve mechanism to generate energy in a steady oscillation containing several harmonically related frequency components. Worman was able to trace out how a set of impedance maxima can work together with the air valve. The particular "playing frequency" chosen by the oscillation (along with its necessarily whole-number multiples) is one that maximizes the total generation of acoustic energy, which is then shared among the various frequency components in a well-defined way.

Experiments with instruments as diverse as the clarinet, the oboe, the bassoon, the trumpet and the French horn show that softly played notes are dominated by the impedance maximum that belongs to the note in the sense of Weber and Helmholtz. As the musician raises the dynamic level, however, the influence of the higher resonances grows in a definite way that is common to all the instruments. As he plays louder and louder, the influence of the impedance at double the playing frequency becomes more marked, and for still louder playing the resonance properties at triple or quadruple frequencies join the regime of oscillation one by one. A look at the input impedance curves for a modern trumpet will show how the peaks in a regime of oscillation cooperate so that the player can sound various notes on his instrument, including even some notes that have no peak at all at the playing frequency [*see illustrations on next two pages*]. Notes in this last category have been known to brass players since the earliest days and were a part of horn-playing technique in the time of Mozart and Beethoven. The need for such notes was reduced, however, as the instrument became more mechanized. In recent years they have returned; for example, they are sounded by musicians who want to play bass-trombone parts without resorting to a special thumb-operated valve that is otherwise required. Tuba players also find the technique useful on occasion.

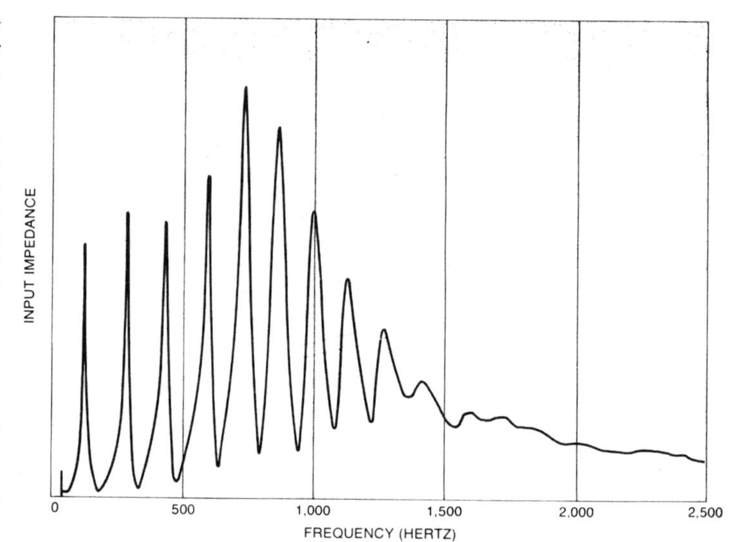


**IMPEDANCE PATTERN OF A 19TH-CENTURY CORNET is typical of most of the trumpet and trombone family. The peaks grow progressively and then fall away sharply. The cornet was made in 1865 by Henry Distin. The third and fourth impedance peaks do not quite follow the smoothly rising pattern required for a genuinely fine instrument. The shortcoming is due chiefly to slight constrictions and misalignments in the valve pistons.**

The reader may be wondering what happens when the valves on a brass instrument are depressed. Does anything radically new happen? The answer is no. The bell, the mouthpipe and the mouthpiece dominate the "envelope," or overall pattern, of the resonance curve; the pattern of peaks for a trumpet rises steadily as one goes from low frequencies to about 850 hertz and then falls away and disappears at high frequencies. When a valve is depressed, thereby increasing the length of cylindrical tubing in the middle of the horn, it merely shifts the entire family of resonance peaks to lower frequencies but leaves them fitting pretty much the same envelope.

In addition to working out the details of the regimes of oscillation in wind instruments Worman gained an important insight into the factors that influence tone color. He was able to show that in instruments with a pressure-controlled air valve (a reed or the lips) the strength of the various harmonics generated in a regime of oscillation (as measured inside the mouthpiece) has a particularly simple relation when the instrument is being played at low and medium levels of loudness. Let us take as given the strength of the fundamental component that coincides with the playing frequency. As one would expect, that strength increases as the player blows harder. Worman's striking result is that when the player blows very softly, there is essentially no other component present in the vibration as it is measured in the mouthpiece, and that as he plays louder the amplitude of the second harmonic grows in such a way that for every doubling of the strength of the fundamental as the player blows harder, the strength of the second harmonic quadruples. Furthermore, the strength of this component proves to be approximately proportional to the impedance of the air column at the frequency of the second harmonic. Similarly, the third harmonic has a strength that is proportional to the impedance at the third-harmonic frequency, and from an even tinier beginning it grows eightfold for every doubling of the strength of the fundamental component. In short, the $n$th harmonic has a strength that is proportional to the impedance at the $n$th harmonic of the playing note, and that component grows as the $n$th power of the fundamental pressure amplitude. The remarkable thing about Worman's observation is that it is totally independent of all details of the flow-control properties of the reed or the lips, provided only that the flow is controlled solely by the pressure variations in the mouthpiece [*see top illustration on page 34*].

Let me summarize what we have found out so far about how the tone

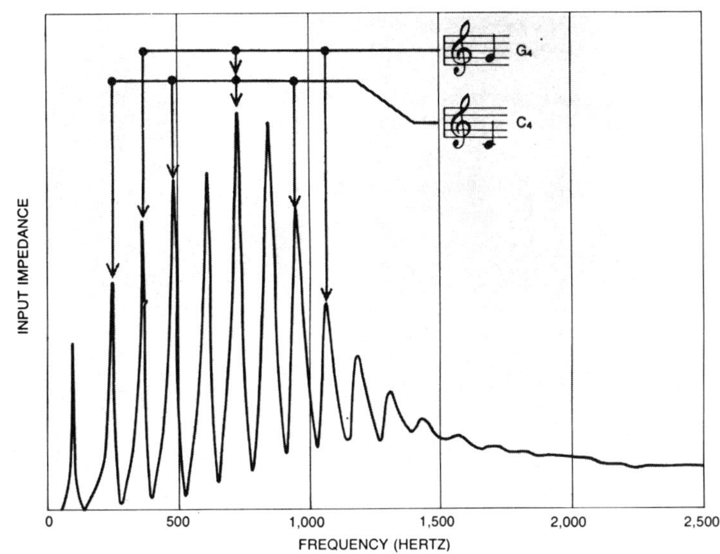


**IMPEDANCE PATTERN OF A MODERN TRUMPET** is annotated to show what happens when a player sounds the notes $C_4$ or $G_4$. When he blows into the horn, a "regime of oscillation" is set up in which several impedance maxima of the air column collaborate with oscillations of his lips to generate energy in a steady oscillation that contains several harmonically related frequency components. The regime of oscillation for the $C_4$ note involves the second, fourth, sixth and eighth peaks in the curve. When the trumpeter plays very softly, the second peak is dominant, but because this peak is not tall the beginner may produce a wobbly note. As he plays louder the other peaks become more influential and the oscillation becomes stabilized. The dominant oscillation for the $G_4$ note corresponds to the third impedance peak; since it is taller than the second peak, $G_4$ is easier than $C_4$ to play pianissimo. As the trumpeter plays louder the tall sixth peak comes in and greatly stabilizes the regime of oscillation, making the $G_4$ one of the easiest notes of all to play.

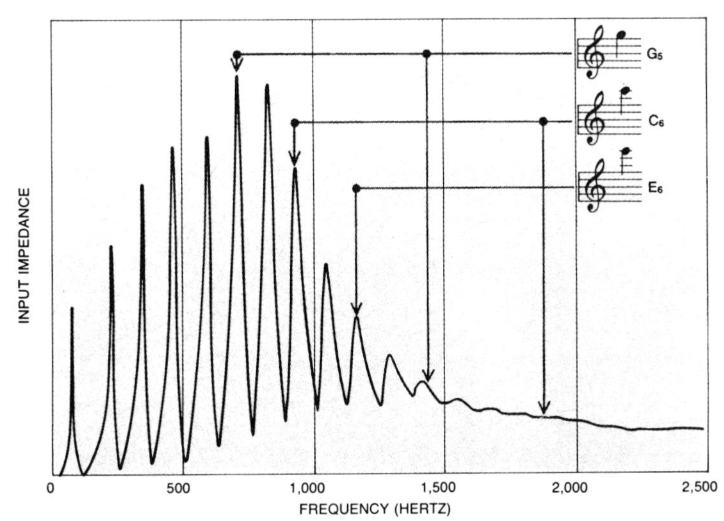


**REGIMES OF OSCILLATION FOR HIGHER NOTES** show why they become increasingly hard to play as one moves up the scale. $G_5$ is still quite easy to play because its regime of oscillation is dominated by the tall sixth impedance peak; the 12th peak makes only a minor contribution. $C_6$ is somewhat more difficult to play because the dominant peak of the note is lower than the peak for $G_5$. It takes an athletic trumpeter to reach the high $E_6$ and higher notes. The trumpet at this point has become virtually a megaphone: the energy production of the instrument is due almost completely to the interaction of the air column with the lips themselves, much as the human larynx operates in producing vocal sounds.

quality develops as measured inside the mouthpiece of the brass instruments. When one plays very softly, only the fundamental component associated with the playing frequency is present. As one plays louder the second, third, fourth and still higher harmonics grow progressively. If the oscillation is in the nature of a regime involving several cooperating resonance peaks, the harmonics grow in the simple fashion described by Worman's theorem; it is only at very loud playing levels that his theorem fails to give simple results. Furthermore, the theorem shows that the strength of the various components is proportional to the height of the various impedance maxima that are cooperating to generate the tone. In other words, when one plays rather loud, the strengths of the various harmonics have heights that correspond roughly to the heights of the impedance maxima from which they draw their chief sustenance. On the other hand, when a tone is generated on the basis of only a single resonance peak, as is the case in the upper part of the trumpet's range, we would be able to describe the strength of the components only if we could specify all the details of the flow-control characteristic.

Up to this point I have been discussing only the strength of the various harmonics as they are measured by a small probe microphone inside the brass instrument's mouthpiece cup. What one hears in the concert hall is, of course, very different. The transformation from the spectrum generated inside the mouthpiece, where the actual dynamics of the oscillation are taking place, into the spectrum found in the concert hall has to do with the transmission of sound from the mouthpiece into the main air column and thence out through the bell. There are many facets to the total transmission process, even without taking into account the complexities of room acoustics or the complications of our perceptual mechanism, which does a remarkable job of processing the great irregularity of room properties to give us clear-cut, definite impressions of the tone quality of musical instruments. I shall only remark that the transformation of the spectrum inside the mouthpiece to the external spectrum has the general nature of a treble boost. In other words, whatever sounds may be generated inside the instrument, it is the higher components that are radiated into the room [*see bottom illustration on page 34*].

The very fact that the bell of an instrument leaks energy preferentially at high frequencies has two important consequences. On the one hand the leakage enhances the relative amount of high-frequency energy that comes out of the horn; on the other it serves to reduce the height of the impedance peaks at high frequencies that lead to the weak generation of the high-frequency part of the spectrum inside the instrument. As a result measurements made outside the instrument in a room do not show nearly as much instructive detail about the dynamics of the entire system as measurements made inside the instrument do.

Let me conclude this discussion of the physics of brass instruments by indicating some of its implications for the musician and the instrument maker. As an illustration of the way physics can help the musician, I shall quote from an article of mine that appeared recently in the magazine *Selmer Bandwagon*. In this passage it was my intention to help French-horn players clarify and systematize their technique of placing one hand in the bell of the instrument to enhance certain frequencies.

"The player's hand in the bell is, acoustically speaking, a part of the bell. ... A properly placed hand provides... resonance peaks out to 1,500 hertz on an instrument that otherwise would lose all visible peaks at about 750 hertz [*see illustration on page* 35]. Suppose you meet a totally unfamiliar horn (perhaps during a museum visit when the curator opens the display cases) and you wish to find out quickly how well the instrument plays. Blow a mid-range note (for example concert $F_3$ in the bass clef) and, keeping your hand absolutely flat and straight, push it into the bell little by little until you feel a slight tingle in your fingertips. At this point (keeping the hand always perfectly straight) move the hand in and out a little until the horn sings as clearly as possible and the oscillation feels secure to your lips. Any listening bystander will agree with your final choice. Keep your hand in this slightly strained position and blow a tone an octave or a twelfth above the first one (say concert $F_4$ or $C_5$). Keeping your fingertips always in their original position, bend the palm of your hand so that its heel moves toward a position more familiar to the horn player. As you do so the tone will again fill out and get a ringing quality to it; also your lips will vibrate with a more solid feel. Your hand will now be in an excellent position for playing all notes on this horn, although an expert will be able to do even better after careful practice.

"Moving your straightened hand in and out while sounding the low *F* allows you to arrange to have an accurately located second helper for the tone. The unstopped horn works somewhat like a trumpet playing $G_5$ above the staff, while putting in the flattened hand serves to set up a regime that is analogous to the one which runs the trumpet's midstaff $C_5$. Bending the palm of one's hand while keeping the fingertips in place will leave the resonance peaks adjusted so far pretty much intact, but will make them taller (and hence more influential). This also gives rise to more peaks at the high-frequency end of things. The frequencies of these peaks move as the hand is bent more, so that once again the player has a means for tuning them for optimum cooperation with the other members of the regime. Trumpet players sometimes find it interesting and technically worthwhile to adapt the horn player's hand technique for their own purposes—especially for playing high passages on a piccolo trumpet."

It is only in the past few years that we have begun to have an understanding of the acoustics of mouthpieces. William Cardwell of Whittier, Calif., has provided a good theoretical basis for dealing with the relation of the mouthpiece dimensions to the tuning of the various resonance peaks. We in Cleveland, with the help of George McCracken of the King Musical Instrument Division of the Seeburg Corporation, have given attention to how the mouthpiece design controls the height of the impedance peaks. I quote again from the article for musicians to indicate the practical implications of mouthpiece acoustics.

"Acoustical theory tells us that, first and foremost, a given instrument will require that the mouthpiece have a certain well-defined 'popping frequency' when its cup is slapped shut against the palm of the hand. In other words, the lowest natural frequency of the mouthpiece alone (with the cup closed) must be of the correct value. It is this requirement

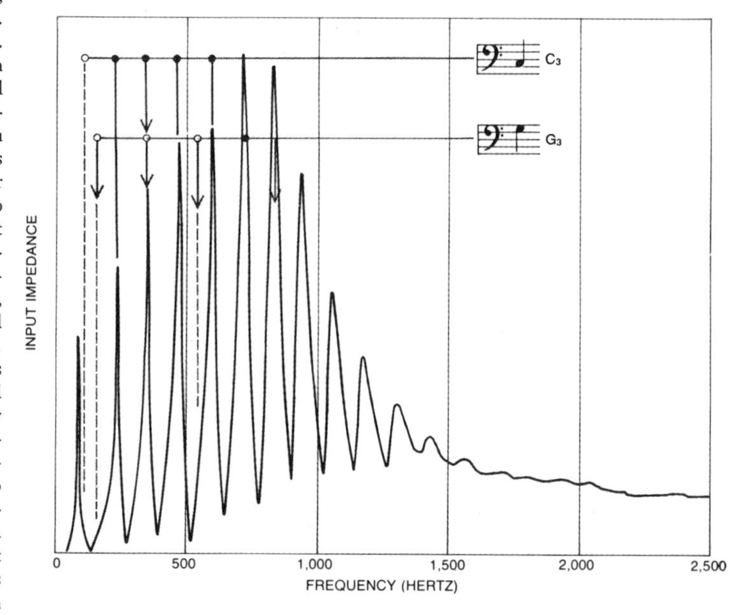


**UNUSUAL REGIMES OF OSCILLATION** are associated with notes whose frequencies correspond to impedances that are close to minimum values. The note $C_3$ in the bass clef is known to musicians as the pedal tone. Its regime of oscillation is such that the second, third and fourth resonance peaks of the trumpet sustain an oscillation that lies at a frequency equal to the common difference between their own natural frequencies. Since there is actually a loss of energy at the fundamental playing frequency for this note rather than a gain, there is only a small amount of fundamental component in the sound, and even the small quantity present is converted to that frequency from the higher components by way of the nonlinearity in the flow-control characteristics of the player's lips. The situation for $G_3$ is even more unusual in that the second and fourth components of the tone are the chief source of oscillatory energy, whereas the fundamental component and the other odd harmonics contribute virtually nothing since the impedance is minimal at their frequencies.

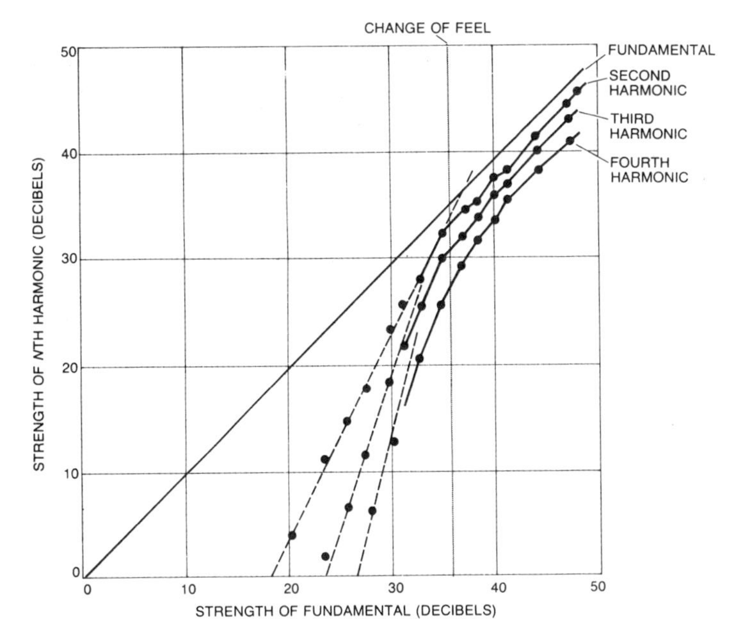


**TONE COLOR OF TRUMPET** is related to the way harmonic frequencies make up an increasing fraction of the total sound emitted as the player blows louder. The strengths of the various harmonic components are plotted as a logarithmic scale (decibels) against the logarithm of the strength of the fundamental component. At low and medium playing levels each harmonic lies on a straight line whose slope is approximately equal to the serial number of the harmonic. As one plays pianissimo essentially no harmonics are present in the vibration as measured in the mouthpiece. For every doubling in strength of the fundamental component the second harmonic increases from an initial tiny value by a factor of four. Similarly, the third harmonic increases in strength by a factor of eight for each doubling in strength of the fundamental, and so on. This finding corresponds to a theory developed by Walter Worman at Case Western Reserve University. At the loudness where Worman's relation begins to break down the player senses a change in "feel" and listeners are aware of a change in sound. The data that are reflected in the curves were obtained with the help of Charles Schlueter, who now plays principal trumpet in the Minnesota Orchestra.

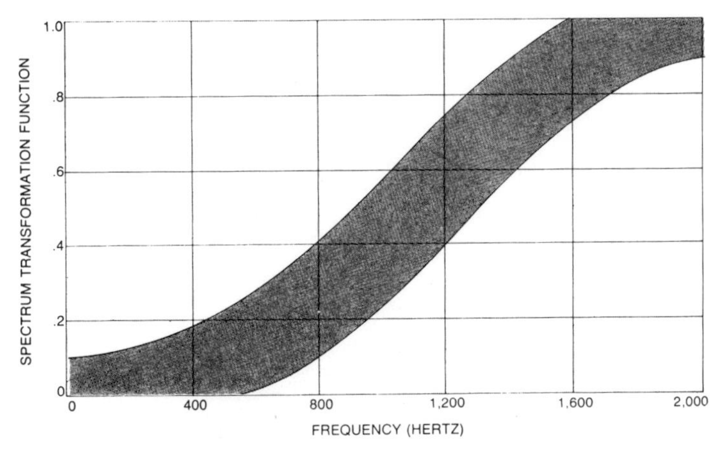


**TRANSMISSION OF TRUMPET SOUND INTO ROOM** is characterized by the "spectrum transformation function," which indicates what fraction of the acoustic energy at each frequency, as measured inside the mouthpiece, is emitted from the bell. Depending on the level of play and characteristics of the instrument, the energy emitted usually falls within the band plotted here. The curve has the qualitative nature of a "treble boost" because the bell leaks energy preferentially at high frequencies. Numbers on vertical scale are arbitrary.

that determines which of the peaks in the trumpet's response curve are the tallest. It also helps the peaks in this region to have the proper frequencies for good cooperation with the low-note regimes. The second most stringent requirement on the mouthpiece is that its total volume be correct (cup plus backbore). We must have this volume right in order to make the bottom two or three regimes of oscillation work properly."

So far I have discussed only the factors that contribute to favorable oscillation inside the horn and have said nothing about the tuning of instruments in the musician's sense: the relation between the pitches of the various tones that the instrument will generate. Fortunately the requirements for good tuning are almost identical with the requirements for favorable oscillation. It is for this reason that the traditional musical-instrument maker, focusing the major part of his attention on the tuning of the notes of the instrument, was able to develop instruments that would "speak" well and have good tone.

In more recent years, as our knowledge of acoustics has grown and the computer has become available, efforts have been made to design good brass instruments with the computer's help. Here the influence of loudspeaker acoustics has been great. Substantial efforts have been made to mathematically piece together a sequence of short loudspeaker-horn segments, each one intended locally to represent the shape of a workable brass instrument. This segmental approach to the problem has certain computational advantages. As we have seen, wherever the bore of a horn has a discontinuity of angle or of cross section there are anomalies in the standing-wave pattern. In spite of this fact it is always possible in principle to find suitable angles and cross sections that will place the impedance maxima of the horn with an accuracy that is acceptable by tuning standards. Although instruments built in this manner may play fairly well in tune, they can be quite disappointing in their musical value because of the neglect of the more subtle cooperative phenomena that ultimately distinguish between mediocrity and genuine excellence. Furthermore, the ability of an instrument to speak promptly and cleanly at the beginning of a tone is extremely sensitive to the presence of discontinuities, so that even though these discontinuities are arranged to offset one another in such a way as to give an excellent steady tone, it does not follow that the instrument starts well. The musician must of course have a "clean attack" as well as a clear, steady tone.

The skillful instrument maker gradually acquires an almost instinctive feel for the subtleties of instruments, so that he can sometimes be astonishingly quick in the use of his empirical store of knowledge to find a correct solution to a tuning or response problem. Consider the problem that such a person must solve when he is asked to correct a trumpet that is faulty, with the sole error being the behavior of the tone corresponding to $C_4$. Let us suppose that the problem is caused by the fourth impedance peak (beginning from the peak of lowest frequency), which is somewhat high in its frequency. When the $C_4$ is played at a pianissimo level, the note will be in tune, but as the loudness increases somewhat the note will tend to run a little sharp as the second member of the regime (the mistuned fourth peak) begins to show its influence. The player will also notice that he can "lip" the tone up and down over a considerable range in pitch without appreciable change in tone color. He will complain that at this moderate dynamic level the tone "lacks center." If he plays louder, the influence of the still properly tuned third and fourth members of the regime becomes strong enough to partly overcome the defect of the second member. When this occurs, the player finds that the tone once again acquires what he calls a core, or center, at a certain playing level, which happens then to fall pretty well back in tune because all but one of the resonances in the regime agree on the desired playing pitch.

In the practical world of the instrument maker or designer one often meets instruments in which one or more notes are "bad" in this way. It has often proved quite difficult to correct such problems with only instinct and experience. Once one understands what is going on, however, it is often possible to bypass laboratory measurements and diagnose the errors with the help of carefully designed "player's experiments." One then uses acoustical perturbation theory to guide the alteration of the shape of the air column to give a desired correction. Such corrections are made by enlarging or reducing the cross section of the bore in one region or more of the air column. The problem is complicated by the need to preserve the locations of the correctly tuned resonance peaks while the faulty peak is being moved.

Whether one is a physicist, a musician or an instrument maker, one tries to make use of any tools at hand to provide an instrument that helps rather than hinders the creative effort of music making. At first it would seem that the computer is ideally suited to be one of these tools and that it could immediately be put to work designing the perfect instrument. As a practical matter one finds that although we have a reasonable understanding of the goals to be achieved, the complexity of the problem is such that it is very difficult to specify the problem for the computer in sufficient detail. I have found that it is much more efficient to start with an already existing good instrument developed by traditional methods and then apply the physical understanding and the technical facilities available to us today to guide the improvement of the instrument, whether it is for an individual player in a symphony orchestra or for the development of a prototype for large-scale production.

In all my work I have found it always important to keep in constant touch both with professional players and with instrument makers. They provide an inexhaustible supply of information about the properties of instruments. They also are a source of questions that have proved enormously fruitful in guiding my investigations. As the subject continues to develop it is becoming increasingly possible for the results of formal acoustical research to be translated into useful information for the player and the instrument maker.

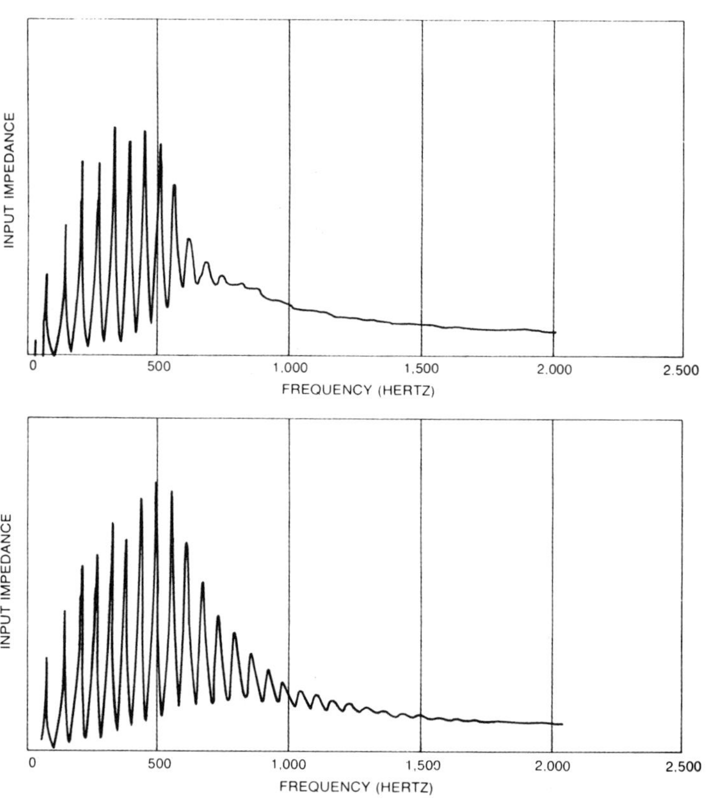


**PLACING HAND IN BELL OF FRENCH HORN** is a well-known technique for extending the frequency range of the instrument. The curve at the top shows the input impedance response of a valveless prototype for the *B*-flat half of a standard French horn when measured without the player's hand in the bell. There are essentially no resonance peaks above 750 hertz. If the player tries to reach a note such as $G_5$ (783 hertz), all he gets is a wobbly scream because there is little or no feedback of acoustic energy from the bell of the instrument to stabilize a note of higher frequency. Notes in the octave below $G_5$ would also be weak and characterless for lack of a strong feedback. The curve at the bottom shows the additional resonance peaks produced when the musician points his flattened hand into the bell until he feels a slight tingling at his fingertips and then bends his palm slightly. The instrument now produces peaks well beyond a frequency of 1,000 hertz, making it possible for the musician to play the note $G_5$ quite dependably and even a few higher notes when he is pressed.

# 12

Copyright © 1967 by the Acoustical Society of America

Reprinted from *J. Acoust. Soc. Am.*, **41**(4), Pt. 2, 1126–1146 (1967)

# Complete Solutions of the "Webster" Horn Equation

EDWARD EISNER

*Bell Telephone Laboratories, Inc., Murray Hill, New Jersey 07971*

Suppose that one solution of the "Webster" equation for any given horn is known, valid for particular boundary conditions and at one frequency. Expressions for the other linearly independent solution and for the derivatives of both solutions with respect to frequency are deduced and given in computable form. This allows the behavior of the horn for any loading, and in a wide range of frequencies, to be derived from a solution with one loading, at one frequency. The originally known solution may be computed, or experimental, or it may be the initial wavefunction in the inverse method of horn design (where the horn contour is derived from the initial wavefunction, which is constructed to satisfy the design requirements). With the new results, it is straightforward to compute the behavior of horns that were designed by the inverse method (for example, the "Terminated Gaussian" and the "Fourier") in conditions not envisaged in their design. Further, the inverse method can now be used to design new horns with specified characteristics at a number of loads (including dissipative loads) and frequencies. The impedances of horns are discussed in the light of the relation between the solutions of Webster's equation, with special reference to the ideal transformer. The general impedance relations are thereby considerably simplified. Some basic results of the theory of horns are briefly reviewed and an annotated bibliography of over 200 references is given. Attention is drawn to very important work on the horn equation and its solution—long before Webster—in particular to brilliant papers by Daniel Bernoulli, by Lagrange, and by Euler in the 18th century.

## INTRODUCTION

IN January 1945, W. P. Mason filed a patent application [*96*]* in which he described the use of an exponentially tapered solid rod to magnify the vibrational particle velocity of a resonant piezoelectric transducer. This invention and the very similar one made independently by Lozinskii and Rozenberg [*91*] in August 1949 have made ultrasonic processing practical, and have resulted in a sizable industry. Thus, interest in horn theory, which had been considered for loudspeakers first, was revived. The emphasis was on solid horns, often in or near resonance.

The propagation of longitudinal acoustic waves of small amplitude in thin, straight, tapered bars is governed by

$$\frac{\partial}{\partial x}\left[E\Sigma\frac{\partial\xi}{\partial x}\right]=\rho\Sigma\frac{\partial^2\xi}{\partial T^2}, \qquad (1a)$$

where $x$ is the length coordinate along the bar, $T$ is the time, $\xi(x,T)$ is the displacement of material (in the direction of $x$) from its equilibrium position, $E$ is Young's modulus, $\rho$ is density, and $\Sigma(x)$ is the cross-sectional area. The quantities $E$ and $\rho$ may be functions[a] of $x$, but for simplicity they are assumed to be constant in the rest of this paper. The modification of the main arguments for variation in material properties is fairly obvious.

The propagation of sound in an ideal fluid contained in a narrow, rigid tube is also governed by an equation of the form of Eq. 1a; so are the transverse vibrations of a completely flexible string under tension, when the mass per unit length of the string varies along its length ($E'=0=\Sigma'$ and $\rho$ is a function of $x$). These two problems were the earliest of the problems that are governed by Eq. 1a to receive mathematical attention. The history of that work is part of the wider story brilliantly told by Truesdell [*176a,b*].

Newton seems to have made only a qualitative remark on the speaking trumpet [*176b*, p. XXIII]. John II Bernoulli gave, but did not solve, a differential equation for the transverse vibration of a string of linearly varying diameter [*176b*, pp. XXX–XXXI]; but he then erroneously stated that this equation also

* Numbers in square brackets refer to the bibliography at the end of the paper, which is arranged alphabetically. When groups of numbers would be too long to be placed conveniently in the text, they are placed in footnotes, referred to in the text by lower-case superscript letters.

[a] Variable $\rho$, $E$ [*17, 19, 22, 27, 42c, d, 43, 46, 51, 54, 70, 90, 107, 121, 123, 138, 139, 158, 162, 170, 190*].

described the *longitudinal* vibrations of the string. It was probably Daniel Bernoulli [*9a*] who first derived the equation for the propagation of sound in a tube of arbitrarily variable section, and who solved it for a cone. He probably did this in the 1740's [*176b*, p. LVIII], but he did not publish until 1764. By that time, Lagrange had published [*84a*] a better derivation of the equation. Further, he had solved it formally for what we should now call "Bessel" horns ($\Sigma \propto x^m$), by an expansion in differential operators, a method that has been largely ignored for our problem [see, however, *168b*]. He obtained explicit solutions for the cone and the wedge. In the same monumental paper, he discussed the relation of this theory to the problem of the transverse vibration of a nonuniform string. The two problems were the subjects of several more papers by d'Alembert [see Ref. *176a*, p. 302], by Daniel Bernoulli [*9b*], and especially by Euler [*42–42f*]. While most of this work is interesting, Euler's papers [*42a*] and [*42d*] are masterpieces. They are milestones in the theory of differential equations and of mechanics. In [*42a*], Euler derived the equations for cylindrical and spherical sound waves, and solved them. According to Truesdell [*176b*, p. XLVII], these papers contain the first example of the solution of a partial differential equation by separation of variables. In Ref. *42d*, Euler gave the dynamical equation for sound of *finite* amplitude, in a fluid of nonuniform density, contained in a tube of arbitrarily varying (small) section, and he included the effect of gravity. He then discussed the solutions for infinitesimal amplitude, introducing first a most interesting method of finding the shape for which the solutions take a specified form that is not necessarily sinusoidal in time. He finished with a detailed treatment of the cone and of the hyperboloid ($\Sigma \propto x^{-2}$). Euler's papers are full of most interesting ideas that seem never to have been followed up.

After this rich harvest in the 18th century, our field seems to have been almost barren in the 19th. Duhamel [*29a*] gave a detailed treatment of the movement of air in cones and wedges, not restricted to small section. But there seem to have been only two works that dealt with arbitrary variation of cross section.

In 1837, George Green showed [*54*] that an equation like Eq. 1a governs the propagation of gravity-controlled water waves in tapered channels of small cross section. He solved the equation for very gradual, but arbitrary, taper. In our notation, with $E$ and $\rho$ constant, the solution is

$$\xi(x,T) = \Sigma^{-\frac{1}{4}} f_1(T - x/c) + \Sigma^{+\frac{1}{4}} f_2(T + x/c), \quad \text{(1aa)}$$

where $c = (E/\rho)^{\frac{1}{2}}$; it corresponds physically to there being no reflection from the taper. The rate of taper allowed by this approximation is too small for horns, but the method gives physical insight, and its result has been used as the starting point for more general discussions [e.g., Refs. *43*, *148*]. Other approximate solutions for small but arbitrary taper have also been given,[b] and a method used for the same problem in flexure [*128*] has its counterpart for longitudinal vibration.

Von Helmholtz [*62a*] considered short, noncylindrical tubes, smoothly joined to cylindrical tubes. He was concerned mainly with an essentially cylindrical musical instrument that has a mouthpiece or that is flared at the open end. He includes an inverse method. Equation 1a does not appear explicitly.

The next important papers in this branch of acoustics were those by Rayleigh (1916) [*168b*] and by Webster (1919) [*187*]. They independently deduced equations of essentially the same form as Eq. 1a. The analogous equation for the propagation of current on a nonuniform electric transmission line had, however, been published (and solved for some interesting cases) by Heaviside in 1892 [*62*] and (independently) by Rüdenberg in 1913 [*146*].

As a contribution to the theory of horns, Rayleigh's paper is much more interesting than Webster's. The fame of Webster's paper should rest on his introduction in it of the concept of acoustic impedance, and his application of it to certain horns. His deduction of Eq. 1a is not clear. In contrast, Rayleigh deduced the space-dependent part of Eq. 1a for harmonic excitation (Eq. 1c, below) from the three-dimensional equation for a gas. He used an expansion in differential operators, reminiscent of Lagrange's [*84a*]. While the convergence of this process is open to question, it does lead to higher-order approximations than Eq. 1c.

Equation 1a is usually called "Webster's horn equation," but we see that there is little justification for this name. Daniel Bernoulli, Euler, and Lagrange all derived the equation and did most interesting work on its solution, more than 150 years before Webster.

Not only does an equation like Eq. 1a describe the propagation of sound in fluids contained a nonuniform, *rigid* tube, but a similar equation applies when the tube is not rigid, as in the problem of the water hammer [*43*, *122*]. A similar equation also holds for torsional waves[c] in solid bars. The results of this paper apply to those cases, with appropriate changes in the meanings of the symbols.

Equation 1a is a good description of the wave propagation, if the bar is thin enough relative to the wavelength of the sound, if it is straight enough and does not taper too fast, and if the waves are of infinitesimal amplitude. The domain of applicability of the equation has been discussed for gas-filled horns[d] and for torsional vibrations in solids [*135*]. There is an extensive literature on the vibration of thick, *uniform* bars [e.g., *100*]; the limitations of one-dimensional theory for such

[b] Slow taper [*13, 17, 19, 23, 30, 50, 74, 82, 107, 133, 134, 191a, 194*].
[c] Torsion [*12, 33, 46, 56, 67, 77, 77a, 80, 94, 105, 115, 135, 155a, 156, 180, 190, 196*].
[d] Gas-filled horn [*4, 14, 15, 53, 57a, 58, 63, 66, 74, 86, 98, 110, 142–144a, 158, 164, 165, 168b, 175a, 188*].

bars have also been specifically discussed [*99, 161, 166, 172*]. Rayleigh's approximate method [*166*] of accounting for the effect of lateral motion ("Poisson contraction") on the frequencies of longitudinal resonance of fairly thin bars has been applied to horns [*101*]. Very recently, equations of motion have been derived for longitudinal waves in tapered bars, based on plane-wave models with Poisson contraction [*18, 95*] and with shear [*95*], and these have been applied to the cone. However, much remains to be done on this subject, as well as on the effects of departures from the nominal shape [*71, 100a, 167, 171*] and the nominal boundary conditions [*191*]. The limitation to small amplitude lies in changes of geometry as a result of vibrational deformation, and in the nonlinearity of elasticity[e]: terms of order $(\partial\xi/\partial x)^2$ and higher are neglected in the relation of force and $(\partial\xi/\partial x)$. These questions are not considered here and discussion is limited to the domain in which Eq. 1a does provide an adequate description. Practical experience suggests that this may be so for bars up to about a quarter of a wavelength in diameter for longitudinal vibrations, and even larger for torsional vibrations [*100, 135*], if the contour function is reasonably slowly varying. While Webster's equation, and therefore the formal treatment of this paper, is not restricted to horns in which there is no energy dissipation, only few published papers have dealt with such dissipation,[f] and I shall not consider it in detail here.

Assume sinusoidal motion of pulsatance $\omega$, and define

$$\xi(x,T)=u(x)e^{i\omega T}, \tag{1b}$$

where $u(x)$ will be called the amplitude of vibration. In general, $u(x)$ will be complex and its magnitude will be the maximum excursion during a cycle of material at $x$ from its equilibrium position, while its angle will be the number of radians by which its cycle of vibration leads $\omega T$. Equation 1a now reduces to

$$U''(X)+[A'(X)/A(X)]U'(X)+\Omega^2U(X)=0, \tag{1c}$$

where

$$U=u/l, \tag{2a}$$

$$X=x/l, \tag{2b}$$

$$A(X)=\Sigma(X)/\Sigma(0), \tag{2c}$$

$$\Omega=2\pi l/\lambda=\omega l/c=\omega l(\rho/E)^{\frac{1}{2}}, \tag{2d}$$

and $l$ is a reference length, which is taken to be the length of the bar (that is, the ends of the bar are at $X=0$ and $X=1$). Dissipation in the material of the bar is represented by complex $E$ and hence by complex $c$, $\lambda$, and $\Omega$. The real part of $(1/\lambda)$ is the reciprocal of the wavelength of longitudinal waves of frequency $(\omega/2\pi)$ in a thin, *uniform* bar of this material, while the imaginary part is the reciprocal of the distance in which the amplitude of such waves falls to $(1/e)$. Differentiation with respect to the independent variable (here $X$) is denoted by primes.

[e] Nonlinearity [*4, 10, 42c, d, 53, 98, 143, 144, 147a, 168a, 175b, 176*].

[f] Losses [*9, 124, 145, 154, 160, 174, 196*].

The problems represented by Webster's equation have been expressed in many different forms,[g] both to bring out different points of physical significance and to suggest methods of solution; but no solution giving $U(X)$ explicitly as a result of finite algebraic operations on $A$ and $\Omega$ is known.* However, the complete solutions for many specific forms of $A(X)$ are known: cylindrical [*166*]; conical[h] $[A\propto(X_0+X)^2]$; exponential[i] $(A\propto e^{kX})$; catenoidal[j] $(A\propto\cosh^2kX)$; "hypex"[k] $[A\propto(\cosh kX+\alpha\sinh kX)^2]$; "Bessel"[l] $[A\propto(X_0+X)^n]$; Gaussian[m] $[A\propto\exp(-kX^2)]$; trigonometric[n] $[A\propto(\cos kX+\alpha\sin kX)^2]$; and several other functions.[o] (There are also some cases for which solutions of the exact, three-dimensional wave equations are known.[p]) Some of the horns for which solutions are known may be regarded as members of more-general families.[q] Complete solutions are also known, of course, for horns that are built up of sections of horns for which complete solutions are known.[r] Principles of duality [*42d, 136*] allow the solutions for some further shapes to be deduced from known solutions (see also the end of Sec. I).

(Since Eq. 1c can be transformed into the one-dimensional Schrödinger equation [e.g., *120, 127, 148, 178*], any distribution of mass for which the problem

[g] Transformations [*2, 6, 12, 13, 13a, 17, 22, 23, 43, 45a, 46a, 50, 62, 65, 66, 67, 69, 72, 74, 75, 76, 77a, 84, 90, 90a, 97, 98a, 103, 104, 119–123, 126, 127, 129, 133, 138, 139, 144–148, 152, 153a–c, 157, 168b, c, 175a, 177, 178, 181, 185, 185a, 186, 190, 192, 194*].

* Rayleigh [*168b*] suggested that a more accurate equation than Eq. 1c (for an ideal fluid in a rigid tube) was $U''+(A'/A)U'+\Omega^2(1-\frac{1}{2}rr'')U=0$, where $r(x)\equiv A^{\frac{1}{2}}$ is the profile function. He then supposed the taper to be sufficiently gradual to allow Green's approximation (Eq. 1aa, above) to be used in evaluating $U$ for use in the term $\frac{1}{2}\Omega^2rr''U$. This allowed him to give an explicit expression for $U$. The method does not seem to have been followed up. Many other examples of explicit expressions resulting from some restrictive assumption are known, of which the outstanding example is in the "WKBJ method" [*111*, Pt. 2, Sec. 9.3, esp. pp. 1092–1105]. Since Eq. 1c itself does not represent the motion exactly, the results given by such approximate methods of solving this equation may sometimes represent the physical processes as well as would an exact solution of Eq. 1c.

[h] Cone [*5, 9a, 13a, 14, 18, 25, 26, 29a, 34, 41, 44, 46, 52, 55, 57a, 61, 63, 64, 68, 70, 77, 84a, 87, 91, 95, 98, 101, 104, 114, 125, 137, 145, 165, 173, 182, 187, 195*].

[i] Exponential [*1, 3, 16, 26, 31a, 38, 52, 53, 55, 57a, 61, 66, 73, 76, 81, 91, 96, 98, 98a, 101, 105, 109, 112, 113a, 114, 115, 118, 124, 131, 135, 143–145, 146a, 147a, 160, 163, 173, 175b, 185, 185a, 187, 189, 195*].

[j] Catenoidal [*88, 101, 114, 169, 173, 175*].

[k] "Hypex" [*77, 104, 108, 149, 154, 169a, 180*].

[l] "Bessel" [*4, 8a, 24, 31a, 45, 49, 55, 56, 57a, 60, 62, 84a, 91, 92, 98, 104, 116, 155a, 156, 162, 163, 180, 184, 185a, 187, 193*].

[m] Gaussian [*11, 13, 38, 115, 120, 127, 187, 195*].

[n] Trigonometric [*77, 104, 127, 180*].

[o] Other shapes [*9a, 13, 23, 29, 42b, d, f, 80, 82 83, 86, 100a, 112, 127, 146, 147, 155, 191a, 194*].

[p] Exact solutions [*5, 14, 20, 21, 42a, 48, 63, 85, 132, 135, 144a, 150, 155a, 168*].

[q] Families of shapes [*9a, 42b, d, f, 49, 77, 97, 120a, 127, 148, 153c, 169a*].

[r] Composite [*3, 7, 9a, 14, 44, 55, 56, 65, 68, 76, 78, 79, 84, 92, 102, 114, 117, 132a, 159, 173, 183*].

of the nonuniform string can be solved must correspond to a family of horn profiles for which the solution of Eq. 1c follows. Many solutions of the string problem are known [see, e.g., *41a*, *42*, *171*, *176a*], but the transition to a horn profile involves the solution of a second-order differential equation that may be no more tractable than Webster's. The same remarks apply to some of the simpler problems in the theory of the propagation of waves in layered media [*13b*] and in wave mechanics [*153a*]. There is also a correspondence [*126*] with the Gaussian approximation of the problem of the electrostatic electron lens [*57*]. Since the solutions in these fields do not seem to have been transformed into solutions applicable to acoustic horns, detailed references are not given in the present bibliography.)

For any such horn, the wavefunction $U(X)$ can be expressed as the sum of two linearly independent, explicit functions of $X$ and $\Omega$. Therefore, the behavior of such a horn can be calculated for any frequency and for any consistent boundary conditions.

But, there are important cases where only *one* wavefunction, valid possibly for only one frequency and one pair of boundary conditions, is known. For instance, the distribution of amplitude in a horn may be found experimentally at one frequency under, say, free–free conditions, where experiments with a different boundary condition may be difficult and experiments at other frequencies very time-consuming. Further, there are horns that have been designed by the inverse method [*35, 38, 39*], such as the "Fourier" [*32, 33*], the "Terminated Gaussian" [*35, 38, 39*], and the "polynomial" [*37*]: for these, only one solution of the Webster equation is known.

When a horn is of one of the shapes for which the complete solution of the Webster equation is known, it will not usually satisfy all the requirements that one may have, even though these requirements may not be inconsistent with each other when general shapes are allowed. For instance, if a free, solid, longitudinally resonant exponential horn were required with a "magnification" (ratio between end amplitudes) of 100, it would be so slender [*32*] that it could hardly be made, and would, if made, be very subject to flexural vibration, and of little use as a tool. On the other hand, a "stepped" vibrator [*3*] would be much stiffer in bending, but would fail in fatigue [*38, 39*] at a much lower amplitude of vibration than the exponential. In the inverse method of design [*35, 38, 39*], the required characteristics are written into a wavefunction, and the corresponding shape function is then derived by integration. Thus, the "Fourier" vibrator [*32, 33*] was designed to give high magnification with reasonable flexural stiffness and reasonable resistance to overstraining; the "Terminated Gaussian" [*38, 39*] was designed to give extremely high amplitude of particle velocity for given maximum strain, while retaining the possibility of a range of magnifications; the "polynomial" [*37*] design was used to investigate the limits ***in principle*** to the particle velocities attainable.

In the inverse method of design, as hitherto described, the vibrational properties of a horn are specified when it is loaded at a particular frequency so that there is no net energy flow across its ends. A (real) wavefunction $U(X)$, of arbitrary form, is then constructed to satisfy the prescribed conditions. Equation 1c may be inverted to give

$$(d/dX)(\ln A) = -[U''(X)+\Omega^2 U(X)]/U'(X). \quad \text{(1d)}$$

The wavefunction $U(X)$ that has been constructed to meet the prescription is inserted into the righthand side of Eq. 1d and a single quadrature yields the shape function $A(X)$ for a horn with the prescribed characteristics. $U(X)$ may contain free parameters so that the properties of the shape function may also be adjusted to meet prescribed conditions or to make optimizations or compromises. The quantity $\Omega$ may also be a free parameter (this means that, at a given frequency, with a given material, the length of the vibrator is a parameter).

Thus, a shape function is derived from a certain wavefunction $U(X)$ and a certain value $\Omega=\Omega_0$ of the frequency parameter, which have been chosen to satisfy prescribed conditions. A different set of conditions, or a different $\Omega$, leads to a different shape of vibrator. Thus, when a vibrator has been designed by the inverse method, the single wavefunction available describes the behavior of the vibrator only at the frequency and under the boundary conditions for which it was designed. It is not immediately possible, therefore, to predict the behavior of such a vibrator at any other frequency, nor at any other loading (and, in particular, not for "power" loading).

Suppose that one wavefunction, valid at one frequency and for one set of boundary conditions, is known. It is the purpose of this paper to show that the behavior for other boundary conditions, and for a range of frequencies, can be deduced. In this sense, complete solutions of the Webster equation can be found.

### I. THE SECOND SOLUTION

It can be shown [*111*, Pt. 1, Sec. 5.2] that, if $U_a(X)$ is known to be a solution of the equation

$$U''(X)+p(X)U'(X)+q(X)U(X)=0, \quad \text{(3a)}$$

then the complete solution is

$$U(X)=\alpha_0 U_a(X)\int\frac{dX}{U_a^2(X)F(X)}, \quad \text{(3b)}$$

where

$$F(X)=\exp\left[\int p(X)dX\right] \quad \text{(3c)}$$

and $\alpha_0$ is an arbitrary constant. Clearly, Webster's

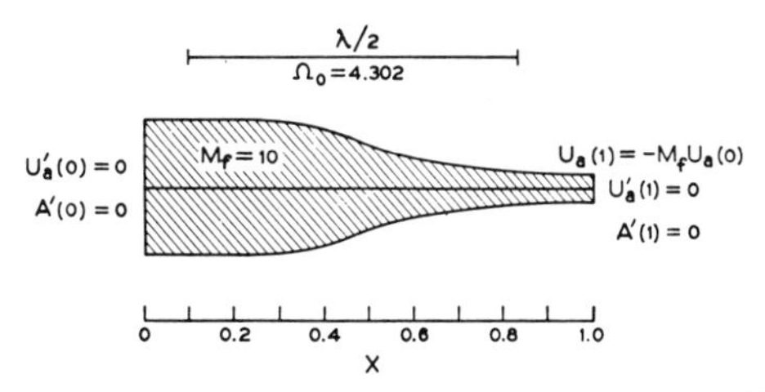


FIG. 1. Profile of the Fourier longitudinal vibrator with magnification 10 (see Fig. 2). The end conditions used in the design are shown.

equation is of the same type as Eq. 3a, and it follows that, if $U_a(X)$ is known to be a solution of Eq. 1c, then the complete solution is

$$U(X)=\alpha U_a(X)+\beta U_b(X), \tag{4a}$$

where

$$U_b(X)=U_a(X)\int_0^X \frac{dt}{A(t)U_a^2(t)}. \tag{4b}$$

This is one of the two basic results of this paper. It means that if one solution of Webster's equation is known, then the complete solution can be deduced. A single quadrature is all that is required. With $U_a$ and $U_b$ both available, the wavefunction with boundary conditions other than those to which $U_a$ applies can be calculated.

By definition, $U_b(0)=0$ if $U_a(0)\neq 0$. If $U_a(0)=0$, the lower limit of integration in Eq. 4b—which is arbitrary since it merely adds to the constant $\alpha$—is best moved to some other point. However, to make the rest of the discussion definite, we exclude those $U_a(X)$ for which $U_a(0)=0$.

If $\Omega$ is real—that is, if the material is nondissipative—and if $U_a(X)$ is complex, then the real and imaginary parts of $U_a(X)$ must *both* be solutions of Webster's equation. Therefore, either the imaginary part is merely constant times the real part—which is trivially different from real $U_a(X)$, since it means no more than a shift in the origin of time—or the real and imaginary parts are two linearly independent solutions. In the latter case, we essentially already have the general solution, and Eqs. 4 yield nothing new. Thus, although the subsequent analysis is valid for complex $U_a$ and $U_b$, this is not more general than real $U_a$ and $U_b$ for lossless materials. In practice, therefore, $U_a$, $U_b$ may be thought of as real solutions, each corresponding to a pure standing wave. Traveling waves are represented by their superposition with complex $\beta/\alpha$.

Computation of the integral in Eq. 4b is not entirely straightforward since $U_a$ will usually have a zero in range. The solution of this problem is given in Appendix A.

As an example, we may consider the "Fourier" vibrator of free–free magnification $M_f=10$ (see Fig. 1). Fourier vibrators were designed [*32*] to have the following vibrational characteristics: (a) to be strainfree at the ends—i.e., $U_a'(0)=U_a'(1)=0$; (b) to have zero surface slope at the ends—i.e., $A'(0)=A'(1)=0$; (c) to have specified magnification at the lowest frequency for free–free resonance—i.e., $U_a(1)=-M_fU_a(0)$; (d) to have low maximum strain for given particle velocity at the thin end; (e) to have the highest-possible static flexural stiffness consistent with the aforesaid conditions. It can readily be shown that, if Conditions (a) hold, then for Conditions (b) to be satisfied it is necessary and sufficient that $U_a''(0)+\Omega_f^2U_a(0)=U_a''(1)+\Omega_f^2U_a(1)=0$ *and* $U_a'''(0)=U_a'''(1)=0$ (where $\Omega=\Omega_f$ at the lowest free-free resonance). Thus, Conditions (a)–(d) are constraints on the wavefunction $U_a(X)$ (and its derivatives) only, and can be applied before the integration of Eq. 1d is carried out. A fourth-order Fourier cosine series was chosen for $U_a(X)$ and Conditions (a)–(c) provided algebraic relations among its coefficients. The two remaining free coefficients were given values by numerically satisfying Conditions (d) and (e). Tables of $U_a(X)$ and of the resulting shape functions $[A(X)]^{\frac{1}{2}}$ have been published in Ref. *32* for a number of values of $M_f$. For $M_f=10$, $U_a(X)$ is shown in Fig. 2. The strain $U_a'(X)$ is shown in Fig. 3(a); note that it is zero at the ends of the vibrator, as required.

In Fig. 2 is also shown the second independent solution $U_b(X)$, obtained by means of Eq. 4b, using the $U_a(X)$ of Fig. 2 and the shape function $A(X)$ for the vibrator of Fig. 1. The two functions shown in Fig. 2 for this Fourier vibrator correspond to $U_a=\cos\pi X$, $U_b=(1/\pi)\sin\pi X$ for a uniform bar, or to

$$U_a=e^{\gamma X}[\cos\pi X-(\gamma/\pi)\sin\pi X],$$
$$U_b=(1/\pi)[1+(\gamma^2/\pi^2)]e^{\gamma X}\sin\pi X$$

for an exponential vibrator with $A=e^{-2\gamma X}$.

R. W. Pyle* has suggested an interesting way in which the possibility of deducing the second solution of a second-order differential equation by means of Eqs. 3 could lead to new contours for which complete solutions of Webster's equation are available. Webster's equation can be transformed [*120, 127, 148, 178*] into the form of Schrödinger's equation, with $rU$ as the dependent variable and $(r''/r)$ as the "potential function," where $r(X)\equiv A^{\frac{1}{2}}(X)$ (i.e., the profile function). Given a profile for which $U(X)$, and hence $rU$, is known, a second-order differential equation for $r$ can be set up. The other solution of this differential equation is a new profile function, for which $rU$ must be the same function as before. The function $U(X)$ for the new profile is therefore also known. [Cf. Ref. *120a*.]

## II. USE OF THE COMPLETE SOLUTION: IMPEDANCES

The most obvious use of the freedom now available is to determine what happens when the loading at one

* Private communication (1966).

end of the vibrator is changed from that represented by $U_a$ alone. For this, we may use impedances. Impedance relations have been given for many of the horns for which complete solutions are found in the literature[s]; there have also been more general discussions of the impedances of horns.[t] We shall examine the general impedance relations in the light of the relation (Eq. 4b) between the linearly independent solutions of Webster's equation.

It can readily be shown [see, e.g., Refs. *31* and *106*] that

$$U'(0)=B_{11}U'(1)+B_{12}U(1), \quad (5a)$$

$$U(0)=B_{21}U'(1)+B_{22}U(1), \quad (5b)$$

where $\|B\|$ is a property of the transmitter of sound between $X=0$ and $X=1$. In our case, this transmitter is a horn obeying Webster's equation [*31*]. This fact considerably simplifies the expressions for $\|B\|$.

The solution of Webster's equation can always be expressed with the linearly independent solutions related by Eq. 4b. (Near the end of the Sec. I, we saw that this is not always the most obvious form.) We may therefore use the facts that $U_b(0)=0$ and that (from Eq. 4b)

$$U_b'(X)=\frac{1}{U_a(X)}\left[U_a'(X)U_b(X)+\frac{1}{A(X)}\right]. \quad (4c)$$

This leads to the following simple expressions:

$$B_{11}=A(1)[U_a(1)/U_a(0)-U_a'(0)U_b(1)], \quad (5c)$$

$$B_{12}=A(1)[U_a'(0)U_b'(1)-U_a'(1)/U_a(0)], \quad (5d)$$

$$B_{21}=-A(1)U_a(0)U_b(1), \quad (5e)$$

and

$$B_{22}=A(1)U_a(0)U_b'(1). \quad (5f)$$

We have thus far assumed that the original solution $U_a(X)$ of Webster's equation is known for only one particular value $\Omega_0$ of the frequency parameter $\Omega$. The wavefunction $U_b(X)$, defined by Eq. 4b, is therefore also a solution only for $\Omega=\Omega_0$. However, in Sec. III it is shown how these solutions can be extended to other frequencies, in a very wide band, by perturbation. In Appendix B, it is shown that these new solutions are still related by Eq. 4b. Thus, Eqs. 4 and 5 apply at all frequencies, as long as $U_a$ and $U_b$ have been derived by the method of Sec. III from solutions related by Eq. 4b.

Equations 5 are very simple to compute with, since $A(1)$ is of course independent of frequency, and since there is no loss in generality in setting $U_a(0)=1$, if this is done consistently.

[If $U_a(X)$ is a solution for which the vibrator is free at $X=0$, then $U_a'(0)=0$ and the expressions for $B_{11}$ and $B_{12}$ simplify even further. From Eqs. 14 and 16, it can be seen that, if $U_a'(0)=0$ for $\Omega=\Omega_0$, then it is zero for all frequencies, if $U_a$ is extended by those equations. If $U_a$ is the solution for a free–free vibrator at $\Omega=\Omega_f$, then, in addition, $U_a'(1)=0$ and Eqs. 5c–5f become $B_{11}=A(1)U_a(1)/U_a(0)$, $B_{12}=0$, $B_{21}=-A(1)U_a(0)U_b(1)$, $B_{22}=U_a(0)/U_a(1)$; but *these* expressions are valid for $\Omega=\Omega_f$ only.]

[s] Special impedance relations [*16, 31, 57a, 73, 81, 93, 94, 102, 106, 109, 110, 146a, 154, 162, 169, 169a, 175, 187, 192, 195*].

[t] General impedance relations [*31, 106, 126, 130, 144, 153, 154, 187, 192, 194, 195*].

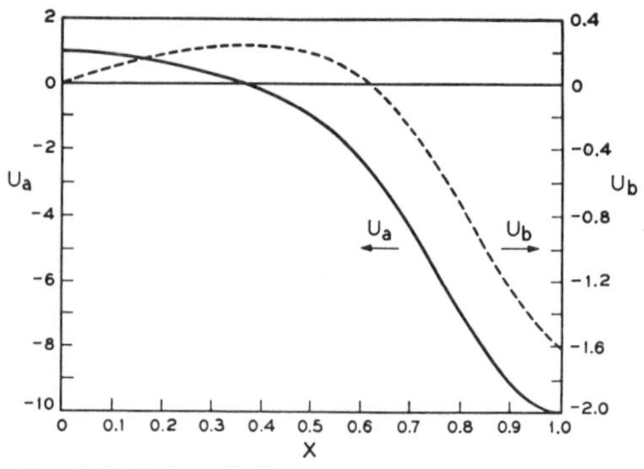


FIG. 2. Original amplitude function $U_a$ and the corresponding second solution $U_b$ of the Webster equation, as deduced from Eq. 4b. The function $U_a$ and its derivatives satisfy the required end conditions shown in Fig. 1, minimize the strain, and maximize the flexural rigidity. The profile in Fig. 1 was deduced from this $U_a(X)$.

Equations 5a–5f give the force [equal to $iE\Sigma(0)AU'$] and the particle velocity (equal to $c\Omega U$) at $X=0$ for given force and velocity at $X=1$. If the distribution of force or velocity is required (from Eq. 4a), then we need

$$\alpha=A(1)[U_b'(1)U(1)-U_b(1)U'(1)], \quad (6a)$$

$$\beta=A(1)[-U_a'(1)U(1)+U_a(1)U'(1)]. \quad (6b)$$

Thus, if $U(1)$ and $U'(1)$ are given, the state of vibration of the rod is completely defined. It is more usual, however, for $U'(1)/U(1)$ to be given in the form of a terminating impedance, so that only $\beta/\alpha$ can be found. While this leaves the magnitude of vibration amplitude undetermined, it permits the calculation of such properties as the positions of minimum vibration (for support) and of maximum strain, the magnification ($|U(1)/U(0)|$), and the figure of merit for ability to give large particle velocity ($\Omega|U|_{\text{MAX}}/|U'|_{\text{MAX}}$) [Refs. *38, 39, 115*].

Let us define impedance as

$$z=\frac{\text{AMPLITUDE OF FORCE}}{\text{AMPLITUDE OF VELOCITY}} \quad (7a)$$

and treat it as real when force and velocity are in phase. Then,

$$z=i(\Sigma EU'/\omega lU)=i(\rho c/\Omega)(\Sigma U'/U). \quad (7b)$$

($\rho c$ is the characteristic impedance of the material.) Let us now define a nondimensional impedance per unit

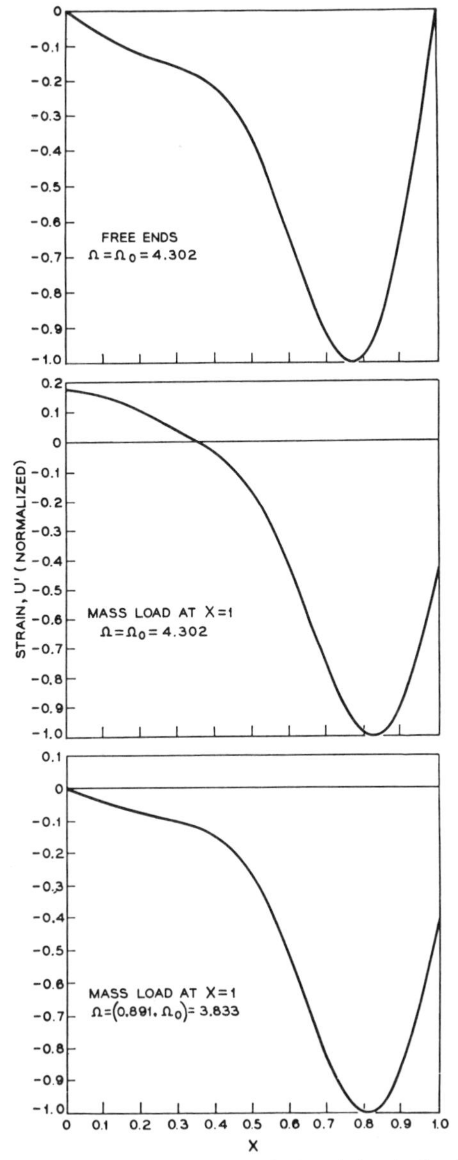


(a) With the ends free and the frequency parameter $\Omega$ equal to that used in the design. Thus, here $U'=U_{a0}'$.

(b) With a rigid mass equal to 1/165 of the mass of the vibrator attached at $X=1$ and the frequency still at the original frequency. The large intercept on the strain axis at $X=1$ shows the force exerted on the mass. A large force is also needed at $X=0$; and the vibrator could not be driven by a free–free resonant driver.

(c) The vibrator loaded as in Fig. 3(b), but with the frequency reduced by 10.9%. The vibrator is once again strainfree at $X=0$, and could be driven by a free–free driver resonant at this frequency.

FIG. 3. Normalized strain function for the vibrator in Fig. 1, under different conditions.

area:

$$Z=z/\Sigma\rho c=iU'/\Omega U. \tag{7c}$$

Suppose, now, that we load the bar at $X=1$ so that $Z(1)=Z_1$; then, using Eqs. 6a and 6b,

$$\frac{\beta}{\alpha}=-\frac{i\Omega Z_1U_a(1)+U_a'(1)}{i\Omega Z_1U_b(1)+U_b'(1)}. \tag{6c}$$

As an example, we may again consider the Fourier vibrator with $M_f=10$ (Fig. 1). If this is driven at the design frequency, with no load at $X=1$, the strain function is as shown in Fig. 3(a). If a rigid mass equal to $6.05\times10^{-3}$ of the mass of the vibrator is attached at $X=1$ and the vibrator is again driven at the same frequency, then $Z_1=0.314i$, $\beta/\alpha=51.7$ (real, because the load is nondissipative) and the strain function is as shown in Fig. 3(b). The large intercept on the $U'$ axis at $X=1$ shows the force exerted on the mass. There is now also a force required at $X=0$ and, if the vibrator is driven there by a transducer that is in free–free resonance at the design frequency, it will vibrate with only very small amplitude at this same frequency when loaded. If the vibrator is to be driven effectively with this load at this frequency, a new resonant transducer is needed that matches the impedance at $X=0$ (see below) at this frequency. If this transducer is of the type employed originally, it will be shorter than before.

This example illustrates the importance of calculating the impedance at $X=0$. From Eqs. 4,

$$-i\Omega Z(0)=\frac{U_a'(0)}{U_a(0)}+\frac{\beta}{\alpha}\frac{U_b'(0)}{U_a(0)} \quad (8a)$$

$$=\frac{U_a'(0)}{U_a(0)}+\frac{\beta}{\alpha}\cdot\frac{1}{U_a^2(0)} \quad (8b)$$

$$=\frac{B_{12}-i\Omega Z_1 B_{11}}{B_{22}-i\Omega Z_1 B_{21}}. \quad (8c)$$

### A. Ideal Transformers and Ideal Impedance Inverters

A horn is not just a general "2+2 pole" device, but has its properties restricted by the properties of Webster's equation and hence by the relation of Eq. 4b between the linearly independent solutions. This restriction has led to the relations that we have just derived. As examples of the application of these relations, we now consider the properties of ideal transformers and impedance inverters. As this is a digression, the reader not especially interested in this aspect of the properties of horns may wish to skip to Sec. III.

#### *1. Ideal Transformer*

In general, $Z(0)$ is not proportional to $Z(1)$, but it can readily be shown from Eqs. 6c and 8 that this *is* so if, and only if,

$$U_a'(0)U_b'(1)-U_a'(1)U_b'(0)=0 \quad (9a)$$

and

$$U_b(1)=0. \quad (9b)$$

[The latter condition is, more fully, $U_a(0)U_b(1)-U_a(1)U_b(0)=0$; but this reduces to Eq. 9b because we deliberately excluded $U_a(0)=0$ in Sec. I and have thus made $U_b(0)=0$. As can be seen from Eq. 8c, the two conditions are equivalent to $B_{12}=B_{21}=0$.] It can be shown that, as would be expected, the conditions of Eqs. 9a and 9b can be satisfied only if the material of the vibrator is lossless. These are the conditions that have to be satisfied if the horn is to behave like an ideal transformer. Even if a horn is of such a shape that these conditions can be satisfied, they will be satisfied only for a set of discrete eigenfrequencies. For the exponential horn, for instance, the conditions are satisfied, but only at the frequencies for which the horn is in free–free resonance.

If the conditions of Eqs. 9a and 9b are satisfied,

$$Z(0)=\frac{U_a(1)U_b'(0)}{U_a(0)U_b'(1)}Z_1, \quad (9c)$$

$$=A(1)\left[\frac{U_a(1)}{U_a(0)}\right]^2 Z_1. \quad (9d)$$

Note that this is true even if $U_a$ does not represent free–free resonance [$U_a'(0)=U_a'(1)=0$], as long as Eqs. 9a and 9b are satisfied. It can be shown that these results are consistent with conservation of energy.

If $\Omega_f$, $U_{af}$, and $M_f$ [equal to $-U_{af}(1)/U_{af}(0)$] are the frequency parameter, the wavefunction, and the magnification in free–free resonance, and if $U_{bf}$ is the corresponding complementary solution (Eq. 4b), then, at frequency $(c/2\pi l)\Omega_f$ only,

$$Z_f(0)=M_f^2A(1)Z_1[1+i\Omega_f Z_1 A(1)U_{af}(1)U_{bf}(1)]^{-1}. \quad (10)$$

Thus, at the frequency of free–free resonance, $Z_f(0)$ is approximately proportional to $Z_1$ *for any horn*, if

$$\Omega_f A(1)|U_{af}(1)U_{bf}(1)Z_1|\ll 1. \quad (11a)$$

It can be shown that, if $|Z_1|$ is small enough, then

$$\Omega_f A(1)\mathcal{R}(Z_1)\simeq \chi\Delta/M_f^2, \quad (12a)$$

where $\chi$ is a dimensionless constant of the order of unity. [For the stepped transformer (double cylinder) and for the uniform bar, $\chi=0.8$; for a complete cone, $\chi=1.6$; for an exponential transformer with $M_f=10$, $\chi=1.9$, while with $M_f=20$, $\chi=2.8$.] The quantity $\Delta$ is the logarithmic decrement of energy per cycle of the vibrator when it is free at $X=0$ and terminated in $Z_1$ at $X=1$. If the reactive part of $Z_1$ is like the impedance of a mass $\mu$, then

$$A(1)\mathcal{I}(Z_1)=\Omega_f\mu/\rho l\Sigma(0). \quad (12b)$$

The criterion of Inequality 11a then becomes

$$|U_{af}(1)U_{bf}(1)|\ll[(\chi\Delta/M_f^2)^2+\Omega_f^2\mu/\rho l\Sigma(0)]^{-\frac{1}{2}}. \quad (11b)$$

In operations such as ultrasonic welding and drilling, $\Delta$ could be of the order of $10^{-2}$ and $\mu/\rho l\Sigma(0)$ of the order of $10^{-4}$; $\Omega_f^2$ and $M_f$ would typically be of the order of 10. The condition of Inequality 11b therefore implies that, if we require $Z(0)$ to be approximately proportional to $Z_1$ throughout the working loads of devices used in such operations, then $|U_{af}(1)U_{bf}(1)|\ll 10^3$. This will not usually be a restrictive condition. If it is important that a vibrator behave like an ideal transformer, then we can use the inverse method to *design* a vibrator for which the inequality of Inequality 11a will be satisfied (see Sec. IV). Indeed, we can design it for $U_{bf}(1)=0$, when Eq. 9d will hold for *all* loads.

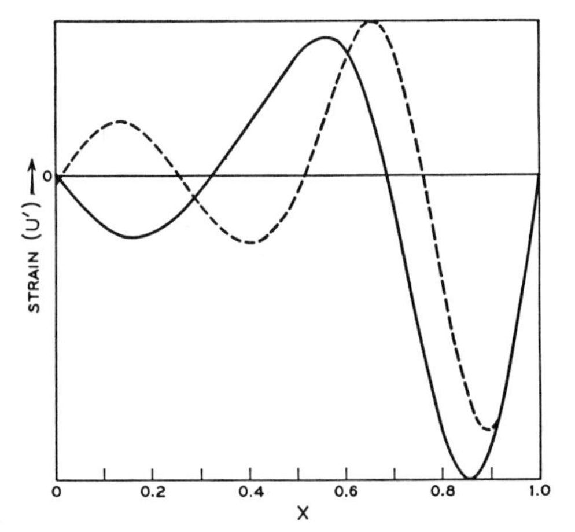


FIG. 4. Two examples, with the vibrator of Fig. 1, of strain distributions that can be handled by 20th-order perturbation computation. At $\Omega=9.679$ (——), the vibrator is in its third free–free resonance and the accuracy in strain is better than 0.01%. At $\Omega=12.91$ (- - -), the vibrator is near its fourth free–free resonance and the accuracy is still about 3%. These curves are obtained by perturbation of the functions in Fig. 2, using Eqs. 16 repetitively, with 100 intervals for all integrations.

### 2. *Ideal Impedance Inverter*

Another possibility that may be interesting also follows from Eqs. 6c and 8. If

$$U_a(0)U_a'(0)U_b(1)-U_a(1)=0 \tag{13a}$$

and

$$[1/U_a(1)][A(1)U_a'(1)U_b(1)+1]=0 \tag{13b}$$

(that is, $B_{11}=B_{22}=0$), then

$$Z(0)=-\frac{1}{\Omega^2}\cdot\frac{U_a'(1)}{U_a^2(0)U_b(1)}\cdot\frac{1}{Z_1}. \tag{13c}$$

The horn is an ideal impedance inverter—a small mass at $X=1$ will behave like a large mass or a strong spring at $X=0$, etc. Such devices are known in electrical theory and may have some uses in acoustics.

## III. CHANGE OF FREQUENCY

While the relations before Sec. II-A apply for any frequency for which $U_a$ is known to be a solution of Webster's equation for a given area function $A(X)$, there are cases, as discussed in the Introduction, when $U_a$ is known only for a particular frequency. When $A(X)$ has been obtained by the inverse method, $U_a(X)$ is generally known for only one $\Omega$; another $\Omega$ would yield a different $A(X)$. However, when we actually have a vibrator with given $A(X)$, it will not usually be enough to know its behavior under different boundary conditions: we will usually want to know what happens when we change the frequency. For instance, having put an end load onto a given horn, we have seen how we can calculate the impedance presented by this to the driver, at the original frequency. But then we will usually want to answer a question such as, "How must we now change the frequency to match the load to the driver; that is, how can we return to 'resonance'?"

It will be shown that this problem may be conveniently solved by perturbation, over a wide range of frequencies. There will usually be no need to resort to numerical solution of the differential equation.

Suppose that we know that $U_0(X)$ is a solution of Webster's equation (Eq. 1c) for the frequency parameter $\Omega=\Omega_0$. We now want to obtain the solution of

$$U''(X)+\frac{A'(X)}{A(X)}U'(X)+\Omega_0^2(1+\epsilon)U(X)=0, \tag{14a}$$

where $A(X)$ is the *same* as in Eq. 1c. We may then write the solution as

$$U(X)=U_0(X)+\epsilon U_1(X)+\epsilon^2U_2(X)+\cdots. \tag{14b}$$

Substituting in Eq. 14a and equating the coefficients of all powers of $\epsilon$ to zero, we obtain

$$U_0''+\frac{A'}{A}U_0'+\Omega_0^2U_0=0, \tag{15a}$$

$$U_1''+\frac{A'}{A}U_1'+\Omega_0^2U_1=-\Omega_0^2U_0, \tag{15b}$$

$$U_2''+\frac{A'}{A}U_2'+\Omega_0^2U_2=-\Omega_0^2U_1, \tag{15c}$$

etc. Equation 15a is just Webster's equation; it is satisfied since $U_0$ is defined as a solution of this equation. The remaining equations are inhomogeneous versions of the homogeneous equation (Webster's), the solution of which is already known. They can therefore be solved by the method of variation of parameters [*8*, Sec. 8, pp. 12–15].

By that method, it can be shown that, if we let

$$U_n=\alpha U_{an}(X)+\beta U_{bn}(X) \tag{16a}$$

[where $U_{a0}$, $U_{b0}$ are the solutions $U_a$, $U_b$ for $\Omega=\Omega_0$ (i.e., $\epsilon=0$)], then, for $n\geq 1$,

$$U_{an}(X)=\Omega_0^2\int_0^X P(X,t)U_{a(n-1)}(t)dt$$

and

$$U_{bn}(X)=\Omega_0^2\int_0^X P(X,t)U_{b(n-1)}(t)dt, \tag{16b}$$

where

$$P(X,t)=A(t)[U_{a0}(X)U_{b0}(t)-U_{b0}(X)U_{a0}(t)]. \tag{16c}$$

Thus, successive functions $U_{a1}$, $U_{a2}$, $U_{a3}$, etc., and $U_{b1}$, $U_{b2}$, $U_{b3}$, etc., can be determined by performing a given set of operations on the last functions computed, starting from the known $U_{a0}$, $U_{b0}$. Also, for the strain,

$$U_{an}'(X)=\Omega_0^2\int_0^X \frac{\partial P(X,t)}{\partial X}U_{a(n-1)}(t)dt$$

and (16d)

$$U_{bn}'(X)=\Omega_0^2\int_0^X \frac{\partial P(X,t)}{\partial X}U_{b(n-1)}(t)dt.$$

The functions that are combined in $P(X,t)$ and $\partial P/\partial X$ need be computed once only. All this is very convenient.

Equations 16 express the second basic result of this paper. By obtaining functions $U_1$, $U_2$, etc., in this way, we can extend the solutions of the form of Eqs. 4 to frequencies other than the original frequency for which $U_{a0}$ was specified. These new solutions can be used for instance in impedance calculations, just as the primary solutions were in Sec. II.

For an example, we return to the Fourier vibrator with $M_f=10$, loaded with a mass at $X=1$. At the design frequency $\Omega_0$, the strain function is shown in Fig. 3(b): there is considerable strain at $X=0$, so that the junction with a transducer would be quite highly stressed. The perturbation was carried to fourth order for a frequency 10.9% below the original frequency (i.e., $\epsilon=-0.206$); $U_a(X)$, $U_b(X)$, and $\beta/\alpha$ were computed, and hence the wavefunction $U(X)$ at the new frequency. The corresponding strain function is shown in Fig. 3(c), and we note that the strain now vanishes at $X=0$. Thus, by decreasing the frequency by 10.9%, the loaded transformer may again be driven at a stressfree boundary by a free–free resonant transducer. (This transducer could not be the same as that originally used. If the original combination of transducer and vibrator were loaded at $X=1$, the resonant frequency would change. The new resonance would be at the frequency at which the impedance at the driving face of the transducer equalled that of the vibrator at $X=0$. To compute this would be a minor extension of the present computation, but would require a knowledge of the properties of the transducer. The driving face would not in general be stressfree.)

It must be emphasized that the value of $\beta/\alpha$ is determined by the boundary condition, and must therefore be evaluated anew when $\epsilon$ is changed.

Because of the form of the Webster equation (Eq. 14a) and because $A'(X)/A(X)$ must be analytic (for $0\leq X\leq 1$) if Webster's equation is to describe the vibration, the infinite series of Eq. 14b converges for all $\epsilon$ [see Ref. *8*, p. 18 and Ref. *89*, p. 44]. Therefore, by using very-high-order $n$, the solutions $U(X)$ would in principle be good even for large $|\epsilon|$ (no computations have been made for $\epsilon\leq -1$, since this corresponds to zero or imaginary $\Omega$). The rate of convergence will depend on the functions $U_{a0}(X)$, $U_{b0}(X)$, but not very strongly. Since the computations were performed on a big, fast machine (IBM-7094 II), high-order perturbation computations presented no problem, and the largest value of $\epsilon$ that could be accommodated with a 20th-order computation was examined (the machine handles this, with 100 intervals in $X$, in under 1 sec). The computations were for a vibrator free at $X=1$ [i.e., $U'(1)=0$ or $Z(1)=0$]. The accuracy of the functions produced by the perturbation computation can be assessed by computing $[U''+(A'/A)U'+\Omega^2U]$ for each $X$ and comparing these numbers (which would be zero if the computation were perfect) with the largest of $|U''|$, $|(A'/A)U'|$, $|\Omega^2U|$. In Fig. 4, the strain functions are drawn for $\Omega=9.679$ (i.e., $\epsilon=4.07$) and $\Omega=12.91$ (i.e., $\epsilon=8.00$). At the first of these frequencies, the strain vanishes at $X=0$ and there are two zeros of strain between the ends: the vibrator is thus at its third free–free resonance. The error due to truncation of the series of Eq. 14b at the term in $\epsilon^{20}$ is still not detectable above the other errors of computation (probably mostly integration errors), which are smaller than one part in $10^4$. At $\Omega=12.91$, *three times* the original frequency, we see that the vibrator is near its fourth free–free resonance: the truncation error has risen to about 3%, and at a slightly higher frequency the 20th-order perturbation computation becomes unusable. As a further demonstration, the computer program was given $U_{a0}=\cos\pi X$ for a uniform bar [$A(X)=1$, $\Omega_0=\pi$] in its lowest free–free mode, and asked to compute the wavefunction for $\Omega=4\pi$, the fourth free–free resonance. The resulting strain function is shown in Fig. 5. The differences between this function and the known analytical solution, $U'=-\sin 4\pi X$, are too small to be shown on the graph (0.006 max).

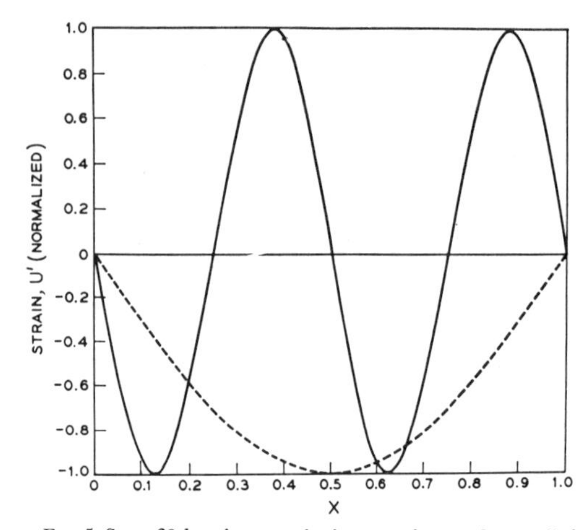


FIG. 5. Same 20th-order perturbation procedure as that applied to the Fourier horn to give the curves of Fig. 4 is here applied to the uniform bar. ---: $U'=-\sin\pi X$, the strain function at the original frequency, for which $\Omega_0=\pi$. ——: Strain function obtained *by perturbation* for $\Omega=4\pi$, the fourth harmonic. The greatest difference between this curve and $U'=-\sin 4\pi X$ is about 0.006, which is too small to show in the Figure.

It is clear that this perturbation method can produce wavefunctions of excellent accuracy even for frequencies very far from the original frequency. With large digital computers able to perform high-order perturbation computations very quickly, we need no longer regard such methods as being restricted to a narrow band of frequencies. The computation was quite arbitrarily limited at the 20th order and there is no reason to doubt that higher order, and consequently larger departures from the original frequency, could be handled. Presumably, computing errors will accumulate in the highest-order $U_n(X)$, but there is no evidence of such an effect at 20th order, so that one can probably go a long way before being limited by this.

This ability to derive high-order mode shapes from low-order ones is a good example of the way that the availability of modern computers should change our attitude to the possibilities of computation. It may often be preferable, when a differential equation is to be solved for many values of a parameter, to solve it for one value, to find and store the perturbation functions [like $U_n(X)$] just once, and to combine these in a Taylor-like series (Eq. 14b) for each of the other values, rather than to solve the differential equation afresh for each value of the parameter.

R. W. Hamming* has used another technique for a similar purpose. He takes an original solution of a differential equation and finds the solution for a fairly close value of the parameter by perturbation. He then makes this new solution the original solution for a further perturbation calculation. By combining this method with the one described here, I have found that very large ranges of a parameter can be covered densely, economically, and accurately.

Clearly, by using Eq. 14b iteratively, these perturbation methods can be used to solve boundary-value problems, and may indeed be very economical. They thus add to the repertory of methods available for the determination of the natural frequencies of vibrating systems [e.g., Refs. *47, 110, 113, 118, 190, 192*].

### IV. INVERSE DESIGN

In the inverse method of design [*35*], as heretofore used, an arbitrary function $U_a$ is devised and the parameters in this are chosen so that $U_a$ fits a particular set of boundary conditions and satisfies some other requirements of the problem [*32, 35, 37, 39*]. If all the parameters of $U_a$ are determined by this, a definite design of vibrator results. Although all the published designs have been for free–free boundary conditions, the same methods can be used for other forms of loading. But, a *change* in boundary conditions or frequency would lead to a change in $U_a$ and, hence, a change in the *designed* $A(X)$.

The application of the algorisms that we have discussed in Secs. I and III to the $U_a$ and $A$ that result from the inverse design procedure allows the behavior of the designed vibrator to be determined when boundary conditions and frequency are changed.

Suppose, however, that the arbitrary $U_a(X)$ is written with more parameters than are needed to satisfy the conditions imposed on $U_a$. The present algorisms can be applied (probably numerically) and the free parameters can be adjusted to satisfy constraints on $U_b$ or on $[U_a+(\beta/\alpha)U_b]$. Thus, designs can be produced that will have required characteristics at any finite number of different loadings and frequencies (in a wide band). For example, as noted in Sec. II-A, a vibrator could be designed to be an ideal transformer. Also, this provides a way of using the inverse method when there is energy flow across the boundaries. This freedom makes the inverse method of design even more powerful.

* Private communication (1966).

### V. CONCLUSION

Expressions have been given from which, if one solution of Webster's horn equation for a given horn and a particular frequency and particular conditions of loading is known, the solutions for any consistent boundary conditions and for other frequencies can be calculated. The impedance relations of a horn have been given from this point of view.

The possibility of deriving a general solution of Webster's equation from one solution will allow the inverse method to be used to design horns to work with complex loads and to optimize such designs.

### ACKNOWLEDGMENTS

I should like to thank R. W. Pyle, Jr., E. N. Gilbert, J. A. Lewis, J. R. Baechle, and H. O. Pollak for useful suggestions, and R. N. Thurston for a most helpful critique of the whole paper. I should also like to thank Rochelle Kellman for writing some of the computer programs.

## Appendix A. Computation of Eq. 4b (Divergent Integrand)

It is very likely that $U_a(X)$ will have at least one zero for $0\leq X\leq 1$. In particular, this will be so if $U_a(X)$ is a free–free solution. The integrand of Eq. 4b will therefore have poles at these zeros.

We restrict the discussion to the lowest mode, in which $U_a$ has one (simple) zero and one zero only in the range $0\leq X\leq 1$. Suppose this zero to be at $X=X_p$, so that

$$U_a(X_p)=0. \tag{A1}$$

We wish to compute

$$U_b(X)=U_a(X)\int_0^X \frac{dt}{A(t)U_a^2(t)}. \tag{4b}$$

[$A(X)$ is everywhere smooth and $>0$.] The integrand

has a pole of order two at $t=X_p$; the integral therefore behaves like $(X-X_p)^{-1}$ near $X=X_p$. Since $U_a$ there behaves like $(X-X_p)$, $U_b$ itself does not diverge. However, difficulties in computation with numerical values certainly arise.

We choose two values of $X$, $X_-$ and $X_+$, such that

$$0<X_-<X_p, \tag{A2a}$$

$$X_p<X_+<1. \tag{A2b}$$

$X_-$ and $X_+$ should be near the middles of their ranges, and should be tabular values of $X$. They must be such that $U_a'(X)$ has no zeros for $X_-\leq X\leq X_+$. We may then divide the computation into three ranges—

**I.** $0\leq X\leq X_-$

In this range, the integrand is well behaved and we can evaluate $U_b$ direct from Eq. 4b. $U_b'(X)$ is conveniently evaluated from Eq. 4c, to avoid numerical differentiation.

**II.** $X_-<X\leq X_+$

In this range, the integrand diverges at $X=X_p$. At the suggestion of H. O. Pollak,* we rewrite Eq. 4b, using

$$Q(X)=\int_0^X \frac{dt}{A(t)U_a^2(t)}: \tag{A3}$$

$$U_b(X)=U_a(X)Q(X_-)$$

$$+U_a(X)\int_{X_-}^X \frac{1}{A(t)U_a'(t)}\cdot\frac{U_a'(t)}{U_a^2(t)}dt \tag{A4a}$$

$$=U_a(X)Q(X_-)+U_a(X)\left\{-\left[\frac{1}{AU_aU_a'}\right]_{X_-}^X\right.$$

$$\left.-\int_{X_-}^X \frac{1}{AU_aU_a'}\left(\frac{A'}{A}+\frac{U_a''}{U_a'}\right)dt\right\}. \tag{A4b}$$

Now, since $U_a$ is a solution of Eq. 1c, it can be seen that

$$\frac{A'}{A}+\frac{U_a''}{U_a'}=-\Omega^2\frac{U_a}{U_a'}. \tag{A5}$$

* Private communication (1966).

Therefore,

$$U_b(X)=-\frac{1}{A(X)U_a'(X)}+U_a(X)Y(X), \tag{A6a}$$

where

$$Y(X)=\frac{1}{A(X_-)U_a(X_-)U_a'(X_-)}+Q(X_-)$$

$$+\Omega^2\int_{X_-}^X \frac{dt}{A.(U_a')^2}. \tag{A6b}$$

The quantities $X_-$ and $X_+$ have been chosen so that $U_a'$ has no zero in this range. (If $U_a$ is for the lowest free–free mode, this is automatic.) Therefore, all the functions in Eqs. A6 are well behaved. Also,

$$U_b'(X)=U_a'(X)Y(X). \tag{A6c}$$

**III.** $X_+<X\leq 1$

$$U_b(X)=U_a(X)Q(X), \tag{A7a}$$

where

$$Q(X)=Y(X_+)-\frac{1}{A(X_+)U_a(X_+)U_a'(X_+)}$$

$$+\int_{X_+}^X \frac{dt}{AU_a^2}. \tag{A7b}$$

This definition of $Q(X)$ is consistent with that of Eq. A3. Also, as in Eq. 4c,

$$U_b'(X)=U_a'(X)Q(X)+\frac{1}{A(X)U_a(X)}. \tag{A7c}$$

Thus, $U_b(X)$ and $U_b'(X)$ have been expressed for the whole range $0\leq X\leq 1$ in computable form.

Although all the integrands remain finite in their ranges of integration, they all diverge *outside* those ranges. In such circumstances, numerical integration formulas (like Simpson's) that fit polynomials may be very inaccurate, and it may be better to use a special method [*28*, *36*, *59*].

## Appendix B. Validity of Eq. 4b for the Perturbed Functions

$U_{a0}(X)$ is a solution of Eq. 14a for $\epsilon=0$ and $U_{b0}(X)$ is the linearly independent, complementary solution given by (cf. Eq. 4b)

$$U_{b0}(X)=U_{a0}(X)\int_0^X \frac{dt}{A(t)U_{a0}^2(t)}. \tag{B1}$$

Let

$$U_a=U_{a0}+\epsilon U_{a1}+\epsilon^2U_{a2}+\cdots \tag{B2a}$$

and

$$U_b=U_{b0}+\epsilon U_{b1}+\epsilon^2U_{b2}+\cdots \tag{B2b}$$

be two linearly independent solutions of Eq. 14a for $\epsilon\neq0$, where $U_{an}$, $U_{bn}(n>0)$ are given by Eqs. 16b and 16c. We now show that $U_a$ and $U_b$ are related by Eq. 4b.

Let

$$U_b^*(X)\equiv U_a(X)\int_0^X \frac{dt}{A(t)U_a^2(t)}. \tag{B3a}$$

Then, since $U_a(X)$ is a solution of Eq. 14a, $U_b^*(X)$ is also a solution and is linearly independent [111]. Therefore,

$$U_b^*(X) \equiv K_1 U_a(X) + K_2 U_b(X). \quad \text{(B4a)}$$

Now, $U_{an}(0)=0$ for $n>0$ (Eq. 16b) and $U_{a0}(0) \neq 0$, by definition. Also, $U_{bn}=0$ for $n \geq 0$ (Eqs. 16b and B1). Therefore, $U_a(0)=U_{a0}(0) \neq 0$ and $U_b(0)=0$. Also, $U_b^*(0)=0$ (Eq. B3a). Therefore, $K_1=0$ and

$$U_b^*(X) \equiv K_2 U_b(X), \quad \text{(B4b)}$$

$$(U_b^*)'(X) \equiv K_2 U_b'(X). \quad \text{(B4c)}$$

From Eq. B3a,

$$(U_b^*)'(X) = U_a'(X) \int_0^X \frac{dt}{A(t)U_a^2(t)} + \frac{1}{A(X)U_a(X)}. \quad \text{(B3b)}$$

Therefore,

$$(U_b^*)'(0) = 1/U_a(0) = 1/U_{a0}(0). \quad \text{(B5)}$$

From Eq. 16d, we see that $U_{bn}'(0)=0$ $(n>0)$. Therefore, from Eqs. B2b and B1,

$$U_b'(0) = U_{b0}'(0) = 1/U_{a0}(0). \quad \text{(B6)}$$

From Eqs. B4c, B5, and B6, $K_2=1$, and, therefore,

$$U_b^*(X) \equiv U_b(X). \quad \text{(B7)}$$

*Q.E.D.*

## Bibliography*

Of the very large literature on tapered electromagnetic transmission lines, only those papers are cited that are thought to be most relevant to acoustics. (Bibliographies on electromagnetic lines are given in Refs. *2*, *75*, and *153c*.) A. G. Caggiano and I hope that we shall shortly publish a much fuller bibliography, in which abstracts will be given for most of the papers.

The comments in parentheses after many of the entries are intended to supplement the titles. Only matter relevant to horn theory is noted. Unless the contrary is stated, the approximation of Eq. 1a has been used, and $E$ and $\rho$ are constant. Occasionally, specific forms of variation of $A$, $E$, or $\rho$ are noted. This does not imply that the author of the paper in question has used this notation, has dealt specifically with the propagation of longitudinal acoustical waves, nor even that an equation more or less of the form of Eq. 1a appears explicitly in his paper. It is simply my interpretation of those variations in my Eq. 1a (or Eq. 1c) on which the paper under discussion might throw light.

The bibliography is arranged alphabetically in the authors named first in each entry. Here is an index to other authors' names:



* The bibliographic references to papers in periodicals are generally given as in the following example: Ser. VI, **5**, No. 10, 12–15 (1926), which means pages 12–15 of issue No. 10 of Vol. 5 in Series VI of that journal for the year 1926. In some of the 18th-century references, dates appear in parentheses after the volume numbers: these are the years during which papers published in that particular volume were communicated to the academy in question. Series numbers are quoted only where confusion might otherwise arise. Issue numbers are quoted only where pagination is by issue, or where we do not know whether it is by volume or by issue. Where reference is to an abstracting journal, "No." refers to the number of an abstract, not of an issue. Initial and final page numbers are given; where only one page number is given, the article is entirely on that page. The symbol (A) or (L) after the page number(s) means that the reference is to an abstract or to a Letter to the Editor. Where no language is stated, the article is in English or in American. If an article is in some other language, but contains an English abstract, we say so, but we do not usually note abstracts in any other languages.

1. **Anon.**, "The Design of Accustic Exponential Horns. Data Sheets on Horns of Square and Circular Cross Section," Electron. Eng. **19**, 286–287 (1947).
2. **N. Amitay, A. Lavi, and F. Young**, "Electromagnetic Field Theory Solution of the Infinite Tapered-Plane Transmission Line," Z. Angew. Math. Phys. **12**, 89–99 (1961). [*Bibliography on electromagnetic lines.*]
3. **L. Balamuth**, "Mechanical Impedance Transformers in Relation to Ultrasonic Machining," IRE Trans. Ultrasonics Eng. **2**, 23–33 (Nov. 1954). [*Origin of the "stepped" (double cylinder), solid horn; also analysis of exponential and various combinations.*]

4. **S. Ballantine,** "On the Propagation of Sound in the General Bessel Horn of Infinite Length," J. Franklin Inst. **203,** 85–102, 852–853 (1927). [*Derives finite amplitude, three-dimensional wave equation for gases and discusses it; uses Webster's equation for analysis of the horn; detailed and clear.*]

5. **E. H. Barton,** "On Spherical Radiation and Vibrations in Conical Pipes," Phil. Mag. Ser. VI, **15,** 69–81 (1908).

6. **P. R. Beesack,** "Isoperimetric Inequalities for the Nonhomogeneous Clamped Rod and Plate," J. Math. Mech. **8,** 471–482 (1959). [*Limits on eigenfrequencies; flexure; there should be similar theorems for longitudinal vibrations.*]; "Linear Differential Equations and Convex Mappings," Duke Univ. Math. J. **27,** 483–495 (1960). [*Properties of* $w''+p(z)w=0$.]

7. **J. F. Belford,** "The Stepped Horn," Proc. Natl. Electron. Conf., 16th, Chicago, **1960,** 814–822 (1960). Available, with errata and addendum, from Clevite Corp., Bedford, Ohio. [*Numerical results on the horn consisting of two cylinders of different diameters and lengths.*]

8. **E.g., R. Bellman,** *Perturbation Techniques in Mathematics, Physics, and Engineering* (Holt, Rinehart & Winston, Inc., New York, 1964).

8a. **A. H. Benade,** "On Woodwind Instrument Bores," J. Acoust. Soc. Am. **31,** 137–146 (1959). [*Resonance of Bessel horns; excitation of overtones by reed requires cylinder or cone.*]

9. **R. W. Benson and J. R. Chapman,** "Distribution of Losses in Longitudinally Excited Vibrators," J. Acoust. Soc. Am. **36,** 1479–1484 (1964). [*Solid, "stepped"; also experiments.*]

9a. **D. Bernoulli,** "Physical, Mechanical and Analytical Researches on Sound and on the Tones of Differently Constructed Organ Pipes" (in French), Mém. Acad. Sci. (Paris) **1762,** 431–485 (1764). Summary in Ref. *176b,* pp. LV–LIX. [*Probably first derivation of Eq. 1c, and its solution for a cone; Ref. 84a was, however, published first.*]

9b. **D. Bernoulli,** "On the Vibration of Strings of Nonuniform Thickness" (in French), Mém. Acad. Sci. (Berlin) **21** (1765), 281–306 (1767); Summary in Ref. *176a,* pp. 307–309. [*Inverse method; i.e., synthesis.*]

10. **R. T. Beyer,** "Nonlinear Acoustics," in *Physical Acoustics—Principles and Methods,* W. P. Mason, Ed. (Academic Press Inc., New York, 1964–), Vol. 2, Pt. B (1965): *Properties of Polymers and Nonlinear Acoustics,* Chap. 10, pp. 231–264.

11. **D. A. Bies,** "Tapering a Bar for Uniform Stress in Longitudinal Oscillation," J. Acoust. Soc. Am. **34,** 1567–1569 (1962). [*Gaussian.*]

12. **V. Blaess,** "On the Computation of the Vibration of Rods with Varying Cross-Section" (in German), Ing.-Arch. **9,** 428–435 (1938). [*Numerical method.*]

13. **E. F. Bolinder,** "Fourier Transforms in the Theory of Inhomogeneous Transmission Lines," Trans. Roy. Inst. Technol. (KTH), Stockholm, No. **48,** pp. 1–84 (1951); Proc. IRE **38,** 1354(L) (1950); *ibid.* **44,** 557(L) (1956). [*Small-reflection approximation; very fruitful method for electric lines; many cases worked out; important.*] Proc. IRE **44,** 1056(L) (1956). [*Nomenclature for forms of taper of transmission lines.*]

13a. **H. Bouasse,** *Pipes and Resonators* (in French) (Delagrave, Paris, 1929); *Wind Instruments* (in French) (Delagrave, Paris, 1929), 2 vols.

13b. **L. M. Brekhovskikh,** *Volny v sloistykh sredakh* (Akademia Nauk SSSR, Moscow, 1957). [English transl.: by D. Lieberman, *Waves in Layered Media.* Ed. R. T. Beyer, (Academic Press, Inc., New York, 1960)]. Especially, Chap. 3: "Plane Waves in Layered-Inhomogeneous Media," pp. 168–233, and "References," pp. 544–553 (English pages).

14. **H. Buchholz,** "The Acoustic Field in a Conical Horn under Different Excitation Conditions" (in German), Akust. Z. **5,** 169–189 (1940). [*Infinite; three-dimensional, axially symmetric; gas; also combination with cylinder.*]

15. **H. Buchholz,** "The Propagation of Sound Waves in a Horn in the Shape of a Paraboloid of Revolution with an Harmonic Source at the Focus" (in German), Ann. Physik (Leipzig) Ser. 5, **42,** 423–460 (1942); Math. Revs. **5,** 249(A) (1944). [*Gas; three-dimensional, axially symmetric.*]

16. **C. R. Burrows,** "The Exponential Transmission Line," Bell System Tech. J. **17,** 555–573 (1938). [*Detailed treatment; cf. Ref. 113a.*]

17. **J. R. Carson,** "Propagation of Periodic Currents over Non-Uniform Lines," Electrician **86,** 272–273 (1921). [*Infinite-series method for general taper, not necessarily continuous; solution for small taper considered.*]

18. **D. S. Chehil and H. S. Heaps,** "Effect of Lateral Motion on the Longitudinal Vibration of Bars with Conical Taper," J. Acoust. Soc. Am. (to be published) [*Plane-wave model for general taper; equation of motion from Hamilton's principle; worked example of cone.*]

19. **C. Chree,** "Bars and Wires of Varying Elasticity," Phil. Mag. Ser. V, **21,** 81–100 (1886). [$A'=0$, *E and* $\rho$ *vary; main interest in resonant frequencies.*]

20. **C. Chree,** "Longitudinal Vibrations of a Circular Bar," Quart. J. Math. **21,** 287–298 (1886); "On Longitudinal Vibrations," *ibid.* **23,** 317–342 (1889) [*Deals with elliptic and rectangular section.*]; "The Equations of an Isotropic Elastic Solid in Polar and Cylindrical Co-Ordinates, Their Solution and Application," Trans. Cambridge Phil. Soc. **14,** 250–369 (1889); "On the Longitudinal Vibrations of Aeolotropic Bars with One Axis of Material Symmetry," Quart. J. Math. **24,** 340–358 (1890). [*Classic three-dimensional solutions for the infinite cylinder.*]

21. **C. Chree,** "Longitudinal Vibrations in Solid and Hollow Cylinders," Proc. Phys. Soc. (London) **16,** 304–322 (1899); reprinted in Phil. Mag. Ser. V, **47,** 333–349 (1899).

22. **R. Codelupi,** "Theory of Non-Uniform Lines" (in Italian), Alta Frequenza **26,** 226–282 (1957). [*Interesting transformation; detailed.*]

23. **R. E. Collin,** "The Optimum Tapered Transmission Line Matching Section," Proc. IRE **44,** 539–547 (1956). [*Synthesis method in small-reflection approximation.*]. *ibid.* **44,** 1056(L) (1956). [*Reply to criticisms; Refs. 13, 82.*]

24. **J. F. C. Conn,** "Vibration of a Truncated Wedge," Aircraft Eng. **16,** 103–105 (Apr. 1944). [*Longit dinal, torsional, flexural.*]

25. **H. D. Conway,** "The Calculation of Frequencies of Vibration of a Truncated Cone," Aircraft Eng. **18,** 235–236 (1946); "Calculation of Frequencies of Truncated Pyramids," *ibid.* **20,** 148 (1948). [*Longitudinal, torsional, flexural.*]

26. **I. B. Crandall,** *Theory of Vibrating Systems and Sound* (D. Van Nostrand Co., Inc., Princeton, N. J., 1926).

27. **A. N. Datta,** "Longitudinal Propagation of Elastic Disturbance for Linear Variations of Elastic Parameters," Indian J. Theoret. Phys. **4,** 43–50 (1956). [$A'=0=\rho'$.]

28. **P. J. Davis and P. Rabinowitz,** "Ignoring the Singularity in Approximate Integration," J. Soc. Ind. Appl. Math. Numer. Anal. **B2,** 367–383 (1965).

29. **F. L. Dimaggio,** "Longitudinal Vibration of a Prolate Ellipsoid," Quart. Appl. Math. **20,** 182–183 (1962). [$A\propto(1-X^2)$.]

29a. **J. M. C. Duhamel,** "On the Vibration of Gases in Cylindrical, Conical, etc., Tubes" (in French), J. Math. Pures Appl. (Liouville) Ser. 1, **14,** 49–110 (1849); Compt. Rend. **8,** 542–543 (1839)]. [*Not restricted to narrow tubes; open and closed; cone, wedge, pyramid.*]

30. **A. M. Dykhne,** "The Theory of Horns" (in Russian), Dokl. Akad. Nauk (SSSR) **126,** 1232–1233 (1959) [English transl.: Soviet Phys.—Dokl. **4,** 651–652 (1959)]. [*Slow taper.*]

31. **G. Eckart,** "Four-Terminal Theory of the Non-Uniform, Ideal Transmission Line" (in German), Hochfrequenztechn. u. Elektroakust. **55,** 173–186 (1940). [*Comprehensive; simplifies general impedance relations for a line.*]

31a. **A. M. Efross,** "Transient Phenomena in Horns" (in Russian), Commun. Inst. Sci. Math. Mécan. Univ. Kharkoff [Zap. Inst. Mat. Mekhan.], Ser. 4, 16, 82–88 (1940); Math. Revs. **3,** 25(A) (1942). [*Exponential, Bessel.*]

32. **E. Eisner,** "Design of Sonic Amplitude Transformers for High Magnification," J. Acoust. Soc. Am. **35,** 1367–1377 (1963). [*Inverse method: "Fourier" vibrator; longitudinal.*]

33. **E. Eisner,** "Torsionally Resonant Amplitude Transformers for High Magnification," J. Acoust. Soc. Am. **36,** 1–9 (1964). [*"Fourier".*]

34. **E. Eisner,** "Resonant Vibration of a Cone," J. Acoust. Soc. Am. **36,** 309–312 (1964). [*Numerical results; strain, magnification, etc., as functions of truncation.*]

35. **E. Eisner,** "The Design of Resonant Vibrators," in *Physical Acoustics—Principles and Methods,* W. P. Mason, Ed. (Academic Press Inc., New York, 1964), Vol. 1: *Methods and Devices,* Pt. B, Chap. 14, pp. 353–365.

36. **E. Eisner,** "Numerical Integration of a Function That has a Pole"; Commun. Assoc. Computer Machinery **10,** 239–243 (1967). [*Explicit formulas.*]

37. **E. Eisner and R. E. Hicks,** "Optimum Longitudinal Horns for Large Particle Velocity," Paper K68 in *Proceedings of the Fifth International Congress on Acoustics, 1965, Liège,* D. E. Commins, Ed. (Imprimerie Georges Thone, Liège, 1965), Vol. 1b. [*Inverse method; "polynomial."*]

38. **E. Eisner and J. S. Seager,** "A Longitudinally Resonant Stub for Vibrations of Large Amplitude," Safety in Mines Res. Establ., Sheffield, England, Res. Rept. No. 216 (1963). [*Inverse method introduced; "terminated Gaussian"; unterminated finite Gaussian; strains in vibrating systems.*]

39. **E. Eisner and J. S. Seager,** "A Longitudinally Resonant Stub for Vibrations of Large Amplitude," Ultrasonics **3,** 88–98 (1965). [*Inverse method; "terminated Gaussian"; strains in vibrating systems.*]

41. **D. Ensminger,** "Solid Cone in Longitudinal Half-Wave Resonance," J. Acoust. Soc. Am. **32,** 194–196 (1960). [*Algebraic expressions for displacement, strain, etc.; experiments.*]

41a. **A. Erdélyi,** "Eigenfrequencies of Inhomogeneous Strings" (in German), Z. Angew. Math. Mech. **18,** 177–185 (1938); see also, **E. Makai,** "On the Calculation of the Eigenfrequencies of Inhomogeneous Strings" (in German), *ibid.* **22,** 167–168 (1942). [*General variation; approximation with estimate of error.*]

42. **L. Euler,** "On the Vibratory Motion of Nonuniformly Thick Strings" (in Latin), Novi Commen. Acad. Sci. Petrop. **9** (1762/1763), 246–304 (1764); reprinted in Ref. *42g,* Ser. II, **10,** 293–343 (1947) (F. Stüssi and H. Favre, Eds.); commentary in Ref. *176a,* pp. 302–307. [*$E'=O=A'$; one of the first major papers in the field.*]

42a. **L. Euler,** "Supplement to (and Continuation of) the Researches on the Propagation of Sound" (in French), Mém. Acad. Sci. Berlin **15** (1759), 210–240, 241–264 (1766); reprinted in Ref. *42g,* Ser. III, **1,** 452–483, 484–507 (1926) (E. Bernoulli, R. Bernoulli, F. Rudio, and A. Speiser, Eds.); commentary in Ref. *176b,* pp. XLV–IL. [*Propagation in two and three dimensions (therefore, in cone and wedge), with solutions and reduction to Riccati's equation; however, no explicit mention of horns; cf., Ref. 84a.*]

42b. **L. Euler,** "Researches on the Motion of Stings of Unequal Thickness" (in French), Misc. Taurinensia (Mélanges Phil. Math., Soc. Roy. Turin) **3** (1762/1765) 25–29 (1766); reprinted in Ref. *42g,* Ser. II, **10,** 397–425 (1947) (F. Stüssi and H. Favre, Eds.); commentary in Ref. *176a,* pp. 309–311. [*Inverse method.*]

42c. **L. Euler,** "More Detailed Elucidation of the Generation and Propagation of Sound and on the Formation of the Echo" (in French), Mém. Acad. Sci. Berlin **21** (1765), 335–363 (1767); reprinted in Ref. *42g,* Ser. III, **1,** 540–567 (1926) (E. Bernoulli, R. Bernoulli, F. Rudio, and A. Speiser, Eds.); commentary in Ref. *176b,* pp. LIX–LXIII. [*Uniform tube containing air of varying density; finite amplitude.*]

42d. **L. Euler,** "Part Four [of a Treatise on Fluid Mechanics]: On the Motion of Air in a Tube" (in Latin), Novi Commen. Acad. Sci. Petrop. **16** (1771), 281–425 (1772), esp. Chap. 4: "On Very Small Vibrations of Air in a Tube of Nonuniform Width," pp. 349–425; reprinted in Ref. *42g,* Ser. II, **13,** 262–369 (1955) (C. A. Truesdell, Ed.), Chap. 4, pp. 310–369; commentary in Ref. *176b,* pp. LXIII–LXX; [German transl. by H. W. Brandes, *Die Gesetze des Gleichgewichts und der Bewegung flüssiger Körper. Dargestellt von Leonhard Euler.* (*The Laws of the Equilibrium and the Motion of Fluid Bodies. Given by Leonhard Euler*) (Leipzig, 1806)]; see Ref. *176b,* pp. CIII–CV. [*Generalization of Eq. 1a to varying density, with inclusion of gravity; very interesting inverse method for horns; exhaustive treatment of hyperboloid and cone; one of the most important papers on the subject.*]

42e. **L. Euler,** "On the Vibratory Motion of Strings of Arbitrarily Variable Thickness" (in Latin), Novi Comment. Acad. Sci. Petrop. **17** (1772), 432–448 (1773); reprinted in Ref. *42g,* Ser. II, **11,** Pt. 1, 98–111 (1957) (F. Stüssi and E. Trost, Eds.); commentary in Ref. *176a,* pp. 314–315.

42f. **L. Euler,** "Elucidation of the Motion of Strings of Nonuniform Thickness" (in Latin), Acta Acad. Sci. Petrop. **1780: II,** 99–132 (1784); reprinted in Ref. *42g,* Ser. II, **11,** Pt. 1, 280–306 (1957) (F. Stüssi and E. Trost, Eds.); commentary in Ref. *176a,* p. 315 [*Inverse method.*]

42g. **L. Euler,** *Leonhardi Euleri Opera Omnia* (Orell Füssli, Zürich, 1911–). Ser. I: *Opera Mathematica.* Ser. II: *Opera Mechanica et Astronomica.* Ser. III: *Opera Physica. Miscellanea.* 74 vols. by various editors, at various dates since 1911. Distributed by Springer-Verlag, Berlin.

43. **G. Evangelisti,** "On the Calculation of the Water Hammer in Piped Flow with Variable Characteristics" (in Italian), Energia Elettrica **16,** 851–854 (1939). [*Transformation that reduces variability of waveform; see also Refs. 122, 152.*]

44. **H. Favre,** "Theoretical Study of the Influence of a Discontinuity of Cross-Section of a Conical Bar on the Propagation of Longitudinal Elastic Vibrations" (in French), Bull. Tech. Suisse Rom. **88,** 353–363 (1962).

45. **M. Federici,** "On a New Type of Non-Uniform Electric Cable" (in Italian), Atti Acad. Naz. Lincei VI, **13,** 128–132 (1931). [*$A\propto X$, $\rho\propto X$, $E'=0$: Bessel.*]

45a. **A. L. Fel'dshtein,** "Nonuniform Transmission Lines" (in Russian), Radiotekhnika **6,** No. 5, 38–46 (1951) [English transl.: Library of Congress, Aerospace Inform. Div., Washington, D. C., AID Rept. T-63-96, pp. 1–12 (1963)]. [*Volterra integral equations; solution by successive approximation.*]; "Generalized Matrix Theory for Nonuniform Transmission Lines" (in Russian), *ibid.* **15,** No. 6, 10–17 (1960) [English transl.: Radio Eng. **15,** No. 6, 12–24(1960)].

46. **H. E. Fettis,** "Torsional Vibration Modes of Tapered Bars," J. Appl. Mech. **19,** 220–222 (1952). [*Pyramids; i.e., $A\propto(X_0+X)^4$ in Eq. 1c.*]

46a. **H. E. Fettis,** "A Modification of the Holzer Method for Computing Uncoupled Torsion and Bending Modes," J. Aeron. Sci. **16,** 625–634 (1949). [*Numerical method.*]

47. **L. Fox,** *Numerical Solution of Two-Point Boundary-Value Problems* (Oxford University Press, London, 1957); also *Numerical Solution of Ordinary and Partial Differential Equations* (Pergamon Press Ltd., Oxford, England, 1962).

48. **J. E. Freehafer,** "The Acoustical Impedance of an Infinite Hyperbolic Horn," J. Acoust. Soc. Am. **11,** 467–476 (1940). [*Three-dimensional solution for gas in hyperboloid of one sheet.*]

49. **V. V. Furduev,** "Some Remarks on the Generalized Group of Bessel Loudspeaker Horns" (in Russian), Zh. Tekhn. Fiz. **9,** 165–167 (1939); Wireless Eng. **16,** No. 3604, 473(A) (1939).

50. **M. E. Gertsenshtein,** "On the Theory of Gradual Transitions with 'Guaranteed' Matching" (in Russian), Radiotekhn. i Elektron. **4,** 1460–1464 (1959) [English transl.: Radio Eng. & Electron. **4,** No. 9, 70–77 (1959)].

51. **S. K. Ghosh,** "Dynamics of the Longitudinal Propagation of Elastic Disturbance through a Medium Exhibiting Gradient of Elasticity," Indian J. Phys. **35,** 22–27 (1961). [$A'=0=\rho'$, $E\propto(X_0+X)$.]

52. **A. N. Goldsmith and J. P. Minton,** "The Performance and Theory of Loud Speaker Horns," Proc. IRE **12,** 423–478 (1924). [*Cone, exponential,* $A\propto X$; *extensive treatment both in theory and experiment.*]

53. **S. Goldstein and N. W. McLachlan,** "Sound Waves of Finite Amplitude in an Exponential Horn," J. Acoust. Soc. Am. **6,** 275–278 (1935).

54. **G. Green,** "On the Motion of Waves in a Variable Canal of Small Depth and Width," Trans. Cambridge Phil. Soc. **6,** 457–462 (1838); reprinted in *Mathematical Papers of George Green,* N. M. Ferrers, Ed. (Macmillan & Co., London, 1871), pp. 225–230. [*Early explicit statement of Eq. 1a; solution for very slow but arbitrary taper.*]

55. **R. W. Gretter and L. S. Wilk,** "Research Investigation of Magnetostrictive Techniques for Obtaining High Frequency Vibrations," Wright Air Develop. Ctr. Tech. Rept. 54-382 (1954) (AD69982). [*Exponential, cone,* $A\propto(X_0+X)$, *first suggestion of Gaussian for constant strain, but did not find it good because of some arbitrarily imposed conditions.*]

56. **O. H. Griffith and E. T. Cranch,** "Torsional and Longitudinal Vibrations of Variable Section Bars," Am. Soc. Mech. Engrs., Winter Meeting, New York, 1961, Papers 61-WA-75 (unpublished). [$A\propto X^n$.]

57. **P. Grivet,** *Electron Optics* (Pergamon Press Ltd., Oxford, England, 1965).

57a. **L. Gutin,** "On the Theory of the Receiving Horn" (in French), Technical Physics USSR **3,** 81–98 (1936); errata inserted between pp. 98 and 99. [*Cone, exponential, paraboloid; impedances; some discussion of limitations of Eq. 1c; detailed, interesting.*]

58. **W. M. Hall,** "Comments on the Theory of Horns," J. Acoust. Soc. Am. **3,** 552–561 (1932). [*Discusses limitations of Eq. 1a for gases; experiments on cone and exponential.*]

59. **R. W. Hamming,** *Numerical Methods for Scientists and Engineers* (McGraw-Hill Book Co., Inc., New York, 1962), p. 163.

60. **C. R. Hanna,** "On the Propagation of Sound in the General Bessel Horn of Infinite Length," J. Franklin Inst. **203,** 849–851 (1927). [*Relation of Bessel and exponential.*]

61. **C. R. Hanna and J. Slepian,** "The Function and Design of Horns for Loud Speakers," Trans. AIEE **43,** 393–411 (1924). [*Was influential tutorial paper for the practising engineer; exponential, cone.*]

62. **O. Heaviside,** "Contributions to the Theory of the Propagation of Current in Wires," Paper XX in *Electrical Papers* (Macmillan & Co., London, 1892), Vol. 1, pp. 141–179, esp. 173–179. [*Various cases, including Bessel; fairly opaque.*]

62a. **H. L. F. von Helmholtz,** *Vorlesungen über die mathematischen Prinzipien der Akustik* (*Lectures on the Mathematical Principles of Acoustics*), A. König and C. Runge, Eds., (Julius Barth, Leipzig, 1898). [*Short, noncylindrical tubes joined to cylinders; inverse method; Eq. 1a not given explicitly.*]

63. **V. A. Hoersch,** "Non-Radial Harmonic Vibrations within a Conical Horn," Phys. Rev. **25,** 218–224 (1925). [*Gas; three-dimensional, axially symmetric solutions.*]

64. **V. A. Hoersch,** "Theory of the Optimum Angle in a Receiving Conical Horn," Phys. Rev. **25,** 225–229 (1925). [*Gas; magnification as function of (large) angle.*]

65. **J. E. Holte and R. F. Lambert,** "Synthesis of Stepped Acoustic Transmission Systems," J. Acoust. Soc. Am. **33,** 289–301 (1961); "Internal Reflections and Low Frequency Cutoff in Nonuniform Transmission Structures," *ibid.* **33,** 1246–1247(L) (1961); "Synthesis of a Stepped Structure for a Prescribed Reflection Coefficient," *ibid.* **34,** 680–681(L) (1962). **L. Young,** "Stepped Waveguide Transformers and Filters," *ibid.* **33,** 1247(L) (1961). [*Riccati impedance equation with low-reflection approximation; graphical method. These papers contain references to other work, mainly in the electrical case, on the synthesis of stepped lines, some of which is less limited.*]

66. **J. Holtsmark, J. Lothe, S. Tjøtta, and W. Romberg,** "A Theoretical Investigation of Sound Transmission through Horns of Small Flare, with Special Emphasis on the Exponential Horn," Arch. Math. Naturvidenskab **53,** 139–181 (1956). [*Gas; less restricted solution than Webster's, specifically for exponential horn; outline of more-general theory; a classic.*]

67. **J. C. Houbolt and R. A. Anderson,** "Calculation of Uncoupled Modes and Frequencies in Bending or Torsion of Nonuniform Beams," Natl. Advis. Comm. Aeron. Tech. Note No. TN 1522 (Feb. 1948). [*Numerical method; examples.*]

68. **E. J. Irons,** "On the Free Periods of Resonators," Phil. Mag. Ser. VII, **9,** 346–360 (1930). [*Gas; spherical waves in cone; coupling to chambers.*]

69. **B. N. Ivakin,** "The Micro- and Macrostructure of Elastic Waves in Single-Dimensional Continuous Heterogeneous Media" (in Russian), Tr. Geofiz. Inst. Akad. Nauk (SSSR) **1958,** No. 39 (166), 1–92 (1958); Appl. Mech. Revs. **14,** No. 1343 p. 201 (1961).

70. **I. Jacobs,** "The Nonuniform Transmission Line as a Broadband Termination," Bell System Tech. J. **37,** 913–924 (1958). [$A$ *and* $\rho\propto(X_0+X)^2$; $E$ *constant.*]

71. **R. P. N. Jones,** "The Effect of Small Changes in Mass and Stiffness on the Natural Frequencies and Modes of Vibrating Systems," Intern. J. Mech. Sci. **1,** 350–355 (1960). **R. P. N. Jones and S. Mahalingam,** "The Natural Frequencies of Free and Constrained Non-Uniform Beams," J. Roy. Aeron. Soc. **64,** 697–699 (1960).

72. **V. K. Kabulov,** "The Integral Equation of the Longitudinal Vibration of Bars" (in Russian), Dokl. Akad. Nauk UzSSR **1956,** No. 3, 7–12 (1956); see Appl. Mech. Revs. **12,** No. 102, p. 16 (1959); *Integral Equations of the Balance Type and Their Application to Dynamic Analysis of Bars and Beams* (in Russian), (Izdatel'stvo Akademii Nauk Uzbekskoi, Tashkent, UzSSR, 1961), pp. 185; see Appl. Mech. Revs. **16,** No. 3858, p. 524 (1963).

73. **J. Kacprowski,** "Analysis of the Wave-Parameters of the Exponential Horn" (in Polish; English sum. pp. 757–758), Arch. Elektrotech. (Warsaw) **5,** No. 4, 719–758 (1956); see Sci. Abstr. **A60,** No. 6963, 637 (1957). [*Detailed treatment of four-terminal characteristics and their significance.*]

74. **B. Z. Katsenelenbaum,** "On the Theory of Irregular Acoustic Waveguides" (in Russian), Akust. Zh. **7,** 201–209 (1961) [English transl.: Soviet Phys.—Acoust. **7,** 159–164 (1961)]. [*Three-dimensional theory for gases.*]

75. **H. Kaufman,** "Bibliography of Nonuniform Transmission Lines," IRE Trans. Antennas Propagation **3,** 218–220 (1955). [*Mainly electromagnetic lines.*]

76. **B. G. Kazansky,** "Outline of a Theory of Non-Uniform Transmission Lines," Proc. Instn. Elec. Engrs. (London) **105C,** 126–138 (1958). [*Impedance formulation, with some unique features; method of synthesis.*]

77. **A. V. Kharitonov,** "Torsional Ultrasonic Concentrators" (in Russian), Akust. Zh. **7,** 387–389 (1961) [English transl.: Soviet Phys.—Acoust. **7,** 310–311 (1962)]. [*Schrödinger form;* $A\propto(X_0+X)^2$, $(e^{\beta X}+\alpha e^{-\beta X})^2$, $(\cos\beta X+\alpha\sin\beta X)^2$ *in Eq. 1c recognized as one family.*]

77a. **N. A. Kil'chevskii**, "Determination of Dynamic Stresses Appearing as the Result of Torsion in Round Rods of Variable Section" (in Russian), Izv. Kiev. Politekhn. Inst. **19**, 252–268 (1956). [*"Exact" and simplified Fredholm integral equations.*]

78. **C. Kleesattel**, "Approximate Formula for Some Frequently Encountered Combinations of Acoustic Conductors" (in German), Acustica **6**, 288–294 (1956). [*Combinations of uniform bars.*]

79. **C. Kleesattel**, " 'Vibrator Ampullaceus,' a Longitudinal Resonator for Maximum Particle Velocity and Transducer Power" (in German), Acustica **12**, 322–334 (1962) [English transl.: Bell Telephone Labs. No. TR63-95 (1963)]. [*Extensive analysis of Gaussian terminated with cylinders and other shapes.*]

80. **C. Kleesattel**, "Torsional Resonators with Uniform Stress," Acustica **17**, 153–161 (1966). [*Hollow Gaussian; solid,* $I \propto (\cosh \alpha X)^{-4}$*; others.*]

81. **P. W. Klipsch**, "A Note on Acoustic Horns," Proc. IRE **33**, 447–449 (1945). [*Impedance of exponential below cutoff frequency.*]

82. **R. W. Klopfenstein**, "A Transmission Line Taper of Improved Design," Proc. IRE **44**, 31–35 (1956). [*Low-reflection approximation.*] "The Optimum Tapered Transmission Line Matching Section," *ibid.* **44**, 1055–1056(L) (1956). [*Comments on Ref. 23.*]

83. **J. S. Kouvelites**, "Free Longitudinal Vibration of a Prolate Ellipsoid, Clamped Centrally," Quart. Appl. Math. **9**, 105–108 (1951). [$A \propto (1-X^2)$.]

84. **K. Y. Kukhta**, "Determination of Natural Frequencies and Forms of Longitudinal Oscillations of a Free Beam of Variable Mass with Concentrated Loads" (in Ukrainian; English abstr. p. 315), Dopovidi Akad. Nauk Ukr. RSR **1966**, No. 3, 312–315 (1966).

84a. **J. L. Lagrange**, "New Researches on the Nature and the Propagation of Sound" (in French), Misc. Taurinensia (Mélanges Phil. Math., Soc. Roy. Turin) **2**, No. 2, 11–171 (errata pp. 171–172) (1760/1761); esp. Secs. 30–32, pp. 92–96, "The oscillations of an elastic fluid enclosed in a pipe whose shape is a general conoid"; Sec. 33, pp. 96–98, "Of the vibrations of strings of non-uniform thickness"; Sec. 59, pp. 157–158 on the harmonics of horns. [Reprinted in *Œuvres de Lagrange*, J. A. Serret, Ed., (Gauthier-Villars, Paris, 1867), Vol. 1, pp. 151–316: Secs. 30–32, pp. 232–236; Sec. 30, pp. 237–238; Sec. 59, pp. 301–303.] For commentary: on Sec. 33, see Ref. *176a*, pp. 301–302; on Secs. 30–32 and 59, see Ref. *176b*, pp. IL–LIV. [*First publication of Eq. 1a, and of its solution for the wedge, the cone, and (formal) the general "Bessel" horn,* $A \propto X^m$*; recognition of the problem of the overtones of flared wind instruments; much else; monumental.*]

85. **H. Lamb**, "On the Vibrations of an Elastic Sphere," Proc. London Math. Soc. **13**, 189–212 (1882). [*Exact solution.*]

86. **R. F. Lambert**, "Acoustical Studies of the Tractrix Horn. I," J. Acoust. Soc. Am. **26**, 1024–1028 (1954). [*Modification of plane-wave theory; experimental paper on pp. 1129–1133.*]

87. **J. W. Landon and H. Quinney**, "Experiments with the Hopkinson Pressure Bar," Proc. Roy. Soc. (London) **A103**, 622–643 (1923), esp. 639–643. [*Solid cone; Webster equation; pulses.*]

88. **T. Lange**, "On the Eigenfrequencies of Horns" (in German), Acustica **5**, 323–330 (1955). [*Impedance; catenoidal, terminated in various ways.*]

89. **S. Lefschetz**, *Differential Equations: Geometrical Theory* (Interscience Publishers, Inc., New York, 1962), 2nd ed. [*Poincaré's expansion theorem.*]

90. **U. S. Lindholm and K. D. Doshi**, "Wave Propagation in an Elastic Nonhomogeneous Bar of Finite Length," J. Appl. Mech. **32**, 135–142 (1965). [$E \propto X^n$, $A' = \rho' = 0$; *free vibration; pulse loading; orthogonality of eigenfunctions.*]

90a. **O. N. Litvinenko and V. I. Soshnikov**, "Synthesis of Heterogeneous Lines by Solution of the Inverse Strum–Liouville Problem" (in Russian), Radiotekhnika **17**, No. 9, 15–23 (1962) [English transl.: Telecommun. & Radio Eng. Pt. 2, **17**, No. 9, 14–22 (1962)].

91. **M. G. Lozinskii and L. D. Rozenberg**, "A Method of Concentrating Ultrasonic Energy," USSR Patent 85,193 (1950). [*Suggest conical, exponential, and parabolic, solid transformers for ultrasonic processing; no analysis.*]

92. **J. L. Lubkin and Y. L. Luke**, "Frequencies of Longitudinal Vibration for a Slender Rod of Variable Section," J. Appl. Mech. **20**, 173–177 (1953). [$A \propto (X_0+X)^n$.]

93. **L. O. Makarov**, "Waveguide Properties of Ultrasonic Rod Concentrators," in *Reports of the All-Union Scientific–Technical Conference on the Application of Ultrasonics in Metal-Working, Metal Physics and Machining of Metals, Kiev, 1958* (in Russian) (Ukrainian Academy of Science, Kiev, 1960), pp. 44–53. [English transl.: John Crerar Library Transl. Pool, Chicago, No. TT-66-14338 (1966)]; "Note on the Operational Characteristics of a Rod Concentrator" (in Russian), Akust. Zh. **5**, 372–374 (1959) [English transl.: Soviet Phys.—Acoust. **5**, 380–382 (1959)]. [*Relations for the dissipatively loaded exponential and "stepped" horns.*]

94. **L. O. Makarov**, "Theoretical Investigation of Selected Torsional Oscillating Systems" (in Russian), Akust. Zh. **7**, 450–456 (1961) [English transl.: Soviet Phys.—Acoust. **7**, 364–369 (1962)]. [*Exponential and step, solid and hollow.*]

95. **G. E. Martin**, "On the Propagation of Longitudinal Stress Waves in Finite, Solid, Elastic Horns," Ph.D. dissertation, Univ. Tex. (May 1966); available from Univ. Microfilms, Inc., Ann Arbor, Mich., or as Univ. Tex. Rept. Off. Naval Res. NONR 4690(00) (June 1966). [*Plane-wave model with lateral inertia and shear, giving one-dimensional wave equation by Hamilton's principle; solution, without shear, for cone, and comparison with experiment; discusses limitations clearly.*]

96. **W. P. Mason**, U. S. Patent 2,514,080 (1950). **W. P. Mason and R. F. Wick**, U. S. Patent 2,573,168 (1951); "A Barium Titanate Transducer Capable of Large Motion at an Ultrasonic Frequency," J. Acoust. Soc. Am. **23**, 209–214 (1951). [*Exponential; analysis and experiment; suggest uses.*]

97. **O. K. Mawardi**, "Generalized Solutions of Webster's Horn Theory," J. Acoust. Soc. Am. **21**, 323–330 (1949). [*Most interesting transformations; method of evaluating impedance of general horn; deduces a generating equation for many new families of horns, and treats some examples.*]

98. **N. W. McLachlan**, *Loud Speakers* (Oxford University Press, London, 1934; reprinted: Dover Publications, Inc., New York, 1960). [*Cone, exponential, Bessel; finite amplitude for gas.*]

98a. **N. W. McLachlan and A. T. McKay**, "Transient Oscillations in a Loud-Speaker Horn," Proc. Cambridge Phil. Soc. **32**, 265–275 (1936). [*Exponential.*]

99. **M. A. Medick**, "One-Dimensional Theories of Wave Propagation and Vibrations in Elastic Bars of Rectangular Cross Section," J. Appl. Mech. **33**, 489–495 (1966). [*Discusses limitations and anisotropy.*]

100. **T. R. Meeker and A. H. Meitzler**, "Guided Wave Propagation in Elongated Cylinders and Plates," in *Physical Acoustics—Principles and Methods*, W. P. Mason, Ed. (Academic Press Inc., New York, 1964), Vol. 1: *Methods and Devices*, Pt. A, Chap. 2, pp. 111–167.

100a. **H. H. Meinke**, "A Modified Exponential Line as an Improved Transformer with High-Pass Characteristics" (in German), Arch. Elek. Übertrag. **7**, 347–354 (1953). [*Includes discussion of effect of departure from nominal shape.*]

101. **L. G. Merkulov**, "Design of Ultrasonic Concentrators" (in Russian), Akust. Zh. **3**, 230–238 (1957) [English transl.: Soviet Phys.—Acoust. **3**, 246–255 (1957)]. [*Cone, exponential, catenoidal; Rayleigh correction to frequency for lateral motion in horns; clear, important.*]

102. **L. G. Merkulov and A. V. Kharitonov,** "Theory and Analysis of Sectional Concentrators" (in Russian), Akust. Zh. **5**, 183–190 (1959) [English transl.: Soviet Phys.—Acoust. **5**, 183–190 (1959)]. [*Detailed analysis of composite horns consisting of uniform cylinders joined to one of cone, exponential, catenoidal.*]

103. **P. Mermelstein and M. R. Schroeder,** "Determination of Smoothed Cross-Sectional Area Functions of the Vocal Tract from Formant Frequencies," Paper A24 in *Proceedings of the Fifth International Congress on Acoustics, 1965, Liège,* D. E. Commins, Ed. (Imprimerie Georges Thone, Liège, 1965), Vol. 1a. Also, **P. Mermelstein,** "Determination of Vocal-Tract Shape from Measured Formant Frequencies," J. Acoust. Soc. Am. (to be published). [*Determine Fourier coefficients of area function.*]

104. **W. Meyer zur Capellen,** "A Method for the Approximate Solution of Eigenvalue Problems with Application to Vibration Problems" (in German), Ann. Physik (Leipzig) Ser. V, **8**, 297–352 (1931). [*Treats a general horn shape as a perturbation of some horn shape for which the solution is known; eigenvalues and eigenfunctions are then obtained by perturbation of the known solutions; applied to flexural and longitudinal vibrations; examples.*]

105. **A. K. Mitra,** "Note on the Torsional Vibration of a Thin Beam of Varying Cross-Section," Indian J. Theoret. Phys. **8**, 23–26 (1960). [*Fixed-free exponential; gives resonant frequencies.*]

106. **A. Mohammed,** "Equivalent Circuits of Solid Horns Undergoing Longitudinal Vibrations," J. Acoust. Soc. Am. **38**, 862–866 (1965). [*General impedance relations of "2+2 pole black box"; specific expressions for "hypex," Bessel, conical, exponential, catenoidal, parabolic.*]

107. **Chi-Hung Mok and E. A. Murray, Jr.,** "Free Vibrations of a Slender Bar with Nonuniform Characteristics," J. Acoust. Soc. Am. **40**, 385–389 (1966). [*Solution for very slow, but arbitrary, taper; longitudinal and flexural.*]

108. **C. T. Molloy,** "Response Peaks in Finite Horns," J. Acoust. Soc. Am. **22**, 551–557 (1950). ["*Hypex.*"]

109. **E. Mori and M. Uno,** "Analysis of Torsional Vibration of an Ultrasonic Exponential Solid Horn with a Tool and Its Design Considering Fatigue Limit," Bull. Tokyo Inst. Technol. No. 51 (PME No. 11), 63–80 (1963); see, however, Appl. Mech. Revs. **17**, No. 3810, 525 (1964).

110. **P. M. Morse,** *Vibration and Sound* (McGraw-Hill Book Co., Inc., New York, 1948), 2nd ed.

111. **P. M. Morse and H. Feshbach,** *Methods of Theoretical Physics* (McGraw-Hill Book Co., Inc., New York, 1953).

112. **D. Muster and A. Christensen,** "Study of Underwater Horns—Single-Loading Exponential and Pseudohemispherical Horns," J. Acoust. Soc. Am. **37**, 1184(A) (1965).

113. **N. O. Myklestad,** *Vibration Analysis* (McGraw-Hill Book Co., Inc., New York, 1944).

113a. **M. S. Neiman,** "Inhomogeneous Lines with Specified Constants" (in Russian), Izv. Elektroprom. Slabogo Toka **1938**, No. 11, 14–25 (1938). [*Exponential; detailed; cf. Ref. 16.*]

114. **E. A. Neppiras,** "A High-Frequency Reciprocating Drill," J. Sci. Instr. **30**, 72–74 (1953); "Design of Ultrasonic Machine Tools," in *Proceedings of the Conference on Technology of Engineering Manufacture, 1958, London* (Institution of Mechanical Engineers, London, 1959), pp. 417–432. **E. A. Neppiras and R. D. Foskett,** "Ultrasonic Machining," Philips Tech. Rev. **18**, 325–335 (1956–1957). [*Exponential, cone, catenoidal, stepped; materials.*]

115. **E. A. Neppiras,** "Mechanical Transformers for Producing Very Large Motion," Acustica **13**, 368–370 (1963); "The Effect of Shape and Internal Impedance on the Power-Handling Capacity and Efficiency of Ultrasonics Transducers," *ibid.* **15**, 58–62 (1965). [*Summaries of results.*]

116. **H. F. Olson and I. Wolff,** "Sound Concentrator for Microphones," J. Acoust. Soc. Am. **1**, 410–417 (1930). [$A \propto X^{\frac{1}{2}}$.]

117. **H. F. Olson,** "A Horn Consisting of Manifold Exponential Sections," J. Soc. Motion Picture Engrs. **30**, 511–518 (1938).

118. **H. F. Olson,** *Acoustical Engineering* (D. Van Nostrand Co., Inc., Princeton, N. J., 1957). [*Impedances of conical and exponential horns; comparison of a number of horns.*]

119. **S. I. Orlov,** "Concerning the Theory of Nonuniform Transmission Lines" (in Russian), Zh. Tekhn. Fiz. **26**, 2361–2372 (1956) [English transl.: Soviet Phys.—Tech. Phys. **1**, 2284–2294 (1956)]. [*Impedances; smoothly varying line as limit of step-varying line, each step being a quadripole; synthesis.*]

120. **M. Parodi,** "Propagation on a Lossless Electric Line Whose Linear Parameters are Exponential Functions of the Square of the Space Coordinate: Analogy with the Solution of Schrödinger's Equation for the Harmonic Oscillator" (in French), J. Phys. Radium Ser. VIII, **6**, 331–332 (1945). [*Gaussian.*]

120a. **M. Parodi,** "Remark on the Propagation of Electricity on a Nonuniform Cable" (in French), Rev. Gén. Élec. **57**, 37–38 (1948). [*Solution for one line leads, via Schrödinger formulation, to solutions for family of lines.*]

121. **M. Parodi,** "On the Determination of Conditions for the Integration of the Equations for the Propagation of Electricity on a Nonuniform Line" (in French), Compt. Rend. **234**, 1674–1676 (1952). [*Family of shapes derivable recursively.*]

122. **H. M. Paynter and F. D. Ezekiel,** "Water Hammer in Nonuniform Pipes as an Example of Wave Propagation in Gradually Varying Media," Trans. ASME **80**, 1585–1595 (1958). [*Detailed discussion of transformation allowing solution for slow, but arbitrary, taper; examples; E, A, and ρ can all vary; cf. Refs. 33, 152.*]

123. **R. G. Payton,** "Elastic Wave Propagation in a Non-Homogeneous Rod," Quart. J. Mech. Appl. Math. **19**, 83–91 (1966). [$E=(a+bX+cX^2)^2$, $A'=\rho'=0$.]

124. **W. D. Phelps,** "Power Transmission Loss in Exponential Horns and Pipes with Wall Absorption," J. Acoust. Soc. Am. **12**, 68–74 (1940).

125. **G. W. Pierce and A. Noyes, Jr.,** "Periods of Longitudinal Vibration of Steel Cones and Truncated Cones," J. Acoust. Soc. Am. **9**, 301–307 (1938). [*Essentially Eq. 1a; also experiments.*]

126. **J. R. Pierce,** "A Note on the Transmission Line Equation in Terms of Impedance," Bell System Tech. J. **22**, 263–265 (1943). [*First note that transmission-line equation can be transformed into Riccati's equation for the impedance; much used subsequently for electric lines.*]

127. **H. F. L. Pinkney and G. Basso,** "On the Classification of Families of Shapes for Rods of Axially Varying Cross-Section in Longitudinal Vibration," Natl. Res. Council Canada, Ottawa, Mech. Eng. Rept. MS-109 (1963). [*Transformation of Eq. 1c into Schrödinger's equation leads to a differential equation for the horn profile; the solutions of this equation in terms of known functions are demonstrated and discussed; they include most of the known horns and a number of new ones; outstandingly clear.*]

128. **E. Pinney,** "Vibration Modes of Tapered Beams," Am. Math. Monthly **54**, 391–394 (1947). [*Flexure; solution for very slow taper.*]

129. **E. N. Pinson,** "Computing Vocal Tract Shapes to Yield Specific Tract Transfer Functions," Paper A37 in *Proceedings of the Fifth International Congress on Acoustics, 1965, Liège,* D. E. Commins, Ed. (Imprimerie Georges Thone, Liège, 1965), Vol. 1a. [*Iterative perturbation of guessed area function to approximate given formant frequencies.*]

130. **L. A. Pipes,** "Computation of the Impedances of Nonuniform Lines by a Direct Method," Trans. AIEE **75**, 551–554 (1956); "Electrical Circuit Analysis of Torsional Oscillations," J. Appl. Phys. **14**, 352–362 (1943). [*Riccati impedance equation (with examples) and numerical solution by "method of reversion."*]

131. **M. M. Pisarevskii,** "Calculation of Transition Rods for Magnetostrictive Transducers" (in Russian), in *Calculation of Magnetostrictive Transducers* (Moskovskii Dom Nauchno-Tekhnicheskoe Propagandy, Moscow, 1957); see also Ref. Zh. Mekhan. **1961,** No. 9V99(A) (1961). [*Exponential, conical, parabolic, catenoidal, composites.*]

132. **L. Pochhammer,** "On the Velocity of Propagation of Small Vibrations in an Infinite, Isotropic, Circular Cylinder" (in German), J. Reine u. Angew. Math. (Crelle) **81,** 324–336 (1876). [*Three-dimensional solution; a classic.*]

132a. **S. D. Poisson,** "On the Motion of Elastic Fluids in Cylindrical Pipes, and on the Theory of Wind Instruments" (in French), Mém. Acad. Sci. (Paris) **2,** 305–402 (1819). [*Two tubes of differing diameter, pp. 354–372; one uniform tube, two materials, pp. 372–402.*]

133. **V. L. Pokrovskii, F. R. Ulinich, and S. K. Savvinykh,** "Local Reflection in Waveguides of Varying Cross Section," Dokl. Akad. Nauk (SSSR) **120,** 504–506 (1958) [English transl.: Soviet Phys.—Dokl. **3,** 580–583 (1958)]; "Non-Local Reflection in Waveguides of Varying Cross Section," *ibid.* **124,** 304–306 (1959) [English transl.: *ibid.* **4,** 108–110 (1959)]. [*Slow, arbitrary taper; modified WKBJ solution.*]

134. **H. Pursey,** "Effect of Variation in Diameter on the Torsional Vibration of Bars," Nature **170,** 502(L) (1952). [*Solution for very slow taper.*]

135. **R. W. Pyle, Jr.,** *Solid Torsional Horns,* Harvard Univ. Acoust. Res. Lab. Tech. Mem. No. TM 55 (NR-384–903) (1963); J. Acoust. Soc. Am. **41,** 1147–1156 (1967). [*Extensive, three-dimensional treatment for cylindrically symmetric horns; discusses forms for which equation is separable; detailed discussion of cone; experiments; in this issue.*]

136. **R. W. Pyle, Jr.,** "Duality Principle for Horns," J. Acoust. Soc. Am. **37,** 1178(A) (1965). [*If solution for $A(X)$ is known, so is that for $1/A(X)$.*]

137. **R. H. Quint,** "Note on Longitudinal Vibrational Amplitudes of Solid Conical Horns," J. Acoust. Soc. Am. **26,** 252(L) (1954). [*Magnification of complete cone; puzzling; cf., e.g., Ref. 29.*]

138. **C. Ravut,** "Propagation of Sinusoidal Currents on Non-Uniform Lines" (in French), Rev. Gén. Éléc. **7,** 611–615 (1920). [*Infinite-series method for general taper; based on Taylor series.*]

139. **F. H. Raymond,** "On Propagation in a Nonuniform Line" (in French), J. Phys. Radium **7,** 171–177 (1946). [*Infinite-series method; especially interested in reflection and transmission coefficients.*]

142. **Y. Rocard,** "Parabolic Surfaces in Acoustics" (in French), Rev. Acoust. **1,** 222–231 (1932). [*Gas; three-dimensional with simplifications.*]

143. **Y. Rocard,** "Propagation of Sound Waves of Finite Amplitude" (in French), Compt. Rend. **196,** 161–164 (1933); "Propagation of Sound Waves of Finite Amplitude; Harmonics Produced during Propagation" (in French), Rev. Acoust. **3,** 192–197, 261 (Erratum) (1934). [*Exponential; cf. Ref. 53.*]

144. **Y. Rocard,** *General Dynamics of Vibrations* (in French) (Masson et Cie., Paris, 1959), 3rd ed. [English transl.: W. T. Stern *et al.*, Ungar, New York, 1960). [*Chapters 22–25* (English ed.) *contain a very illuminating treatment of gas-filled horns, including finite amplitude, and behavior below cutoff frequency,*]

144a. **A. Rosenblatt,** "On the Hyperbolic Horn with Elliptic Section. I. Fundamental Equations. II. Expression for the Impedance" (in Spanish), Rev. Cienc. (Lima) **47,** 301–324, 361–388 (1945). [*Solution of $c^2\Delta V - \partial^2 V/\partial t^2 = 0$, by separation of variables.*]

145. **W. T. Rouleau and F. J. Young,** "Distortion of Short Pulses in Tapered Tube Pulse Transformers," J. Basic Eng. **87,** 465–470 ("Part I—Inviscid Liquid"), 471–477 ("Part II—Viscous Liquid") (1965).

146. **R. Rüdenberg,** "The Propagation of Electric Waves on Conductors with Nonuniform Characteristics" (in German), Elektrotech. u. Maschinenbau **31,** 421–429 (1913). Also comment on this paper by **J. Wallot,** *ibid.* **32,** 607–608 (1914). [*Very interesting, early, detailed treatment, including a transformation of the usual equations and a method of synthesis of lines; not all the conclusions are sound.*]

146a. **A. A. W. Ruhrmann,** "The Propagation of Energy on Transmission Lines with Exponentially Varying Characteristic Impedance" (in German), Hochfreq. u. Elektroakust. **58,** 61–69 (1941); "Improvement of the Transformation Characteristics of the Exponential Line by Compensating Loads" (in German), Arch. Elek. Übertrag. **4,** 23–31 (1950); "The Exponential Line at the Critical Wavelength and in the Cutoff Region" (in German), *ibid.* **4,** 401–412 (1950). [*Very comprehensive.*]

147. **L. T. Russell and H. S. Heaps,** "Family of Cylindrical Velocity Transformers; Study by Analog Computer Techniques," J. Acoust. Soc. Am. **38,** 47–49 (1965). [*Set a special form of solution (cf. Refs. 77, 127) and study horns belonging to that class.*]

147a. **H. Ryffert,** "On the Propagation of 'Exponentially Bounded' Waves of Finite Amplitude" (in German), Acta Phys. Polon. **14,** 435–445 (1955). [*Curved wavefronts; air.*]

148. **V. Salmon,** "Generalized Plane Wave Horn Theory," J. Acoust. Soc. Am. **17,** 199–211 (1946). [*Schrödinger form, leading to separation of effects of profile and frequency and to method of synthesis; extensive discussion; a classic.*]

149. **V. Salmon,** "A New Family of Horns," J. Acoust. Soc. Am. **17,** 212–218 (1946). [*Method of Ref. 148 leads to important family $A \propto (e^{\beta X} + \alpha e^{-\beta X})^2$, "hypex."*]

150. **Y. Satô and T. Usami,** "Basic Study on the Oscillation of a Homogeneous Elastic Sphere," Geophys. Mag. (Tokyo) **31,** 15–62 (1962). [*Computed results of exact theory.*]

152. **S. A. Schelkunoff,** "Remarks concerning Wave Propagation in Stratified Media," Commun. Pure & Appl. Math. **4,** 117–128 (1951). [*From point of view of reflections, but not restricted to very small reflections; cf. Refs. 33, 122.*] "Solution of Linear and Slightly Nonlinear Differential Equations," Quart. Appl. Math. **3,** 348–355 (1946). [*Solution, especially of transmission-line equations, as perturbations of known solutions; very clear.*]

153. **W. Schottky,** "Elementary Theory of the Band Loudspeaker" (in German), Elek. Nachr.-Tech. **2,** 157–175 (1925).

153a. **E. Schrödinger,** "Quantization as an Eigenvalue Problem" (in German), Ann. Physik (Leipzig) Ser. 4, "Part 1: The Hydrogen Atom," **79,** 361–376 (1926); "Part 2: The Hamiltonian Analogy between Mechanics and Optics," **79,** 489–527 (1926); "Part 3: Perturbation Theory, with Application to the Stark Effect of the Balmer Lines," **80,** 437–490 (1926); "Part 4," **81,** 109–139 (1926). [English transl.: *E. Schrödinger, Collected Papers on Wave Mechanics* (Blackie & Son, London, 1928), pp. 1–12, 13–40, 62–101, 102–123; summary, pp. ix–xiii.]

153b. **M. R. Schroeder,** "Determination of the Geometry of the Human Vocal Tract by Acoustic Measurements," J. Acoust Soc. Am. **41,** 1002–1010 (1967). [*From eigenfrequencies or from impedance at lips.*]

153c. **R. F. Schwartz,** "Transformations in the Analysis of Nonuniform Transmission Lines," J. Franklin Inst. **278,** No. 3, 163–172 (1964). [*New solutions from known solutions; bibliography.*]

154. **R. I. Ŝcibor-Marchocki,** "Analysis of Hypex Horns," J. Acoust. Soc. Am. **27,** 939–946 (1955). [*Impedances; Riccati equation; use of Smith chart; losses.*]

155. **H. J. Scott,** "The Hyperbolic Transmission Line as a Matching Section," Proc. IRE **41,** 1654–1657 (1953). [*Low-reflection approximation.*]

**155a. B. Sen,** "Torsional Oscillations in a Conical Rod" (in German), Z. Tech. Phys. **14**, 428–429 (1933). [*Three-dimensional solution; not restricted to thin rod.*]

**156. A. K. Sengupta,** "Note on the Torsional Vibration of a Thin Beam of Varying Cross-Section," Indian J. Theoret. Phys. **11**, 101–103 (1963). [*Fixed-free Bessel; $A \propto (X_0+X)$ in Eq. 1c.*]

**157. C. B. Sharpe,** "An Alternative Derivation of Orlov's Synthesis Formula for Non-Uniform Lines," Proc. Inst. Elec. Engrs. (London) **109C**, 226–229 (1962). [*Integral equation; cf. Ref. 119.*]

**158. V. V. Shevchenko,** "Irregular Acoustic Waveguides" (in Russian), Akust. Zh. **7**, 484–491 (1961) [English transl.: Soviet Phys.—Acoust. **7**, 392–397 (1962)]. [*Extension of Ref. 74 to varying $\rho$, E.*]

**159. E. Sittig,** "An Acoustic Impedance Transformer Using an Inverted Solid Cone," IEEE Trans. Ultrasonics Eng. **10**, 104–106 (Sept. 1963).

**160. J. C. Snowdon,** "Longitudinal Vibration of Internally Damped Rods," J. Acoust. Soc. Am. **36**, 502–510 (1964). [*Graphs for several systems, including exponential horn and cylinder of finite diameter.*]

**161. S. Spinner and R. C. Valore, Jr.,** "Comparison of Theoretical and Empirical Relations between the Shear Modulus and Torsional Resonance Frequencies for Bars of Rectangular Cross Section," J. Res. Natl. Bur. Std. (U.S.) **60**, 459–464 (1958). **S. Spinner, T. W. Reichard, and W. E. Tefft,** "A Comparison of Experimental and Theoretical Relations between Young's Modulus and the Flexural and Longitudinal Resonance Frequencies of Uniform Bars," *ibid.* **64A**, 147–155 (1960).

**162. A. T. Starr,** "The Nonuniform Transmission Line," Proc. IRE **20**, 1052–1063, 1553–1554 (Errata) (1932). [*Bessel; $A \propto X^{\alpha}$, $\rho \propto X^{\beta}$.*]

**163. H. Stenzel,** "On the Theory and Application of Horn Loudspeakers" (in German), Z. Tech. Phys. **12**, 621–627 (1931); Allgem. Elek. Ges. Mitteil. **5**, 310–316 (1931). [*Bessel, exponential.*]

**164. A. F. Stevenson,** "Exact and Approximate Equations for Wave Propagation in Acoustic Horns," J. Appl. Phys. **22**, 1461–1463 (1951). [*Gas; three-dimensional theory for general horn; important.*]

**165. G. W. Stewart,** "The Performance of Conical Horns," Phys. Rev. **16**, 313–326 (1920); "Note on Hoersch's Theory of the Optimum Angle of a Receiving Conical Horn," *ibid.* **25**, 230–231 (1925). [*End effects.*]

**166. J. W. Strutt, Lord Rayleigh,** *The Theory of Sound* (Macmillan & Co., London, 1894; reprinted Dover Publications Inc., New York, 1945), 2nd ed., Vol. 1, Chap. 7, pp. 242–254. [*Longitudinal vibration of uniform bars; correction for lateral motion, Art. 157, pp. 251–252.*]

**167. Reference** *166*, Arts. 90–91, pp. 113–118. [*Treatment of one system as a perturbation of another.*]

**168. J. W. Strutt, Lord Rayleigh,** *The Theory of Sound* (Macmillan & Co., London, 1896; reprinted Dover Publications Inc., New York, 1945), 2nd ed., Vol. 2, Arts. 280–281, pp. 112–115. [*Spherical waves in a cone; gas.*]

**168a. Reference** *168*, Art. 249, pp. 30–32. [*Nonlinearity in gases.*]

**168b. J. W. Strutt, Lord Rayleigh,** "On the Propagation of Sound in Narrow Tubes of Variable Section," Phil. Mag. Ser. 6, **31**, 89–96 (1916); reprinted in *Scientific Papers by Lord Rayleigh* (Cambridge University Press, London; Vols. 1–6, 1899–1920; reprinted by Dover Publications, Inc., New York, 1964), Vol. 6, paper No. 402, pp. 376–382. [*Two cases: (1) little change in a wavelength; (2) change complete in much less than a wavelength. In (1), assumes circular section and deduces equations of successively higher approximation from specialization of $\nabla^2\phi+k^2\phi=0$. One of these is Eq. 1c. Solutions in quadratures. Also solutions of successively higher approximation for (2).*]

**168c. I. Sugai,** "A New Exact Method of Nonuniform Transmission Lines," Proc. IRE **49**, 627–628(L) (1961). [*Inverse method; families of solutions.*]; "Variationally Minimum Reflection Coefficient for Nonuniform Transmission Lines," Proc. IEEE **51**, 1789–1790(L) (1963).

**169. C. Sugi,** "Analysis of Catenoidal Solid-Horn and Its Design Method" (in Japanese; English abstr.), J. Acoust. Soc. Japan **18**, No. 2, 54–64 (1962) English transl.: No. 96U99J from Assoc. Tech. Services, Inc., P.O. Box 271, E. Orange, N. J.; filed with Special Libraries Transl. Pool, Chicago]. [*Includes treatment of loads; detailed.*]

**169a. C. Sugi,** "Four-Terminal Equivalent Circuit of Solid Horn and Its Transmission Characteristics" (in Japanese; English abstr.), Yamanashi Univ. Dept. Eng. Res. Rept. No **11**, 95–103 (Dec. 1960) [English transl.: No. 95U99J from Assoc. Tech. Services, Inc., PO Box 271, E. Orange, N. J.; filed with Special Libraries Transl. Pool, John Crerar Library, Chicago]. [*Impedance relations for "hypex," with cone, exponential, catenoidal, and parabolic given as special cases; many graphs; detailed and thorough.*]

**170. S. P. Sur,** "A Note on the Longitudinal Propagation of Elastic Disturbance in a Thin Inhomogeneous elastic Rod," Indian J. Theoret. Phys. **9**, 61–67 (1961). [$A'=0=\rho'$; $E \propto e^{\beta X}$]

**171. B. de Szent Nagy,** "Vibration of a Nonhomogeneous String" (in French), Bull. Soc. Math. France **75**, 193–208 (1947); see Math. Revs. **10**, 269(A) (1949). [*Perturbation treatment for change of mass distribution.*]

**172. W. E. Tefft and S. Spinner,** "Torsional Resonance Vibrations of Uniform Bars of Square Cross Section," J. Res. Natl. Bur. Std. (U.S.) **65A**, 167–171 (1961); "Cross-Sectional Correction for Computing Young's Modulus from Longitudinal Resonance Vibrations of Square and Cylindrical Rods," *ibid.* **66A**, 193–197 (1962).

**173. I. I. Teumin,** *Ultrasonic Vibrating Systems* (in Russian) [Gosudarstvennoe Nauchno-Tekhnicheskoe Izdatel'stvo Mashinostroitel'noi Literatury (Mashgiz), Moscow, 1959]. [*Practical aspects, e.g., horn with tool; exponential, cone, catenoidal, composites.*]

**174. I. I. Teumin,** "Efficiency of Ultrasonic Focussing Devices" (in Russian), Akust. Zh. **9**, 205–208 (1963) [English transl.: Soviet Phys.—Acoust. **9**, 165–167 (1963)]. [*Assumptions not clear, at least in translation; not as general as suggested.*]

**175. G. J. Thiessen,** "Resonance Characteristics of a Finite Catenoidal Horn," J. Acoust. Soc. Am. **22**, 558–562 (1950). [*Numerical results; particularly concerned with horn radiating at large end.*]

**175a. F. Thomas,** "Propagation of Current on General Transmission Line," (in French), Rev. Gén. Éléc. **26**, 567–569 (1929).

**175b. A. L. Thuras, R. T. Jenkins, and H. T. O'Neil,** "Extraneous Frequencies Generated in Air Carrying Intense Sound Waves," J. Acoust. Soc. Am. **6**, 173–180 (1935). [*Exponential.*]

**176. R. N. Thurston and M. J. Shapiro,** "Interpretation of Ultrasonic Experiments on Finite-Amplitude Waves," J. Acoust. Soc. Am. **41**, 1112–1125 (1967).

**176a. C. A. Truesdell, III,** *Leonhardi Euleri Opera Omnia*, Ser. II, Vol. 11, Pt. 2: *The Rational Mechanics of Flexible or Elastic Bodies, 1638–1788* (Orell Füssli, Zürich, 1960); principally pp. 301–316. [*Nonuniform string.*]

**176b. C. A. Truesdell, III,** "The Theory of Aerial Sound, 1687–1788," being the Editor's Introduction (pp. VII–CXVIII) to Ref. *42g*, Ser. II, **13** (1955), *Commentationes mechanicae ad theoriam corporum fluidorum pertinentes* (Second Part).

**177. R. Uhrig,** "Finite Computation of Vibrators with Continuously Distributed Mass and Compliance" (in German), Ing.-Arch. **34**, 95–108 (1965). [*Numerical method treating continuous variation as limit of discontinuous.*]

178. **G. Ungeheuer,** *Elemente einer akustischen Theorie der Vokalartikulation* (*Elements of an Acoustic Theory of Vocal Articulation*) (Springer-Verlag, Berlin, 1962), Appendix. [*This contains an excellent summary of the transformations of the Webster equation and their treatment.*]

180. **W. R. Utz,** "Differential Equations of the Torsional Vibration of Tapered Bars," Indian J. Theoret. Phys. **11,** 81–84 (1963). [*Essentially as Ref. 77; fixed-free.*]

181. **V. Vodička,** "A Class of Problems on Longitudinal Vibrations," Quart. Appl. Math. **16,** 11–19 (1958); "Longitudinal Vibrations of a Composite Bar," Z. Angew. Math. u. Phys. **7,** 345–349 (1956). [$A'=0$; *general formulation in terms of discontinuous variation of* $E$ *and* $\rho$.]

182. **V. Vodička,** "Longitudinal Vibrations of a Conical Bar," Appl. Sci. Res. **A11,** 13–16 (1962). [*Fixed-fixed, with otherwise arbitrary initial conditions.*]

183. **V. Vodička,** "Longitudinal Vibrations of a Composite Conical Bar," Öster. Ing.-Arch. **17,** 249–254 (1963). [$E$ *and* $\rho$ *discontinuously variable; otherwise like Ref. 182.*]

184. **V. Vodička,** "Longitudinal Vibrations of Homogeneous Bars with Variable Cross-Section," Czech. J. Phys. **B13,** 771–780 (1963). [*Bessel; initially at rest; force suddenly applied at one end and maintained.*]

185. **V. Vodička,** "On Longitudinal Vibrations in Semi-Infinite Bars" (in Czech.; English abstr.), Česk. Časopis Fys. **13,** 81–86 (1963). [*Exponential; arbitrary initial conditions.*]

185a. **K. W. Wagner,** "The Theory of Nonuniform Transmission Lines" (in German), Arch. Elektrotech. **36,** 69–96 (1942). [*Comprehensive; general loads and "shapes"; detailed treatment of Bessel and exponential.*]

186. **L. R. Walker and N. Wax,** "Non-Uniform Transmission Lines and Reflection Coefficients," J. Appl. Phys. **17,** 1043–1045 (1946). [*Riccati form; reflection coefficient; resonant lengths.*]

187. **A. G. Webster,** "Acoustical Impedance, and the Theory of Horns and of the Phonograph," Proc. Natl. Acad. Sci. (U.S.) **5,** 275–282 (1919). [*The classic, basic paper; introduces acoustic impedance; gives Eq. 1a; analyses cone in some detail, exponential briefly, and says he can solve Gaussian.*]

188. **E. S. Weibel,** "On Webster's Horn Equation," J. Acoust. Soc. Am. **27,** 726–727 (1955). [*Gas; using Hamilton's principle, obtains a simple equation more broadly valid than Webster's.*]

189. **H. A. Wheeler,** "Transmission Lines with Exponential Taper," Proc. IRE **27,** 65–71 (1939). [*Conditions for impedance matching.*]

190. **H. Wittmeyer,** "A Simple Method for the Approximate Computation of All the Torsional Eigenfrequencies of a Rod of Variable Cross-Section" (in German), Ing.-Arch. **20,** 331–336 (1952); "On the Simple, Approximate Calculation of the Flexural Eigenfrequencies of a Bar of Variable Section, Encastred at One End, as Well as the Eigenvalues of Similar Variational Problems" (in German), Z. Angew. Math. u. Mech. **36,** 355–367 (1956); "A New Method for Developing Simple Formulae for the Eigenvalues of Linear, Ordinary, Self-Adjoint Differential Equations," J. Soc. Ind. Appl. Math **6,** 111–143 (1958). [*Remarkably simple method to use.*]

191. **H. Wittmeyer,** "The Influence of Small Changes in the Boundary Conditions on the Fundamental, Torsional Eigenfrequency of a Rod of Variable Section, Built in at One End" (in German), Z. Angew. Math. Mech. **37,** 293–294 (1957); "Torsional Eigenfrequencies of a Rod of Variable Section, Built in at One End, or with Boundary Conditions Differing Slightly from This" (in German), Forsch. Gebiete Ingenieurw. **24,** No. 2, 37–49 (1958).

191a. **R. F. H. Yang,** "Parabolic Transmission Line," Proc. IRE **43,** 1010(L) (1955). [*Arbitrary (cubic) impedance function to match at ends; small-taper approximation; reflection coefficient relatively independent of frequency.*]

192. **F. J. Young,** "The Natural Frequencies of Musical Horns," Acustica **10,** 91–97 (1960).

193. **F. J. Young,** "Family of Bars of Revolution in Longitudinal Half-Wave Resonance," J. Acoust. Soc. Am. **32,** 1263–1264 (1960). [*Algebraic formulas for Bessel horns.*]

194. **F. J. Young,** "Impedance of Tapered Structures," J. Acoust. Soc. Am. **39,** 841–846 (1966). [*Smooth profile as limit of stepped; synthesis.*]

195. **F. J. Young and B. H. Young,** "Impedance of Tapered Structures," J. Acoust. Soc. Am. **33,** 1206–1210 (1961); "Smoothly and Step Tapered Structures," *ibid.* **33,** 813(L) (1961). **A. V. J. Martin and F. J. Young,** "On the Calculation of Lines of Smoothly Variable Impedance" (in French; English abstr.), J. Phys. Radium Ser. 8, **19,** No. 7, Suppl., 65A–70A (1958). [*Include examples.*]

196. **S. Ziemba,** "The Influence of Mass and Internal Friction on Free Torsional Vibrations of a Bar," Arch. Mech. Stos. **9,** 51–72 (1957). [See Math. Revs. **19,** p. 478 (1958), and Appl. Mech. Revs. **12,** No. 6000, 833(A) (1959).]

# 13

*Copyright © 1968 by the New York Academy of Sciences*

Reprinted from *Ann. N.Y. Acad. Sci.*, **155**, 247–263 (1968)

## SOUND PRODUCTION IN WIND INSTRUMENTS*

A. H. Benade
*Case Western Reserve University, Cleveland, Ohio*

D. J. Gans
*University of Illinois, Urbana, Ill.*

### I. Introduction

This report on sound production in musical wind instruments is intended, first, to sketch the basic nonlinear mechanism whereby oscillations are maintained. Experimental evidence to support the theory is then presented, after which several applications of the theory are made to various aspects of the behavior of wind instruments. Following this, an outline of the way in which a wind instrument distributes the player's input energy among the various kinds of dissipation is presented. It sets forth briefly the relation between these dissipative effects and the generally small amount of radiated energy that constitutes the desired musical output of the instrument.

Many parts of the data referred to in this report were obtained from experiments that were performed at Case Institute (now Case Western Reserve University), and most of the analysis is carried out using theoretical methods that have already been published. The section on nonlinear oscillation theory had its origin in some rough and speculative calculations contained in a report written by the senior author early in 1958 for the C. G. Conn company at the request of Earl L. Kent. A more developed version of the theory formed the background for much of the discussion of sound production in a book on musical acoustics that was published in 1960.[1] Later, the two present authors collaborated in a more detailed analysis of the problem, and our report here is a condensation and extension of that analysis, as supported by a considerable body of later experimental observation.

This report has been designed as a summary of our present understanding of the subject as a whole rather than as a detailed report on the exact numerical relations that apply to any particular musical instrument. An attempt has been made, however, to indicate the methods that have been used in obtaining each particular piece of information and to point out features of particular musical instruments that might illustrate the important principles. In keeping with this, our references to the literature have been chosen to be illustrative rather than to be complete in any sense.

### II. Nonlinear Excitation of Air Column Oscillations

We assume that we are dealing with a self-excited system in which a disturbance originating at the reed (flow-controller) end travels the length of the air column, is reflected, and returns to the reed to initiate and control the next cycle of operation. In making the round trip, the disturbance may be changed in both form and amplitude because of the filtering action of the finger holes, the peculiarities of

* Parts of this work have been assisted by grants from The Case Research Fund, The Cleveand Foundation, and The Research Corporation.

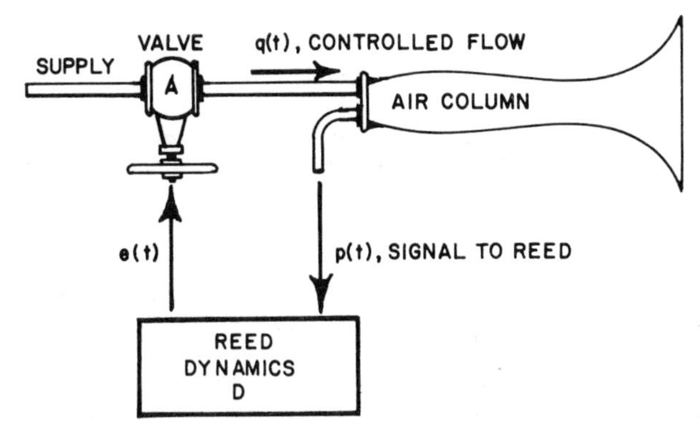


FIGURE 1. Schematic diagram of the feedback mechanism of a pressure-controlled wind instrument. The relation between the flow rate, q(t), and the pressure, p(t), is mediated by the reed dynamics, and the valve opening is a nonlinear function of the control signal, e(t).

air column shape, the radiation from the open end, the energy losses to the pipe walls, etc., all of which are sensitive functions of frequency. We make the further (realistic) assumption that the new disturbance initiated by the reed under the influence of the reflected impulse will be functionally complicated, not only because of such factors as reed inertia, elasticity, and damping, but more importantly, because in its action as a valve, the reed does not give a flow that is in simple proportion to the signal that controls it. Consider the schematic representation given in FIGURE 1. The volume flow, q(t), of air into the pipe is determined at any instant by the valve signal, e(t), according to the transconductance relation given by Equation 1.

$$q = A_0 + A_1 e + A_2 e^2 \ldots\ldots A_N e^N$$
$$= \sum_{k=0}^{N} A_k e^k \qquad (1)$$

The $k = 0$ term in this summation represents steady leakage of air through the valve independently of the size of the valve signal. The second term, $A_1[e(t)]^1$, represents a flow that is directly proportional to the first power of the activating signal, while the higher-order terms represent contributions to the flow that are proportional to higher powers of the controlling signal.

### *A. The Pressure-Controlled Reed: Formulation*

If the feedback system is pressure-controlled, as in the reed woodwinds and brasses, the signal e(t) that controls the air flow is derived from p(t), the pressure in the bore at the mouthpiece, as modified by the physical response characteristics (elasticity, damping, and inertia) of the reed. This modification is symbolized in FIGURE 1 by the box labeled Reed Dynamics, while the mathematical representation of this aspect of the reed behavior is implied by the symbol D. In terms of observable quantities, then, the controlled airflow through the valve is related to the mouthpiece pressure p as follows:

$$q = \sum_k A_k (pD)^k \qquad (2)$$

Upon the basis of the ordinary definition of the input impedance of an air column, the relation between the pressure and the flow rate at the input end is given by

$$p(t) = Z \cdot q(t) \tag{3}$$

We can combine Equations 2 and 3 now to give a symbolic representation for the (air column + reed) feedback system, as shown in Equation 4:

$$p/Z = \sum_{k}^{N} A_k (pD)^k \tag{4}$$

It is to be borne clearly in mind that Equations 3 and 4 have no more than formal significance, because p(t) and q(t) are general waveforms whose Fourier spectra contain many frequencies, whereas the Z and D coefficients represent changes in magnitude and phase, which have meaning only for a definite single frequency. In any event, Equation 4 represents the regeneration of the *system,* and since the disturbances of interest are necessarily periodic (if N is finite), we may expand p(t) in a Fourier series of cosines, using the playing frequency $\omega$ as the fundamental.

$$p(t) = \sum_{n=o}^{\infty} p_n \cos n\omega t \tag{5}$$

Incorporating Equation 5 into Equation 4, and observing the convention that the lower-case letters $z_n$ and $d_n$ represent the magnitudes of the quantities Z and D evaluated at the frequencies $n\omega$, which are harmonics of the playing frequency, and that $\alpha n$ and $\beta n$ represent the tangents of the phase shifts produced by these parameters, we obtain

$$\begin{aligned} &\sum_{n} (p_n/z_n)(\cos n\omega t + \alpha_n \sin n\omega t) \\ &= \sum_{k} A_k \left\{ \sum_{n} (p_n d_n)(\cos n\omega t + \beta_n \sin n\omega t) \right\}^k \end{aligned} \tag{6}$$

Equation 6 is an extremely unwieldy expression from the point of mathematical solution or even manipulation. It will, therefore, be necessary to chip away at it in segments, to find out some of its major implications. In what follows, certain examples will be presented to illustrate important features, with the assertion that the conclusions drawn with the aid of these examples have been verified by numerous algebraic experiments and that they are also supported by experimental observations on various musical instruments. The important results of our investigations will be summarized in the form of numbered "Fundamental Principles" that are set off from the body of the text.

### *B. The Linear Pressure-Controlled Case (N = 1)*

In conventional oscillation theory, the assumption is made that the entire system is linear, with the result that each normal vibrational mode of the air column interacts with the reed mechanism independently of the possible existence of other modal vibrations. Let us see how this appears in the present format, by restricting the summation over k on the right side of Equation 7 to the values 0 and 1:

$$\begin{aligned} &\sum_{n} (p_n/z_n)(\cos n\omega t + \alpha_n \sin n\omega t) \\ &= A_0 + A_1 \sum_{n} (p_n d_n)(\cos n\omega t + \beta_n \sin n\omega t) \end{aligned} \tag{7}$$

If the solution is to be independent of time, there must be a "spectral balance" between the two sides of Equation 7. That is, the coefficients of each cosine term taken by itself must be consistent, and the same is true for each sine term. For the n'th harmonic, we find then for the cosines ($n = 0$)

$$(P_n/z_n) = A_1 (p_n d_n) \qquad \textbf{(8a)}$$

and for the sines

$$(\alpha_n P_n/z_n) = A_1 (\beta_n p_n d_n) \qquad \textbf{(8b)}$$

These equations together show that for a given reed system (specified A's and D's), the system can oscillate steadily a frequency (represented here by $n\omega$) for which $\alpha_n = \beta_n$, provided that at this frequency

$$z_n = 1/(A_1 d_n) \qquad \textbf{(9)}$$

From this, we see among other things that the input impedance z, which can be kept in oscillation by a given reed, must be larger than a certain minimum value, so that the favored frequencies are approximately equal to the closed-pipe resonances of the air column. Thus for a "linear" type of clarinet we would expect the playing frequencies to be members of the 1, 3, 5 harmonic sequence based on $\omega_{min} = (\pi c/2L)$ for a cylindrical pipe of length L.

Traditionally one ignores the possibility of $z_n$ being larger than the threshold value implied above, and various self-limiting mechanisms are (correctly) invoked, without investigating the wider implications of their presence. For present purposes we may summarize the salient features of a linear regeneration process as follows:

Fundamental Principles (Linear Pressure-Controlled Systems)

1. A given reed structure will tend to maintain oscillation at any frequency where the air column input impedance is large.
2. The actual oscillation frequency is off resonance by just enough to make the phase shift $\alpha_n$ between pressure and flow in the mouthpiece offset the phase shift $\beta_n$ arising from the inertia and stiffness of the reed.
3. The linearity of the system implies that a number of such oscillations can take place simultaneously at the different impedance maxima *without mutual interaction* (as shown by the fact that there is no mixing of different values of n in Equation 8).
4. Because the frequencies of maximum input impedance coincide with the normal mode resonance frequencies belonging to the air column if it were closed off at the reed end, the linear oscillator gives sounds which correspond to the traditional "stopped pipe" schema. *The form of the regeneration equations shows, however, that this behavior is independent of whether or not the reed actually does close the pipe.*

If the condition of Equation 9 is *precisely* satisfied, oscillation is possible for the n'th harmonic. In reality, Equation 9 cannot be precisely satisfied. If $z_n$ does not equal $1/(A_1 d_n)$, the oscillation of the n'th harmonic is unstable and grows or shrinks exponentially in amplitude according as $z_n$ is too large or too small. This implies that in an (almost strictly) linear musical instrument, the tonal quality (Fourier spectrum) would be undefined, and the various harmonics would grow or die away according to the vagaries of the player, of the air column, and of the reed. This is clearly not the case in practice: Every instrument, in association with its own player, has a characteristic tone color. This can be altered within limits, but in musically useful fashion, by the player as he changes the detailed nature of his reed and embouchure.

*C. The Quadratic Pressure-Controlled Case ($N = 2$)*

Let us turn now to the simplest possible nonlinear case, where the transconductance of the reed is such that one part of the airflow through it is proportional to the square of the internal pressure in the mouthpiece. Our basic equation (Equation 6) now has the appearance of Equation 7 with an additional set of terms proportional to $A_2$. These *new* terms are set out in Equation 10:

$$\left\{\sum_n (p_n d_n)(\cos n\omega t + \beta_n \sin \omega t)\right\}^2$$

$$= \tfrac{1}{2}\sum_{i,j}^{N} (p_i d_i)(p_j d_j) \cdot \left\{\begin{array}{c} (1 - \beta_i\beta_j)\cos(i + j)\omega t \\ (1 + \beta_i\beta_j)\cos(i - j)\omega t \\ +(\beta_i + \beta_j)\sin(i + j)\omega t \\ +(\beta_i - \beta_j)\sin(i - j)\omega t \end{array}\right\} \qquad \textbf{(10)}$$

Let us write out schematically the equation that governs the amplitudes of the first three harmonic cosine terms. These are based on Equation 6 and filled out with the help of Equation 10:

$$p_1/z_1 = A_1 p_1 d_1 + A_2 \cdot \left\{\begin{array}{l} \text{sum of combinations} \\ \text{of } p_i \text{ and } p_j \text{ with} \\ i \pm j = 1 \end{array}\right\} \qquad \textbf{(11a)}$$

$$p_2/z_2 = A_1 p_2 d_2 + A_2 \cdot \left\{\begin{array}{c} \text{terms with} \\ i \pm j = 2 \end{array}\right\} \qquad \textbf{(11b)}$$

$$p_3/z_3 = A_1 p_3 d_3 + A_2 \cdot \left\{\begin{array}{c} \text{terms with} \\ i \pm j = 3 \end{array}\right\} \qquad \textbf{(11c)}$$

It is apparent that the terms in $(i \pm j)$ on the right intercouple the equations, so that each pressure component of the generated sound spectrum is affected by all the rest. It is at this place that we learn formally the basis of an idea that we may enunciate as the first of a pair of fundamental principles:

Fundamental Principle 1 (Nonlinear Pressure-Controlled Systems)

Because of the intercoupling of spectral terms, a nonlinear reed mechanism automatically leads to a definite sound spectrum, whose nature is controlled by the detailed nature of the air column impedance function $Z(n\omega)$ and that of the reed response as represented by the function $D(n\omega)$.

We now illustrate the major difference between the conditions favoring oscillation in linear systems and those required in nonlinear systems. Let the air column be of such a shape that all the z's are negligibly small, except for $z_2$ and $z_4$. This implies that the pressure amplitudes of all the Fourier harmonics are essentially "shortcircuited" except for the two components whose frequencies are 2 and 4. Equations 11a, 11b, and 11c then reduce to two, as follows:

$$p_2/z_2 = A_1 (p_2 d_2) + A_2 (p_4 d_4)(p_2 d_2)(1 + \beta_1 \beta_2) \qquad \textbf{(12a)}$$

$$p_4/z_4 = A_1 (p_4 d_4) + A_2 (p_2 d_2)^2/2(1 - \beta_1 \beta_2) \qquad \textbf{(12b)}$$

Let us solve these simultaneously for the transconductance coefficients $A_1$ and $A_2$:

$$A_1 = \left[\frac{1}{z_2 z_4 d_2}\right] \cdot \left[\frac{(p_2 d_2)^2 z_4 - 2(p_4 d_4)^2 (d_2/d_4)\, z_2}{(p_2 d_2)^2 - 2(p_4 d_4)^2}\right] \quad \textbf{(13a)}$$

$$A_2 = \left[\frac{(p_4 d_4)}{z_2 z_4}\right] \cdot \left[\frac{(z_2/d_4) - (z_4/d_2)}{(p_2 d_2)^2 - 2(p_4 d_4)^2}\right] \quad \textbf{(13b)}$$

The fact that *both* $A_1$ and $A_2$ must, among other things, be proportional to the *product* of $z_2$ and $z_4$ shows that for a given reed (specified A's) oscillation is favored when *both* impedances are large and remains possible if one of them is large enough so that the product of the two is sufficiently large. This result is an illustration of a general property of this class of nonlinear systems. The property can be expressed as the second of our fundamental principles:

Fundamental Principle 2 (Nonlinear Pressure-Controlled Systems)

Oscillation is favored at a frequency for which the air column input impedance is large (as in linear systems), and oscillation is also favored if the impedance is large at some or all of the harmonics of this frequency.

### *D. The Velocity-Controlled Reed System*

The physical structure and playing behavior of the flute and recorder family of instruments show that here the feedback mechanism is of a different sort from that described above. In the flute family, there is an aperture to the open air at the upper end of the instrument across which an air jet is blown by the player. This air jet is caused to blow alternately into the air column and out into the air, as a result of the waves set up in the instrument bore. We are not interested here in the specific details of the viscoaerodynamics of this interaction, but only in the fact that there is such an interaction. It has been generally accepted that this is a velocity-dependent interaction (if only because of momentum considerations), but this assumption has been disputed from time to time. We shall shortly see in a very direct way that the overt behavior of actual instruments confirms the velocity-control assumption.

Let us assume that the flow-control signal, $e(t)$, of Equation 1 is derived from the flow-rate, $q(t)$, at the player's end of the air column, instead of being derived from the pressure at the top end of the air column. Equation 2 then takes on the form

$$q_{input} = \sum_k A_k\, (qD)^k \quad \textbf{(14)}$$

where $q_{input}$ represents the controlled flow into the air column from the player's lungs, $q$ is the flow in and out of the air column through the aperture, and the other terms keep the essentials of their earlier meanings. Standard transmission-line theory now permits us to write the analog to Equation 3, a relation between $q_{input}$ and $q$ as it is determined by the input admittance $Y$ ($=1/Z$) of the air column:

$$q(t) = Y\, q(t)_{input} \quad \textbf{(15)}$$

From here on, the analysis goes exactly as before, with the word "flow" replacing the word "pressure," and with "admittance" replacing "impedance." Attention is called to the fourth of the linear-system fundamental principles enunciated in

Section II, *B*. In the present case, we have a relation between favorable regeneration conditions and the normal mode frequencies of a traditional "unstopped pipe" resonator, and it is for this reason that one can assert that the flute family is indeed a member of the velocity-controlled group of oscillators.

## III. The Tacet Horn: A Test of the Theory

The validity of a theory of nonlinear regeneration in wind instruments is best supported by study of their behavior under conditions of actual use. While certain such examples will be presented in the next section, it is worthwhile to describe some experiments performed on an instrument that was designed to behave in an extremely "pathological" manner, as viewed in the light of traditional (linear) concepts of regeneration, although it acts predictably from the point of view of nonlinear analysis.

### *A. Description of the Instrument*

A horn was designed on the basis of well-known principles to provide an air column whose natural stopped-pipe frequencies (frequencies of maximum input impedance) were chosen to avoid all possible integer relations between them. In a nonlinear system, conditions for oscillation would then be most unfavorable at the normal-mode frequencies, since the impedance would be small at harmonics of the playing frequency. On the other hand, if the reed mechanism were essentially linear in its behavior, oscillation would easily take place at any one of the resonance frequencies, and no other frequencies. Calculation showed that a horn whose radius varies as the square root of the distance from the apex, coupled via a short cylindrical passage to the tapered cavity in the beak of a modified clarinet mouthpiece, should give the desired characteristics.[2] Such an

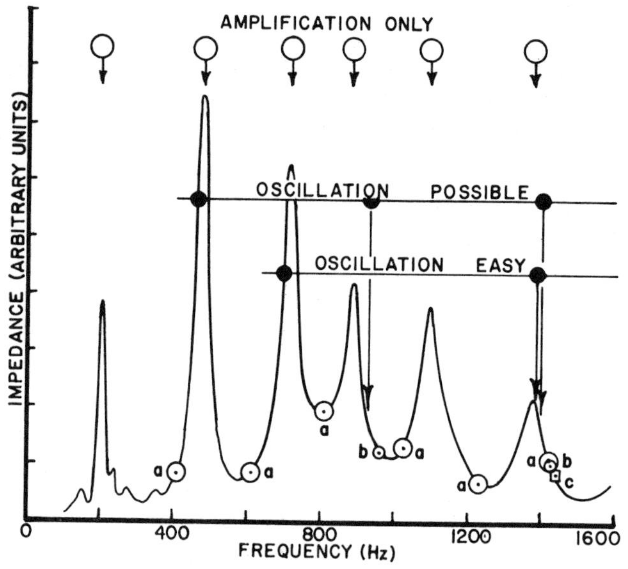


FIGURE 2. Measured impedance curve of the tacet-horn. The circles marked "a" indicate the low impedance valves observed at frequencies that are harmonics of the lowest resonance frequency. The circles "b" and "c" indicate similarly the impedances at harmonics of the second and third resonances.

instrument was constructed out of fiberglass and epoxy in the spring of 1964, and its characteristics were found to agree exactly with those desired. FIGURE 2 shows, among other things, the input impedance of this horn as a function of frequency. The design's success is shown by the low value of the impedance at harmonics of the first-mode frequency (indicated by open circles marked "a") and also at harmonics of the second and third mode-resonance frequencies (as shown by the points marked with "b" and "c" respectively). Viscous losses in the horn throat, the shunting effect of the mouthpiece cavity volume, and radiation losses at the open end cause the input impedance to remain small and relatively uniform at frequencies above 2kHz. During its construction, considerable humor was engendered in the laboratory concerning this horn, and since it was designed to be maximally difficult to play, it came to be called the tacet horn, in anticipation of success.

### *B. Experiments with the Horn*

When a clarinetist attempts to play upon this horn with the help of a standard reed, he eventually succeeds in obtaining a raucous sound whose fundamental frequency is 692 Hz. This is considerably lower than the 724 Hz frequency of the third normal mode of the horn, but the impedance is still reasonably high (see FIGURE 2). Furthermore, the impedance at the second harmonic of the playing frequency is also high, falling as it does near the peak of the sixth resonance. The black dots on the horizontal line labelled "Oscillation Easy" in FIGURE 2 indicate the frequency of the fundamental and its harmonic, as just described. The possibility of an oscillation of this sort is consistent with the second of the fundamental principles enunciated for nonlinear systems in Section II, *C*, and clearly inconsistent with the principles as set forth for linear systems in Section II, *B*, since none of the sounds associated with the separate normal modes of the horn could be excited at all.

It is possible also to start an oscillation whose fundamental frequency lies at 472 Hz, just below the second resonance peak (located at 477 Hz.). In FIGURE 2, this frequency and its harmonics are indicated as black spots on the horizontal line labelled "Oscillation Possible." Here we see an oscillation that is favored because the impedance is large not only at the playing frequency, but also at one of its harmonics. The regeneration is made slightly difficult here because the impedance is low at the second harmonic, even though it is large again at the third harmonic. We omit comment here on the effect of change in the phase relations between airflow and pressure at frequencies that lie above and below a resonance, since it is a matter for straightforward analysis.

Although the damping of the resonances in this horn is considerably lower than that which a clarinet reed can overcome in sustaining oscillation in a more conventional air column, we have seen that the present system is not able to set up oscillations at the ordinary resonance frequencies. The blown reed *can*, however, amplify at these frequencies. If a small earphone is driven by means of an audio oscillator at one of the air column resonance frequencies, a microphone placed next to it will pick up the radiated sound. Bringing the open end of the horn near these two transducers will alter the observed signal only slightly due to ordinary resonance effects. If now the reed is blown, a signal gain of 10 to 30 decibels is easily obtained, due to the cooperation of the reed mechanism with the injected sound wave. The subjective "feel" of the reed to the player also becomes less abnormal. This amplification phenomenon is observed to take place most strongly at frequencies in the immediate neighborhood of the resonances, but it takes place to a lesser extent elsewhere. In FIGURE 2, the frequencies at which strong amplification can take place without sustained oscillation are indicated at the top of the drawing by means of open circles with arrows.

## IV. Musical Implications of Nonlinear Regeneration

In this section we shall sketch the relation of our fundamental principles governing nonlinear regeneration to various phenomena that are observed in musical wind instruments. Some of these phenomena are familiar to the practising musician, and some are familiar to the makers of these instruments as part of their trade, often to the point where they are taken for granted as being intuitively obvious.

### *A. Privileged Notes*

The players of brass instruments sometimes become aware of notes that can be played more or less easily, located at frequencies different from the natural frequencies of the air column. Forty years ago, Bouasse[3] gave these additional notes the felicitous name "privileged notes" to set them apart from the normally expected harmonic series that the brasses are designed to produce. These extra notes are found at frequencies that are integral submultiples of the normal-mode frequencies of the air column. That is, regeneration can take place at privileged frequencies $\omega_{mn}$, which are related to the frequencies $\omega_n$ of the normal modes according to the formula

$$\omega_{mn} = \omega_n/m \qquad (16)$$

Here n is the serial number of th normal mode, and m is an integer. An elementary account of some of the musical consequences of these privileged notes, along with a description of an easily-performed experiment to measure some of them, is described in Chapter VIII of Reference 1. An identical behavior is observed in reed organ pipes when the voicer slides the tuning wire over a large range: The pitch seems to "hang up" at certain well-defined frequencies, and Equation 16 gives their relation to the resonances of the pipe.

The explanation of these privileged notes is to be found in terms of Fundamental Principle 2 in Section II, *C,* to the effect that oscillation is favored at frequencies of such a type that the impedance is large either *at* these frequencies or *at their harmonics.* We have remarked already that the normal mode frequencies are those for which the input impedance is high, so that the privileged frequency $\omega_{mn}$ is found at a frequency of such a type that its m'th harmonic lies near the n'th-mode resonance peak. The forms of Equations 6 and 10 indicate that the order N of the nonlinearity sets an upper limit to the value of m. It also shows that in general, oscillation is favored more for small values of m than it is for large.

### *B. Effect of Bore Shape on Ease of Regeneration and on Intonation*

The heuristic power of the privileged-tone concept is well demonstrated when we consider the relation of the shape of an instrument's bore to the ease with which a given note is produced. The bore shape determines the ratios of the normal-mode (maximum impedance) frequencies, and the favorability for regeneration at particular frequency is greatly increased if the impedance is large simultaneously at the playing frequency *and at its harmonics.* That is, if the frequencies of a whole set of privileged notes coincide (for a particular system), then the regeneration is greatly facilitated. When $\omega_F$ is one of these particularly favored frequencies, the air column is one whose shape gives the relation

$$\omega_F \cong \omega_{mn} \ (= \omega_n/m) \qquad (17)$$

which is to be satisfied for many pairs of integers m and n. This implies that a horn whose shape gives resonance frequencies that are members of a harmonic series is particularly easy to excite by means of a reed mechanism.

As a musical example of this behavior, consider the ordinary trumpet or trombone: Here the bore shape is such that the measured resonance frequencies $\omega_n$ for $n = 2, 3, 4, \ldots$ lie quite close to a 2, 3, 4, . . . harmonic series based on a fundamental frequency that is half the resonance frequency of mode 2. This fundamental frequency is known to brass players as the pedal note. We see that the privileged frequencies for which $m = n$ all cooperate to give good regeneration at the pedal frequency, so much so that it is useful musically in spite of the fact that the lowest mode of these horns, $\omega_1$, lies several semitones (20% to 30%) lower than the pedal note frequency, so that the input impedance is small *at* the pedal note frequency.

Makers of brass instruments are familiar with the fact that moving the resonance frequency of a single one of the higher modes will cause a shift in the playing frequency of notes that are based on lower modes, particularly if these are subharmonically related to the altered resonance. While this is not expected in a strictly linear system, the explanation is clear. Due to nonlinearities, the playing frequency is determined jointly by the impedance of the perturbed resonance, and by the (unaltered) impedances at other frequencies of the played note, so that the change is present, but in diluted form. Very similar effects are also observed in woodwinds, although the small number of air-column modes that are consciously used by the woodwind player makes it a little less easy for him to identify the phenomenon clearly.

Experiments using many shapes of air column, excited by both the clarinet and the oboe type of reeds, indicate that what the musician calls "good resonance," or "easy blowing," as well as "clarity of tone," all correlate well with the presence of a sequence of resonances that are aligned to make the air column input impedance maximally large, not only at the played-note fundamental, but also at several of its neighboring harmonics. It becomes possible to understand, then, why even a slight alteration of a woodwind bore by means of a short hand-reamer can considerably alter the tone and feel of certain notes. The bassoon and the Viennese oboe are particularly sensitive to slight changes produced by reaming, because their construction involves a set of critically proportioned discontinuities at the joints of the bore. Similarly, the instability of the note E on the French-style oboe is at least in part due to a reaction back through the main bore onto the reed of several fortuitous resonances (which are in approximately harmonic relation to one another and to the frequency belonging to the note E) of two lower segments of the bore and bell. These extra resonances arise as a result of the particular way in which the key mechanism provides open and closed holes at the bottom of the instrument. The problem is not present in the Viennese oboe, the so-called military-system oboe, nor in the recently designed Uebel-system oboe, all of which have very different key mechanisms.

### *C. Action of the Register Key in Woodwinds*

The register key acts to shift the played note from an oscillation based on the lowest vibrational mode of the pipe to one based on the second mode. It provides an important illustration of the role played by nonlinearities in the regeneration process in woodwinds. A preliminary investigation in 1958 showed that it would be worthwhile to obtain accurate numerical information on the resonances of a pipe provided with a small side hole placed as is conventional for register holes. A simple case was worked out with the help of a computer in 1959 through the kindness of James Gibson, and in 1964 a similar but much more general calculation was made for us by Robert Stieglitz. The following discussion is based on these calculations, as confirmed by experiment.

FIGURE 3 presents a schematic representation of the impedance curve of a cylindrical tube provided with a closable vent hole whose size and location is consistent with a typical situation obtaining in a clarinet (the pair of notes A and E). In the upper diagram (vent hole closed), the black dots indicate the frequencies of the harmonics belonging to the low-register and to the upper-register played notes. We see that for a clarinet type of instrument, alternate harmonics lie at low points on the impedance curve. Various second-order effects in the theory make the low-register oscillation more favorably sustained than the higher-register oscillation is, as is observed by musicians.

Let us turn now to the case where the vent hole is opened, as illustrated in the lower half of FIGURE 3. Here we see that the major effect of the hole is to raise the lowest resonance frequency by about 23%, leaving the higher modes roughly unchanged. It is at once apparent that an oscillation based on the new lowest mode is unfavored, since most of the harmonics of this frequency fall at points where the impedance is low. On the other hand, the upper-register oscillation conditions have hardly been affected, so that the clarinet settles on this vibrational type for its oscillation. An inexpert player sometimes gets an accidental grunt from his instrument as a part of the starting transient of a note in the upper register. This

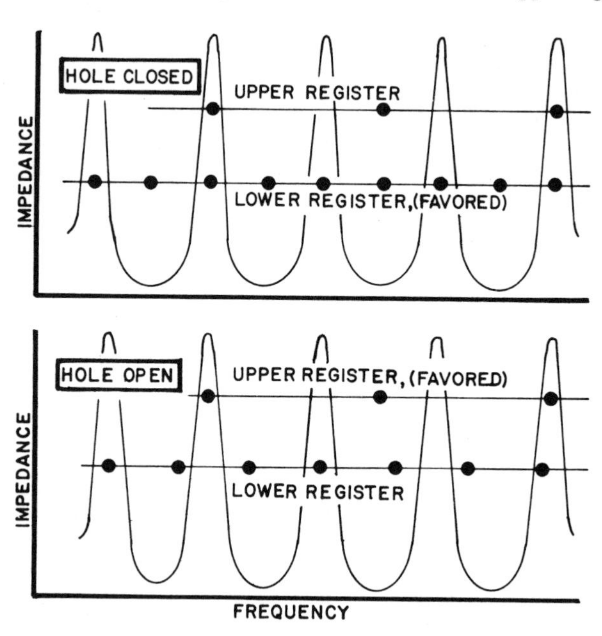


FIGURE 3. Schematic diagram of the relation of the impedance curve to the played-note harmonics for a clarinet with its register key open and closed.

grunt may be identified in frequency as being an unsuccessful beginning of regeneration at the lowest-mode frequency.

The following experiment shows that it is the inharmonicity induced by the vent hole rather than the increased damping that leads to a transition from low to second register: A suitably chosen set of glass-wool tufts can be placed within the tube to lower the resonance peaks of several of the even-numbered modes to values a factor of two below those of the odd-numbered ones. Upon opening the register key, the clarinet makes an unhesitating transition from the lower to the upper register, even though the upper register is more heavily damped. When the key is closed, the tone makes a very prompt transition downward, as is expected for both linear and nonlinear devices.

### D. *Nonlinear Effects in the Flute Type of Instrument*

As pointed out in Section II, *D*, the behavior expected of velocity-controlled nonlinear oscillators is very similar to that of pressure-controlled instruments, if certain systematic modifications are made to the theory. Relatively little work has been done on the flute family to investigate nonlinear effects. These seem, however, to be important, but not so clearly dominant as in the reed woodwinds. A brief report calling attention to the essential presence of nonlinear behavior in flue organ pipes has been published recently.[4] Evidence is presented of the resulting sensitivity of the generated sound spectrum on flue organ pipes to small changes in resonance frequencies and dampings (to changes in the impedance curve).

## V. The Energy-Budget of Wind Instruments

It is of interest to trace the expenditure of the energy that is provided to a wind instrument by its player, and to indicate the mechanisms whereby this energy is ultimately dissipated into heat. We shall not discuss any of the measurements that have been published recently on the actual energy input to wind instruments[5] nor speculate upon the implications of work published in this conference volume. Our attention will instead be focused chiefly on the physics of the instrument itself as it interacts with the airflows through it.

### A. *Preliminary Survey of Loss-Mechanisms*

Figure 4 is a schematic diagram that shows the apportionment of energy expenditure among the various parts of the instrumental mechanism. Let us describe these expenditures briefly in a general way before examining some of them more closely.

First on the list is the reed loss, one contributor to which is the dissipation of energy in friction within the reed material itself and/or in the player's lips as they come in contact with the reed (this distinction between reed and lips is, of course, meaningless in the case of brass instruments). Another contribution arises from the viscous and turbulent loss of energy from the airflow as it is acted on by the valve mechanism of the reed. Very little information is available about the magnitude of this energy expenditure, although there is indirect evidence that suggests that a good-quality instrument played mezzforte and above spends only about 10% of its total budget in this way.

The fact that there is a large-amplitude sound present within the instrument's mouthpiece suggests that energy can be transmitted back through the reed into the player's vocal tract. Stethoscopic observations confirm this, but little is known

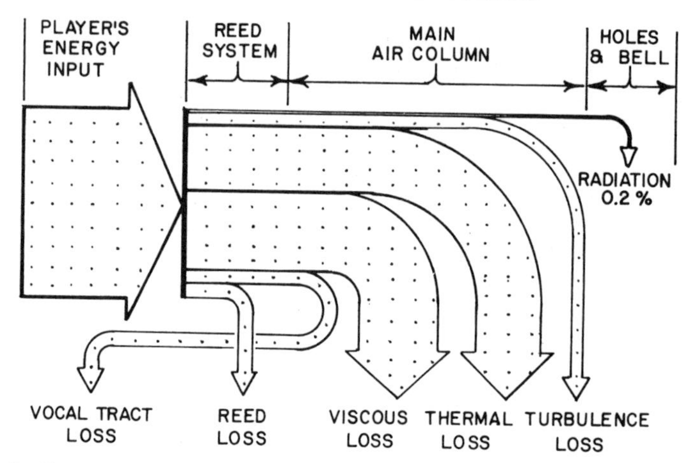


FIGURE 4. Energy budget of a wind instrument. Note the minute amount of energy that is radiated as sound. This amount is increased for the high notes of a saxophone and the highest notes of a brass instrument.

about the amount of energy that escapes from an instrument by this route. An estimate made for the flute type of instrument shows that the loss in the vocal tract might be as high as 15%. One would expect somewhat smaller losses in brass and reed instruments. Estimates of this sort are treacherous, however, because they gloss over the backward transfer of energy through an active, nonlinear, amplifying device.

The viscous loss of energy to the pipe walls, and the loss due to conduction of heat into and out of the air column from the walls during each cycle of the sound wave, together contribute the dominant energy expenditure of most instruments, except in the case of high notes played on saxophones and on brass instruments. This assertion is based on the assumption that the playing is not so loud that there is an appreciable turbulence set up where the instrument's internal wave reacts with the outside wave (at the fingerholes of woodwinds). Considerable study has been given to the mechanism of wall losses, and in the main they are well understood, so that we shall shortly consider them in more detail.

The loss of energy via turbulence at the open finger holes of loudly played woodwinds is easily apparent from the hissing noises that are generated at these holes. There is also a possibility of turbulent loss due to the oscillatory airflow into and out of the *closed* finger holes higher up the bore. There is almost no information on the amount of energy that is abstracted from a musical instrument through the mechanism of turbulence. It is possible to say, however, that laboratory resonance measurements that maintain sound levels with the bore comparable with those attained in pianissimo playing show a *net* energy loss that is equal to the viscous and thermal loss plus the loss to sound that is radiated into the room. We may assume temporarily that only a few percent of the total energy is normally expended in turbulence.

Last on our list, and smallest in magnitude most of the time, is the energy that is radiated from the bell, or from the finger holes of the instrument. It is ironical that the very thing for which a musical instrument is constructed, the generation of sound, should normally find itself as a minor appendage to the other expenditures in the energy budget. The radiation of sound by various systems has been intensely studied for many years, so that the calculation of the radiation from musical instruments is, in principle at least, thoroughly understood. We shall therefore consider it more carefully in subsequent paragraphs.

### *B. Discussion of Viscous Thermal and Radiation Losses*

It can be shown[6] that the rate of thermal energy loss through the boundary layer of a sound field to an area element of its confining walls is proportional to the square of the sound pressure acting on this element of the wall. Similarly, the viscous energy loss rate depends on the squared tangential velocity of the air at the boundary surface element.

Consider the air column enclosed by a horn of length L that lies along the x-axis of a coordinate system, and let the radius of the horn at any point along it be given as r(x). We can write the following expression for the rate of wave-energy loss to the walls of the horn:

$$dW/dt = K_p \int_0^L 2\pi r(x)\,dx\,p^2(x,t) + K_v \int_0^L 2\pi r(x)\,dx[f(x)(\partial/\partial x)p(x,t)]^2 \qquad (18)$$

Here $K_p$ and $K_v$ represent coefficients of proportionality (which rise as $\omega^{1/2}$ and are calculable for smooth surfaces of various materials), and the combination $f(x)(\partial/\partial x)\,p(x,t)$ expresses the tangential velocity in terms of the wave pressure and a function of the air column shape that is obtainable from the theory of horns. In a musical instrument, p(x,t) is a linear combination of disturbances, each of which is associated with one of the Fourier components of the net sound spectrum. We have seen that many of the components of the Fourier series for a given played note lie close to the natural frequencies of the air column. For these components, it is a good approximation to make the loss calculation using the ordinary standing wave functions belonging to these particular normal modes. For the Fourier components that do not lie near the air column resonance frequencies, it is necessary to make a special calculation of the pressure distribution. Fortunately, however, in most instruments the observed pressure amplitudes of these off-resonance components are small enough that their neglect will not materially change the estimated total dissipation by more than a very few percent.

Numerical estimates for the wall losses to be expected in the various simple horns used for woodwind instruments are given in Section VI, A, of Reference 2, along with an empirically determined loss-coefficient to allow for the presence of surface roughness. Examination of the possible alteration of the wall absorption by changes in the wall material has shown that to within a few percent, any reasonable material may be considered to act as an isothermal boundary. Analysis and experiment show that these estimates apply equally well to the family of brass instruments. The question as to how much energy is abstracted via the compliance of the wall is as yet unsettled, but it is known that the effect is usually relatively small. A larger source of variation in the wall losses appears to arise from the nature of the surface finish. Rough measurements show that the losses of a brand new clarinet in normal use may fall as much as 10% as the bore becomes polished by successive passages of the swab. In conclusion, we may assert that the wall losses in all wind instruments are of such magnitude that (for all the resonances that are significant for the regeneration process) during each cycle of oscillation, the walls absorb between 15% and 40% of the total vibrational energy *stored* in the air column.

We turn now to the question of radiation from woodwind instruments, where the radiation is emitted from a series of open holes at the lower end of the bore. Calculation shows the power radiated to be a complicated function of frequency,[7] but it is possible to verify that at most frequencies of interest, the total radiated power is within a factor of two above the amount that would be emitted from the open end of the simple bore. Suppose we set in motion one of the natural frequency oscillations of an air column and provide it with an initial amount of energy, $W_0$. If it is not kept going by means of some external regeneration mechanism, the energy is dissipated exponentially so that the stored energy at time is given by Equation 19:

$$W(t) = W_0 \exp(-gt) \quad \textbf{(19)}$$

Here the symbol g symbolizes the summed effects of the various loss mechanisms that are at work. Differentiation of this equation shows at once that g is the fractional rate of loss of energy, at any time. It may usefully be remarked that g is a measure also of the width of the resonance curves that have been so much discussed. In Section VII of Reference 2, it is shown that for clarinet-like and flute-like instruments the open-end radiated power is related to the losses to the walls according to the following formula:

$$g_{rad}/g_{wall} = B \cdot (\omega/\omega_b)^{3/2} \quad \textbf{(20)}$$

Here $\omega$ is the frequency of interest, $\omega_b$ is the frequency of the bottom-register note played with a given fingering, and B is a constant characteristic of the wall itself. The experimental value of B is in the neighborhood of 0.002 so that over almost the whole of the musical spectrum and radiation loss is minute as compared with the wall dissipation. The situation is more complicated in the case of conical-bore instruments. The foregoing remarks remain approximately valid for the oboe and bassoon, while the saxophone shows a rapidly increasing relative importance of the radiation as frequency goes up beyond the third harmonic of a low-register note.

The radiation from the bells of brass instruments will now be discussed. Consider a cylindrical middle section of a typical brass instrument that is smoothly attached to a bell of length L, small-end radius r, and large-end radius R. Many instruments have a bell shape that is well approximated by the following formula:

$$r(y) = K/(y + b)^{\alpha} \quad \textbf{(21)}$$

Here y is the distance along the horn measured from the large end, and the constants K and b are chosen together to give the desired diameters at the bell ends, in terms of the desired rate of flare $\alpha$. It is possible to show[8] that the fractional rate of radiated power $g_{rad}$ (as already defined in connection with woodwinds is a function of the bell proportions and frequency as given approximately in Equation 22:

$$g_{rad} \cong \text{const.}(\omega L)^{(3 + 2\alpha)}(r/R)^{(3 + 2\alpha)/\alpha} \quad \textbf{(22)}$$

FIGURE 5 gives experimental curves for a trombone bell with a measured flare parameter $\alpha = 0.63$, smoothly fitted to the end of a 6-ft length of medium-wall ¾-inch copper water tubing. Data are presented here for both radiation and loss to the air column walls. The well-fitting solid line drawn through the experimental points for radiation loss has a slope *calculated* for the particular horn using Equation 22. The line through the wall-loss points has the slope expected from a first-principles calculation for an ideally smooth hard pipe and bell, and its intercept is less than 10% above the ideal value.

We may remark that if other losses do not intervene, the upper-frequency limit

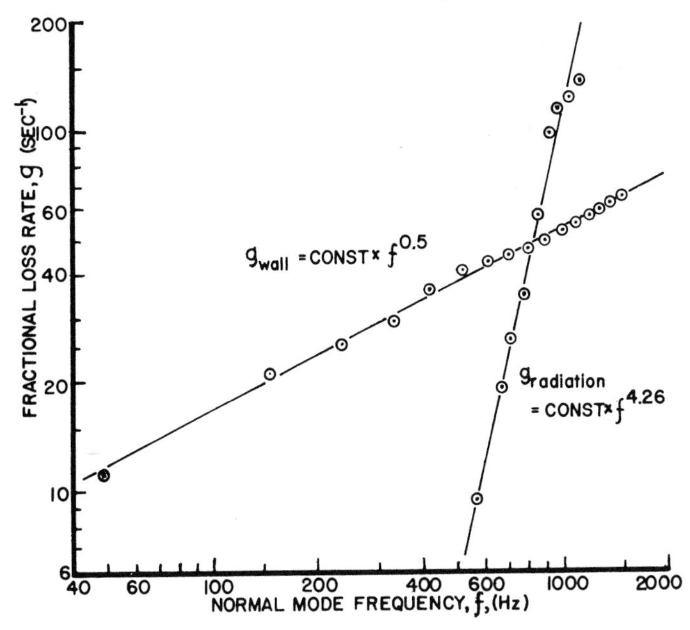


FIGURE 5. Experimental data compared with theoretical curves for the fractional energy loss rate to walls ($g_{wall}$) and to radiation ($g_{rad}$) for a trombone-like brass instrument.

of playability, $\omega_u$, in a brass instrument lies somewhat below a criterion set by the simplest of linear oscillation theory. The resulting inequality is the following:

$$1 \leqq \omega_p/(g_{wall} + g_{rad}) \qquad (23)$$

Here $\omega_p$ is the frequency of the instrument's own pedal note, and the g's are to be evaluated at the limiting frequency $\omega_u$.

## ACKNOWLEDGMENTS

It is very difficult to make proper acknowledgment to everyone, who has contributed to our understanding of the material discussed in this report, so that we confine ourselves in listing those who were of most direct and tangible assistance, with apologies to the others.

The interest and well-aimed questions of John Schelleng, Erwin Shrader, Bruce Shoffner, and Donald Garber on the technical side have been particularly valuable. Robert Pyle and William Cardwell have provided both technical and musical information and stimulation, particularly with regard to the brass instruments. Harry Sargous contributed much hard work to the measurement, playing, diagnosis, and successful correction of a misbored Viennese oboe, while Edwin Hausl provided us with information about these interesting instruments as well as detailed measurements of the bores of several excellent specimens. Stanley Maret joined with Alan Fox to give a spectacular demonstration of the effect of reaming near the middle tenon of a bassoon, and the latter has been most helpful along with John Stavash, Earle Kent, James Feddersen, and Vito Pascucci in providing information of the construction of good-quality woodwinds. Certain measurements connected with the radiation and wall losses of brass instruments were carried out by John Rosenberg and Harold Gordon. Last but not least, we acknowledge the continual helpfulness and skill of August Hruschka, who has advised in the design of and supervised the construction of many peculiar kinds of apparatus over the years.

The aid given parts of this work by grants from The Case Research Fund, The Cleveland Foundation, and The Research Corporation is gratefully acknowledged.

## References

1. Benade, A. H. 1960. Horns, Strings, and Harmony. Doubleday & Co., Inc. New York, N. Y.
2. Benade, A. H. 1950. J. Acoust. Soc. Amer. **31**: 137 (Sections II and III).
3. Bouasse, H. 1930. Instruments à Vent. Chap. I, Sec. 11 (note especially the final two paragraphs). Librairie Delagrave. Paris, France.
4. Benade, A. H. 1966. J. Acoust. Soc. Amer. **40**: 247.
5. Bouhuys, A. 1965. J. Acoust. Soc. Amer. **37**: 453.
6. Lambert, R. F. 1953. J. Acoust. Soc. Amer. **25**: 1068.
7. Benade, A. H. 1960. J. Acoust. Soc. Amer. **32**: 1591.
8. Benade, A. H. 1966. J. Acoust. Soc. Amer. **39**: 1220(A).

# 14

*Copyright © 1942 by the Acoustical Society of America*

Reprinted from *J. Acoust. Soc. Am.*, **13**(3), 305–308 (1942)

## Lip Vibrations in a Cornet Mouthpiece*

DANIEL W. MARTIN
*Physics Department, University of Illinois, Urbana, Illinois*
(Received October 28, 1941)

A BRASS wind instrument may be considered as consisting of the player's lips which act as the source of vibration, and the horn which is an acoustical system with selective transmission and radiation characteristics.

Webster[1] and Richardson[2] have advanced hypotheses concerning the action occurring at the mouthpiece. The former author suggests that "the principle employed is that of the squeaky faucet or fluttering safety valve. A spring of variable tension holds the valve in place and the proper pressure causes a puff of air, which generates a sound wave in the horn, which on reflexion arrives at the valve in the proper phase to maintain vibration." Richardson considers a combination of valve action and edge-tone production.

This paper describes a photographic experimental study of the lip action at a cornet mouthpiece. Lip action is dependent upon reaction from the horn, and horn properties are in turn dependent upon the lips since one end of the horn is terminated by them. Therefore isolation of these two parts of the instrument either for theoretical consideration or for experiment is permissible only if the missing part is replaced by something nearly equivalent to it. To obviate such replacement the experimental mouthpiece shown in Fig. 1 was used.

*I* is a Lucite rim which is threaded to *II*, the brass ring which is the body of the unit. *III* is a Lucite plug which provides a window facing the lips of the player. *IV* is a brass tube tapered like the similar part of a conventional mouthpiece. *V* is a small probe tube used in another experiment. The radius of the rim and the depth of the cavity are equal to the corresponding dimensions of a cornet mouthpiece, making the volume somewhat larger than usual, and lowering the normal frequencies appreciably (e.g., about 5 cycles at 230 c.p.s.). The higher harmonics in the acoustic spectrum were diminished slightly, as might be expected when the acoustic capacitance of the cavity is increased. Since the mouthpiece is used only for photographic purposes, the changes in frequency and spectrum are unimportant as long as the lips act in a nearly normal manner.

Three types of photographs were made. Single pictures having random phase relationship were taken with a General Radio Strobolux and Kodatron Panchromatic film. To correlate the pictures with a time scale, apparatus was used as shown in Fig. 2. The flashing rate of about 50 per second was set just enough below an integral divisor of the vibration frequency to give the desired positive phase shift between consecutive pictures. Use of less sensitive film than in the single pictures required moving the lamp from the unit to within several inches of the mouthpiece. Application of a liquid of low surface tension kept the breath from fogging the Lucite window. The third type of picture was obtained by interchanging lamp and camera positions to photograph the vibration along the axis of the mouthpiece. Distortion by the action of the Lucite rim as a cylindrical lens did not affect the measurements taken along the axis of the mouthpiece. Samples of all three types of pictures are shown in Fig. 3.

Phase shifts between consecutive pictures varied from one trial to another, from one-sixth

TABLE I. Harmonic analysis of lip separation curves for cornet.

| No. of harmonic | 225 Amp. mm | 225 *LG* below fund. | 340 Amp. mm | 340 *LG* below fund. | 460 Amp. mm | 460 *LG* below fund. | 570 Amp. mm | 570 *LG* below fund. | 690 Amp. mm | 690 *LG* below fund. |
|---|---|---|---|---|---|---|---|---|---|---|
| 1 | 1.20 | — | 0.77 | — | 0.67 | — | 0.54 | — | 0.36 | — |
| 2 | 0.18 | 17 | 0.13 | 16 | 0.11 | 16 | 0.08 | 17 | 0.06 | 16 |
| 3 | 0.05 | 27 | 0.08 | 20 | 0.08 | 18 | 0.05 | 21 | 0.03 | 22 |
| 4 | 0.05 | 27 | 0.04 | 26 | 0.03 | 27 | 0.03 | 25 | 0.03 | 22 |
| Constant | 1.28 | | 0.76 | | 0.66 | | 0.59 | | 0.50 | |

(Column groups 225–690 are under the spanning header "Fundamental frequency".)

* This paper was presented at the Rochester Meeting of the Acoustical Society of America, May 5, 1941. It is the first of several which are based on the thesis submitted by the author in partial fulfillment of the requirements for the degree of Doctor of Philosophy in Physics at the University of Illinois.

[1] Webster, Phys. Rev. **13**, 164 (1919).

[2] Richardson, *Acoustics of Orchestral Instruments* (Arnold, 1929).

to one-twentieth of a vibration. Lip separation at the center was measured for the front views and the axial displacement for both lips on the side views so that both vertical and horizontal components of the motion were determined. Zero phase was assigned to pictures showing zero lip separation and to those in which the upper lip had minimum axial displacement. Phase was assigned to other pictures on the assumption that the frequency of lip vibration and the flashing rate remained constant for intervals of two-fifths of a second or less. The constancy of measurements on pictures taken with the frequencies nearly synchronous justified the assumption.

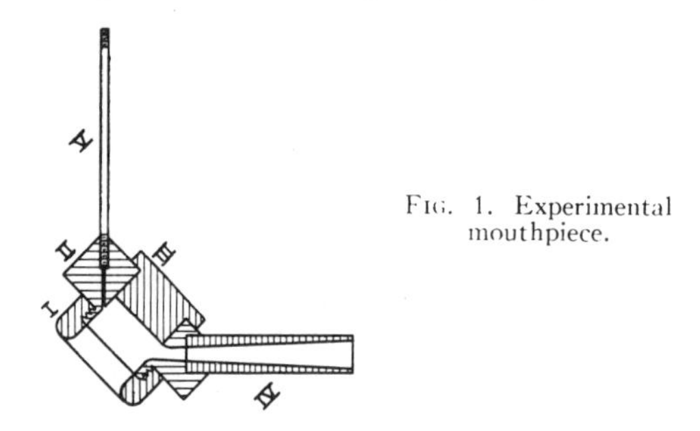

FIG. 1. Experimental mouthpiece.

In a given set of data, all values corresponding to phases lying in the same ten degree interval were averaged to obtain the ordinates of the points shown in Figs. 4 and 5. On account of small uncontrollable frequency fluctuations in a note played by a performer, it would be worth while to take the pictures at a much faster rate, when facilities are available, making such averaging unnecessary. About 150 pictures were measured to plot each curve.

It is estimated that the tones were played mezzo forte, although no serious attempt was made to maintain constant musical expression of loudness. Frequencies shown in the figures are approximate, the notes played being the series with no keys pressed.

As expected, the amplitude decreases markedly with increasing frequency for both separation and axial vibration curves. The front surfaces of the upper and lower lips become farther apart as the frequency rises, and the upper lip does most of the vibrating on high notes. The phase at which maximum separation occurs increases with frequency.

The conductivity of a small orifice depends upon the shape, cross-sectional area, and depth. Sivian[3] has shown that the relation is not simple even in the geometrical cases of circular and rectangular orifices. If lip separation remains small compared to the length of the orifice, one might for theoretical consideration replace the lip orifice by a rectangular opening of equivalent area, comparable length, and variable width. At high frequencies the lip orifice area is nearly proportional to the central separation, as shown in Fig. 6. At such frequencies an harmonic analysis of a separation curve will provide a mathematical expression for the area function also. For the larger amplitudes at low frequencies, however, the ratio of area to separation is not constant. Harmonic analyses of the curves in Fig. 4 are tabulated in Table I. These were made by the Runge[4] method using the tabulation scheme of Grover.[5] Comparison of the analyses is made directly by expressing the amplitudes in logarithmic units ($LG = 20 \log_{10} a_n/a_1$) below the fundamental amplitude for that frequency.

Ordinates chosen for the analysis were estimated only to 0.02 mm, so the smallest amplitude values in the table are meaningless. The analyses are more similar at different frequencies than one might anticipate, indicating that the differences between this type of analysis for a low note and that for a high note are not in any way comparable to the large differences observed in the acoustic spectrum of the instrument when

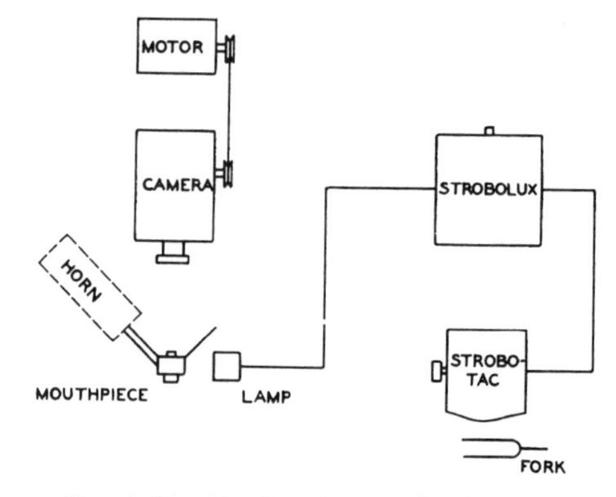


FIG. 2. Lip-vibration photography. Schematic drawing of apparatus.

[3] Sivian, J. Acous. Soc. Am. **7**, 94 (1935).
[4] Runge, Zeits. f. Math. und Physik **48**, 443 (1903).
[5] Grover, Bull. Nat. Bur. Stand. **9**, 567 (1913).

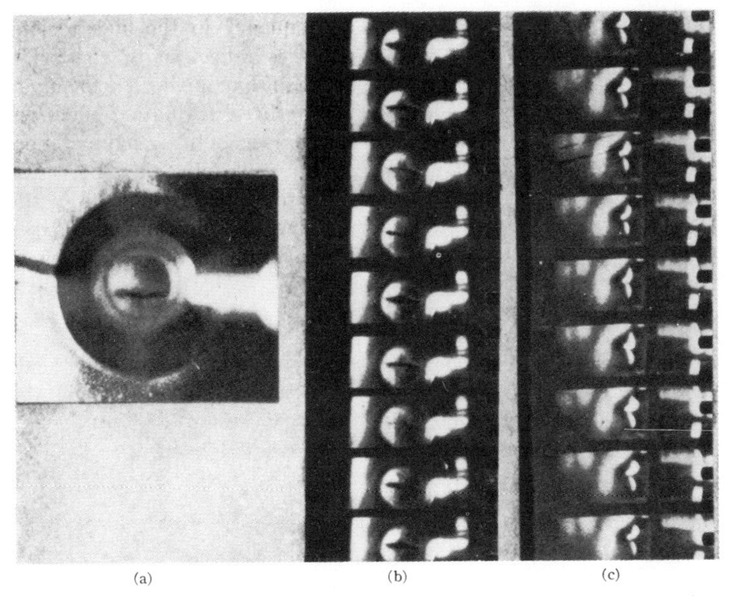


FIG. 3. Lip vibration at low frequency. a—single flash; b—front view series; c—side view series.

these same notes are played. This observation leads one to conclude that major differences in the acoustic spectra for different notes played on the same cornet are due to properties of the horn or of the medium in the horn or both, and not primarily due to lip action.

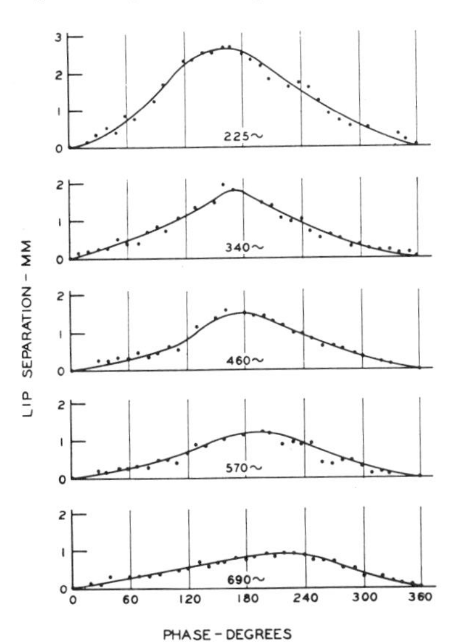


FIG. 4. Lip-vibration curves for cornet of central separation of the lips.

## REMARKS

The factors influencing lip action are so numerous as to require further experiment before adequate quantitative theory can be formulated. Webster stated that the arrival of the reflected

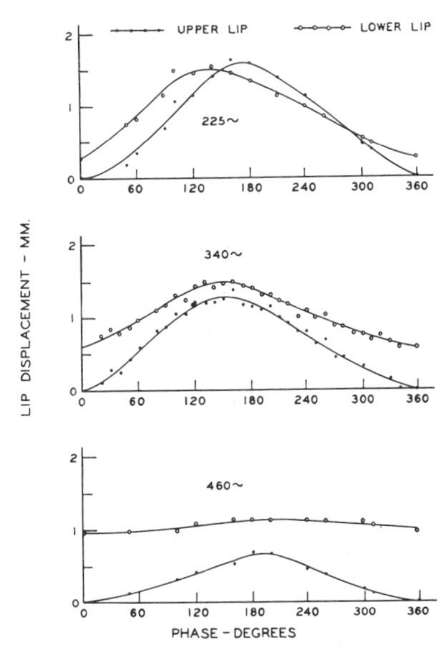


FIG. 5. Lip-vibration curves of displacement of the lips along the mouthpiece axis of cornet.

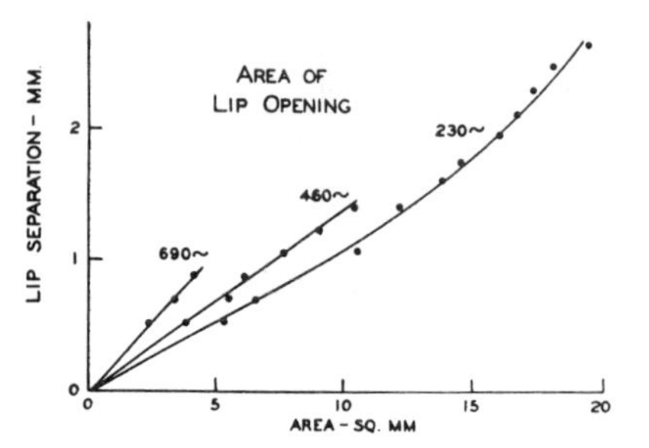


FIG. 6. Central separation *vs.* area of lip opening.

pressure wave regulates the lip-vibration frequency. Yet a player can control the frequency enough to force the tone sharp or flat, and an expert player can produce a continuous change of frequency in the high register. At high frequencies reflection at the bell of the horn is small so that the horn acts only as a transmitter, having little regulating effect on the frequency. An analysis of lip action in a mouthpiece coupled to an infinitely long horn would provide a solution which could be modified when the amount of reflection at the bell has been determined for the lower frequency range.

ACKNOWLEDGMENT

The author is grateful to Professor F. R. Watson and Dr. R. H. Bolt for their interest and suggestions, and to C. G. Conn, Ltd. for instruments loaned.

# 15

*Copyright © 1947 by the Acoustical Society of America*

Reprinted from *J. Acoust. Soc. Am.*, **19**(5), 902–906 (1947)

## An Electrical Method of Measuring the Intonation of Cup-Mouthpiece Instruments

J. C. Webster*
*C. G. Conn Ltd., Elkhart, Indiana*

(Received July 29, 1947)

An electrical driving system has been worked out for intonation tests on cup mouthpiece instruments. The system amounts to driving an acoustic transmission line from a closed end and measuring the resonant frequencies. It is shown experimentally that these resonant frequencies correspond quite precisely (within about 10 cents) to the frequencies normally played, except at the lower end of the scale where the player habitually corrects the defective intonation of the usual instrument. The experimental work includes tests on specially designed instruments that could not be played "in tune" with standard fingering.

### INTRODUCTION

EARLIER explanations of the operation of brass wind instruments have been based on the general theory that the lips are capable of exciting any frequency over a rather wide range, and that the general resonant characteristics of the air columns determined what frequencies are heard. The pitches that can be played with any given valve combination are related to each other substantially as the integers of the complete harmonic series with the pedal note missing. This makes it *seem* quite obvious that the air column of a trumpet acts as an open-ended resonator. However, these resonant frequencies simply are not the frequencies sounded in normal playing of such an instrument; the difference is substantially one semitone or more throughout the playing range of the instrument.

It has been found possible with a fairly simple set-up to drive the acoustic transmission line involved from a closed end, and when this closed end corresponds in position to the mouthpiece constriction of a trumpet for instance, the resonant frequencies correspond quite precisely to the frequencies actually played.

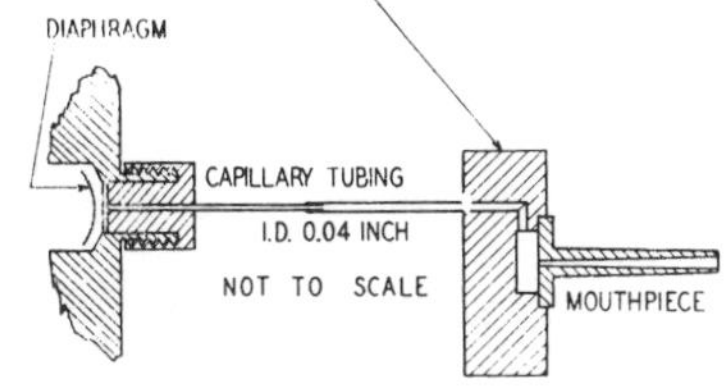

Fig. 1. System for measuring acoustic characteristics by driving from a "closed end."

* On leave of absence at State University of Iowa.

### CLOSED-END DRIVING SYSTEM

The more direct methods of precisely measuring the resonant frequencies of an acoustic transmission line closed at one end are experimentally awkward.

It has been found possible to drive such a system from the closed end by using the arrangement shown in Fig. 1. The precaution which has to be taken in this sort of driving system is to isolate the resonant acoustic system from the driving element. If there is any interaction between the two systems the indicated maxima (from the pick-up microphone at the open end) are not the resonant points of the tube alone but of the tube and driver. The capillary tubing used decouples the two systems sufficiently. This is shown experimentally by the close agreement of the two velocity *vs.* frequency curves of Fig. 2a in which the solid curve was obtained by conventional open-ended resonance measurements, and the dotted curve was obtained from the arrangement of Fig. 1.

In the use of the equipment shown in Fig. 1, the instrument or component to be measured is attached to the coupling device and the frequency of the audio oscillator slowly increased until a maximum on the vacuum-tube voltmeter indicates the resonance for the first mode of vibration; this frequency is read on the Stroboconn (formerly called Conn Chromatic Stroboscope) to 0.01 semitone. The frequency is then increased until the next resonance, corresponding to the third mode of vibration, is reached, and so on.

The same set-up and general method are used for measuring the performance of a tube open at both ends, except that the coupling device and its capillary tubing are omitted, there is an air gap between the loud speaker and the open end being driven, and the successive modes of vibration form the complete series rather than the odd series.

Each of the curves of Fig. 2a represents data taken on a number of different lengths of cylindrical tubing, and the measurement of a number of modes of vibration on each tube. The maximum experimental deviation from the average curves drawn was below one percent, and was less than one-half of that value for the open-ended resonant system.

### ANALYSIS OF TRUMPET COMPONENTS

It will be convenient in the work that follows to express the relation between sound velocity and frequency in the various parts of a typical brass instrument as a relation between effective length and frequency. By effective length is meant that length of acoustic-transmission line that would be required to account for the observed transit time of sound waves if the sound waves were transmitted with an assumed standard velocity of 13,650 inches per second. Such effective lengths are additive. (Fig. 2b.)

Figure 3 shows the variation in effective length as the frequency is changed for a mouthpiece and mouthpipe combination of a typical trumpet. The marked difference between the curves for closed-end resonance and of open-ended resonance will be observed.

As has already been indicated in Fig. 2a, the sound velocity in cylindrical tubing is independent of the type of resonance that occurs. In fact, that is the reason that Fig. 2a was presented as evidence of the success of the arrangement for driving an acoustic-transmission line from its closed end.

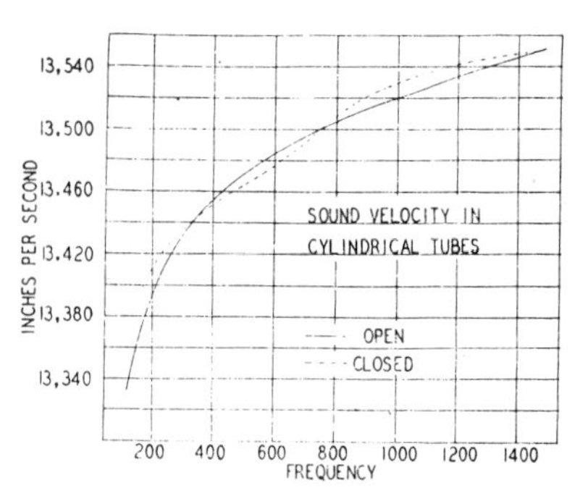


FIG. 2a. Sound velocity *vs.* frequency in 0.438-inch inside-diameter tube: comparison of measurements by closed-end and open-ended resonance.

In the case of the flaring part of the horn, in normal playing the large end is open and this establishes a pressure node at that point. In order to get sufficient points to draw a smooth curve it is necessary to measure the effective lengths of the bell in combination with various lengths of cylindrical tubing attached to the small end of the bell. The effective length of the extra cylindrical tubing is subsequently subtracted in each case. As long as the flared end is open the effective length of any given trumpet bell is the same whether activated as a closed-end or open-end resonant system.

Figure 4 shows the variation of effective length *vs.* frequency for a typical trumpet bell. It can be seen that the effective length changes substantially with frequency, and that the fastest rate of change occurs at the lower frequencies. The effect of this changing length on the resonant-frequency series (corresponding to the different numbered modes of vibration) is that the second mode, for instance, occurs at a frequency substantially less than twice the frequency of the first mode, and the third mode occurs at substantially less than three times the frequency of the first mode, and so on.

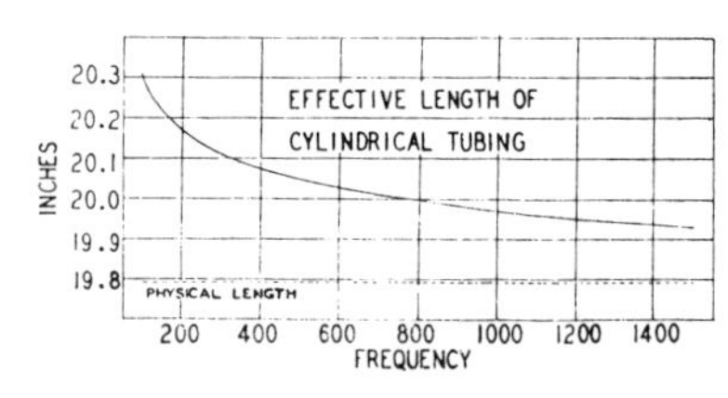


FIG. 2b. Effective length *vs.* frequency for 0.438-inch inside-diameter tube.

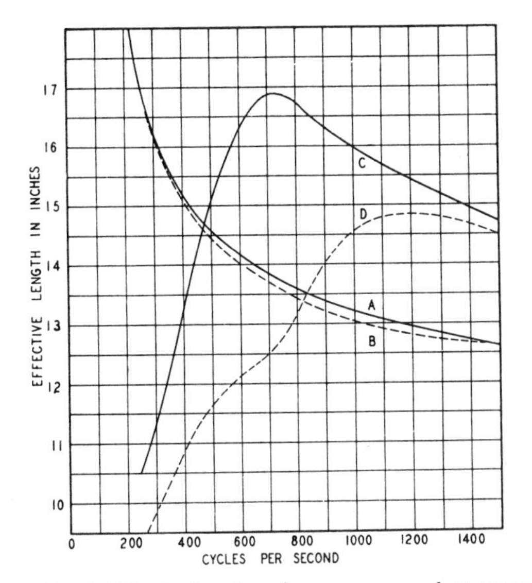


FIG. 3. Effective length *vs.* frequency curves for trumpet mouthpiece-mouthpipe combination.
*A* and *C* = mouthpiece complete
*B* and *D* = mouthpiece complete only to narrowed part
*A* and *B* = pressure node at mouthpiece
*C* and *D* = pressure antinode at mouthpiece.

This condensing of the series of modes not only occurs when using the bell by itself but also happens when the bell is used to terminate any length of cylindrical tubing. Adding cylindrical tubing lowers the fundamental frequency but the modes are still condensed.

It is apparent that unless some other component of the trumpet can counteract this increasing effective length with increasing frequency the trumpet could not possibly resonate in the successive frequencies of the complete harmonic series when open at both ends. Qualitatively the mouthpiece-mouthpipe combination does show a decreasing effective length with increasing frequency when resonated with the mouthpiece end open, but quantitatively this rate of change is not sufficient to give the conventional integer-ratio frequency relationship to the playing modes. This is brought out in Fig. 5 which shows the appropriate effective length curves of the mouthpiece-mouthpipe combination added to the effective length of the bell and cylindrical tubing actually involved. For the upper end of the frequency range involved the combined effective length of the instrument components is substantially independent of frequency, but the resonant points are all one semitone sharp to the pitches ordinarily blown by a player.

It is in the mouthpiece-mouthpipe combination that the location of the pressure antinode becomes important in arriving at the effective length of this component. As mentioned above, when a pressure node exists at the mouthpiece end of the system its effective length decreases with increasing frequency; but when a pressure antinode exists at the mouthpiece end (equivalent to a closed-pipe resonant system) the effective length increases with increasing frequency (see Fig. 3). A pressure antinode can be made to exist at the mouthpiece end by driving the system with the coupling device described in Fig. 1. Furthermore, it is of great interest to note that if this pressure antinode is made to exist precisely at the smallest constriction of the mouthpiece, the effective length increases with frequency at a rate such that when this effective length is added to the effective length of the bell the condensing of the series of modes is

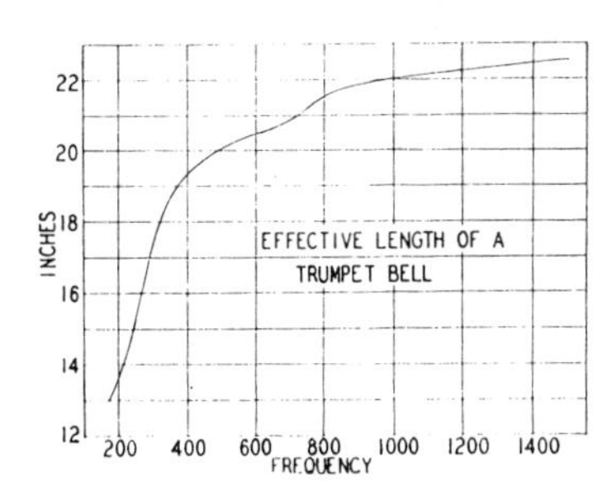


FIG. 4. Effective length *vs.* frequency for *B♭* trumpet bell.

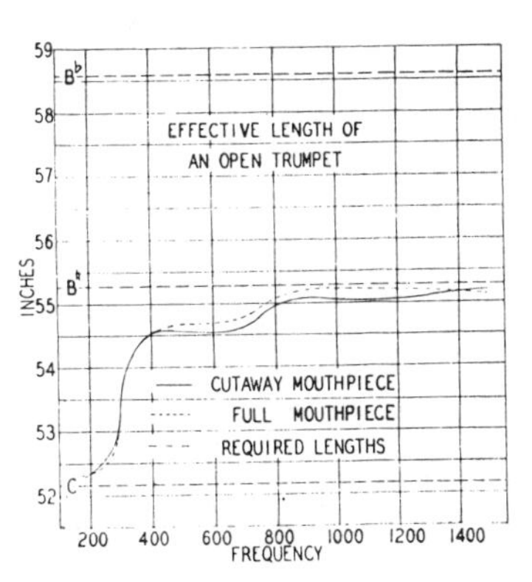


FIG. 5. Sum of the effective lengths of trumpet components *vs.* frequency; based on existence of pressure node at mouthpiece.

almost exactly such that the frequency of the third mode is twice that of the first mode, and the frequency of the fifth mode is three times that of the first mode, the seventh four times, etc. This is true for a given frequency range independently of the length of cylindrical tubing that may be involved between the bell and mouthpipe. Figure 6 shows the sum of the effective lengths of typical trumpet components taken on this basis compared to the required effective length for just intonation. The deviation between the sum and the required length is a great deal less throughout the playing range of the instrument than is the corresponding deviation in Fig. 5.

It must be remembered that if a pressure antinode exists at the mouthpiece constriction, the bell end being open, the combined system acts like a closed-pipe resonant system where there are no even-numbered modes of vibration; but the paradox remains that the odd-numbered modes give in this case the complete integer-series relation between the corresponding frequencies.

These facts having been determined from the sum of the parts of the trumpet, it need only be shown that combining the parts with the correct length of cylindrical tubing and driving the total system as a closed-pipe system from the mouthpiece constriction gives resonant points which coincide with the pitches customarily blown by a player. When combined and tried the resonant points do indeed coincide in general with the played pitches. As a corollary to this the resonant points were determined when both ends of the trumpet were open and these pitches in no cases were closer than one semitone of the played pitches.

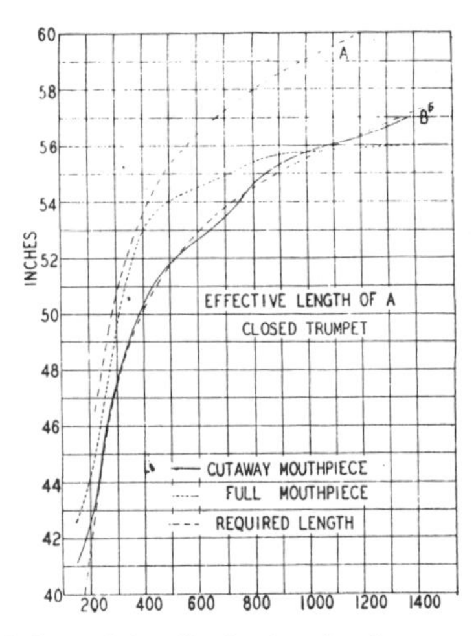


FIG. 6. Sum of the effective lengths of trumpet components *vs*. frequency; based on existence of pressure antinode at mouthpiece.

### APPLICATION OF CLOSED-END DRIVING SYSTEM TO COMPLETE TRUMPET

In order to see if the resonant frequencies obtained in this manner could be used to predict the pitches a player would ordinarily play, a trumpet was made up with detachable bells and extensive tests were made. Detachable bells were used so that the intonation of the trumpet could be changed by merely changing bells. One bell in particular, the "conical" bell, altered the frequencies so far from what is expected of a trumpet that no amount of player "favoring" could bring it into tune, when the standard fingerings were used. Another precaution taken to minimize the effect of the player's ear from correcting any bad pitches was to arrange the test pitch sequence in as unmelodic an order as possible (see Fig. 7). These precautions, however, could not alter the player's habitual lip set, which in the case of more experienced players seems to be quite definite.

For this study two "testers" were used, and they played each pitch twice a day for two weeks in the sequence referred to above under constant temperature conditions. The player data on Figs. 8 and 9 are an average of the twenty trials of the two players, and the individual points represent each player's average. As a basis for stating that player lip set is an important consideration and that it was not eliminated from these data, notice that on both Figs. 8 and 9 player 1 (●) goes decidedly flat on $B\flat_4$ while going markedly sharp on $B\flat_3$. Also, player 1 is constantly sharp

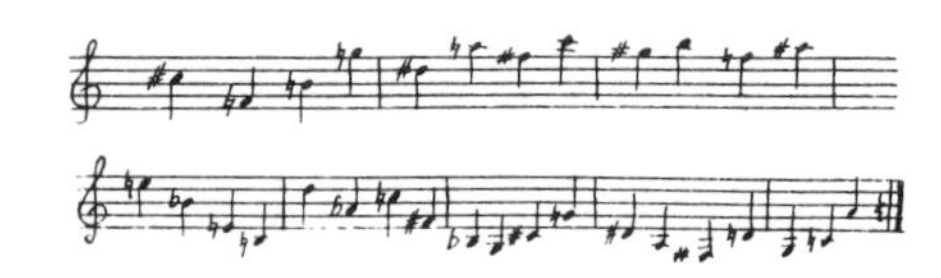

FIG. 7. Test schedule for player tests; this succession of intervals was selected in an effort to discourage pitch correction by ear.

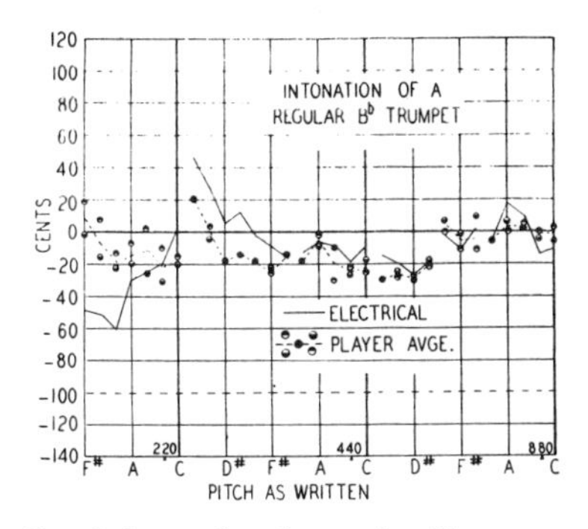


FIG. 8. Intonation of a regular $B\flat$ trumpet.

of player 2 in the lower ranges, but in the upper ranges there is no uniformly marked difference between the players.

In comparing the average player data to the electrical data, which is an average of 10 readings taken over ten days at constant temperature, it will be noticed that from $F\sharp_3$ to $C_4$ there is very little agreement. In this range, however, it should be noticed that regardless of the position of the electrical data the players tend to correct the pitches to the "in tune" (0-cent deviation) position; that is, if the air-column resonant frequencies are too flat the players sharpen these played pitches in an attempt to bring them into tune, and conversely, when the resonant frequencies are too sharp the played pitches are flatted.

Above $C_4$ the agreement between the electrical and player data is much closer; and this is especially true of the "conical" trumpet, which as can be seen, is so much out of tune that not much attempt is made to correct its faulty intonation. It is on the basis of the close agreement between the player and the electrical data on the "conical" trumpet, where it is believed the player's ear has the least influence on his intonation data, that the methods and devices described above are considered to be a means of electrically determining the intonation characteristics of a trumpet and, in general, any brass instrument. The disagreements below $C_4$ are not considered faults of the electrical equip-

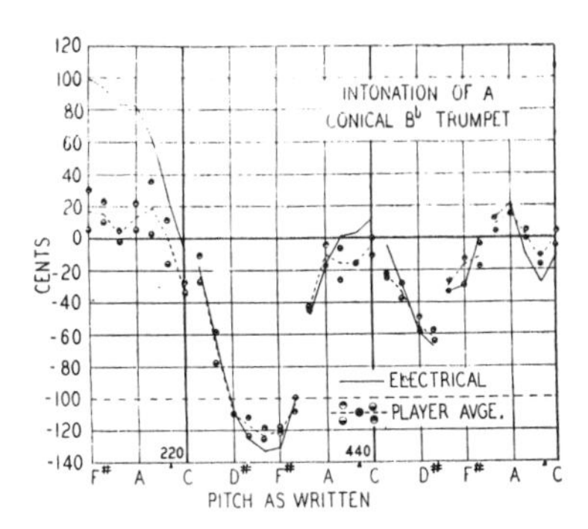


FIG. 9. Intonation of a special $B\flat$ trumpet with a conical bell; this bell is described in some detail in a companion paper by T. H. Long entitled "The performance of cup mouthpiece instruments."

ment but are more an indication of how widely the lower pitches of brass instruments can be varied by the player; and in this case are a tribute to the good pitch judgment of the two players participating. It is thought that if beginning players could hold their pitches constant enough to be measured, and were not already conditioned into "sharpening" their lower pitches, a closer agreement could be demonstrated. "Sharpening" is used because on the standard trumpets measured, which included three well-known brands of trumpets, all tested electrically flat below $C_4$. It is only with a few special bells that the low ranges could be made sharp, and on these the players "flattened" the pitches to bring the trumpet back into tune.

In conclusion, it should be said that more tests are contemplated which, it is hoped, will yield additional information on the relative importance of lip set and the ear in making player-intonation tests.

**ACKNOWLEDGMENTS**

I wish to acknowledge the help given to this study by E. L. Kent, under whose direction it was carried out, to T. H. Long for many helpful suggestions and aid in electrical circuits, and to C. E. Miller who helped to take and treat the experimental data.

# 16A

*Copyright © 1947 by the Acoustical Society of America*

Reprinted from *J. Acoust. Soc. Am.*, **19**(5), 892–901 (1947)

## The Performance of Cup-Mouthpiece Instruments

T. H. LONG
*C. G. Conn Ltd., Elkhart, Indiana*

(Received July 18, 1947)

It is shown by a qualitative analysis that the playing of cup-mouthpiece instruments must be associated with the existence of a pressure antinode at or near the mouthpiece, and that harmonic production in such instruments can be adequately explained by the acoustic overload in the air column.

A quantitative analysis discloses the "mechanism" by which the odd series of modes of vibration occur at frequencies related to each other by the 1, 2, 3, 4 integers of the complete harmonic series.

### INTRODUCTION

LITERATURE on the general subject of air column musical instruments seems to have been in a sufficiently deplorable state that the late John Redfield was justified in devoting a paper[1] before this Society to the defects of theory. These defects are most apparent in woodwind instruments, and can best be summarized by quoting the data that Redfield presented. These data show the ratio of pulse length to instrument length as follows:

For the bassoon, oboe, and saxophone this ratio of pulse length to instrument length varies from 2.3 to 2.4 as compared to the 2.0 required by theory. The discrepancy is +20 percent. For the clarinet, on the other hand, the actual ratio is 3.5 and the theoretical requirement is 4.0, so that the deficiency amounts to −12 percent.

Redfield further insisted that discrepancies of the same sort existed between fact and theory for the brass (cup-mouthpiece) instruments, but admitted that more careful measurement is required to show them.

A concise statement of a theory that has been "generally accepted" on a default basis may be expected to be hard to find. The idea seems to have been to assert the general equivalence to a cone, and thus to a doubly open cylindrical pipe of those roughly conical instruments that "overblow" to the octave, or that are played in several modes related to each other by the frequency ratios 1, 2, 3, 4, ···, of the complete harmonic series. There is an intriguing theoretical reason for such an assertion, since it was shown mathematically by Rayleigh[2] that "A cone, which is complete as far as the vertex, may be treated as though the vertex were an open end. . . . " Such a cone resonates at successive frequencies related to each other by substantially 1, 2, 3, 4, ··· ratios just as does a cylindrical pipe open at both ends. So there is at least an external equivalence between the instruments in question, the complete cone, and the open cylindrical pipe. Any internal equivalence that may exist seems to have been badly misunderstood.

The present work has been confined almost exclusively to trumpets. The trumpet is a representative member of a group of musical instruments in which the lips of the player act as the reeds. Such instruments are characterized by cup mouthpieces and an air column of variable length in its cylindrical part. This variation may be in discrete steps as is usually the case, or the variation may be continuous as in the trombone.

With a fixed length of air column (as in the bugle) such instruments can be played in several different modes having fundamental frequencies corresponding to the complete harmonic series. In most cases, the first mode of vibration is difficult to sound and is not of pleasing quality so is not used. The normally used modes for the trumpet are apparently 2, 3, 4, 5, 6, and 8. It will be shown that the actual vibrations are in modes 3, 5, 7, 9, 11, and 15.

It is well known that the frequency of any particular tone played on such an instrument can be varied over a limited range at the will of

---

[1] John Redfield, "Certain anomalies in the theory of air column behavior in orchestral wind instruments," J. Acous. Soc. Am. 6, 34–36 (1934).

[2] Lord Rayleigh, *Theory of Sound* (Dover Publications, New York, 1945), Vol. 2, p. 114.

the player; in fact it is something of an art to sound a tone steadily.

It seems likely that some of the conclusions developed are applicable to all air column musical instruments.

### QUALITATIVE ANALYSIS OF CUP-MOUTHPIECE INSTRUMENTS

In this section arguments will be presented to show that

(1) There must be a pressure antinode at the mouthpiece end of the instrument;

(2) The harmonic content of the radiated sound can be explained on the basis of overloading of the air column;

(3) Theoretical reasons are advanced for several more or less well-known characteristics of the instruments.

Cup-mouthpiece instruments are sounded by buzzing the lips as they are pressed against the mouthpiece. The lips can be similarly buzzed independently of the instrument, but the sound output is then reduced to the order of 1 percent. It is evident that the presence of the instrument serves to match the impedance of the lips to the impedance of the air. In other words the instrument acts as an acoustic transformer. A certain amount of this transformer action is necessarily associated with the taper of the air column. But in order to get the maximum of transformer action from an air column that is open at the far end, it is necessary that there be a pressure antinode at the driving end. This follows for instance from Morse's[3] equation for the specific acoustic impedance at the driving end of a small-diameter open tube:

$$z(0) = i\rho_0 c \tan[(2\pi/\lambda)(l+8a/3\pi)],$$

in which the argument of the tangent function is $2\pi$ times the effective length of tube divided by wave-length. This argument becomes an odd multiple of $\pi/2$ when the effective length of the tube is an odd multiple of a quarter wave-length. This condition corresponds to infinite impedance under the assumed conditions of zero radiation from the open end, and zero losses. Appreciable radiation will make the impedance finite.

In order to establish a sense of proportion in dealing with what happens in the air column of this type of instrument, it will be necessary for a moment to consider some figures. Sivian, Dunn, and White[4] have given the figure of 0.3 watt for the peak sound power of a trumpet. A typical trumpet has a bore of 0.438-inch diameter or a cross section of 0.972 square centimeter in its cylindrical section. This corresponds to a radiation intensity of $3.09\times10^6$ erg per second per square centimeter. Depending on the valve combination played, up to 45 inches or roughly 100 centimeters of tubing is working at maximum excess sound pressure equal to or greater than 15,700 dynes per square centimeter if the presence of a standing-wave system is ignored.

Thuras, Jenkins, and O'Neil[5] made a study of the generation of harmonic (and difference) frequencies in air carrying intense sound waves. The upper limit of excess pressure on which they reported was 8000 dynes per square centimeter. The maximum length of tubing available for distortion measurements was 705 centimeters. In this length they found substantial harmonic production, closely approximating in magnitude the predictions made theoretically by Lamb. They pointed out, for instance, that a solution of the differential equation for overloaded sound transmission by successive approximations required the second harmonic production to be proportional to the length of the path, to the frequency, and to the square of the excess pressure; their experiments confirmed this.

For a rough estimate of the maximum excess pressure at the throat of a trumpet mouthpiece multiply the above figure of 15,700 dynes per square centimeter by 5 to account for the standing waves, and multiply that product by 3 to account for the constriction at the throat of the mouthpiece. The result is 236,000 dynes per square centimeter or about 3.4 pounds per square inch. This is undoubtedly the highest sound pressure that exists in any familiar device.

An understanding of why it is that overloading of the air column causes substantial production of harmonics can be reached by considering what is actually happening. In that part of a plane

[3] P. M. Morse, *Vibration and Sound* (McGraw-Hill Publishing Company, Inc., New York, 1936), p. 200, p. 222-3.

[4] Sivian, Dunn, and White, "Absolute amplitudes and spectra of certain musical instruments and orchestras," J. Acous. Soc. Am. **2**, 369 (1931).

[5] Thuras, Jenkins, and O'Neil, "Extraneous frequencies generated in air carrying intense sound waves," J. Acous. Soc. Am. **6**, 173–180 (1934).

progressive sound wave where the pressure is high, the temperature is above normal, and so the higher the pressure the more rapidly the pressure is propagated with reference to the medium. Where the pressure is high the medium itself is moving in the direction of pressure propagation, and this "drift" velocity is to be added directly to the wave velocity. So we find that the pressure crests are propagated with a velocity substantially above that of the zero excess pressure part of the wave, which is propagated with the normal velocity of sound; conversely the pressure troughs are transmitted with a substantially lower velocity.

The usual derivation of the equations describing plane progressive sound waves assumes very small excess pressure and displacement, and arrives at the conclusion that the velocity of sound transmission $c=(\gamma p_0/\rho_0)^{\frac{1}{2}}$. In any plane progressive sound wave that does not involve pressure discontinuities let us consider a point $x$ that shall move with the wave. Any other point sufficiently close to $x$ will differ in pressure from the pressure at $x$ by as little as we may choose. Therefore the velocity with which these pressures are propagated through the medium will be

$$c'=(\gamma p/\rho)^{\frac{1}{2}}, \qquad (1)$$

where $p$ and $\rho$ refer to the pressure and density at the point $x$. Let $p/p_0=n$. Then the value of $p/\rho$ in Eq. (1) may be evaluated from the adiabatic law:

$$n=p/p_0=(\rho/\rho_0)^{\gamma}=(\theta/\theta_0)^{\gamma/(\gamma-1)}$$

and we find that

$$c'=(\gamma p_0 n^{(\gamma-1)/\gamma}/\rho_0)^{\frac{1}{2}}=(\gamma p_0\theta/\rho_0\theta_0)^{\frac{1}{2}}=cn^{(\gamma-1)/2\gamma}. \qquad (2)$$

It is evident that in order to find the total velocity $C$ of sound transmission relative to a fixed point we must add the value of $c'$ from Eq. (2) to the velocity of the medium at the point $x$. This value is (at least approximately) $c's$ where $s$ is the condensation $=\rho/\rho_0{}^{-1}=n^{1/\gamma}-1$. Therefore we conclude that $C=c'(n^{1/\gamma}-1)+c'=c'n^{1/\gamma}$ so

$$C=cn^{(\gamma-1)/2\gamma}n^{1/\gamma}=cn^{(\gamma+1)/2\gamma}. \qquad (3)$$

In other words the velocity of sound transmission is increased at the crest of the pressure wave by $(p/p_0)^{0.858}$ for air over the value that obtains at small excess pressures.

If there is a standing-wave system, the situation is more complicated but still of a type that can be qualitatively analyzed. Let the components of the standing-wave system be referred to as forward and reverse in direction, and assumed to be equal in magnitude and somewhat sinusoidal in shape (being originated by sinusoidal excitation for instance). The problem will be further arbitrarily simplified by ignoring the difference in magnitude between positive and negative excess pressure peak values.

Then consider a point at the excess pressure crest of the forward wave; such a point will never experience negative resultant excess pressure from the addition of the two waves. This point will then experience only positive particle velocities, varying more or less sinusoidally from zero when the resultant pressure is a maximum to $2c's$ when the resultant excess pressure is zero; $s$ in this case is to be understood to refer to the maximum condensation existing in either component by itself.

The average value of this positive particle velocity is the main component of the increase in propagation velocity that the pressure crest experiences, and apparently will not be much different from what it would have been in the absence of the reverse wave. The same line of reasoning may be followed with other points on the forward (or reversely directed) wave with the same result, namely, that the presence of the oppositely directed wave makes only a minor difference in the average propagation velocity of any selected pressure level of the other wave.

It should not be concluded from this "analysis" that the standing-wave system of an air column instrument is not associated with an increased harmonic production. If it be assumed that there is no reflection at the lips, the increasing reflection from the open end of the instrument as the exciting frequency is reduced means that in order to maintain the radiated energy constant the peak excess pressure in the forward wave must be increased. This is an important consideration since it has been shown that the harmonic production at a given excess pressure is proportional to the path length measured in terms of wavelengths over which that excess pressure exists. As the frequency is reduced (from one playing mode to a lower numbered mode) the number of wave-lengths in the path will be reduced (in discrete steps). If there were no increase in the maximum excess pressure in the forward wave there would be a marked decrease in the harmonic production as the frequency of excitation was reduced. Of course there is actually something at least analogous to reflection occurring at the lips, but it might more properly be termed regeneration.

It will also be instructive to consider just what happens in a standing-wave system when that system exists within the air column of a musical instrument. In this case there is at least one open end to be considered, and at the open end there will be some radiation, and the sound energy that is not radiated will be reflected with reversal of phase. It has been shown that in the forward wave train the crests of excess pressure gain substantially on the troughs. After phase reversal, that part of the wave that is most advanced in phase position is the trough, and the crests of the reflected wave are in the most phase-retarded position. If there were no radiation from the open end, the mechanism that causes harmonic production in the forward wave would restore the reflected wave to the initial shape of the forward wave. This restoration could hardly be perfect, even in the assumed case.

This situation is complicated by the frequency-selective radiation from the open end of the instrument, which favors the radiation of the higher frequencies. This frequency-selective characteristic will (over-simplifying) cause a loss in phase position of that part of the wave that is a rarefaction after reflection, and a gain in the phase position of the condensations. This would lead us to suspect that the wave would be restored substantially to its original form before it gets back to the mouthpiece, so that when it does get back, the condensations will again be ahead of their nominal (sinusoidal) phase position. If this analysis is correct we would expect to find harmonics present in the motion of the lips but to a lesser extent than in the sound from the horn. This is precisely what Martin[6] found.

A possible objection to the *necessity* of the above line of reasoning is the theoretical possibility that the gain in phase position of the reflected condensation would properly match its loss in amplitude, so that the wave train would not be restored to its original shape until it had just reached the mouthpiece. Recalling the weak radiation of the fundamental (which mainly determines the amplitude of the standing wave) this seems most unlikely in the lower frequency range of the instrument.

Attention is directed to the fact that Martin's results show a variation in the phase of peak separation of the lips with variations in frequency. It does not seem possible in this qualitative analysis to establish anything conclusive based on phase position. It should be pointed out however, that a variation in phase is to be expected since the bell, and to a lesser extent the mouthpiece, are frequency-dispersive devices, transmitting low frequencies with markedly higher velocities than high frequencies, as will be shown.

An interesting corollary of this qualitative analysis is the support it gives to what might be called the "broad-formant" theory. By broad-formant is meant the idea that those musical instruments to which it applies, especially air column instruments, have a frequency range in which, for a normal resulting sound level, the radiation is a maximum provided only that the fundamental frequency is lower. This frequency range may approach an octave in width and is sometimes specified simply by the center frequency of the formant, without any implication that the formant is closely confined to that frequency. For instance Martin[7] found evidence of a formant for the trumpet centering around 1000 c.p.s. and for the french horn centering around 500 c.p.s.

It follows from what has been said previously that energy at any frequency too low for efficient radiation will simply contribute to the standing-wave system in the horn. The more intense the standing-wave system, the more energy is converted into harmonics of sufficiently high order to be radiated rather than reflected. This means that there will not be any substantial generation of harmonics of higher order than is necessary for efficient radiation, and no pronounced radiation

[6] Daniel W. Martin, "Lip vibrations in a cornet mouthpiece," J. Acous. Soc. Am. **13**, 305 (1942).

[7] Daniel W. Martin, *A Physical Investigation of the Performance of Brass Musical Wind Instruments* (University of Illinois thesis (May 12, 1941)).

of low frequencies. This reasoning is also supported by Martin's measurements, according to which the maximum radiation occurs within a limited frequency range that is more or less independent of how much lower the fundamental frequency is.

One or two other consequences of this analysis may be of greater practical significance in explaining observed phenomena:

(1) The fact that relative harmonic content decreases with decreasing sound level. It is well known that this happens.

(2) The standing-wave system should have a higher harmonic content than the lip motion, and a lower harmonic content than that of the radiated sound energy.

(3) The regenerative action at the mouthpiece between the air column and the lips divides the frequency spectrum into permitted and excluded ranges. Over part of the permitted range the instrument exerts only slight influence on the frequency sounded.

Item 3 of the above tabulation suggests the describing of the influence of the instrument in terms of *nominal frequency sounded/permissible frequency deviation*. J. G. Woodward[8] found that the range through which a cornet can be "forced" to be substantially 20 vibrations per second in any part of the playing range of the instrument. This would make the influence of the instrument on the frequency played substantially proportional to the frequency played, and would seem to be a necessary consequence of item 3 above.

The writer has found that proficient trumpet players are able to "force" their tones through almost the same frequency range reported above, and that the amount of forcing possible varies somewhat with the reciprocal of the player's proficiency. For instance a tyro can buzz anything through a six semitone range in the apparent second mode of a trumpet with a little application: some of the results are definitely unmusical, and undoubtedly the more proficient player simply will not allow himself to get them.

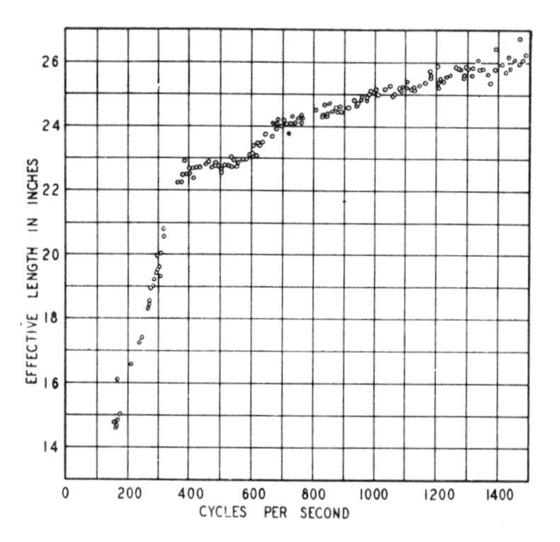


FIG. 1. Effective length *vs.* frequency for typical B♭ trumpet bell. Actual length 25.69 inches; inside diameter from 0.438 inch to 4.5 inches.

[8] J. G. Woodward, "Resonance characteristics of a cornet," J. Acous. Soc. Am. **13**, 156 (1942).

## QUANTITATIVE ANALYSIS OF A TRUMPET

In the following it will be shown that the variation of wave velocity with frequency in the various parts of a trumpet is such as to cause the odd numbered modes of vibration to produce a series of tones having their frequencies related substantially as the integers of the complete harmonic series.

### INTRODUCTION

Morse[3] has shown that the wave velocity of sound in an exponential horn is $c/[1-(\lambda/2\pi x_0)]^{\frac{1}{2}}$. where $c$ is the velocity of sound in air, $\lambda$ the wavelength in air, and $x_0$ is a measure of the flare of the horn, being the length along the axis between cross sections whose radii have a ratio of $\epsilon = 2.718\cdots$. He comments on the somewhat surprising nature of this result since it states that the wave velocity is always greater than in air, and that there is a frequency below which wave motion cannot exist in the horn. This later frequency has come to be identified as the cut-off frequency $f_0$ of the horn. The conclusion that the wave velocity is always greater than in air seems to be substantially confirmed by experiment. But the same experiments (by Wm. M. Hall[9]) showed that wave motion exists below the cut-off frequency and that the wave velocity was then several times that in open air. The cut-off frequency idea still furnishes a useful concept in acoustic design by establishing an approximate lower limit for efficiently transmitted frequencies.

It is suggested as a result of the work reported here that the most surprising characteristic of the

[9] Wm. M. Hall, "Comments on the theory of horns," J. Acous. Soc. Am. **3**, 552 (1932).

exponential horn is that the wave velocity is independent of the position of the wave along the axis of the horn. It is further suggested that this is a unique quality of exponential horns and that in any other flaring horn the wave velocity depends both on the frequency and on the part of the horn being considered. It is almost obvious that this should be so since the exponential curve is itself unique.

It is possible to measure the wave velocity, as an average velocity through the entire horn, in a simple and precise manner. The system amounts to determining the resonant frequencies for the horn open at both ends, and from these frequency measurements and the known modes of vibration, the wave velocity can be calculated quite precisely, except for the question of the corrections for the two open ends of the system. A quite precise correction can ordinarily be made for the small end of the horn, and the question of the end correction for the large end avoided in so far as the application of the results to musical instruments is concerned.

Information on the wave velocity through, for instance, the bell of a trumpet, is not directly useful, since there will be one velocity for the bell, one for the cylindrical tubing section, and yet another for the mouthpiece and mouthpipe combination, and each of these will be a different function of frequency. It is a great deal simpler to assume a standard velocity (13,650 inches per second is used here) and express the velocity data in terms of the effective length, or the physical length that would be required to account for the transit time if the wave velocity were the assumed standard velocity. Then $l_e = l_a 13{,}650/v$, in which $l_e$ is the effective length, and $l_a$ is an arbitrary (or actual) length for which the velocity $v$ in inches per second was calculated. The effective length can usually be calculated more directly for most purposes as

$$l_e = 13{,}650m/2f, \tag{4}$$

where $m$ is the mode number and $f$ is the open-ended resonant frequency.

By comparing the effective lengths of various known lengths of cylindrical tubing it has been established that the proper end correction for an unflanged open end of 0.438-inch tubing is $0.67R$, $\pm$about $0.01R$, where $R$ is the radius of the tube.

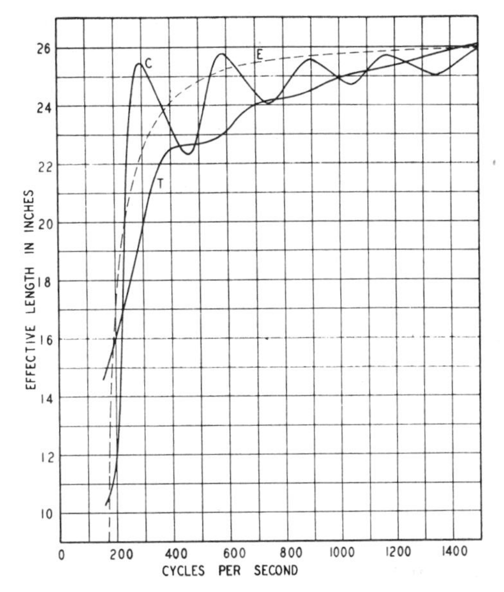


FIG. 2. Effective length *vs.* frequency curves for trumpet bells. $T$=smooth curve from Fig. 1; $C$=effective length of conical bell, made as follows: 2.63 inches of 0.438 I.D. tubing, 21.0 inches of straight cone 0.438 to 1.68 inches I.D., 1.9 inches substantially identical to last 1.9 inches of Fig. 1 bell; $E$=calculated effective length of exponential horn; cut-off frequency 150 c.p.s.; length 26 inches.

## TRUMPET COMPONENTS

### Bell

Since the bell of the trumpet is to be joined to some cylindrical tubing it is necessary to correct the effective length arrived at in the method stated above by subtracting the appropriate correction for the small end. The end effect at the large end of the bell is intrinsically a part of the acoustic performance of the instrument and so it should remain in the effective length, whether known or not.

By measuring the several resonant frequencies of a trumpet bell the effective lengths at those frequencies can be calculated, but when the effective length is plotted as a function of frequency, the resulting curve is not smooth, and more information is necessary. This may be obtained by repeating the process with successively different lengths of cylindrical tubing attached to the small end of the bell. In these

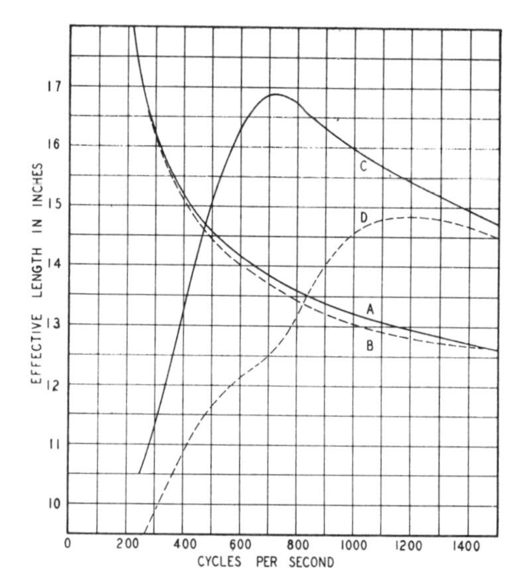


FIG. 3. Effective length *vs.* frequency curves for trumpet mouthpiece and mouthpipe combination. A and C=complete mouthpiece; B and D=mouthpiece complete only to narrowest part. Both A and B are for open-ended resonance. Both C and D are for pressure antinode at mouthpiece end.

cases, the effective length of the cylindrical tubing plus one end correction for an unflanged open end is to be subtracted from the effective length of the combination in order to arrive at the effective length of the bell at the several frequencies involved. Attention is directed to the fact that this procedure measures the effective length of the bell under actual operating conditions in so far as the location of nodes and antinodes in the standing-wave system is concerned.

The results of a series of about 150 such effective length measurements are plotted in Fig. 1. This is for a typical B♭ trumpet bell having an actual length of 25.69 inches, 0.438-inch minimum inside diameter, and 4.5 maximum inside diameter.

In Fig. 2, *T* is a smooth curve through the points of Fig. 1, and, for comparison, the effective length of a special experimental bell substantially conical in shape is identified by curve *C*. This bell was made up as follows: 2.63 inches of 0.438 inside diameter cylindrical tubing, 21.0 inches of straight cone, 0.438-inch to 1.68-inches inside diameter, 1.9 inches substantially identical to the last 1.9 inches of the typical B♭ trumpet bell referred to above. These experimentally measured curves will perhaps be surprising until they are compared with the curve identified as E which is the calculated effective length (exclusive of the end effect for the large end) for an exponential horn having a physical length of 26 inches and a cut-off frequency of 150 cycles per second.

Attention is directed to the well-defined scallop in the effective length curve of the trumpet bell. It will be shown later that for a cup-mouthpiece instrument (without using valve loops) to sound a series of tones having as fundamentals the complete harmonic series it is necessary for the curve of effective length *vs.* frequency to increase smoothly (actually it is a rectangular hyperbola). In order to get the tempered scale from the instrument the 5th mode (so called) must be 14 cents sharp with respect to the harmonic series. For a B♭ trumpet the *apparent* fifth mode extends from 494 to 587 cycles per second. In other words, the irregularity noted above is in just the right place, and substantially correct in amount to bring the *apparent* fifth mode in tune with the tempered scale.

### Mouthpiece and Mouthpipe

Since the mouthpiece and mouthpipe overlap somewhat, it is not possible to consider them separately, add the results, and come out with anything useful. It is therefore expedient to consider them as a unit. Following the method stated above the effective length of the combination as a doubly open resonator may be obtained as a matter of academic interest, and such a curve is plotted at A of Fig. 3.

In order to measure the effective length with a pressure antinode at the mouthpiece there are alternative procedures available. The mouthpiece may be closed and the corresponding resonant frequencies measured; this is rather difficult. The other method is to set up a symmetrical system involving two mouthpiece and mouthpipe combinations clamped together cup-to-cup and used with successive matched length pairs of cylindrical tube. In this latter case measurements are made just as in arriving at the effective length of the bell, except that only the odd numbered modes of vibration are used. After subtracting corrections for two unflanged open ends, the remainder is halved to arrive at the actual effective length of the mouthpiece and mouthpipe combination with a pressure antinode at the mouthpiece. The latter method seemed the more reliable of the two and was used to obtain curve C of Fig. 3.

Curves B and D of Fig. 3 are curves corresponding to A and C, but for the case in which the mouthpiece was cut off at the narrowest part of the throat, and the cup part discarded. The difference between the curves for open-end resonance and for closed-end resonance are sufficiently pronounced to make the resonant frequencies for the complete trumpet with the mouthpiece open almost the same as the resonant frequencies with the mouthpiece closed. The difference is ordinarily about one or two semitones, and the frequency associated with the open mouthpiece will be the higher of each pair of resonant frequencies that come close together. This near coincidence of open- and closed-end resonant frequencies has served for a long time to disguise the fact that the actual playing modes of cup-mouthpiece instruments are the odd-numbered modes, even though the fundamental frequencies of these modes are related to each other substantially by the integers of the complete harmonic series.

### Cylindrical Tubing

The velocity of sound through cylindrical tubing on the order of one-half-inch in diameter falls off by one or two percent as the frequency is reduced through the musical range. This can be handled on an effective length basis just as the other components have been handled. In the summation of the several parts given below the variation in the effective length with frequency has been ignored for the sake of simplicity, and the effective length of the cylindrical tubing has been assumed constant at the arbitrary figure of 17 inches. The actual length of that part of the cylindrical section involved in the valve mechanism cannot be measured readily with a high degree of accuracy, and on account of mechanical imperfections the effective length will vary with the position of nodes and antinodes as well as with frequency, although these variations are normally only a few cents in terms of frequency.

### Sum of Parts

We are now in a position to add up the various component effective lengths and compare this total with the effective length required to make a trumpet play in tune. This has been done in Fig. 4, in which the curves identified as C and D correspond to the same curves of Fig. 3.

The plotted points of the smooth curve are the calculated required effective lengths to give just intonation rather than tempered intonation. These points have been calculated for the normally played modes of the trumpet and show the required effective length *vs.* frequency for the trumpet exclusive of valve loops. By calculating for just intonation the discontinuities that would be associated with tempered intonation have been avoided and certain useful conclusions are possible, as will be seen. The required effective length has been taken as

$$l_e = mV/4f, \qquad (5)$$

where $V$ is the assumed standard sound velocity, and $m$ is the mode number for the type of vibration actually occurring and not the conventionally assigned node number for the playing modes of the instrument referred to in the introduction. For instance the conventional 2nd mode corresponds to an actual third mode type of vibration,

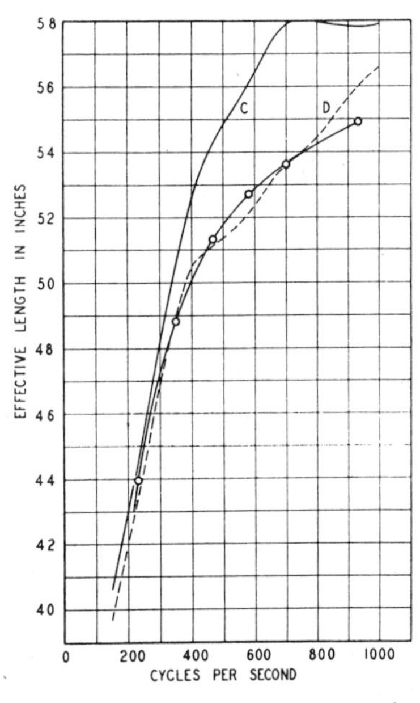


FIG. 4. Effective length *vs.* frequency curves for complete trumpet. o = required length for B♭ just scale; C = Fig. 1 plus curve C of Fig. 3; D = Fig. 1 plus curve D of Fig. 3. Both o and C include 17-inch effective length of cylindrical tubing.

and so we would use $m=3$ in Eq. (5) to arrive at the required effective length. Likewise, for what is conventionally called the 3rd mode the actual vibration is of the 5th mode type and so we would use $m=5$ in Eq. (5). This can be generalized by substituting for $m$ in Eq. (5) the expression $2m'-1$, where $m'$ is the conventional mode designation. Then we have

$$l_e=(2m'-1)V/4f=2m'V/4f-V/4f, \quad (6)$$

but $m'$ is proportional to $f$ and so we can write

$$l_e=V/2f_1-V/4f, \quad (7)$$

where $f_1$ is the frequency that would correspond to the first mode of the conventional designation. This is at once recognized as a branch of a rectangular hyperbola. This is quite remarkable since it indicates that all such instruments should have the same curve of effective length *vs.* frequency except for a constant (length of cylindrical tubing) depending on the key of the instrument. The customary requirement of tempered intonation disrupts this beautiful simplicity.

The agreement between the sum of the parts and the theoretically required effective length is reasonably good throughout the normal range of the instrument, usually within a small fraction of a semitone. This is especially the case when the requirement of tempered intonation in the *apparent* fifth mode is considered.

### VALVE-LENGTH PROBLEM

A casual inspection of Fig. 4 makes it *seem* obvious that, for instance, it will be impossible to lower the frequency by one semitone from the third octave B♭ with the same length of cylindrical tubing that will be required for lowering the frequency by one semitone from the fifth octave B♭. Any one familiar with such instruments knows that the length of cylindrical tubing required for one case is quite adequate for the other because the system has been working nicely for a very long time. A little calculation will explain what happens:

The required effective length is $vm/4f$ or 13,650 $m/4f$.
The required mode numbers are 7 and 15.
The required frequencies are 220, 233, 880, and 932 c.p.s.

The required effective lengths may be calculated and the actual effective lengths of the trumpet exclusive of the valve loops read from the curve of Fig. 4 or calculated from Eq. (7), and the information tabulated as follows:

| Frequency | 220 | 233 | 880 | 932 |
|---|---|---|---|---|
| $l_e$ (inches) required | 46.6 | 43.9 | 58.2 | 54.9 |
| $l_e$ (inches) trumpet | 43.1 | 43.9 | 54.7 | 54.9 |
| Valve loops | 3.5 | 0.0 | 3.5 | 0.0 |

The tabulated differences above show the length of valve loop required to produce the specified frequencies, and it is seen that the same length, 3.5 inches, is required in either case. Of course what has happened is that the total effective length of the trumpet has changed by about 6 percent in both cases, and the extra length in the valve loop over and above that required for the 6 percent change has been used in offsetting the inherent change in the effective length of the instrument (which has been assumed to follow Eq. (7)).

It is interesting to note that under the usual *assumption* of open pipe resonance the required effective lengths in the above example would have been 58.5 and 62.0 inches, so that the required length of the valve loop would again have been 3.5 inches. In other words the required valve loop lengths can still be calculated accurately by the older and simpler method provided the effective length *vs.* frequency curve of the trumpet follows Eq. (7) and as modified by the requirement for tempered intonation.

### CONCLUSIONS

It is believed that on the basis of the work described here the following conclusions are necessary:

1. That the velocity of sound wave propagation in the flaring bell of air column instruments varies quite markedly with frequency, being higher at low frequencies, at least when there is a standing-wave system present and the large end of the bell is open.
2. That the velocity of sound wave propagation in the mouthpiece and mouthpipe combination varies markedly with frequency and with the position of a pressure antinode with regard to the mouthpiece. When a pressure antinode is at or near the mouthpiece increasing frequencies are associated with at first decreasing velocities and finally increasing velocities.
3. That only those frequencies can be sounded on a cup-mouthpiece instrument by buzzing with the lips that

correspond to a pressure antinode within approximately $\frac{1}{8}$ wave-length of the mouthpiece constriction.

4. That within a small frequency range corresponding to a total range in pressure antinode positions of approximately 0.1 wave-length the influence of the instrument on the frequency sounded is small or negligible.

5. That harmonic production in a cup-mouthpiece instrument (and probably in other reed-air-column instruments) is due almost entirely to overloading of the air column in combination with frequency-selective radiation.

6. That the action of cup-mouthpiece (and probably all reed-air-column) instruments is properly described as regenerative rather than resonant.

7. That in instruments of the type described only the odd numbered modes of vibration are possible in normal playing. In connection with this last item, the habit of ascribing to thet rumpet, for instance, the modes of the complete harmonic series is so firmly established that it will be difficult to correct. The established custom has the merit of simplicity, and the logical procedure might be to continue the use of the established mode numbers where their simplicity is advantageous but refer to them as *apparent* modes.

## ACKNOWLEDGMENTS

The writer is considerably indebted to Mr. J. C. Webster who made most of the measurements reported here, and who besides brought an open mind and a critical attitude to the job. The writer is also indebted to Mr. Earle L. Kent, Director of Engineering Research, C. G. Conn Ltd., for an introduction to the problem treated here. (There was some difficulty in persuading me that the problem existed.)

# 16B

Copyright © 1948 by the Acoustical Society of America

Reprinted from *J. Acoust. Soc. Am.*, **20**(3), 345–346(L) (1948)

## On the Performance of Cup Mouthpiece Instruments

ROBERT W. YOUNG
*U. S. Navy Electronics Laboratory, San Diego 52, California*
February 16, 1948

IN a recent paper[1] entitled "The performance of cup mouthpiece instruments," certain conclusions appear which are not entirely apparent from the evidence presented. It is stated "that the velocity of sound wave propagation in the flaring bell of air column wind instruments varies markedly, being higher at low frequencies, at least when there is a *standing wave system* present and the large end of the bell is open" and "that the velocity of sound wave propagation in the mouthpiece and mouthpipe combination varies markedly with frequency and *with the position of a pressure antinode* with regard to the mouthpiece." The italics are the present writer's. If the usually assumed principle of superposition[2] is valid, it is difficult to see why the speed of one of two waves traveling in opposite directions (which together result in the particular standing wave and thus the position of the antinode) should depend upon the presence of the other wave. Certainly in a cylindrical tube the speed does not vary with the precise position of an antinode. On the other hand, if indeed the principle does not hold, the fact merits particular comment.

The conclusion was drawn "that in instruments of the type described only the odd numbered modes of vibration are possible." The author also suggested that since the custom of describing the modes of vibration of a trumpet by a complete series of integers is so firmly established, it would be advantageous to continue to use them but to refer to them as *apparent* modes. These remarks seem to be entangled with the manner of assigning the mode number.

There are at least three conceivable methods (and combinations thereof) by which mode numbers may be assigned, but which in idealized cases may all give the same result:

(a) The arbitrary assignment of a series of numbers which are approximately proportional to the frequencies of the corresponding modes of vibration.

(b) The designation of the different standing wave patterns in order of complexity, starting with the simplest as the first mode, the next as the second mode, regardless of the actual frequency, etc.; for example, in a tubular resonator the mode number can be designated as equal to the number of vibration nodes present.

(c) The assignment of the odd integers as mode numbers if a tubular resonator is closed at one end and open at the other; or the assignment of the full series of integers if the resonator is open at both ends, regardless of any taper of the resonator.

Apparently, the author followed method (*c*). Although not explicitly described as such, his calculation scheme for the resonant frequencies appears to have been to find as frequency dependent functions: (1) the length of cylindrical resonator open at both ends to represent the bell and central cylindrical part of a trumpet and (2) the length of a cylindrical resonator closed at one end and open at the other end to represent the mouthpipe part. He then assumed that these two "effective" parts in combination would function as a single closed-open cylindrical resonator. Thus, since the calculation scheme in the final stage required the usual formula for the closed-open cylinder, inevitably only the odd integers appear as mode numbers. The fact that the observed frequencies are not actually in the ratios of the odd integers is explained on the assumption that the velocity within the tapered tubes (and thus the "equivalent" length of the corresponding "equivalent" resonator) varies with the frequency in such a manner that the formulas give the proper frequencies.

Blaikley has demonstrated[3,4] how in a complete cone or a bugle there can be a vibration node at the small end, and yet the standing wave is such that the resulting frequencies form a complete harmonic series. Then according to method (b), he assigned numbers to the successive standing wave patterns, which are the same as the currently used mode numbers. Blaikley's evidence on the standing wave pattern is quite plausible; there seems to be little justification for calling his modes "apparent." The author's modes numbered on method (c) differ; it seems to the present writer that they should be called the *apparent* ones.

In view of the largely empirical scheme set up by the author, one wonders how satisfactory it would be if there were little cylindrical tubing connecting the tapered portions of the instruments being tested. Consider as a limiting case two tapered parts which when joined constitute a single truncated cone closed at the small end. On the often assumed approximate theory,[5] the sound velocity in a cone (aside from "small tube" effects) is the same as in free air. That is, the shape of the cone does not modify the wave velocity as does an exponential horn, for example. If one applies the approximate boundary conditions[6] of zero particle velocity and zero pressure, respectively, at the closed and open ends of the truncated cone, one obtains

$$-kr_1 = \tan k(r_2 - r_1),$$

where $r_1$ is the slant length from the extrapolated apex of the cone to the closed end; $r_2$ is the distance to the open end from the same origin; $k$ is $2\pi f/c$, where $f$ is the frequency and $c$ the speed of sound in free air. A similar transcendental relation is obtained when the same boundary conditions are applied to an exponential horn. The solutions of the transcendental equation certainly do not result in a series of frequencies related as odd integers. If the author's calculation scheme for an equivalent closed-open cylinder involves a true velocity which in the cone is a constant, then it cannot hold for the theoretical example just given.

The open end correction for an unflanged tube determined in the course of this work is given as 0.67, ± about $0.01R$, where $R$ is the radius of the tube. The fact that this value is somewhat larger than the commonly quoted[7,8] value of $0.58R$ is perhaps worthy of further investigation, since the difference is large in relation to the estimated error.

In a companion paper on electrical intonation tests,[9] it is stated that "if a pressure antinode exists at the mouthpiece constriction, the bell end being open, the combined system acts like a closed-pipe resonant system where there are no even-numbered modes of vibration; but the paradox remains that the odd-numbered modes give in this case the complete integer-series relation between the corresponding frequencies." In view of the arguments just presented, there is serious question as to whether the trumpet does in all respects act as a closed-open cylindrical resonator; there is no paradox if one accepts the picture of the standing wave system given by Blaikley.


[1] T. H. Long, J. Acous. Soc. Am. 19, 892-901 (1947).
[2] E. G. Richardson, *Sound* (Edward Arnold and Company, London, England, 1919), p. 37.
[3] D. J. Blaikley, Phil. Mag. 6, 119-128 (1878).
[4] E. H. Barton, *A Textbook on Sound* (The Macmillan Company, New York, 1919), p. 261.
[5] P. M. Morse, *Vibration and Sound* (McGraw Hill, 1936), p. 217.
[6] See reference 4, p. 255.
[7] See reference 2, p. 165.
[8] A. E. Bate, Phil. Mag. 24, 453-458 (1937).
[9] J. C. Webster, J. Acous. Soc. Am. 19, 902-906 (1947).


## ERRATUM

Page 345, column 2, line 24 should read: "the resonance frequency appears to have been to find as. . ."

# 16C

*Copyright © 1948 by the Acoustical Society of America*

Reprinted from *J. Acoust. Soc. Am.*, **20**(6), 875–876(L) (1948)

## On the Performance of Cup Mouthpiece Instruments

T. H. LONG
*C. G. Conn Ltd., Elkhart, Indiana*
July 26, 1948

IN a letter dated February 16, 1948, Dr. Robert W. Young[1] has raised a number of questions about some conclusions reached in my paper on the above subject that was presented before the Acoustical Society in May of 1947.[2] I am indebted to Dr. Young for this opportunity to elaborate a little on the points in question, and especially indebted to him for his reference to the quite instructive work of Blaikley,[3] with which I was not familiar and which seems to have been rather sadly neglected by modern writers on the subject.

The questions raised by Dr. Young will be taken up in the order in which they appear in his letter.

The principle of ***superposition*** does not pertain where the system is nonlinear. The non-linearity of the medium would seem to be of secondary importance here. The major item of non-linearity is evidently a combination of a small tube effect and a tapered tube effect. In a tube that is sufficiently small by comparison to the wave-length involved, the velocity of sound transmission is appreciably reduced by the energy lost in viscous friction. It must be obvious that this energy loss will be greatest, and the propagation velocity least, where the particle velocity is the greatest. If, therefore, we have a tube of varying diameter such that some part of the length is of "small tube" size by comparison to the wave-length, then the effective length of the entire tube for a standing wave system will depend on the location of pressure nodes and anti-nodes with regard to the small tube section. In a cup mouthpiece instrument the mouthpiece and mouthpipe constitute this sort of a tube, in which the mouthpiece constriction is the "small tube" section. The statement in the letter that "Certainly in a cylindrical tube the speed does not vary with the precise position of an anti-node,"[1] seems incorrect for this limiting case. This implies no variation of velocity with intensity.

The above discussion does not consider the taper of the tube, which is perhaps the most important factor and is taken up in more detail a little later. The non-linearity of this factor may be questionable.

I hesitate to debate the numbering of modes since it makes little difference how we number the possible modes of vibration as long as every one understands what we are talking about, and as long as we use the numbers in the proper manner in equations that correspond to what goes on.

Perhaps it should be pointed out that, even at the time of Blaikley's work, cup mouthpiece instruments were of great antiquity, and that Blaikley only reported what the musicians called these modes then—and still do.

The usage adopted in my paper was based on the logic of using a numbering system that conveyed the most information about what goes on, and the understanding that the odd series was always assigned to the possible modes of excitation of a quarter-wave transmission line. If this is not the case, it would seem that it should be.

The system of calculation employed was to find as a frequency dependent function: (1) the length of cylindrical resonator open at both ends to represent the bell and the central cylindrical part of a trumpet, and (2a) the length of a cylindrical resonator closed at one end and open at the other to represent the mouthpiece-mouthpipe part, or (2b) the length of cylindrical resonator open at both ends to represent the mouthpiece-mouthpipe part; all this was explicitly stated, the letter to the contrary; the entire statement was not given in one sentence however. There was no assumption that these two "effective" parts in combination would function as a single closed-open cylindrical resonator, but to the contrary. The ***assumption*** was that either part (1) plus part (2a) would function as a closed-open cylindrical tube resonator, or that part (1) plus part (2b) would function as an open-open cylindrical tube resonator. Since the sum of parts (1) plus (2b) varied by from 6 to 12 percent (too short) from the constant length required to obtain the complete harmonic series from an open-open cylindrical tube it was ***concluded*** that something else was happening Calculations were then made of the effective length *vs.* frequency required to obtain the complete harmonic series from a closed-open cylindrical tube and this was plotted on the same curve with, and shown to coincide quite precisely with, the sum of parts (1) plus (2a). (See Fig. 4 of the paper.) From this it was *concluded* that the instrument must be analagous to the quarter-wave transmission line rather than to the half-wave transmission line usually assumed.

The assertion in the letter that the variation of sound velocity within a *tapered tube* is only an assumption would be more nearly understandable if it had been accompanied by some alternative explanation for the information presented either in my paper, in Mr. J. C. Webster's paper,[4] or in the paper by Blaikley[3] on which a good deal of the letter seems to depend.

It is difficult to understand why the letter presented an equation illustrating quite precisely the variation of sound velocity in a truncated cone as an argument that the velocity of sound does not vary in such a cone. The equation in question is

$$-kr_1 = \tan k(r_2 - r_1), \tag{1}$$

where $k$ is $2\pi f/c$, and $r_1$ and $r_2$ are the slant lengths from the extrapolated apex of the cone to the closed end and open end respectively. Let us make out of this truncated cone something that will at least remotely resemble a $B^b$ trumpet by making $r_2/r_1 \approx 30$. Then arguments of the transcendental satisfying the equality will be 0, and approximately $0.97\pi$, $1.94\pi$, and $2.91\pi$, etc. If we make $r_2 - r_1 = 57$ inches the resonant frequencies are 116.5, 233, and 349.5 c.p.s. and so on, forming the complete harmonic series. These frequencies correspond to the travel of sound waves, within the horn, of 1/2 wave-length (for the round trip), 3/2 wave-length, and 5/2 wave-length respectively. These in turn correspond to sound velocities of 26,600, 17,700, and 15,950 inches per second respectively. These velocities are in each case an assumed average that is required to account for the transit time of the sound wave, and no implication is intended that the velocity is constant over the length of the cone, but rather the contrary. The corresponding effective lengths for these frequencies are 29.3, 43.9, and 48.8 inches respectively. The latter two points will be found plotted in Fig. 4 of the paper;[2] the first point is off scale.

It is interesting to note that the average velocities for the first three modes in a truncated cone sounding slightly higher pitches (based on $C$) are 26,880, 17,920, and 16,128 inches per second respectively, according to Blaikley's paper.

The above seems reasonably straightforward, but the letter goes on to say: "If the author's calculation scheme for an equivalent closed-open cylinder involves a true velocity which in a cone is a constant, then it cannot hold for the theoretical example just given." Now the velocity of a sound wave in a cone is substantially constant only when the distance from the vertex is more than a few wave-lengths, as was illustrated graphically in Fig. 2 of the paper.[2]

It is of course possible, by making appropriate errors, to conclude from the transcendental equation quoted that the velocity of sound in the truncated cone is constant. It is only necessary to assign the complete series of mode numbers and use the equation relating this series of mode numbers to the resonant frequencies of an open-open or closed-closed cylindrical tube resonator. It is submitted that this procedure bears no relation to what happens in the truncated cone.

There remains the apparent discrepancy between these results and Morse's[5] statement about constant phase velocity within a cone. (It seems that this is explicitly stated only in the revised edition, at p. 272, but the first edition reference certainly implies the same thing.) In approaching this question it might be well to use Morse's definition of phase velocity (reference 5, p. 115) as "the velocity of propagation of a simple harmonic wave." Morse's equations for wave propagation in a conical horn are in rather awkward shape for our present use, so we will take Crandall's[6] equation 155 as a starting point, drop the constant coefficient as being of no present use, arbitrarily define his $f'(\ )$ and include a term for the oppositely directed wave so that we will have a standing wave system representative of resonance in a cone. We then have

$$p = \{\cos(\omega t - kr) - \cos(\omega t + kr)\}/r. \tag{2}$$

The significance of this equation near the vertex of the cone where $r$ approaches 0 can best be appreciated by separating the variables, so that

$$p = 2\sin\omega t(\sin kr)/r, \tag{3}$$

but

$$(k/kr)\sin kr \approx k\cos(kr/2), \quad 0 < kr < \pi \tag{4}$$

and this approximation is especially precise for $kr = 0$ and $\pi$. So we may write

$$p \approx 2k\sin\omega t\cos(kr/2). \tag{5}$$

In other words a quarter wave-length of a standing wave system next to the vertex of a cone is equal in length to a half wave-length elsewhere in the cone. Therefore we must conclude that the propagation velocity, or phase velocity, is twice normal in that quarter of a wave-length that is next to the apex of the cone.

The stated *end correction* of $0.67R$ for a 0.438 inch diameter tube was the average of upwards of 20 calculations based on the measured resonant frequencies of more than 10 different lengths of tubing open at both ends, and in no case was the calculated correction as small as $0.58R$. It might appropriately be pointed out that the end correction of $0.58R$ mentioned in the letter seems to derive from, or at least agree with some measurements made by Blaikley and quoted by Rayleigh.[7] These measurements were made on tubes 2.08 inches in diameter, closed at one end, and the frequency range was from 253 to 507 cycles per second.

It would seem that a more complete consideration of Blaikley's work on the truncated cone, and of Morse's text, along the lines outlined above will allow *the paradox* mentioned in the companion paper by Mr. J. C. Webster[4] to stand.


[1] R. W. Young, J. Acous. Soc. Am. **20**, 345–6 (1948).
[2] T. H. Long, J. Acous. Soc. Am. **19**, 892–901 (1947).
[3] D. J. Blaikley, Phil. Mag. **6**, 119–128 (1878).
[4] J. C. Webster, J. Acous. Soc. Am. **19**, 902–6 (1947).
[5] P. M. Morse, *Vibration and Sound* (McGraw-Hill, New York, 1936), p. 217.
[6] Irving B. Crandall, *Theory of Vibrating Systems and Sound* (D. Van Nostr. Company, Inc., New York, 1927), p. 117.
[7] Lord Rayleigh, *Theory of Sound* (Dover Publications, New York, 1945), Vol. 2, Section 314.

Reprinted from U.S. Patent No. 2,987,950 (June 13, 1961)

1

2,987,950

# WIND INSTRUMENT OF THE CUP MOUTHPIECE TYPE

Earle L. Kent, Elkhart, Ind., assignor to C. G. Conn, Ltd., Elkhart, Ind., a corporation of Indiana

Filed Apr. 24, 1958, Ser. No. 731,581
10 Claims. (Cl. 84—388)

This invention relates generally to musical wind instruments of the type using cup-shaped mouthpieces, and more particularly to such an instrument in which the brass or metal tubing forming the same is constructed to provide better intonation and tone quality.

Musical wind instruments having cup-shaped mouthpieces have been constructed over a large number of years and are in quite widespread use. In such instruments various notes are played by use of frequency derived by resonance modes resulting from the length and general construction of the passage through the instrument. To provide other frequencies which may be spaced between these resonance modes, slides of different length are selectively connected into the passage of the instrument to change the effective length thereof. Resonance modes produced by these various lengths together with resonance modes at the basic length are used to provide the different tones of the instrument.

The frequencies of the tones of the equally tempered musical scale which it is desired to produce by musical instruments do not, however, correspond with the frequencies which are produced by the resonant modes. Therefore the resonance frequencies produced by an instrument as mentioned above do not correspond accurately with the frequencies in the equally tempered musical scale. Further to limit the number of slides which change the length of the passage through an instrument, various slides are used in combination and by this arrangement compromises must be made resulting in variation in the lengths provided as compared with the desired lengths. These two factors contribute to provide the undesired result that the tones produced by cup-mouthpice type instruments do not accurately conform to the frequencies of the equally tempered musical scale, so that the notes are not completely in tune, the instrument does not respond as desired by the musician, and the tone quality is imperfect.

It is therefore an object of the present invention to provide an improved wind instrument of the cup-mouthpiece type which produces better intonation and tone quality.

Another object of the invention is to provide a cup-mouthpiece type wind instrument wherein frequencies produced by resonance are modified to conform to the equally tempered musical scale.

The invention relates to wind instrument having valve slides which change the frequency thereof and which are used in combination to provide certain frequencies, but in which the frequencies produced by the slides differ from the desired frequencies, and it is a further object to compensate for such differences in frequency caused by the use of the valve slides.

Still another object of the invention is to provide an improved method of designing a cup-mouthpiece instrument so that the instrument has better intonation.

A feature of the invention is the provision of a brass wind instrument of the cup-mouthpiece type which includes sections of varying diameter which change the effective length of the instrument with the frequency of the tone played, to thereby compensate for differences

2

between frequencies produced by resonance and the frequencies required by the equally tempered scale, and/or differences due to the use of slides in combination which provide improper slide lengths.

A further feature of the invention is the provision of a brass type wind instrument having a mouthpiece, a mouthpipe and a bell which include tapered sections, with the tapers of the various sections being constructed to provide effective lengths of the over-all instrument which differ at different frequencies and fit a desired pattern. The bell may be formed of a plurality of portions each constructed to provide a desired change in the effective length of the instrument.

Another feature of the invention is the provision of a method of designing a cup mouthpiece instrument wherein the design variables for various parts are considered, and each part is constructed to have a particular effective length characteristic with respect to frequency in conjunction with the remainder of the instrument, so that the instrument has the over-all effective length to provide desired intonation characteristic over the entire range of the instrument. Nomograms may be used to determine changes in flared sections to provide the required changes in effective length to correct for intonation errors in an instrument.

A still further feature of the invention is the provision of an instrument as described above having a cavity formed by the mouthpiece and the mouthpipe, the size and shape of which may be controlled to adjust the effective length of the instrument at different frequencies.

Still another feature of the invention is the provision of a brass type wind instrument having a mouthpiece in which the volume of the cup of the mouthpiece is so related to the orifice area of the mouthpiece to provide a change in the effective length of the instrument over a predetermined frequency band.

Further objects, features and the attending advantages of the invention will be apparent from a consideration of the following description when taken in connection with the accompanying drawings in which:

FIG. 1 is a perspective view of a cornet constructed in accordance with the invention;

FIG. 2 shows in detail the taper of the various tubular portions of the cornet of FIG. 1;

FIG. 3 illustrates the deviation in cents of the frequency of a cylinder open at both ends from the desired frequency over a frequency band;

FIG. 4 shows the effective length required in an instrument in accordance with the invention to produce tones in accordance with equally tempered scale;

FIG. 5 illustrates variations of the effective length of the mouthpieces having different constructions;

FIG. 6 illustrates the change of the effective length of the instrument as a function of frequency and shows variations resulting from change in the length of the cavity formed between the mouthpiece and the mouthpipe;

FIG. 7 illustrates the change of the effective length of the instrument as a function of frequency and shows variations resulting from changes in the length and taper of the mouthpipe;

FIG. 8 shows the variation of effective length of the instrument as a function of frequency, which may be produced by construction of the bell of the instrument;

FIG. 9 includes curves of the effective length of an instrument considered as a cylinder open at one end and shows the configuration required to provide the tones of the equally tempered musical scale;

FIG. 10 includes curves illustrating changes in effective length with changes in physical length; and

FIG. 11 is a nomogram for use in calculating the effective length of flaring sections of an instrument.

In practicing the invention there is provided a musical instrument of the cup-mouthpiece type which in the example illustrated is a cornet. This cornet is made up of a mouthpiece having a cup adapted to be positioned adjacent the lips of the person playing the instrument, a mouthpipe having a portion attached to one end thereof in which the mouthpiece is inserted, a length of cylindrical tubing to which additional slide portions may be selectively coupled by valves, and a bell connected to the cylindrical tubing and having a flaring end from which the musical tones are discharged. The mouthpiece, the mouthpipe and the bell each have portions which are tapered, with the small ends being in the direction of the mouthpiece and the larger ends in the direction of the bell. The taper of these sections is effective to change the effective length of the entire passage through the instrument with the frequency involved. The length of a cavity formed by the mouthpiece and mouthpipe may also be varied to change the effective length of the instrument. The valve slides may also be constructed to have different effective lengths at different frequencies. The bell may be constructed with three or more portions which are individually designed to provide further variables which may be controlled. Accordingly, the instrument has different effective lengths at different frequencies and this feature is used to correct the effective length at particular notes where the actual length is improper to provide the tone which fits in the equally tempered musical scale. This compensates for differences between the equally tempered musical scale and a series of frequencies produced by resonance, and also for improper length which results from the use of the valve slides.

Referring now to the drawings, in FIG. 1 there is illustrated a cornet which is constructed in accordance with the invention. This instrument is made up of a mouthpiece **10**, a mouthpipe **11**, tubing sections **12** joining the mouthpipe in which valves **13** are provided for selectively connecting slides **14**, **15** and **16** to the tubing **12**. The tubing **12** extends from the valve section and joins with the bell **17** which terminates in a flared end **18**.

FIG. 2 shows the mouthpiece **10** more in detail and also shows in a schematic way the mouthpipe **11**, the uniform tubing **12** and the bell **18**. As shown in FIG. 2, the mouthpiece includes a cup **20** adapted to receive the lips of the person playing the instrument. The cup has an orifice therein with a tapered back bore **21** extending therefrom which increases in diameter relatively rapidly. The mouthpipe **11** also increases in diameter but at a much lesser rate. The mouthpipe may extend all the way to the valve slides. The section **12** which is broken away and is indicated by the letter K is usually formed of cylindrical tubing which is all of constant diameter. The valve slides **14**, **15** and **16** are usually of constant diameter. The bell **17** starts out at a relatively small taper and with the taper continually increasing until it becomes a very steep flare at the outlet or mouth of the bell.

Before considering the construction of the instrument further, it is necessary to consider the operation of the instrument which produces the problems solved by the invention. A cup mouthpiece instrument may be generally compared for analysis purposes to a cylindrical tube open at both ends. It is to be pointed out that the characteristics of the instrument are not exactly the same as that of a uniform cylindrical tube open at both ends, and the instrument has some characteristics approaching that of a cylindrical tube open at one end and closed at the other. However, it is believed to be more helpful to consider the analogy of the cylindrical tube open at both ends. Such a cylindrical tube will resonate at a plurality



of frequencies which are the fundamental resonant frequency of the open tube and the harmonics thereof. The resonant frequencies of a tube open at both ends are indicated by the following simple formula:

$$f_r = \frac{nc}{2L}$$

where $f_r$ is the frequency of the harmonic, $n$ is an integer corresponding to the fundamental or harmonic frequency, $c$ is the velocity of sound in the tube, and L is the physical length of the tube. In order to provide the different tones needed in such an instrument, it is necessary to have tones in between the harmonics provided by the above formula and to accomplish this, the slides are provided which change the physical length L so that additional series of harmonics are provided.

Considering first the problem of the resonant frequencies themselves, we may consider, for example, a cylinder of such a length that the fundamental frequency is 116.54 cycles per second. It will then resonate at the following harmonic frequencies:

| Harmonic | Harmonic Frequency | Equally tempered scale frequency | Note |
|---|---|---|---|
| 2 | 233.08 | 233.08 | $A_3$# |
| 3 | 349.62 | 349.23 | $F_4$ |
| 4 | 466.16 | 466.16 | $A_4$# |
| 5 | 582.70 | 587.33 | $D_5$ |
| 6 | 699.24 | 698.46 | $F_5$ |
| 7 | 815.78 | ---------- | |
| 8 | 932.32 | 932.33 | $A_5$# |
| 9 | 1,048.86 | 1,046.5 | $C_6$ |

The above table also lists the frequencies of the equally tempered scale which it is desired to produce. Although some of the harmonic frequencies coincide exactly with the frequencies of the equally tempered scale, others do not. It will be noted from the above that whereas $A_3$#, $A_4$# and $A_5$# are accurate, $F_4$ is slightly off, $D_5$ is substantially off, and $F_5$ and $C_6$ are slightly off.

As stated above, in order to provide frequencies intermediate the frequencies produced by the harmonics it is necessary to change the length of the passage through the instrument and this is done by the use of slides which may be selectively coupled to the instrument tubing by valves or the like. It is necessary to selectively add various different lengths to provide all of the tones necessary to make up the equally tempered scale. Normally it is deemed preferable to provide only three valves in such an instrument, and to do this three different slide lengths may be provided. To produce other variations in length the slides are used in combination. This introduces a problem since if the slides are the proper length when used alone, the use of a plurality of slides to provide a different change in tone is not accurate and does not provide the true length required.

The reason that the slides are of improper length when used in combination is that the slide lengths are computed as a percent of the fixed length of the instrument which is necessary to change the tone by a particular amount, a semitone, two semitones, etc. However, when one slide is already inserted in the passage the fixed length is greater so that the operation of a second slide does not increase the fixed length by the percent required to produce the change in tone normally provided by use of such slide. Compromises are made by changing the slide lengths so that they are slightly off when used alone and are reasonably close when used in combination. However, errors still exist. The following table shows the errors resulting when the slide lengths are made proper for individual use and also the errors resulting when compromise slide lengths are used. It will be apparent that the maximum error is greatly reduced by the use of compromise slide lengths.

SLIDE LENGTH ACCURATE FOR INDIVIDUAL USE

| Valve | Correct Length | Actual Length | Error |
|---|---|---|---|
| 2 | 3.49 | 3.49 | 0 |
| 1 | 7.17 | 7.17 | 0 |
| 3 | 11.08 | 11.08 | 0 |
| 1 and 2 | 11.08 | 10.66 | −.46 |
| 2 and 3 | 15.22 | 14.57 | −.65 |
| 1 and 3 | 19.61 | 18.25 | −1.36 |
| 1, 2 and 3 | 24.25 | 21.74 | −2.51 |

COMPROMISE SLIDE LENGTHS

| Valve | Correct Length | Actual Length | Error |
|---|---|---|---|
| 2 | 3.49 | 3.66 | +.17 |
| 1 | 7.17 | 7.36 | +.19 |
| 3 | 11.08 | 11.77 | +.69 |
| 1 and 2 | 11.08 | 11.02 | −.06 |
| 2 and 3 | 15.22 | 15.43 | +.21 |
| 1 and 3 | 19.61 | 19.13 | −.48 |
| 1, 2 and 3 | 24.25 | 22.79 | −1.46 |

As stated above, the errors resulting from the use of resonant frequencies which differ from the frequencies of the equally tempered scale and the errors resulting from the use of slides which are somewhat inaccurate add together to produce improper tones. The following table lists the note, the frequency, the resonant mode, the valves used, the lengths provided, the lengths required and the errors in length for a cylinder open at both ends which has been described. The instrument simulated by this cylinder without use of valves has a natural resonant frequency of 116.54 cycles per second as in the previous example. The length of the tubing without use of slides is 58.56 inches. The length of the slides are the compromise lengths stated above; that is, slide No. 2 is 3.66 inches, slide No. 1 is 7.36 inches, and slide No. 3 is 11.77 inches.

| Note | Frequency | Mode | Valve | Length Attained (open cylinder) | Length Required (open cylinder) | Error (Inches) | Length Required for open cylinder) | Change in Length Required (Percent) |
|---|---|---|---|---|---|---|---|---|
| $E_3$ | 164.81 | ------ | 1, 2, 3 | 81.36 | 82.82 | −1.46 | 60.02 | +2.49 |
| $F_3$ | 174.61 | ------ | 1, 3 | 77.70 | 78.17 | +.47 | 59.03 | +.80 |
| F# | 185.00 | ------ | 2, 3 | 74.00 | 73.79 | +.21 | 58.35 | −.36 |
| $G_3$ | 196.00 | ------ | 1, 2 | 69.59 | 69.64 | −.05 | 58.62 | +.10 |
| G# | 207.65 | ------ | 1 | 65.92 | 65.74 | +.18 | 58.37 | −.32 |
| $A_3$ | 220.00 | ------ | 2 | 62.22 | 62.05 | +.17 | 58.38 | −.32 |
| A# | 233.08 | 2 | 0 | 58.56 | 58.56 | 0 | 58.56 | 0 |
| $B_3$ | 246.94 | ------ | 1, 2, 3 | 81.36 | 82.91 | −1.55 | 60.12 | +2.66 |
| $C_4$ | 261.63 | ------ | 1, 3 | 77.70 | 78.26 | −.56 | 59.13 | +.97 |
| C# | 277.18 | ------ | 2, 3 | 74.00 | 73.87 | +.13 | 58.43 | −.22 |
| $D_4$ | 293.66 | ------ | 1, 2 | 69.59 | 69.72 | −.13 | 58.70 | +.24 |
| D# | 311.13 | ------ | 1 | 65.92 | 65.81 | +.11 | 58.45 | −.19 |
| $E_4$ | 329.63 | ------ | 2 | 62.22 | 62.12 | +.10 | 58.45 | −.19 |
| $F_4$ | 349.23 | 3 | 0 | 58.56 | 58.63 | −.07 | 58.63 | +.12 |
| F# | 369.99 | ------ | 2, 3 | 74.00 | 73.79 | +.21 | 58.35 | −.36 |
| $G_4$ | 392.00 | ------ | 1, 2 | 69.59 | 69.64 | −.05 | 58.62 | +.10 |
| G# | 415.30 | ------ | 1 | 65.92 | 65.74 | +.18 | 58.37 | −.32 |
| $A_4$ | 440.00 | ------ | 2 | 62.22 | 62.05 | +.17 | 58.38 | −.32 |
| A# | 466.16 | 4 | 0 | 58.56 | 58.56 | 0 | 58.56 | 0 |
| $B_4$ | 493.88 | ------ | 1, 2 | 69.59 | 69.10 | +.49 | 58.07 | −.84 |
| $C_5$ | 523.25 | ------ | 1 | 65.92 | 65.22 | +.70 | 57.86 | −1.20 |
| C# | 554.37 | ------ | 2 | 62.22 | 61.56 | +.66 | 57.90 | −1.13 |
| $D_5$ | 587.33 | 5 | 0 | 58.56 | 58.10 | +.46 | 58.10 | −.79 |
| D# | 622.25 | ------ | 1 | 65.92 | 65.81 | +.11 | 58.45 | −.19 |
| $E_5$ | 659.26 | ------ | 2 | 62.22 | 62.12 | +.10 | 58.45 | −.19 |
| $F_5$ | 698.46 | 6 | 0 | 58.56 | 58.63 | −.07 | 58.63 | +.12 |
| F# | 739.99 | ------ | 2, 3 | 74.00 | 73.79 | +.21 | 58.35 | −.36 |
| $G_5$ | 783.99 | ------ | 1, 2 | 69.59 | 69.64 | −.05 | 58.62 | +.10 |
| G# | 830.61 | ------ | 1 | 65.92 | 65.74 | +.18 | 58.37 | −.32 |
| $A_5$ | 880.00 | ------ | 2 | 62.22 | 62.05 | +.17 | 58.38 | −.32 |
| A# | 932.33 | 8 | 0 | 58.56 | 58.56 | 0 | 58.56 | 0 |
| $B_5$ | 987.77 | ------ | 2 | 62.22 | 62.19 | +.13 | 58.53 | −.05 |
| $C_6$ | 1,046.5 | 9 | 0 | 58.56 | 58.70 | −.14 | 58.70 | +.24 |
| C# | 1,108.7 | ------ | 2, 3 | 74.00 | 73.87 | +.13 | 58.43 | −.22 |
| $D_6$ | 1,174.7 | ------ | 1, 2 | 69.59 | 69.72 | −.13 | 58.70 | +.24 |
| D# | 1,244.5 | ------ | 1 | 65.92 | 65.81 | +.11 | 58.45 | −.19 |
| $E_6$ | 1,318.5 | ------ | 2 | 62.22 | 62.12 | +.10 | 58.45 | −.19 |
| $F_6$ | 1,396.9 | 12 | 0 | 58.56 | 58.63 | −.07 | 58.63 | +.12 |

Valve slide lengths used—#2=3.66″. #1=7.36″. #3=11.77″.

Referring now to FIG. 3 of the drawings, this curve shows the error in intonation (cents) resulting from the two factors mentioned above, that is, the difference of the resonant frequencies and the frequencies of the equally tempered musical scale, and second the incorrect lengths of the valve slides. FIG. 3 is based on a cylinder open at both ends. The unit used in FIG. 3 is cents with 100 cents being equal to one semitone. This curve corresponds generally to the error in inches shown in the above table, but in FIG. 3 the error is shown in deviation of the tuning or intonation rather than in deviation of the length of the instrument. As stated above, the errors in tuning or intonation can be compensated for by changing the length of the instrument. It is, of course, not desired to make a physical change in the length of the instrument as this would require additional mechanisms, but it has been found that the effective length of the instrument can be changed in various ways to provide an effective length of the basic instrument which compensates for the errors referred to above to produce an instrument providing accurate tones at all the desired notes.

FIG. 4 shows the effective length of the basic open cylinder which is necessary to provide accurate tones. In the example used, the instrument has a physical length of 58.56 inches without the use of slides. However, the effective length of the instrument must vary from 60 inches at the low notes to less than 58 inches in the intermediate tones, with minor variations being required at various points along the musical scale.

As shown by the formula presented above, the frequency of a tone produced in an open cylinder depends upon the velocity of the sound in the tube as well as upon the effective length of the tube. The velocity of sound in turn varies with the frequency, in a tube wherein the walls flare. Accordingly, by providing flared portions in various sections of the instrument, the effective length of the instrument can be changed. In conic section the effective length also changes with frequency because of the changing phase relation between the outgoing wave and the reflected wave. In accordance with the invention, the construction of the mouthpiece, the mouthpipe and the bell of the instrument are designed to provide configurations which control the effective length of the instrument. Between the mouthpipe and the bell is a section of tubing which is of constant diameter and this section, although effecting the tone produced, may not be modified to produce a change in the effective length. No substantial change in velocity is produced by change in frequency in constant diameter tubing of the size generally used and in order to produce the instrument conveniently this section to which the slides are coupled is retained at constant diameter.

In some respects, it is more nearly a true analogy if the cylinder closed at one end is chosen as a reference for a cup mouthpiece instrument. First, the cup-mouthpiece instruments have a pressure node at or near the bell of the instrument and a velocity node at or near the mouthpiece. Secondly, the effective length of a cylinder closed at one end would need to increase with frequency if its resonant frequencies followed those required for the musical scale and this would mean that the effective velocity of sound in the tube would be an inverse function of frequency. In flaring horns, such as an exponential, this is actually the case.

It is well known that a cylinder closed at one end resonates only at the odd integral multiples of the fundamental resonant frequency. Therefore, a cylinder closed at one end and of the proper length to resonate at, say, 116.54 cycles per second, as in the prior example, would resonate at 349.62 c.p.s., 582.70 c.p.s., 815.78 c.p.s. etc. if the physical length and the speed of sound in the cylinder are held constant. In order for this cylinder to resonate at 233.08 c.p.s. as required for $A_3\#$, it would be necessary for its effective length to be increased as the frequency is increased so that by the time the frequency reached 233.08 c.p.s. the cylinder would be suitably longer than it was at 116.54 c.p.s. (the fundamental) and the next mode of resonance, which would be 349.62 c.p.s. if the length remained constant, is now 233.08 c.p.s.

The required effective length, $L_e$, for the complete harmonic series is:

$$L_e=\frac{nc}{4f_r}$$

where

$n$=odd integer indicating mode of vibration

$c$=speed of sound

$f_r$=frequency at resonance.

Thus, to return to our example, the effective length required for a fundamental resonance ($n$=1) of 116.54 c.p.s. would be:

$$L_e1=\frac{13,650}{466.16}=29.28 \text{ inches}$$

The effective length required to resonate at the second harmonic of 116.54 c.p.s., or 233.08 c.p.s., would be:

$$L_e2=\frac{3(13,650)}{932.32}=43.92 \text{ inches}$$

These calculations can be carried on as far as desired and an $L_e$ will be a smoothly increasing function of frequency if the harmonic series is followed for the values of $f_r$.

As was mentioned before, the fifth mode of the instrument will resonate at too low a frequency if it follows the harmonic series and:

$$L_e5=\frac{9(13,650)}{2330.8}=52.71 \text{ inches}$$

To be of the proper interval with respect to a 116.54 c.p.s. fundamental it would have to be:

$$L_e5=\frac{9(13,650)}{4\times 587.33}=52.29 \text{ inches}$$

This means that it would be necessary for the rate of increase in effective length to be reduced as the frequency passes through the fifth mode, so that the instrument will resonate at the proper frequency to be in tune with the equally tempered scale. The solid curve of FIG. 9 shows the lengths required to provide the tones of the equally tempered scale and this is an irregular curve. The light smooth curve follows the harmonic series.

Once it has been determined what the effective length should be for each frequency of the scale by this process, the next step is to determine suitable parameters of bore calibration to produce the correct variation of effective length as a function of frequency. Explanations of the effect of the dimensions of the various parts of a horn on the effective length are set forth below. These apply to the analysis of a horn when considered either as a cylinder open at both ends or as a cylinder open only at one end.

Considering first the mouthpiece of the instrument **12**, it has been found that the effective length of the mouthpiece can be changed widely by control of the volume of the inlet cup in relation to the orifice area at the most restricted point of the mouthpiece. FIG. 5 includes six curves which show the effective length of the mouthpiece, and show variation of the effective length with frequency with the length vs. frequency curve being of different shape for different ratios of cup volume to orifice area. Curve *a* is for a ratio of one, *b* for a ratio of two, *c* for a ratio of three, *d* for a ratio of four, *e* for a ratio of five, and curve *f* for a ratio of six. It will be apparent that the mouthpiece can be used to provide an increase in the effective length in the region from 500 to 700 cycles per second as is shown to be needed by the curve of FIG. 4.

The taper of the mouthpiece back bore beyond the restrictive orifice may also be changed to change the effective length of the instrument. The change in taper changes the cutoff frequency and this changes the effective length for different frequencies. Increasing the cutoff frequency decreases the effective length for lower frequencies and increases the effective length for higher frequencies.

A second point in the instrument which may be controlled to change the effective length of the instrument is the small region at the end of the mouthpiece at its junction with the mouthpipe. A cavity with a square shoulder has been provided at this point which is designated C in FIG. 2. Change in the volume and shape of this cavity will change the effective length of the instrument. FIG. 6 shows changes in effective length resulting from change in the length of this cavity. The center line designated *g* in FIG. 6 is used as a reference and is based on a cavity having a length of 7/64 inch which is illustrated in FIG. 2. To reduce this length by half results in the changes in effective length indicated by curve *h*, and to completely eliminate the cavity would produce the curve *j*. To increase the length of the cavity by 50% produces curve *k* and to increase the length of the cavity by 100% would produce the curve *l*.

The next part of the instrument which can be controlled to provide change of effective length is the mouthpipe which has been designated **11**. This is the portion of tubing shown in FIG. 1 extending between the cavity designated C and the tubing of fixed diameter designated K. The shape and length of the mouthpipe changes the effective length of the instrument and the use of a conical taper has been found to provide an improved result. In order to hold the diameters of the ends of the mouthpipe fixed and thereby permit the use of a standard mouthpiece and standard bore for the tubing K which is of fixed diameter, the taper of the conical bore through the mouthpipe can be changed by changing the length thereof. In the mouthpipe shown in FIG. 2 the diameter at the small end is .330 inch and at the large end is .438 inch. FIG. 7 shows the deviation in effective length resulting from change of the length of the mouthpipe from 8 inches to 12 inches. In FIG. 7 a standard mouthpipe 10 inches long is used as a reference and is designated by center line *m*. Curve *n* shows the deviation in frequency produced by a mouthpipe 8 inches long, curve $o$ is the deviation for a 9 inch mouthpipe, curve $p$ the deviation for an 11 inch mouthpipe, and curve $q$ the deviation for a 12 inch mouthpipe. It is obvious from the curves that relatively sharp changes in effective length can be produced by changing the length and thereby the taper of the mouthpipe, and this is particularly effective to bring the notes $F_4\sharp$, $G_4\sharp$ $A_4$ and $A_4\sharp$ in tune.

It has been found that the use of a mouthpipe which is longer and has a smaller inlet has produced the required change in effective length to improve intonation in certain instruments which have been constructed. For example, the intonation of a euphonium was improved by reducing the small diameter of the mouthpipe from .437 to .418 inch and increasing the length thereof from 7.57 to 8.36 inches. The outlet diameter was retained at .555 inch to match the constant diameter tubing. In a trumpet designed in accordance with the invention, the mouthpipe inlet diameter was .330 inch as compared with .340 inch to .346 inch for prior accepted constructions. The mouthpipe inlet diameter at the junction with the cavity indicated $c$ in FIG. 2 may be substantially the same as that of the outlet of the mouthpiece.

Although the constant diameter tubing which is represented in FIG. 2 as the section K is not usually modified to change the effective length or tone characteristics, this length must be adjusted to provide the required total length of the instrument. That is, when the length of the mouthpipe is changed as illustrated by FIG. 7, the length of the constant diameter tubing is subject to change to provide the required total fixed length. The following table shows the change in the constant diameter tubing K for changes in mouthpipe lengths.

| Mouthpipe length, inches | Constant Diameter Tubing, inches |
|---|---|
| 8.0 | 21.47 |
| 9.0 | 20.44 |
| 10.0 | 19.30 |
| 11.0 | 18.21 |
| 12.0 | 17.17 |

It may be desired to construct the third valve slide to provide a change in the effective length thereof with frequency to thereby compensate for incorrect effective length resulting from use of the third valve slide in combination with other valve slides. Referring to FIGS. 3 and 4 and to the table showing the valves used to produce the various notes, it will be observed that a large and abrupt change in effective length is required when going from $A_3\sharp$ to $B_3$. To produce such a change in effective length of the instrument as a whole may be difficult because of this abruptness, but since the third valve slide is used for $B_3$ and not for $A_3\sharp$, compensation of the effective length of the third valve slide which will be effective for the frequency of $B_3$ will have no effect on $A_3\sharp$ and therefore need not be so sensitive to frequency change.

The bell may also be constructed with the tapered and flaring portions selected to adjust the effective length of the over-all instrument at different frequencies. The bell may be considered as made up of three parts: first, the stem designated S which is made up of the full length shown in the third section of FIG. 2 and the portion designated S in the bottom section, second, the throat designated T in the bottom section, and third the mouth M which includes the remainder of the bell. The taper, length and cut-off frequency of each of these sections may be controlled to change the effective length of the bell. FIG. 8 illustrates the effective length at the various frequencies for the bell configuration as shown in FIG. 2. This shows that the effective length increases with frequency, and although there are no sudden changes in the curve it is not a uniform curve, with the rise at certain points being relatively steep and the curve at other points being substantially flat. This curve can be made to have wide variations by making the taper of the stem, where it is connected to the constant diameter tubing, greater to provide a greater discontinuity.

In considering the effective length of various flaring sections of a horn to provide the overall effective length which produces the desired intonation, the following equation for a flaring section has been found to be helpful:

$$y=y_0 \cosh ms-\frac{y'_0}{m} \sinh ms$$

where

$y$=diameter at any point $s$ on section
$y_0$=diameter of the small end of the section
$y'_0$=slope at the smaller end of the section

$m=\frac{2\pi}{c} f_c$=parameter dependent on flare of section

$f_c$="cut-off" frequency of the section
$s$=contour distance measured from smaller end of section
$c$=velocity of sound=13,650 inches per second

Each section is, therefore, defined by four parameters, $s$, the contour length or distance from the small end of the section, $m$, the rate of flare, $y_0$, the diameter of the small end of the section, and $y'_0$, the slope at the small end of the section. Variation of any one of these parameters will cause a variation in the effective length of the section defined thereby. The section defined by the above equation may be conical, exponential, or catenoidal in shape depending upon the relative values of $y_0$, $y'_0$, and $m$. When $m$ is zero and $y'_0$ and $y_0$ have a particular relation, the shape is conical, when $y'_0/y_0m=1$, the section is exponential, and when $y'_0/m$ equals zero, the shape is catenoidal.

The following equation defines the effective length of a first section open at its outlet and joined to a second section at its inlet, with the sections being of various shapes as encompassed by the above equation:

$$L_e=\frac{c}{2\pi\sqrt{f^2-f_2^2}} \cot^{-1}\left[\frac{\sqrt{f^2-f_1^2}}{\sqrt{f^2-f_2^2}} \cot \left(2\pi/c\sqrt{f^2-f_1^2}L\right)\right]$$

where

$L_e$=effective length.
$f$=frequency at which $L_e$ is to be determined.
$f_1$=cutoff frequency of the first section.
$f_2$=cutoff frequency of the second section.
$L$=contour length of the first section.

Note that if the second section is a cylinder, $f_2=0$ and

$$L_e=\frac{c}{2\pi f} \cot^{-1}\left[\frac{\sqrt{f^2-f_1^2}}{f} \cot \left(\frac{2\pi}{c}\sqrt{f^2-f_1^2}L\right)\right]$$

As the velocity of sound is constant, the effective length as indicated by this equation is dependent upon the cut-off frequency $f_1$, and the contour length L.

It will be apparent from the above that the equation for determining the effective length of a flaring section as set forth above is quite difficult to use. It has been found that nomograms can be prepared by the use of a computer to facilitate determination of the effective length of such a section at a particular frequency $f$. FIG. 11 shows a nomogram which may be used for this purpose, and which applies to the length of a catenoidal section which is smoothly joined to another catenoidal section. In using these curves, it is necessary to compute

$$\frac{2fL}{c}$$

$$\frac{f_1}{f}$$

and

$$\frac{f_2}{f}$$

where $f_1$ is the cutoff frequency of the section involved and $f_2$ is the cutoff frequency of the section to which it is joined. After these calculations are made, the calculated value of

$$\frac{2fL}{c}$$

is used as the abscissa and the corresponding point is located on the

$$\frac{f_c}{f}$$

curve which corresponds to the calculated value for

$$\frac{f_1}{f}$$

Then the ordinate is located on the

$$\frac{f_c}{f}$$

curve corresponding to the calculated value of

$$\frac{f_2}{f}$$

The abscissa for this point provides the value for

$$\frac{2fL_e}{c}$$

so that $L_e$, the effective length, can be determined.

By use of the above equations and/or the nomogram, it is possible to design an instrument, or correct the design of an instrument, so that it conforms more closely to the desired curve. This is illustrated in FIG. 9 wherein the dotted curve illustrates the effective length of an euphonium constructed prior to the invention and the dot-dash curve illustrates the effective length of the instrument when changed in accordance with the teachings of the invention. Although the dot-dash curve does not coincide exactly with the desired curve shown by the heavy solid line, it will be apparent that it is much closer at certain critical notes. For example, $B_2$ is considerably improved and $F\sharp_4$, $G_4$, $A_4$, and $A\sharp_4$ are all greatly improved. The improvement shown was achieved by changing the shape of the mouthpiece and the mouthpipe of the instrument, and by the use of a cavity between the mouthpiece and mouthpipe having square shoulders.

The deviations from the smooth resonance curve, as illutstrated by the heavy curve in FIG. 9, may be provided by making the cut-off frequencies of various sections out of line with the cut-off frequencies of other sections, and the equations set forth and the nomogram make it possible to determine the configuration which should be used. As an example, the three sections of the bell described above may be constructed as catenoidal sections with cut-off frequencies having such a relation that the effective length curve will be irregular at a particular point where the equally tempered musical scale differs from a harmonic relationship.

Deviations from the smooth curve can also be provided by joining sections of different shapes. For example, a catenoid smoothly joined to a cylinder will produce effective length variations as shown in FIG. 10. Such variations can be located at various points on the curve by changing the physical lengths of the catenoidal section. In FIG. 10 the dotted curve and the dot-dash curve show deviations from the smooth solid curve, with the dot-dash curve being produced by a catenoidal section having twice the length of the section represented by the dotted curve.

A total of at least seven design variables determine the bell shape. These are rate of taper at the small end or stem of the bell and the cut-off frequencies and lengths of the three sections of the bell referred to above. There are at least six variables which define the mouthpiece and mouthpipe configurations and control the effective lengths thereof. These are the ratio of the volume of the mouthpiece cup to the area of the mouthpiece orifice, the ratio of the diameter of the orifice to the rate of taper of the mouthpiece back bore, the length of the back bore, the length of the cavity formed by the mouthpiece and mouthpipe, and the length and the rate of taper of the mouthpipe. This makes a total of 13 variables which may be changed to control the effective length. The bell may, of course, be divided into more sections to provide more variables. Also other parts of the instrument may be constructed to provide change in the effective length with change in frequency.

It will be apparent from a consideration of FIGS 5, 6, 7 and 8 that by control of configuration of the mouthpiece, mouthpipe and bell, the effective length of the instrument can be changed with frequency to provide the desired effective lengths at the frequencies of the various notes to be played so that the notes produced have the desired tone frequencies to fit in the equally tempered musical scale. Due to variations produced by the musician and to changes in the velocity of sound in the instrument because of changes in temperature, and even due to acoustic coupling of waves in a room into the instrument, the intonation is influenced in any given instrument construction. Accordingly variations of intonation apart from the design of the instrument can cause intonation discrepancies and therefore small intonation variations due to the instrument construction, such as $\pm 3$ cents, become insignificant as compared to other influencing factors. It is important however to eliminate large variations in intonation resulting from the design and construction of the instrument.

It is to be pointed out that the design variables mentioned above which can be chosen to provide optimum intonation may also effect the tone quality of the instrument and the response of the instrument (the feel) to the musician. Since there is no unique set of variables required to provide optimum intonation, the selection of variables should be made giving consideration to tone quality and feel as well as intonation. Improved intonation resulting from the teachings of this invention will however provide improved tone quality and feel when the selection of variables is properly made.

This application is a continuation-in-part of my application Serial No. 568,784 filed March 1, 1956, now abandoned.

I claim:

1. A musical instrument of the cup mouthpiece type, said instrument having at least four major tubular sections, said sections comprising a tapered bell, a valve section connected to said bell, a tapered mouthpipe connected to said valve section, and a mouthpiece, said valve section being of substantially cylindrical form, said mouthpipe having one end shaped to receive said mouthpiece, said bell having at least three sections, each of said bell sections having a progressively increasing diameter outwardly thereof, and the rate of increase in diameter of each bell section extending outwardly from said valve section being of greater magnitude, the cut-off frequencies and the effective lengths of said three bell sections being different whereby the effective length of the instrument increases with the frequency of the instrument so that the tones produced substantially follow the equally tempered musical scale.

2. A musical instrument of the cup mouthpiece type, said instrument having at least four major tubular sections, said sections comprising a tapered bell, a valve section connected to said bell, a tapered mouthpipe connected to said valve section, and a mouthpiece, said valve section being of substantially cylindrical form, said mouthpipe having one end shaped to receive said mouthpiece, said bell having at least three sections, each of said bell sections having a progressively increasing diameter outwardly thereof, and the rate of increase in diameter of

each bell section being of greater magnitude as the bell sections are positioned outwardly from said valve section, the cut-off frequencies of said three bell sections being different and the effective length of each bell section varying with frequency, said mouthpipe and said mouthpiece also being shaped so that the effective lengths thereof vary with frequency, whereby the overall effective length of the instrument increases with frequency in an irregular manner and the effective length is different for different tones produced by the instrument so that the tones substantially follow the equally tempered musical scale.

3. A musical instrument in accordance with claim 2 wherein said one end of said mouthpipe which receives said mouthpiece has an annular recess therein forming a cavity with a square shoulder facing said mouthpiece.

4. A musical instrument as defined in claim 2 wherein the bore of said mouthpipe has a conical taper throughout its length.

5. A musical instrument in accordance with claim 2 wherein said one end of said mouthpipe which receives said mouthpiece has an annular recess therein forming a cavity with a square shoulder facing said mouthpiece, and the bore of said mouthpipe has a conical taper throughout its length.

6. A musical instrument as defined in claim 2 wherein said valve section includes a plurality of slides and valve means for selectively connecting said slides to increase the physical length of said valve section, with at least one of said slides being constructed to have an effective length which varies with frequency.

7. A musical instrument as defined in claim 2 wherein said mouthpiece includes a cup-shaped portion adapted to be placed against the lips of a person playing the instrument, an orifice at the base of said cup-shaped portion and a back bore extending from said orifice and tapering outwardly toward the end of said mouthpiece received in said mouthpipe, and wherein the ratio of the volume of said cup-shaped portion of said mouthpiece to the area of said orifice thereof is selected to provide different effective lengths of said mouthpiece for different tones played on the instrument.

8. A musical instrument as defined in claim 2 wherein said mouthpiece includes a cup-shaped portion adapted to be placed against the lips of a person playing the instrument, an orifice at the base of said cup-shaped portion and a back bore extending from said orifice and tapering outwardly toward the end of said mouthpiece received in said mouthpipe, and wherein said back bore of said mouthpiece is shaped to have a cut-off frequency which produces different effective lengths of said mouthpiece for different tones played on the instrument.

9. A musical instrument as defined in claim 2 wherein said tapered mouthpipe has a conical bore throughout its length and the end thereof which receives said mouthpiece has an annular recess therein forming a cavity with a square shoulder facing said mouthpiece, and wherein said mouthpiece includes a cup-shaped portion adapted to be placed against the lips of a person playing the instrument, an orifice at the base of said cup-shaped portion and a back bore extending from said orifice and tapering outwardly toward the end of said mouthpiece received in said mouthpipe, with the ratio of the volume of said cup-shaped portion of said mouthpiece to the area of said orifice thereof, and the cutoff frequency of said back bore thereof, providing different effective lengths of said mouthpiece for different tones played on the instrument.

10. A musical instrument as defined in claim 2 wherein said valve section includes a plurality of slides and valve means for selectively connecting said slides to increase the physical length of said valve section, at least one of said slides being constructed to have an effective length which varies with frequency, and wherein said tapered mouthpipe has a conical bore throughout its length and the end thereof which receives said mouthpiece has an annular recess therein forming a cavity with a square shoulder facing said mouthpiece, and wherein said mouthpiece includes a cup-shaped portion adapted to be placed against the lips of a person playing the instrument, an orifice at the base of said cup-shaped portion and a back bore extending from said orifice and tapering outwardly toward the end of said mouthpiece received in said mouthpipe, with the ratio of the volume of said cup-shaped portion of said mouthpiece to the area of said orifice thereof, and the cutoff frequency of said back bore thereof, providing different effective lengths of said mouthpiece for different tones played on the instrument.

**References Cited** in the file of this patent

UNITED STATES PATENTS

1,509,104 Hickernell ---------- Sept. 23, 1924
1,759,824 Gulick ---------- May 20, 1930
2,033,183 Dewey ---------- Mar. 10, 1936
2,288,743 Reed ---------- July 7, 1942
2,376,453 Ruettiger ---------- May 22, 1945
2,504,336 Kleczka ---------- Apr. 18, 1950

FOREIGN PATENTS

378,157 France ---------- Aug. 1, 1907
198,960 Great Britain ---------- June 14, 1923
448,869 Germany ---------- Aug. 26, 1927

**June 13, 1961** E. L. KENT **2,987,950**

WIND INSTRUMENT OF THE CUP MOUTHPIECE TYPE

Filed April 24, 1958 4 Sheets-Sheet 1

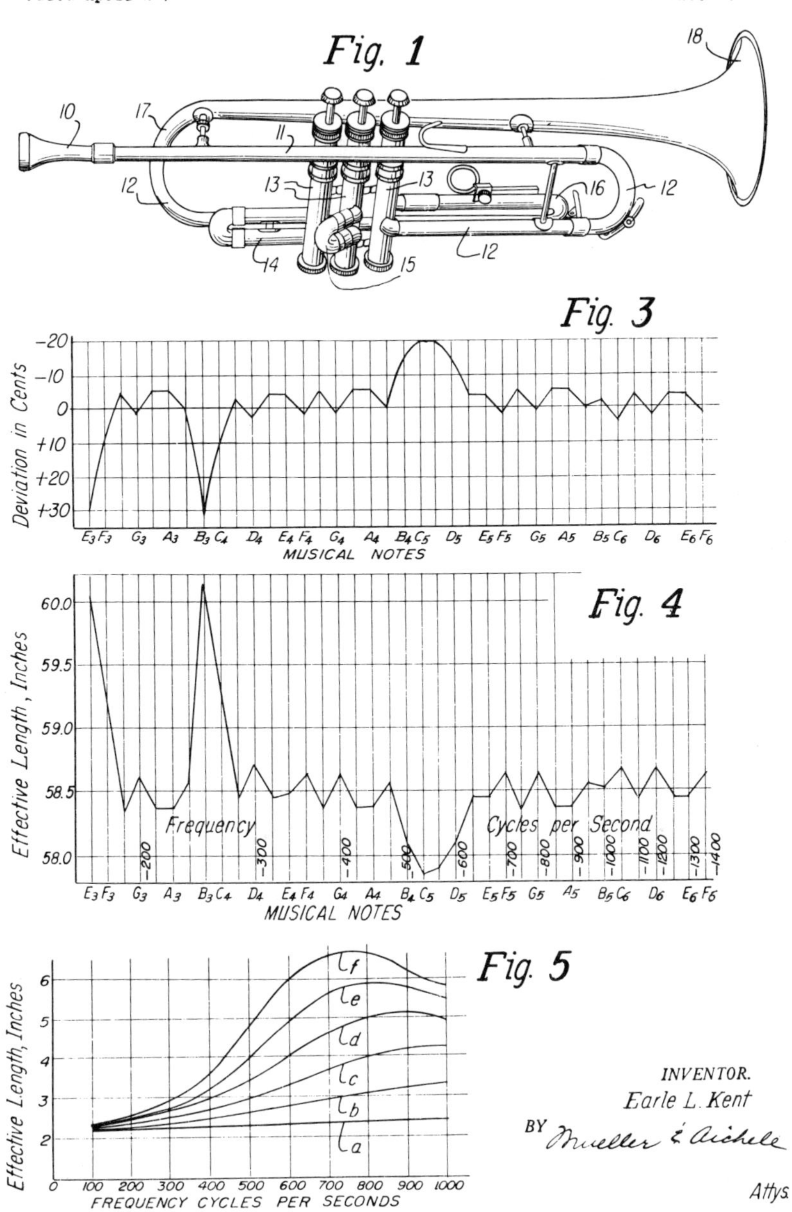


INVENTOR.
Earle L. Kent
BY Mueller & Aichele
Attys.

WIND INSTRUMENT OF THE CUP MOUTHPIECE TYPE

Filed April 24, 1958 4 Sheets-Sheet 2

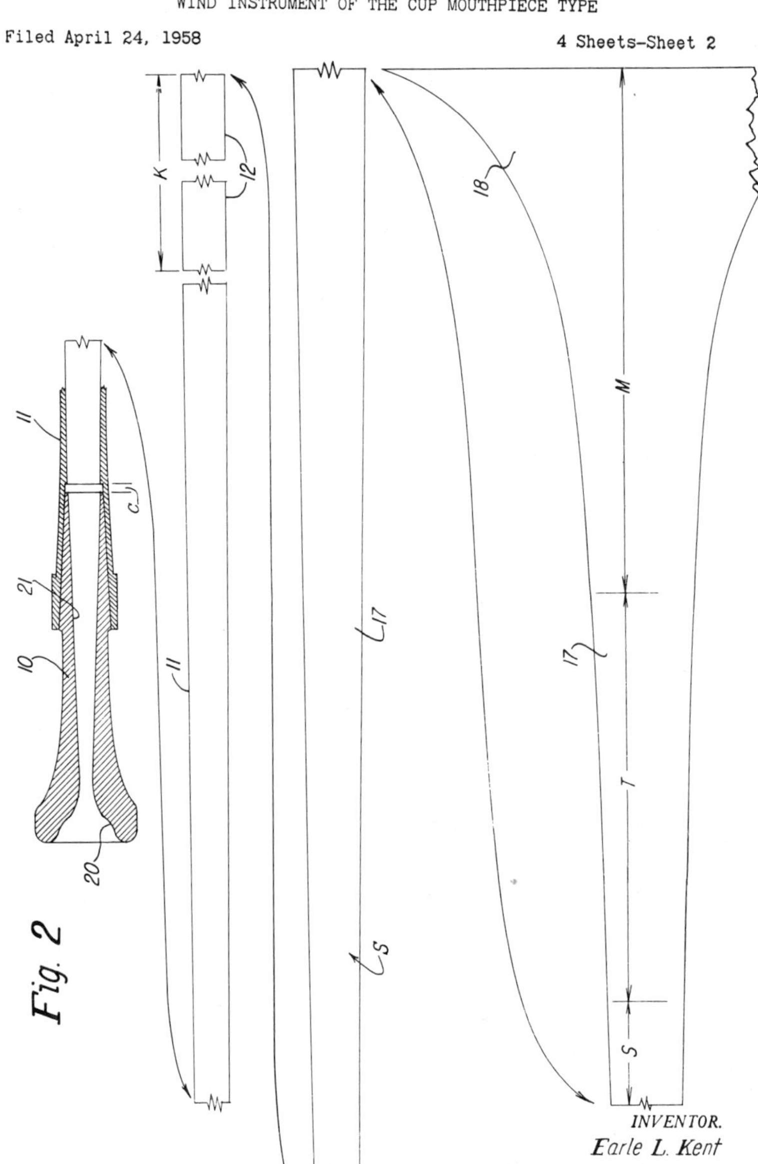

WIND INSTRUMENT OF THE CUP MOUTHPIECE TYPE

Filed April 24, 1958 4 Sheets-Sheet 3

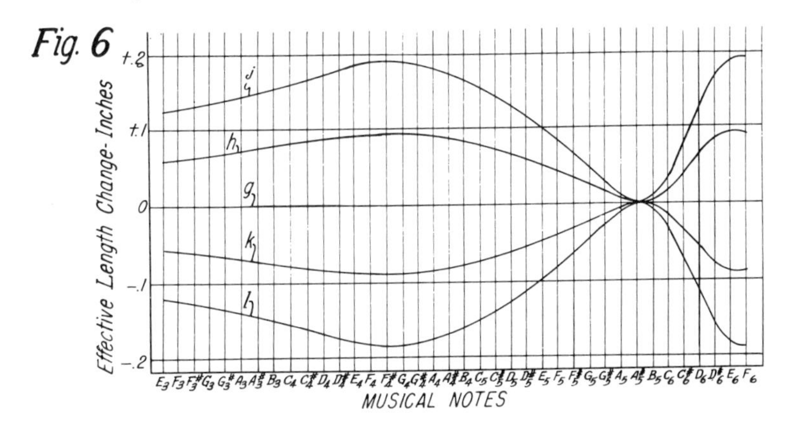


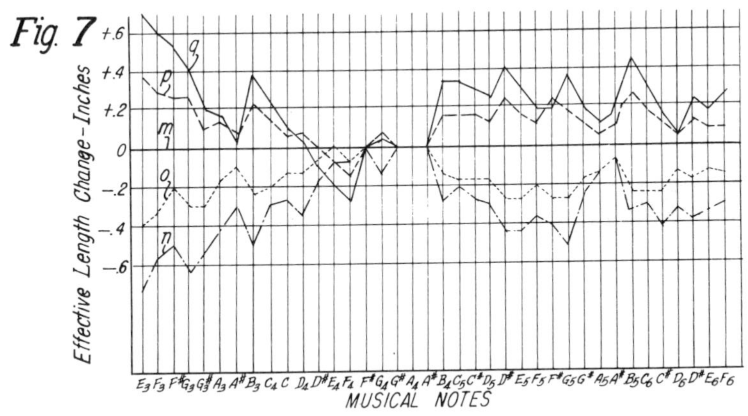


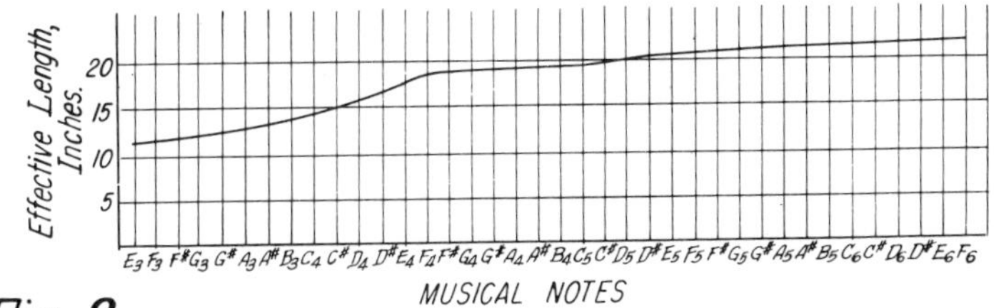


Fig. 8

INVENTOR.
Earle L. Kent
BY Mueller & Aichele
Attys.

June 13, 1961 E. L. KENT 2,987,950

WIND INSTRUMENT OF THE CUP MOUTHPIECE TYPE

Filed April 24, 1958 4 Sheets-Sheet 4

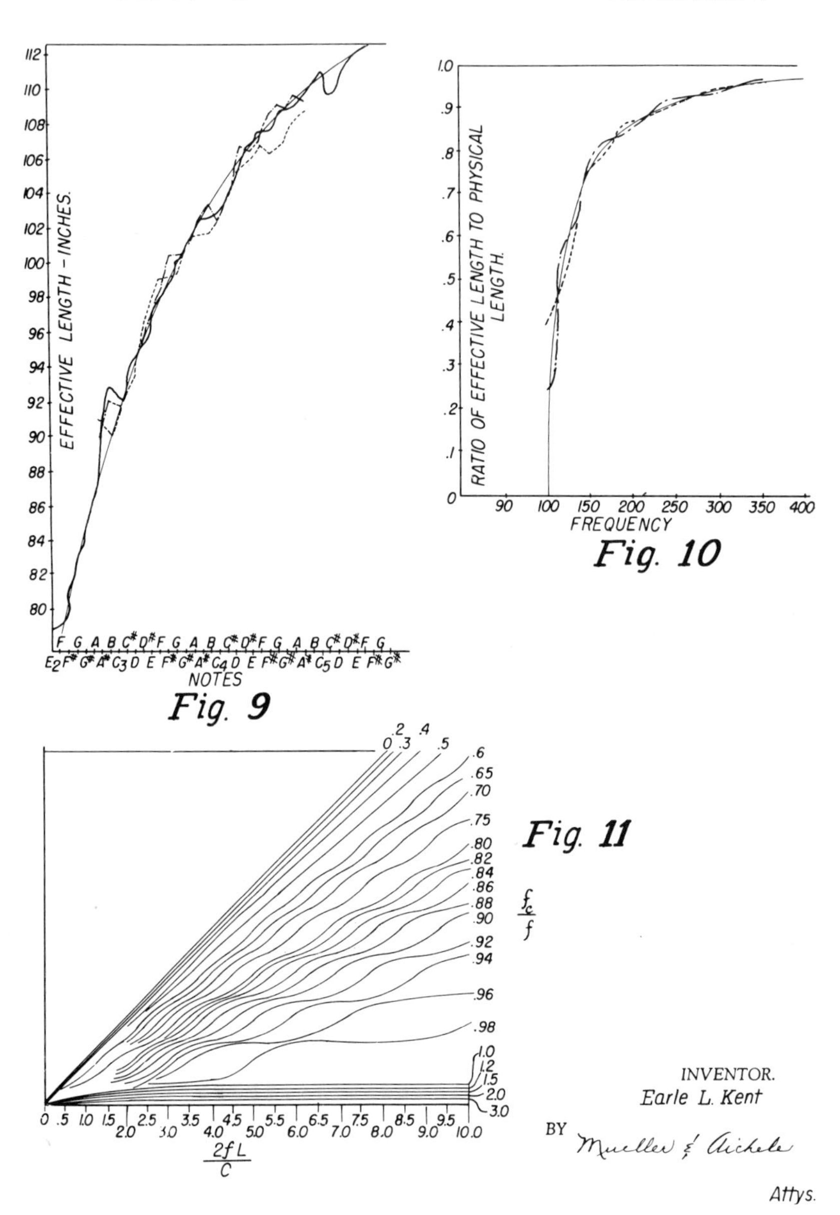


Fig. 9

Fig. 10

Fig. 11

Reprinted from U.S. Patent No. 3,507,181 (April 21, 1970)

1

3,507,181

# CUP-MOUTHPIECE WIND INSTRUMENTS

William T. Cardwell, Jr., 16731 Ardita Drive, Whittier, Calif. 90603

Filed Oct. 25, 1967, Ser. No. 678,042
Int. Cl. G10d *7/10*
U.S. Cl. 84—388 7 Claims


## ABSTRACT OF THE DISCLOSURE

A method is described of determining an optimum shape for the air-column of a trumpet, trombone, or similar cup-mouthpiece wind instrument, so that the intonation of the instrument will approximate ideal intonation. The shape determination is ab initio; it does not merely correct, or improve known empirical shapes. The method involves initial measurements of the Helmholtz-resonator-termination effect of a mouthpiece representative of the mouthpiece to be used on the final instrument. The air-column, particularly the bell stem, is then shaped to give optimum intonation with that mouthpiece.


## BACKGROUND OF THE INVENTION

### Field of the invention

This invention pertains generally to the manufacture of musical wind instruments of the cup-mouthpiece family, which includes trumpets, trombones, alto horns, baritone horns, and tubas. It pertains particularly to the members of that family that are true trumpets in the classical sense that at least one-half of their air column is untapered. It pertains most particularly to the modern instrument that is known by the name "trumpet," which in the mid-twentieth-century is most commonly made "in B-flat," with a "tuning note" at 466 Hz., but which is also made in C with a tuning note at 523 Hz., in D with a tuning note at 587 Hz., etc. It is in the shaping of the smaller trumpets of higher pitch that the invention has found its chief use.

### Description of the prior art

Trumpets have been made and played for literally thousands of years; and for at least several hundred years it has been known that the shape of the air column inside the trumpet (or one of its modern relatives, e.g. the trombone) determines the resonant frequencies to which the instrument responds. However, the air column shapes have been developed empirically, by trial and error, and no working theory of design has existed to enable a trumpet maker to determine the optimum shape, beginning only with a knowledge of the musically-desirable frequencies to which the instrument is supposed to respond. To the knowledge of the present inventor the nearest approach to a working theory of trumpet design, ab initio, was made by H Bouasse: Instruments à Vent," Librarie Delagrave, Paris, 1929. Bouasse was fully aware of the fundamental mathematical-physical problem of trumpet design, which is best stated in the form of the so-called mode paradox: (1) the frequencies of the open tones (the unvalved tones) of the trumpet are those that the trumpet air-column itself responds to as a passive resonator if it is closed off at the lip-plane of the mouthpiece, and yet (2) the ratios between the modal frequencies are those we would expect from a simple resonator that was open at both ends. Bouasse knew that the physical answer to this mode paradox is that the trumpet air column behaves as if it had a length that varies with frequency. (It should be emphasized here that *actual* length variation, such as produced by valves, or slide motion, is not being discussed). Bouasse knew that the flare

2

of the bell stem must produce an apparent length variation with frequency and he tried to calculate what shape a bell should have to produce the musically-desired open tones. He came to a gloomy conclusion that it was impossible, using classical mathematical theory, to calculate the needed bell shape.

I have found that the approach of Bouasse to bell design was more nearly correct than Bouasse himself realized. The essential deficiency of his theory was that he tried to make the bell account for all of the apparent length variation, and the bell does not have to account for all of it. I have shown that the cup mouthpiece performs a significant part of the apparent length variation, and if the help that it provides to the bell is taken into account, it becomes possible to do what Bouasse tried to do, to make a quantitative calculation of the required shape for a bell that will produce correct intonation on a trumpet (or related cup-mouthpiece wind instrument).

Since Bouasse, and up to the present time, the nearest approach to the present invention was made in a 1961 patent to E. L. Kent, U.S. 2,987,950. FIGURE 5 of that patent shows an experimental awareness that the mouthpiece plays some role in varying the apparent length of a cup-mouthpiece wind instrument. However, the qualitative connection to bell design, ab initio, was not made by Kent. The Kent patent was concerned principally with improvements and modifications of existing shapes to make their intonaton better.

The distinction between trumpet bells made according to the present invention, and bells made according to the teachings of Kent in U.S. 2,987,950, may perhaps be most clearly indicated by pointing out that, in one sense, they are simpler than the Kent bells, which were composed or "at least three" catenoidal sections. Instead of using a plurality of corrective sections, each one intended to compensate for deficiencies of the others, I have discovered how to design a single catenoidal section so that it cooperates optimally with the cup-mouthpiece to be used, and produces a closer approach to ideal intonation.

Another distinction over the Kent invention is the avoidance of the phase-matching problems that were necessary to handle when three or more catenoidal bell sections of various flare rates were joined. The single catenoidal section of the bell stem in the present invention, whose main purpose is to raise the natural frequency of the second mode of the instrument, is joined to untapered tubing at the nodal position of the second mode to make a perfect phase-match at the frequency of that mode.

## SUMMARY OF THE INVENTION

In all of the following text, the word "trumpet" will be intended to cover relatives of the trumpet, such as the trombone, particularly those relatives that come under the classical definition mentioned hereinafter. In accordance with the present invention, the design of a trumpet begins with a series of acoustic measurements on a mouthpiece representative of the one to be used on the final instrument. The mouthpiece is fastened to a tubing of constant inside diameter like that to be used in the middle part of the final instrument. The lip-plane of the mouthpiece is closed off with a microphone, and the distal end of the attached constant diameter tubing is left open. The open, distal end is then exposed to ambient sound of adjustable, continuously variable, frequency, and the response of the system, acting as a passive resonator is determined at a series of frequencies. The so-called resonance peaks are determined. From the noted resonance frequencies, the apparent-length-varying function of the mouthpiece can be calculated, and the lengths of the unflared, and flared, portions of the trumpet can be calculated, but it is more conservative to continue the experimental determinations until an actual experimental length of tubing is found, which in cooperation with the mouthpiece, produces upper modes closely approximating the musically desirable upper modes of the final instrument. The discovery, that (1) the intonation of the upper modes is regulated mainly by the mouthpiece, and (2) the mouthpiece and bell must cooperate properly over the entire, upper and lower, playing range, is the underlying essence of the present invention. After the system is found which will produce the musically desirable upper modes, a bell shape is calculated, using known theory relating apparent-acoustical-length to frequency, which bell does not upset the determined placement of the upper modes, but raises the lower modes, particularly the second mode, into its proper musical place. The entire trumpet comprises a mouthpiece acoustically similar to the one used in the experiments, a section of tubing of substantially constant diameter, and a catenoidal bell section, all with properly mated acoustical properties. It may comprise also certain other features commonly found on conventional, commercial modern trumpets: a leaderpipe between the mouthpiece and the constant-diameter section, a set of valves, and a terminating bell skirt of much greater flare rate than that of the main stem of the bell. Methods of taking these additional features into account are described in the detailed disclosure which follows the section immediately below.

## BRIEF DESCRIPTION OF THE DRAWINGS

FIGURE 1 consists of two definitional diagrams, one of the trumpet as a whole, and the other of the frontal part of the trumpet, showing and naming the important parts of the mouthpiece.

FIGURE 2 represents the experimental apparatus that is desirable to use in carrying out the method of the present invention.

FIGURE 3 shows typical resonance data obtained by measuring trumpets with the apparatus of FIGURE 2. The frequencies of resonance peaks, such as those illustrated, are the main data used in the method of the present invention.

FIGURE 4 shows how a mouthpiece helps to give a trumpet its musically desirable intonation in its uppper playing modes.

FIGURE 5 shows a resonance curve for a modern commercial trumpet mouthpiece, when it is not coupled to a trumpet, but is acting alone as a Helmholtz resonator, picking up ambient sound through its backbore.

FIGURE 6 illustrates, in terms of alterations in resonance frequencies, the experimental design and construction of an improved trumpet in high-F (tuning note, 698 Hz.), according to the method of the present invention.

FIGURE 7 shows eight intonation plots on musical staves, plots of a sort sometimes used to show musicians the intonational imperfections of their instruments. The data are from experimental measurements. Seven of the plots represent modern commercial trumpets of high reputation both in Europe and the United States. The eighth plot represents an F-trumpet constructed according to the method of the present invention.

## DESCRIPTION OF THE PREFERRED EMBODIMENTS

Referring to FIGURE 1A, a trumpet is, by classical definition, an instrument having over half of its length untapered. If it tapers all the way, or most of the way, it is, by classical definition, not a trumpet, but a cornet. As the following description progresses, it will become evident that the musical wind instruments to which the invention applies most readily, are those which have a significant untapered or unflared part, although parts of the teachings apply to all cup-mouthpiece wind instruments. The trombone is obviously a member of the



trumpet family, because the entire slide portion must necessarily be untapered in order to slide.

Referring to FIGURE 1B, the trumpet or any other member of the trumpet family, begins with a cup against which the lips are applied, and the cup is followed by a constriction, usually called the throat, which is exceedingly important to note for purposes of this specification. The cup and throat configuration turns out to have a vital acoustic relation to the bell on the distal end of the trumpet.

Referring to FIGURE 2, which illustrates apparatus necessary in the design and testing of a trumpet according to the method of this invention, a trumpet, or part of a trumpet, for example, a mouthpiece and a piece of cylindrical tubing, or even just a mouthpiece, is closed off at the lip plane of the mouthpiece by a condenser microphone. The response of the microphone is amplified and read on a vacuum tube voltmeter. The air column of the system is excited by an external loudspeaker, which is actuated by a power amplifier that in turn is actuated by a variable frequency oscillator. However, the input to the power amplifier is controlled by a feedback loop involving a monitor microphone, so that the acoustic level of the speaker output is held constant. Frequencies may be read by various devices, but the present inventor has found it advantageous to use a digital counter that counts cycles for exactly a second and then reads out directly in Hz.

FIGURE 3 shows typical data obtained with the apparatus of FIGURE 2. All of the abscissae run from zero to 1700 Hz., and the ordinates are in millivolts, representing directly-read responses of the mouthpiece-end microphone. FIGURE 3C represents a conventional B-flat trumpet. FIGURE 3B represents the F trumpet whose design and construction is described below, and FIGURE 3A represents a high-B-flat piccolo trumpet. Briefly stated, the objective of all the efforts to be described below is to get the frequencies of the vibrational modes that are represented in FIGURE 3, into their musically desirable places on the frequency scale.

It has already been mentioned in a previous section that the physicist, Bouasse, knew that the frequencies of the open (unvalved) tones of the trumpet are those that the trumpet air-column itself responds to as a passive resonator if it is closed off at the lip plane of the mouthpiece, and yet the ratios between the modal frequencies are those one would expect from a simple resonator that was open at both ends. Here it is necessary to discuss that point mathematically.

If a simple pipe, of constant diameter, is closed at one end and open at the other, the air column inside that pipe will have natural vibrational frequencies given by Equation 1:

$$f_n = \frac{(2n-1)c}{4l} \qquad (1)$$

where

$f_n$=frequency of the $n$th mode, of a closed-open pipe, in Hz.

$n$=number of mode

$c$=velocity of sound

$l$=length of the closed-open pipe.

The natural frequencies of such a pipe are, in accordance with the factor (2n—1) in the ratios of the odd numbers 1, 3, 5, 7, 9, etc. A set of such frequencies would not be useful in music as we now know and play it. For music, the natural open tone frequencies of a trumpet, or similar instrument, must have ratios comprising a complete harmonic series of whole numbers 2, 3, 4, 5, 6, etc. Such a set of frequencies would be obtainable from a simple pipe, open at both ends, which would have natural vibrational frequencies given by Equation 2:

$$F_n = \frac{nc}{2L} \qquad (2)$$

where

$F_n$=frequency of the $n$th mode of an open-open pipe, in Hz.

L=length of the open-open pipe.

However, when a trumpet tube is placed to the lips of a blower, the effect is to produce closure at one end, or in more precise, modern terms, to terminate the tube with a high impedance, which for modal purposes, is substantially equivalent to closure.

It is not difficult to state mathematically what must happen if a closed-open system is to give modes like those of an open-open system. If the length of the closed-open system acted as if it varied with frequency in the particular way given by equating $f_n$ of Equation 1 and $F_n$ of Equation 2, treating $l$ as a variable, then the frequencies of the closed-open system would be in the ratios of the complete series of whole numbers. Equation 3 states the mathematical condition:

$$l=L(1-\tfrac{1}{2}n) \qquad (3)$$

Some grasp of the implications of Equation 3 is fundamental to the understanding of the entire remainder of this disclosure. Knowing, for instance, that the modern trumpeter must use the open tones of his instrument that correspond to the modes from the second to at least the eighth, one may first put $n=2$ into Equation 3 and then $n=8$, and calculate that at the second mode, a trumpet must act as if it were only 75 percent as long as a simple open-open resonator responding to the same frequency, and at the eighth mode, a trumpet must act as if it were 94 percent as long as the same simple, open-open resonator. Based on the theoretical open-open resonator length, this is a 19 percent variation, but based on its own shortest apparent length, this is a 25 percent variation in apparent length over the musically useful playing range.

Now, it has been known for decades that if a tubular acoustic resonator were not just a simple tube of constant cross section, but had a changing cross section, or flare, it would act as if its length were changing with frequency. The flare causes changes in phase velocity of the waves in the resonator, so that the phase velocity departs significantly from the ordinary velocity of sound, and this produces an effect as if the length of the resonator were changing. Flared horns have apparent acoustical lengths shorter than their actual length and the apparent lengths rise asymptotically toward the actual lengths as the frequency rises. (A good, general reference on this phenomenon is P. M. Morse, "Vibration and Sound," 2nd ed., McGraw-Hill (1948, pp. 265–288).)

So flaring horns have at least qualitatively, the property that is necessary for a trumpet, of increasing apparent-acoustic-length with frequency. However, as Bouasse found out, four decades ago, quantitative calculations of required horn shapes can be very discouraging (H. Bouasse: "Tuyaux et Resonateurs," Librairie Delagrave, Paris, 1929, esp. pp. 370–386; also, same author, publisher, and date: "Instruments à Vent," vol. I, esp. pp. 314–328). Calculations of required horn shapes to give the correct musical behavior lead to flares that are absurdly greater than the flares on existing instruments that are known to work satisfactorily.

The key to the solution of previous theoretical difficulties is a recognition of the fact that the flared horn part of a cup-mouthpiece musical instrument does not do the whole job of changing the apparent acoustical length with frequency. Part of the job is done by the cup-mouthpiece itself. This can be shown both experimentally and theoretically. FIGURE 4 shows the results of some experiments by the present inventor. The solid curve of FIGURE 4 shows the theoretical idea apparent-acoustic-length variation of a modern B-flat trumpet, the plotted points represent apparent-acoustic-lengths calculated directly from the experimentally determined resonance frequencies of a high quality, commercial modern B-flat trumpet. The circles represent behavior with the mouthpiece, and the squares represent behavior without the mouthpiece. The points are for the first eight modes of the trumpet air column.

The points for the first mode, either with, or without the mouthpiece are far away from the musically desirable curve, but this is of no importance because the first vibrational mode of a modern trumpet is not used musically. The second modal points are correctly on the curve, and with the mouthpiece, the third and fourth modal points, and also the eighth modal point, are correctly on the curve. The fifth, sixth, and seventh modal points are not quite on the curve, even with the mouthpiece; but the seventh mode like the first, is not musically useful, and it can be shown that the deviations of the fifth and sixth modes are musically tolerable. However, without the mouthpiece, the deviations of the upper modes are well beyond the musically tolerable. The main observation to be made is that for all modes above the second, the mouthpiece itself somehow performs a significant part of the lengthening effect.

The explanation of how the mouthpiece adds apparent-acoustic-length to the trumpet as the frequency rises, has been given in a technical paper presented orally to the Acoustical Society of America, in November 1966. The mouthpiece, viewed from the trumpet side, is a cavity fronted by a relatively small orifice, and so it should act as a Helmholtz resonator. As a matter of experimental fact, it does. FIGURE 5 shows the frequency response of a mouthpiece only, tested in the system of FIGURE 2. This particular mouthpiece has a strong resonance at about 870 Hz. This is between the seventh and eighth modal frequencies of a modern B-flat trumpet.

By equating the acoustic wave impedance in a tube to the acoustic impedance of a terminating Helmholtz resonator, the present inventor has derived an equation for the apparent lengthening effect, $\Delta x$, of a terminating Helmholtz resonator. It is:

$$\mathrm{ctn}\left(\frac{2\pi\Delta x}{\lambda}\right)=S(b/AV)^{1/2}\left(\frac{f_r}{f}-\frac{f}{f_r}\right) \qquad (4)$$

where

$\Delta x$=the apparent lengthening (e.g. in cm.)

$\lambda$=the wavelength (in cm.)

S=the cross-sectional area of the tube (in cm.$^2$)

$b$=the effective length of the orifice of the resonator (in cm.)

A=the effective cross-sectional area of the orifice (in cm.$^2$)

V=the volume of the resonator cavity (in cm.$^3$)

$f$=frequency (in Hz.)

$f_r$=the resonant frequency of the resonator

Using Equation 4 as a starting point, several useful deductions can be made. One of the most useful is the answer to an old question: Where is the effective beginning of the acoustic air column of the trumpet? Bouasse taught that it was the throat of the mouthpiece (in French, the "grain"). Others have thought that it was at the same location as the actual beginning, that is, at the lip-plane of the mouthpiece. It can be shown with Equation 4 that at very low frequencies, the front end of the trumpet, acoustically, acts the same as if it were terminated by its own substantially constant diameter of tubing, extended by just exactly the length that would enclose a volume equal to the internal volume of the mouthpiece. This correct answer does not necessarily correspond to either of the previously taught answers, but in practical cases it is not far from the answer of Bouasse. The most important use of Equation 4 is to show that as the frequency rises, the mouthpiece adds an apparent-acoustic-length, increasing as the frequency increases, and that this length rises to a maximum a little beyond the resonant frequency of the resonator, and then slowly declines again with frequency.

Equation 4 can be used to estimate by calculation, some of the quantities to be described below, which are best determined by experiment, and this specification, and the claims that follow, are intended to cover an over-all method, in which some of the experimental steps can have calculational substitutes, but it should be made clear that for confident results, all of the taught experimental steps are best performed experimentally, rather than computationally. One of the reasons for this is that the geometrical shape of a mouthpiece is complicated; and it is even hard to tell where the resonator cavity ends, and the orifice begins. So the numbers to be inserted into Equation 4 are hard to estimate. Equation 4 is best used as an over-all theoretical packaging tool, holding all the relevant physical quantities together, showing their interdependence, and showing which quantities may be varied to compensate for given variations in any of the other quantities.

The best way to determine the apparent-acoustic-length adding function of a mouthpiece is to insert the mouthpiece into a long piece of unflared tubing; the longer the better, for closeness of modes in the frequency range of interest. Then, with apparatus like that of FIGURE 2, determine all the modal frequencies through the frequency range of interest (e.g. 100 to 1600 Hz). Finally, from the experimental data, calculate the apparent-length of the system according to Equation 1, and subtract from the apparent length, the actual length. If it is desired to do this experiment with accuracies of the order of one percent, an end correction must be made for the open end of the tube, and it is even advisable to make Helmholtz-Kirchhoff corrections for the small variations of sound velocity with frequency in the unflared tube. Such corrections are well known to those skilled in acoustics.

From this point forward, the description will turn specifically toward the making of a trumpet in high-F (tuning note 698 Hz.) but like all the previous descriptions, it is intended to represent trumpets in general. One reason for choosing a trumpet in high-F for illustration is that, in such a trumpet, the mouthpiece effect is even more significant than it is in a conventional B-flat trumpet.

Reference is now made to FIGURE 6, which represents, in terms of modal frequencies, the essential steps leading to the construction of the trumpet. FIGURE 6 shows model frequencies on a logarithmic scale plotted against mode numbers also on a logarithmic scale. With such coordinates, the plot of the modal frequencies of a theoretically perfect instrument would lie on a straight, 45-degree, line. Furthermore, equal distances in the vertical direction represent equal intervals on the musical scale. The vertical distance corresponding to the musical interval of a semitone is indicated on the graph.

The plotted circular points on FIGURE 6 represent the completion of what may be considered to be the first two steps of determining the shape of the trumpet air column.

First, a long piece of unflared tubing is attached to the mouthpiece. The inside diameter of the tubing here was 0.44 inch (nominally 0.4375 inch but the four figures are not acoustically significant). This is the "valve bore" of certain "small bore" B-flat trumpets. It is actually a large bore for an instrument in high-F. The largest diameter of the flared backbore of modern commercial mouthpieces is not this large, and so it is desirable to couple the mouthpiece to the unflared tubing with a transition section, tapered from the one diameter to the other, to prevent excessive acoustic wave reflections, as well as useless turbulence of the direct current air that is to be blown through the completed trumpet. However, such a transition section is merely desirable; it is not absolutely necessary. The transition section may be made up to several inches long, in which case, its action significantly supplements the action of the mouthpiece in changing the apparent-acoustic-length with frequency. Most contemporary commercial trumpets have such a section, called a "leaderpipe." It will be understood that if a leaderpipe is used, its action and the action of the mouthpiece are to be measured in coop-



eration, and it is their combined acoustic-length changing effect that is to be taken into account in the final bell design.

After the mouthpiece is attached to the unflared tubing, either with, or without a transition section, the resonant frequencies of the air-column inside the system composed of the mouthpiece closed off at its lip plane, and the attached length of tubing are measured in an apparatus like that of FIGURE 2. It will be found that the lowest natural modes have frequencies that would be expected from Equation 1, except that the length, $i$, will not be the actual length of the system. Instead, it will be equal to the actual length of unflared tubing plus an apparent length which will be equal to the internal volume of the mouthpiece (plus transition section if any) divided by the internal cross-sectional area of the unflared tubing. For the modes above the lowest modes, this added apparent length will seem to increase, and these modes will be increasingly lower in frequency than they would be expected to be, if Equation 1 were obeyed and if $l$ were constant. FIGURE 6 shows how they will actually appear on the frequency scale. The solid line represents the natural modes of a simple 33.0 inch tube. The circular experimental points represent the modes of a composite tube and mouthpiece system that behaves as a 33.0 inch tube in its first two modes and then increases in apparent length because of the mouthpiece effect. It will be noticed that the circular points almost lie on a 45-degree line, or that the mouthpiece effect almost causes the system to behave as an ideal trumpet throughout its upper modes. It does not do so exactly, but the deviation from ideality is not musically significant.

The circular points of FIGURE 6 show qualitatively how any length of tubing attached to a mouthpiece will behave, and they show quantitatively what happened when the length of tubing was experimentally varied until a length was found, for which the fourth to eighth modal frequencies best approximated the musically-desirable fourth to eighth model frequencies of a trumpet in high-F.

After the upper modes are properly placed, the problem remains of properly placing the lower modes, down to the second. In the case represented in FIGURE 6, adjustment is needed of only the second mode. The problem is to raise the second mode without destroying the already good placement of the upper modes. This can be done with a bell stem, so designed that it has the proper apparent-length-varying properties in the low frequencies but attains a substantially constant apparent length approximately equal to its actual length, at the upper frequencies.

Reference is now made to P. M. Morse, "Vibration and Sound," 2nd ed., McGraw-Hill, New York (1948) especially pp. 279–282. Morse teaches that catenoidal, horns transmit sound with phase velocities higher than the normal velocity of sound, and that this higher velocity, $c'$ is related to the normal velocity of sound, $c$, by the expression

$$c'=c/[1-(f_0/f)^2]^{1/2} \qquad (5)$$

where

$f$=frequency (Hz.)
$f_0$=the "cutoff frequency."

The "cutoff frequency" is calculable by another expression in terms of the flare rate of the horn:

$$f_0=c/2\pi h \qquad (6)$$

where $h$=the flare constant in the horn shape equation

$$D=D_0 \cos h(x/h) \qquad (7)$$

where

D=the diameter at the axial position $x$
$D_0$=the diameter at $x$=0.

Inserting $f_0$ from Equation 6 into Equation 5 gives

$$c'=c/[1-(c/2\pi hf)^2]^{1/2} \qquad (8)$$

In the terms of interest here, this means that the catenoidal horn acts as if its apparent length, $l$, were less than its actual length, $l_a$ according to the expression:

$$l = l_a[1-(c/2\pi hf)^2]^{1/2} \qquad (9)$$

The problem stated above of raising the second mode, without raising the upper modes, can be solved with the aid of Equation 9. The physical solution is to replace part of the unflared tubing distal to the mouthpiece, with a catenoidal section that will have the correct shorter apparent-acoustic-length at the second modal frequency, but will have an apparent-acoustic-length equal substantially to its actual length at the upper frequencies, when the contraction coefficient of Equation 9 becomes substantially equal to unity.

At this point there is a subtlety involved. One cannot replace part of an unflared tubing by a flared section, and expect the unreplaced part of the acoustic column to do exactly what it was doing before, except under very restricted conditions. There must be proper phase matching at the junction. Reference may be made here to the already cited Kent patent, U.S. 2,987,950. It will be appreciated that the complexity of the equations in column 10, and of the curves in FIGURE 11, of that patent, represents phase matching difficulty.

The present inventor solves the phase matching problem at the second modal frequency by cutting the unflared tubing at the position of the velocity node at that frequency, and replacing the cut-off section with a catenoid whose first modal frequency (closed at the small end and open at the large) is the intended second modal frequency of the new composite air column. Then both the unreplaced portion of the original acoustic column and its new catenoidal ending can cooperate exactly in natural resonance at the desired second mode of the composite system.

It will be appreciated from the theory that there could be an infinite number of catenoidal horns having a first modal frequency (closed at the small end and open at the large) that would equal the desired second modal frequency of the composite system, but only one of these would also have the desired actual length at higher frequencies, which would cause it to act just as the desirable length of unflared tubing acted at those frequencies.

At this point, one can give an almost complete description of the required catenoidal section. To do this, it is most convenient for clarification, to neglect end effects, and to describe the required catenoidal section as follows:

Let $L(u)$ be the length of unflared tubing found to give the best approximation to the musically desirable upper modes, let $L(2)$ be the lesser length, for which the determined second modal frequency, $f_2$, is correct, and let $\lambda_2/4$ be the length that a quarter-wave of the frequency $f_2$ would have in unflared tubing. Then one can say that the required catenoidal section should have an actual length:

$$l_a = \lambda_2/4 + L(u) - L(2) \qquad (10)$$

and it should have an apparent-acoustic-length at the frequency $f_2$:

$$l(f_2) = \lambda_2/4 \qquad (11)$$

If such a section is attached to the unflared tubing at the position, $L(2)-\lambda_2/4$, then the apparent acoustic length of the system must become $L(2)$ at the frequency, $f_2$, and it must become $L(u)$ at the upper frequencies.

It will now be appreciated that because the actual length of the required catenoidal section has been specified in Equation 10, and the apparent length at frequency, $f_2$, has been specified in Equation 11, these two quantities may be used with Equation 9 to calculate the flare constant, $h$. Then the final shape of the catenoidal section may be computed.

For the trumpet represented in FIGURE 6, the quantity $L(u)-L(2)$ was determined to be 4.1 inches and $\lambda_2/4$ (taking into account a Helmholtz-Kirchhoff correction) was 9.6 inches, so the actual length of the desired catenoidal section was 13.7 inches and the desired apparent length at 349 Hz. was 9.6 inches. This gave a flare constant, $h$, of 8.70 inches. The catenoidal section was made, and attached to the cut-off unflared tubing, and as indicated in FIGURE 6, the second mode was corrected up to the musically desirable frequency.

In order to avoid possible confusion, it should perhaps be mentioned that in the phrase "catenoidal section" as used in this specification, the word "section" means a section of the musical instrument, not an arbitrary part of the catenoid. The catenoidal curve of the catenoidal bell stem alway beings at $x=0$ of Equation 7, and so is itself without flare at the very beginning. Therefore it joins perfectly, in an acoustic sense, to the unflared tubing.

At this point, the description has covered the essential steps in making a trumpet that has improved relative intonation among its so-called open tones. However, there is another step remaining if such a trumpet is to have presently conventional tonal quality, and even presently conventional appearance. The catenoidal section, as prescribed above, has an inside diameter of only 1.22 inches at its large end, which is 13.7 inches in the axial direction from its small end of internal diameter, 0.44 inch. As is well known, modern trumpets in the familiar key of B-flat have final bell diameters of about 5 inches. The less well known trumpets in high-F have final bell diameters of about 4 inches. It is important to the understanding of the present invention to appreciate that the bell can be considered to comprise two sections, the long stem determining the intonation, and the final flare, or "skirt" determining the tonal quality and aesthetic appearance. That the bell can be so considered is not a new concept. It was stated in 1878 by Blaikley (Philosophical Mag. Ser. 5, v. 6, pp. 119–128, esp. p. 127) that "the pitch is not altered by the extension of the flange curvature beyond a point at which its tangent would make an angle of about 40 degrees with the axis of the instrument, although the quality of tone is decidedly altered by such extension." In more modern terms one does not try to specify a particular angle of the profile curve at which the acoustic column seems to terminate. One thinks rather of the flare constant, $h$, as determining whether or not waves of certain frequencies can be held within a horn in a standing wave condition, or will radiate away from the internal surface of the horn as if it were merely a baffle. This suggests that at the axial position where one wishes the standing wave column to terminate, one should markedly increase the flare rate of the bell curve, or in terms used here, decrease the effective flare constant, $h$. One must make this marked flare rate increase so as to expand the bell to, say, 4 inches within an axial distance of, say, 1.25 inches, and the only important restriction is that, mainly for aesthetic reasons, one must not change the slope of the profile curve stepwise; the slope change must be perfectly gradual. Mathematically, there are infinitely many ways this can be done. One way is to start, at the axial position where the acoustic column is to be effectively terminated, multiplying the diametral ordinate of the bell stem profile curve by a function which has the ordinal value of unity, and has zero slope at that axial position, but which increases in slope very rapidly. The present inventor chose a multiplying function of the form:

$$y = \exp[0.1][(1+w^2/0.01)^{1/2}-1] \qquad (12)$$

where $w$ = the axial coordinate, in inches, minus 13.7, but the detailed reasons for his choice are not important for purposes of this specification. The analytical form of the flare increasing function is unimportant. All that is important is that the profile curve of the bell skirt should be tangent to the profile curve of the catenoidal section at its large end, and the profile curve should have a flare rate several times that of the catenoidal section.

Reference is now made to FIGURE 7 showing intonation plots of eight trumpets, the first seven of them being modern commercial trumpets of high reputation, both in Europe and the United States, and the eighth being the trumpet in high-F whose construction has been described. The plots are presented in musician's terms, the ideal, or intended, open-tone frequencies being represented by their musical scale positions and the intonation errors being represented by horizontal displacement from a vertical line through the tuning note. The deviations plotted in FIGURE 7 are with reference to the ideal intended notes. The deviations are measured in musical cents, or hundredths of a semitone.

It will be understood that, in musician's terms, the vertical scale positions do not always represent the same musical frequencies. The fourth mode tuning note for a trumpeter may always be written "third space C" on the musical staff, but it is played as C (standard pitch, 523 Hz.) only when the trumpeter is using a "C" trumpet." When he is using the conventional B-flat trumpet, third space C is played as third line B-flat (standard pitch, 466 Hz.); when he is using a trumpet in high F, third space C is played as fifth line F (standard pitch, 698 Hz.); and when he is using a trumpet in high B-flat, third space C is played as high B-flat (standard pitch, 932 Hz.).

FIGURES 7A to 7C represent experimental measurements, with the apparatus of FIGURE 2, on three conventional B-flat trumpets; FIGURES 7D and 7E represent C trumpets, FIGURE 7F represents a trumpet in high B-flat, and FIGURE 7G represents a trumpet in high F. FIGURE 7H represents the trumpet of the present invention.

The diagrams of FIGURE 7 clearly indicate that the intonation of the new trumpet is superior. However, some explanation may be in order to clarify the meaning of some of the large intonational errors shown for the previous trumpets. Obviously, modern trumpeters, especially trumpeters in the better symphonic orchestras, do not play with intonational errors of the magnitude of those indicated in FIGURE 7. They subconsciously correct, by varying lip tension and breath pressure, for the intonational errors of their instruments, so that the played notes are in error by only small fractions, say, less than one-eighth, of a semitone. Therefore, a trumpet having better intonation than a modern conventional trumpet is not an absolute necessity for a good trumpeter who can play the existing trumpets satisfactorily. But it is obvious, without the necessity of argument, that a trumpet with better intonation will allow the trumpeter to spend less of his energy fighting the primitive imperfections of his instrument, and more of his energy in artistic nuances.

A highly-skilled trumpeter, with a good musical ear, who can achieve correct pitch with only subconscious effort, has less absolute need for good intonation in his instrument than has a beginning trumpeter. Obviously, however, good intonation helps them both.

There are other, technical, advantages to better relative intonation between the various open tones of the trumpet, advantages which are not yet completely understood. When the various vibrational modes are more nearly true harmonics of each other, they assist each other in the transient building up of vibration within the instrument, the transition from silence to full sound, or from one frequency to another frequency. In musican's terms, this means an improvement of "the attack," and an improvement in such things as trilling ability. Symphonic trumpeters have noticed these musical features about the trumpet of the present invention.

The foregoing material completely describes a method of making an improved trumpet (or other member of the trumpet family) and the essential parts of the trumpet itself. In order that the claims at the end of this specifica-



tion may be completely understood, it is appropriate to add some final remarks about mouthpieces and leaderpipes. Because the trumpets of the present invention are designed and constructed to cooperate optimally with particular mouthpieces (and when they are used, particular leaderpipes) it is, of course, ideal if the identical mouthpieces, and leaderpipes can be used on a final instrument that were used in its design. But this ideal is not attainable if a particular trumpet is to be reproduced many times, for commercial purposes. It is sufficient that the mouthpiece that was used in the design of the trumpet was representative of the mouthpiece to be used on the final instrument, or was acoustically similar to it. This is a somewhat looser requirement than that the original and the final mouthpieces should be of exactly the same shape. They need not be. One can deduce from Equation 4, together with equations not given, which lead to Equation 4, that to be acoustically similar, two mouthpieces need only have approximately the same cup volume and approximately the same ratio of effective throat area to effective throat length. The experimental proof of acoustic similarity is, of course, a test on apparatus like that of FIGURE 2 to determine apparent-acoustic-length versus frequency.

Leaderpipes are usually of uncomplicated profile curvature. Their air columns are usually merely conic frusta, of uniform taper. It can be said of them, that acoustic similarity does imply similar shape.

A remark should be added also about "end corrections," which have been briefly mentioned hereinbefore. The end correction for the catenoidal section will necessarily be different from the end correction for the tube of valve bore diameter, but it is not worthwhile to try to calculate that difference, because the bell skirt will alter it unpredictably. However, the unknown end correction differences are small, and they are substantially frequency independent, so they can be readily compensated by minor adjustments of the main tuning slide of the trumpet, after it built.

No description of valves, or of their placement in a trumpet, has been given, because the shaping and the placement of the valves in the trumpet of this invention is no different from that in known commercial trumpets.

In summary, a method has been described of determining the shape of the air-column of a trumpet (or other member of the trumpet family) so that the relative intonation of its open tones will be superior to that of previous trumpets. The bell of the instrument is specifically designed to cooperate optimally with a representative mouthpiece. The trumpet is easier for any player to play in tune, and it enables highly skilled players to spend less effort in achieving proper intonation, and more in artistic nuances.

I claim:

**1.** A method of shaping the air-column of a cup-mouthpiece wind instrument of the trumpet-trombone family, so that the intonation of the instrument will approximate ideal intonation, in which method account is taken of the apparent-acoustical-length-varying property of a mouthpiece representative of the mouthpiece to be used on the final instrument, comprising:

(a) measuring the modal resonant frequencies of the air-column inside the system composed of said representative mouthpiece closed off at its lip plane and at least one attached length of unflared tubing of substantially constant diameter, said tubing having a diameter substantially equal to the desired "valve bore" diameter of said instrument and open at the end distal to said mouthpiece.

(b) determining the length of said tubing $L(u)$, required best to approximate the musically-desirable fourth to eight modal frequencies of said instrument,

(c) determining the lesser length, $L(2)$, for which the second modal frequency of said system equals the musically desirable second modal frequency of said instrument, which second modal frequency has a wavelength $\lambda_2$ in said unflared tubing,

(d) attaching to a length, $L(2)-\lambda_2/4$, of said unflared tubing, a catenoidal bell stem of actual length

$$\lambda_2/4+L(u)-L(2)$$

whose apparent-acoustical-length at said musically desirable second modal frequency is $\lambda_2/4$, so that the apparent-acoustical-length of the unflared tubing plus said catenoidal bell stem is $L(2)$ at the musically desirable second modal frequency and $L(u)$ at the upper modal frequencies.

**2.** The method of claim **1**, in which step (a) is extensively carried out with one length of said tubing sufficiently long to give enough measured modes over the desired musical frequency range to permit accurate determination of the apparent-acoustic-length versus frequency function of said representative mouthpiece, and at least one of said steps (b) and (c) may then be carried out by calculation.

**3.** The method of claim **1** in which said tubing is attached to said representative mouthpiece through a tapered leaderpipe, and the system whose resonant frequencies are measured, as well as the finally determined instrument air column, therefore includes said leaderpipe.

**4.** The method of claim **1** in which the air-column is further prolonged at the bell end by a bell skirt whose profile curve is tangent to the curve of said catenoidal bell stem at the large end of said catenoidal bell stem, but whose profile curve has a flare rate several times that of said catenoidal bell stem so that said bell skirt does not significantly affect the resonant frequencies of the first eight modes of said air-column.

**5.** A cup-mouthpiece wind instrument of the trumpet-trombone family, whose intonation approximates ideal intonation when it is used with a mouthpiece acoustically similar to the mouthpiece that was used in designing the air-column of said instrument, comprising:

(a) a length $L(2)-\lambda_2/4$ of tubing of constant, "valve bore" diameter, and

(b) a length $\lambda_2/4+L(u)-L(2)$ of a single section catenoidal bell stem, whose small, beginning diameter is said "valve bore" diameter, and whose flare rate is chosen so that said catenoidal bell stem has the apparent-acoustical length $\lambda_2/4$ at the musically desirable second modal frequency of said instrument,

where: $L(u)$ is the length of said tubing of constant "valve bore" diameter that, attached to said mouthpiece so that with said mouthpiece closed off at its lip plane and said tubing being open at the end distal to said mouthpiece, forms an acoustic system whose fourth to eighth modal frequencies best approximate the musically-desirable fourth to eighth modal frequencies of said instrument; $L(2)$ is the lesser length of said tubing that, attached as described, produces the musically desirable second modal frequency; and $\lambda_2$ is the wavelength of the second modal frequency in said tubing of constant diameter in said acoustic system.

**6.** The cup-mouthpiece wind instrument of claim **5**, in which said tubing of length $L(2)-\lambda_2/4$, is preceded at the mouthpiece end by a tapered leaderpipe forming a transition section between the largest diameter of the backbore of the mouthpiece, and the still larger, constant, "valve bore" diameter, and the length definitions of $L(u)$ and $L(2)$, are based on experimental measurements involving said leaderpipe, rather than direct attachment to said mouthpiece.

**7.** The cup-mouthpiece wind instrument of claim **5**, wherein the air-column is further prolonged at the bell end by a bell skirt whose profile curve is tangent to the curve of said catenoidal bell stem at the large end of said catenoidal bell stem with the flare rate of said bell skirt being several times that of said catenoidal bell stem so that said bell skirt does not significantly affect the resonant frequencies of the first eight modes of said air-column.


**References Cited**

UNITED STATES PATENTS

2,987,950 6/1961 Kent ............... 84—388



RICHARD B. WILKINSON, Primary Examiner

L. R. FRANKLIN, Assistant Examiner

U.S. Cl. X.R.

84—398

CUP MOUTHPIECE WIND INSTRUMENTS

Filed Oct. 25, 1967 4 Sheets-Sheet 1

*Fig. 1.*

A.

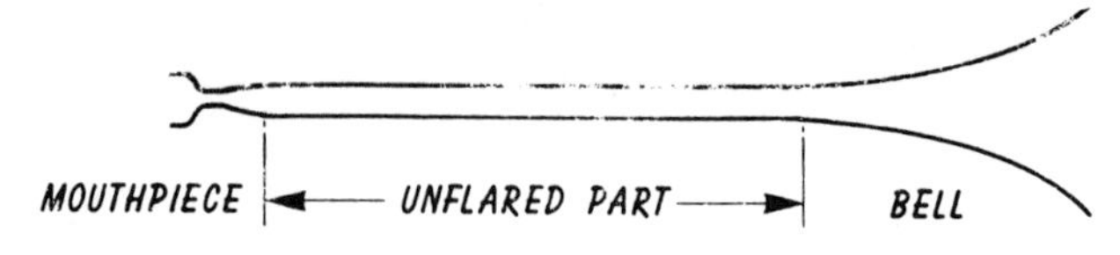


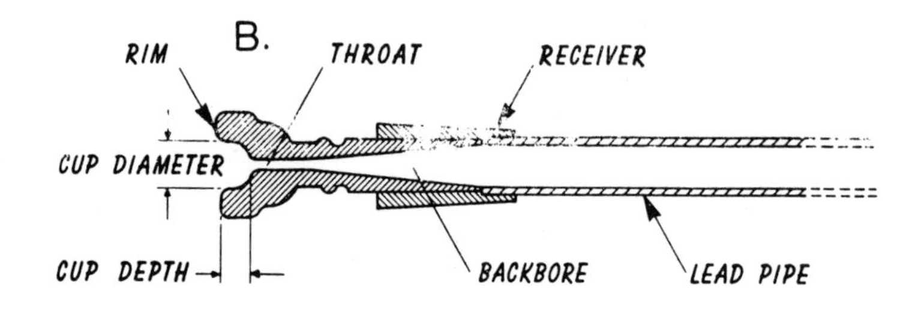


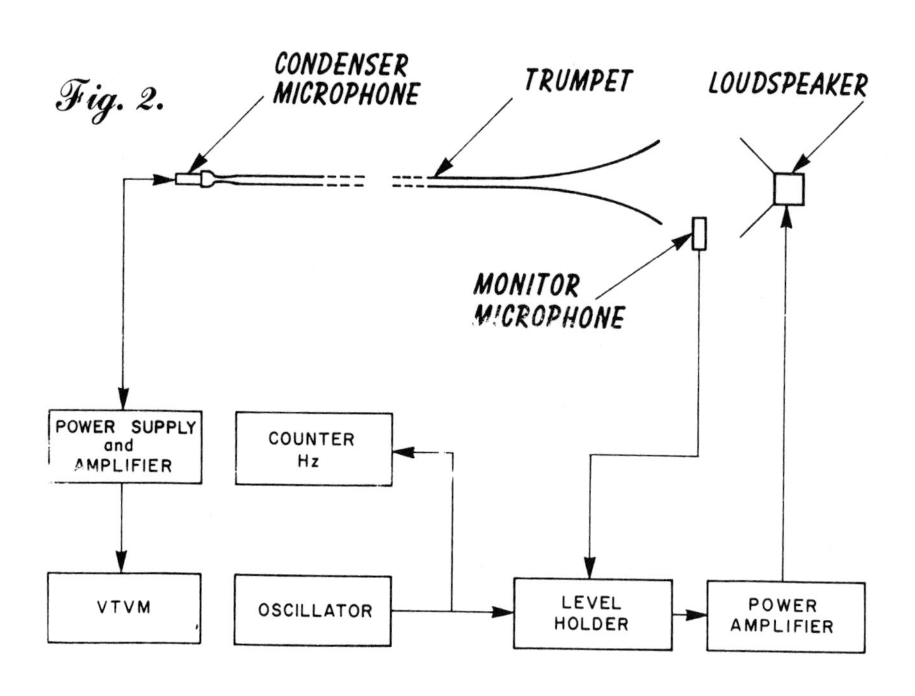

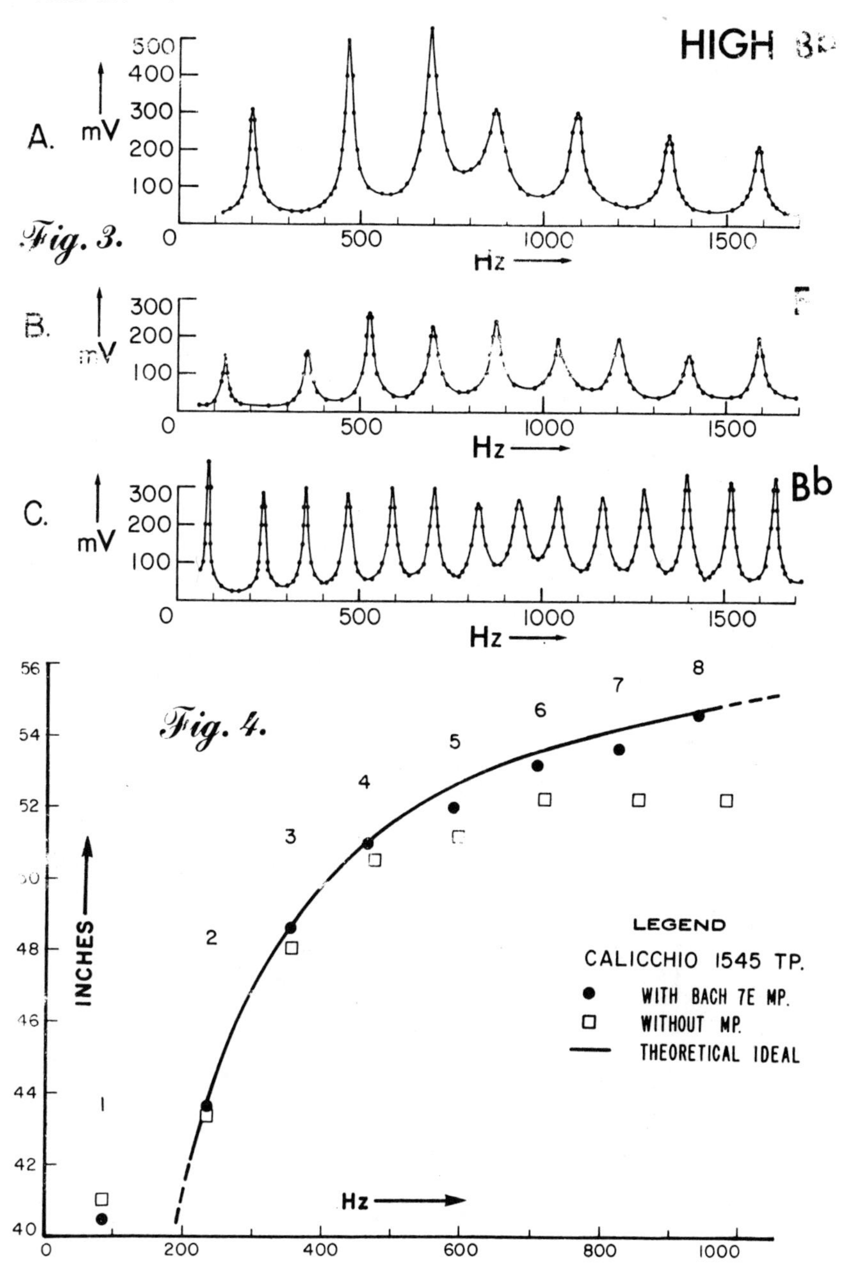
HIGH
A.
mV
500
400
300
200
100
0
500
1000
1500
Hz
Fig. 3.
B.
F
300
200
100
C.
Bb
Fig. 4.
INCHES
LEGEND
CALICCHIO 1545 TP.
WITH BACH 7E MP.
WITHOUT MP.
THEORETICAL IDEAL
56
54
52
48
46
44
42
40
200
400
600
800
1000
1
2
3
4
5
6
7
8

April 21, 1970 W. T. CARDWELL, JR 3,507,181

CUP-MOUTHPIECE WIND INSTRUMENTS

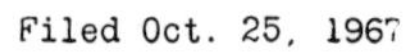
Filed Oct. 25, 1967

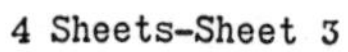
4 Sheets-Sheet 3

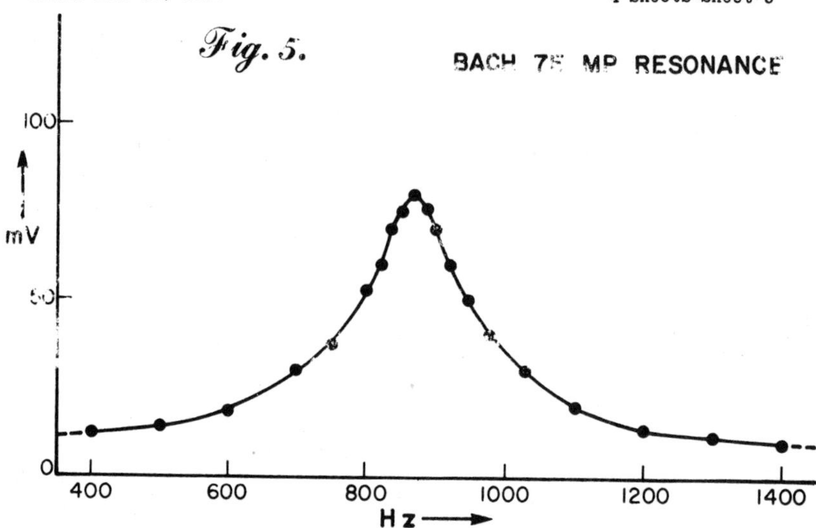


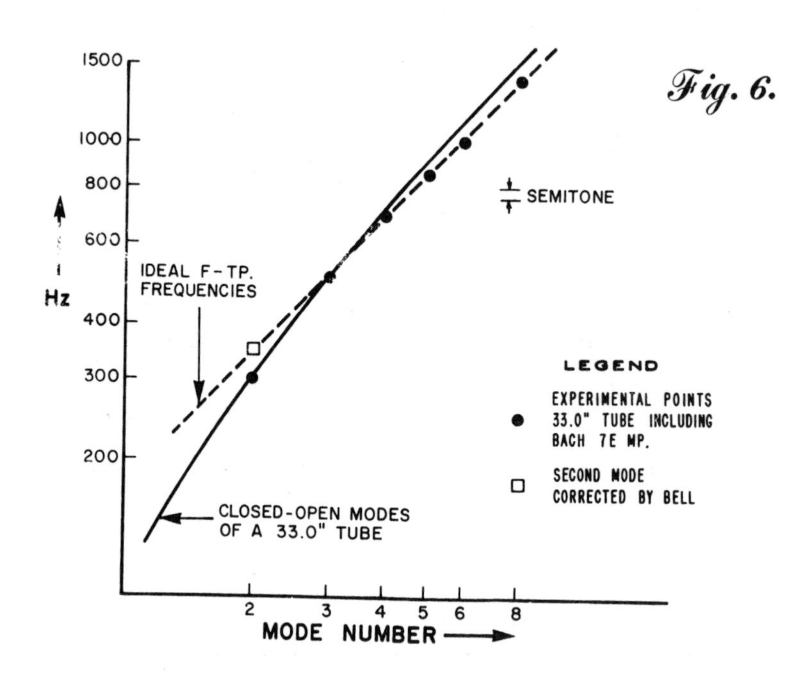

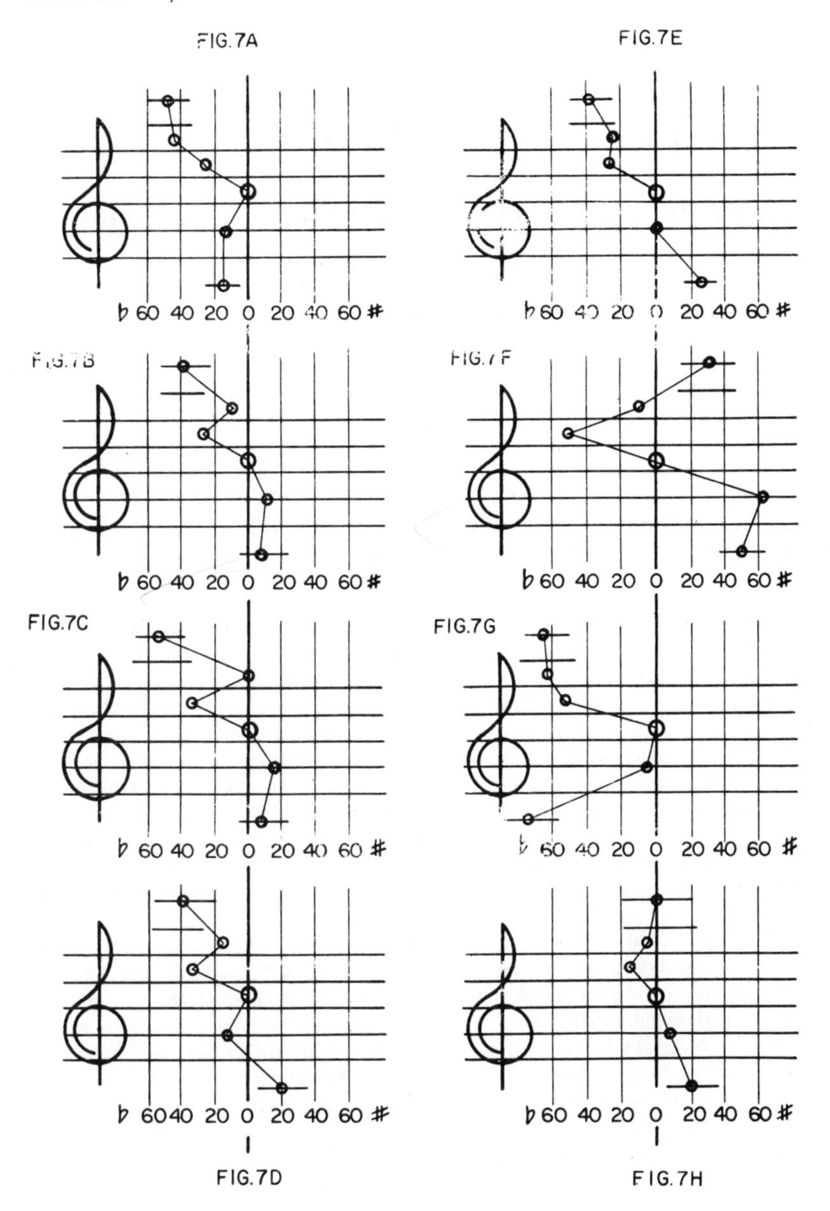
FIG.7A
FIG.7E
FIG.7B
FIG.7F
FIG.7C
FIG.7G
FIG.7D
FIG.7H
♭ 60 40 20 0 20 40 60 #

# 19A

Copyright © 1974 by S. Hirzel Verlag, Stuttgart

Reprinted from *Acustica*, **31**(2), 80–98 (1974)

# On Plane and Spherical Waves in Horns with Nonuniform Flare

## I. Theory of Radiation, Resonance Frequencies, and Mode Conversion

by A. H. Benade
Case Western Reserve University, Cleveland, Ohio 44106 U.S.A.

and

E. V. Jansson
The Department of Speech Communication, The Royal Institute of Technology (KTH), Stockholm 70, Sweden

[*Editor's Note:* Summaries in English, German, and French have been deleted because of limitations of space.]

### 1. Introductory remarks

The calculation of axially symmetric sound waves in a horn of varying cross sectional area has been of great interest for many years, as indicated for example by the large bibliography compiled by Eisner in his thoughtful review of the subject [1]. Because the wave equation is not separable in the coordinate systems that are natural to many of the horns of physical interest, solutions have been found by various approximation methods. One general approach involves finding and solving a brute-force simplification to the basic equation, although it is sometimes difficult to know how good the approximation is. Another approach calls for the development of iterative, or variational procedures to generate an improved solution on the basis of a simpler one. In principle this second approach can lead to accurate solutions, but the mathematical complexities often make physical understanding difficult.

It is the purpose of this paper, and its experimental companion, to discuss a slightly altered methodology that is related to the first approach but which is strongly influenced by the second one. We find that the systematic use of a spherical-wave representation rather than the more familiar plane wave version changes the Webster equation from first approximation to second without major upheaval to its nature. Our modified approach gives considerable accuracy in the calculation of resonant frequencies, and leads to reasonable estimates of the radiation properties of horns whose flare rate changes drastically from one end to the other. In addition it serves to clarify the nature of waves in such horns in a way that permits us to better understand the discrepancies we find between our calculations and our experiments. Furthermore our approach provides easy connections between the mathematics and its physical implications, making the limitations of the approach clear. Because of this, further computational improvements suggest themselves, and new phenomena are brought forward for possible study in the laboratory.

Our interest in the subject of horn acoustics arises in connection with studies of the properties of brass musical instruments, which start out nearly cylindrical, but end with an exceedingly rapid flare. The design specifications for such musical horns are quite different from those which are appropriate to loudspeaker horns, chiefly because interest is directed toward the attainment of specified resonance frequencies in a horn of high cut-off frequency, rather than toward the achievement of efficient radiation from a low cut-off horn [2]. These musical requirements focus attention on aspects of horn acoustics which have been relatively little studied, to wit, the detailed nature of the radiation process below and near cut-off, the values of the resonance frequencies in horns whose rate of flare is far from constant, and the general mechanisms of mode conversion in a horn in which the wave front changes form drastically from one end of the horn to the other. A brief summary of our major results was presented some years ago [3], but the elucidation of many subtleties in the relation between theory and experiment required a considerable further effort.

As remarked earlier, the present paper is essentially theoretical in nature, but theoretical in two senses. Firstly, we are interested in making a thorough examination of the propagation processes that take place in a flaring horn, and secondly we wish to provide the technical basis for dealing systematically with the various corrections and secondary phenomena which inevitably arise in connection with our experimental studies. As our understanding has grown, these two theoretical aspects have become more and more thoroughly intertwined with each other, and with the implications of our experimental results. It is for this reason that we have devoted considerable care to the formal relationships to be found between the relatively simple waves that propagate in cylindrical and conical ducts, and their more complex cousins that belong to flaring structures. Mode-conversion being inevitable in flaring horns (with easily observed experimental consequences), our formulation has been set up in a manner that permits us to visualize the nature and even estimate the magnitude of the effects. Because of thermal gradients and boundary layer effects which are always present in any experimental horn, we will initially formulate the horn equation in a way that includes the effects of non-uniform (and even complex) bulk modulus and density parameters. The major part of our discussion will however be confined to the case where the geometrical cross-section is the only variable parameter in the description of the horn. Boundary layer and thermal effects will then be dealt with by perturbation methods, along with the consequences of air column irregularities in the physical horn.

## 2. Theoretical preliminaries

For the purposes of orientation to the subject, we may initially consider a horn-like symmetrical waveguide either as being like a cylindrical pipe whose radius $R(x)$ slowly varies from point to point along the horn's geometrical axis $x$, or as being like a more or less conical horn whose apical half-angle $\theta_0(x)$ varies with axial distance along the horn. The cylindrical approximation is clearly appropriate to the case where the rate of change of waveguide radius is small, i.e. $(\mathrm{d}R/\mathrm{d}x) \ll 1$. Similarly, the second way of looking at the horn (conical approximation) is manifestly appropriate when the rate of change of angle, $(\mathrm{d}\theta_0/\mathrm{d}x)$, is small. We may note in passing that as long as the angle $\theta_0$ is itself fairly small, the realm of the conical approximation can easily be written in the notation of the cylindrical approximation thus:

$$\mathrm{d}\theta_0/\mathrm{d}x \cong \mathrm{d}^2R/\mathrm{d}x^2 \ll 1\,. \tag{1}$$

We might summarize these remarks by suggesting that the use of the cylindrical approximation appears appropriate only for horns of small taper, while the conical approximation is essentially exact for horns of any taper, and for more general shapes it remains reasonably accurate as long as the horn has small flare.

The air column of a trumpet, for example, starts out at its small end in the region of validity of the cylindrical approximation, and then traverses the region where one should think of it as being a varying cone, on out to where the flare is so great that one might possibly consider whether it needs to be represented by a cone of higher dimensionality. A better way to think about the effects of flare changes is in terms of mode-conversions between different types of propagation which remain distinct if the horn keeps constant flare. One expects mode conversion to take place whenever the actual disturbance within a horn is represented by mode functions which are only approximately correct for the horn in question. The propagating modes remain distinct only for horns which are representable in one of the coordinate systems in which the wave equation is separable.

As a continuation of our preliminary remarks, several succeeding sections will be devoted to a review of some properties of the solutions to the wave equation in cylindrical and spherical coordinates, keeping an eye on their similarities and differences.

### 2.1. *The cylindrical pipe*

In a cylindrical pipe of radius $R$, lying along the $x$-axis, the circularly symmetrical waves $p(r,x)$ obey the following pair of separated differential equations:

$$(1/r)(\mathrm{d}/\mathrm{d}r)\,[r\,\mathrm{d}T/\mathrm{d}r] + \beta^2\,T = 0\,, \tag{2a}$$

$$\mathrm{d}^2X/\mathrm{d}x^2 + [k^2 - \beta^2]\,X = 0\,. \tag{2b}$$

Here $X(x)$ is the longitudinal (or axial) part of the solution, and $T(r)$ is the transverse (i.e., radial) solution. The symbol $k(=\omega/c)$ gives the free space wave-number in terms of the angular frequency $\omega$ of a sinusoidal disturbance, $c$ is the ordinary speed of sound, and $\beta$ is the separation constant that relates the two equations. The transverse solution must obey the requirement that $T$ be finite on the pipe axis, and further that $\mathrm{d}T/\mathrm{d}r$ vanish at $r=R$, in order that the normal component of particle velocity vanish at the wall. The form of eq. (2a), along with the first requirement on $T(r)$, shows immediately that the axially symmetric transverse solution is the ordinary Bessel function of order zero:

$$T(r) = J_0(\beta r). \tag{3}$$

The second boundary condition may then be used to find the acceptable values for the separation constant. As is well known, the first few values of $\beta$ are implied by the sequence $(\beta R) = 0, 3.832, 7.016, 10.173$, etc., etc. [4]. For each value of $\beta$, the axial equation (eq. (2b)) has exponential solutions of the form

$$X(x) = \mathrm{e}^{iqx} \tag{4a}$$

where

$$q = (k^2 - \beta^2)^{1/2}. \tag{4b}$$

We recognize $q$ to be the wave-number for a sinusoidal disturbance propagating axially along the tube with a phase velocity different from $c$.

We see further that for each acceptable value of $\beta$ beyond the first, there is a cut-off frequency below which sinusoidal axial waves are not possible (i.e., $q$ becomes imaginary). The fact that these cut-off frequencies are inversely proportional to the pipe radius $R$, has important consequences in pipes of varying diameter. The most familiar case belongs to $\beta=0$, which has zero cut-off frequency, making it an all-pass mode of wave propagation. The disturbances of this propagation mode are simple plane waves, with wave number $k$ along the horn axis. The $\beta=0$ solutions have no transverse (radial) nodes, and there is no radial flow of the gas. The next propagation mode (corresponding to $\beta R = 3.832$) has one cylindrical nodal surface within the pipe, lying at a radius $r=r_\mathrm{p}$ belonging to the first zero of the Bessel function found in eq. (3). In this second mode of propagation, there is radial motion of the air, as well as a longitudinal motion. Conservation of flow within the bulk of the gas requires that if there is radial flow, then the longitudinal motion at any instant within the nodal surface is opposite to the motion outside this surface. Recognition of this fact will prove to be of considerable significance to us when we take up the question of mode conversion within a flaring horn. It is worthwhile here to notice further that the wave-number $q$ for the second mode of propagation is always smaller than the free space value $k$. This implies that, in a pipe of varying radius, the wavelength varies from place to place in those parts of the horn where propagation is possible. An increase of radius corresponds to a decrease in wavelength, and hence an increase of the local phase velocity.

### 2.2. *The conical horn*

In a conical horn with its apex at the coordinate origin and having a half-angle $\theta_0$ surrounding the $x$-axis, the axially symmetric waves $p(\theta, x)$ obey the following pair of separated spatial differential equations (analogous to eqs. (2a) and (2b)):

$$\left(\frac{1}{\sin\theta}\right)\frac{\mathrm{d}}{\mathrm{d}\theta}\left(\sin\theta\,\frac{\mathrm{d}T}{\mathrm{d}\theta}\right) + \beta^2 T = 0, \tag{5a}$$

$$\frac{\mathrm{d}^2\Phi}{\mathrm{d}x^2} + \left[k^2 - \left(\frac{\beta}{x}\right)^2\right]\Phi = 0. \tag{5b}$$

Here the transverse (angular) solution is $T(\theta)$, and the axial solution is represented by the "reduced" function $\Phi(x)$, such that $\Phi(x)/x = X(x)$. These transformations are of course entirely familiar in content, if not in notation. As before, $k\ (=\omega/c)$ is the free space wave number belonging to the frequency $\omega$. $T(\theta)$ is a Legendre function, whose order $\mu$ is in general nonintegral because the domain of $\theta$ is restricted to lie between 0 and $\theta_0$, instead of between the more familiar limits 0 and $\pi$:

$$T(\theta) = P_\mu(\cos\theta). \tag{6a}$$

The axial dependence of these highest-order waves is given by the corresponding solutions to eq. (5b). These are [5]:

$$X(x) = (kx)^{-1/2} J_{\mu+1/2}(kx). \tag{6b}$$

Although $\mu$ is nonintegral in both eqs. (6a) and (6b), it is connected with the separation constant $\beta$ in the familiar way [6], [7] given in eq. (7). The boundary condition that must be met at the horn wall

$$\beta^2 = \mu(\mu+1) \tag{7}$$

requires that $\mathrm{d}T/\mathrm{d}\theta$ vanish at $\theta=\theta_0$. This condition is met [8] by adjusting the value of the index $\mu$.

The simplest solution belongs to $\mu=0$, independent of $\theta_0$. This corresponds to a spherical wave in the cone, with no conical nodal surfaces at any value of $\theta \leq \theta_0$. It is the exact analog to the $\beta=0$ plane-wave mode which we have already noticed in our review of wave motion in a cylindrical pipe. Adapting for our own use a terminology that is usual in quantum mechanics, we shall refer to all such waves (i.e., those which are axially symmetrical, and without nodes in the transverse direction), as "s-waves", regardless of whether they are found in cylindrical, conical, or flaring horns. The letter s is not intended as a historical reminder of early optical spectroscopy, but rather as a mnemonic for the sphericity and/or the simplicity of this class of waves. Inspection of eq. (5b) reveals that there is no cut-off frequency for s-wave solutions in a cone (since $\beta^2 = 0$), and the axial solution is of sinusoidal form with wave number $q = k$, as was also found for the $\beta = 0$ case in cylindrical pipes. The next class of solutions has a single conical nodal surface at the transverse position $\theta = \theta_p$, the angle at which $P_\mu(\cos\theta)$ has its first zero. To find these solutions we must choose $\mu(\theta_0)$ such as to put the first $(\theta \neq 0)$ maximum of $P_\mu$ at the wall. This second type of solution is completely analogous to the solution belonging to $\beta R = 3.832$ which we found for a cylindrical pipe. Once again we borrow terminology from quantum mechanics, and adapt it to our own purposes. Waves with a single nodal surface of the sort just described, give rise to the principal departures from simplicity that are experimentally observed in horns, and hence will be referred to as "p-waves". Higher order waves, with more nodes, do not differ essentially in their behavior from p-waves, except that their cut-off frequencies are higher. We will not need any particular nomenclature for them, although their quantum mechanical relatives are normally referred to as d, e, f, g, etc., waves.

The two types of solution (cylindrical and conical) join together smoothly in the limit of small $\theta_0$, as we may demonstrate as follows: in a narrow cone, $\sin\theta$ may be replaced by $\theta$ itself, in which case the transverse equation eq. (5a) for the cone becomes formally identical with the analogous transverse equation (eq. (2a)) for the cylinder; we have only to notice now that the radial coordinate in the cylindrical version is expressible as $h$ in the conical version, where $h$ is the (very large) distance from the cone apex.

Eq. (5b) shows that, for any given excitation frequency, waves of sinusoidal type having $\beta \neq 0$ are only possible in the outer (larger) parts of a flaring horn. Furthermore there is a region extending from the cone apex to a minimum distance $x_m$ within which the disturbance is one of exponential type. In other words, in the smaller-diameter part of the horn (where $x < x_m$), the axial wave number $q$ is imaginary. If the free space wave number $k$ is given, the point $x_m$ which separates the region of real $q$ in the cone from the region where $q$ is imaginary, is given by eq. (8):

$$x_m^2 = \mu(\mu + 1)/k^2 \tag{8}$$

### 2.3. *Horn with varying angle*

The discussion so far has been intended to imply that as long as the horn changes cross-section gradually (the strict WKB limit), the plane surfaces of equal phase found in a cylindrical pipe smoothly develop sphericity as the horn angle increases. Furthermore we have seen that for s-waves (waves having no transverse nodes), the pressure amplitude is constant over the whole of any iso-phase surface.

The p-wave case was found to be somewhat different: these waves have a non-uniform pressure distribution over an iso-phase surface; the pressure is maximum on the horn axis, and falls to zero part way out, and then rises to a second maximum of opposite sign at the horn wall. Because of the relation between flow velocity and the pressure gradient we found that the existence of a nodal surface implies that there is a reversal of axial flow direction as one crosses the nodal surface. Furthermore there is a transverse flow of gas across the nodal surface.

Because of its importance to our examination of the higher-order corrections to the simple s-wave propagation theory in horns, we need to look further into the behavior of p-waves in a horn of varying flare. With this end in view, let us examine the most elementary features of p-waves in a Bessel horn whose radius $R(y)$ is given by

$$R(y) = B/y^\alpha. \tag{9}$$

Here we have found it convenient to use a reversed coordinate system with its origin at the place where the horn radius has a singularity (see Fig. 1). For the moment we ignore the possibility of complications which arise because the horn angle changes

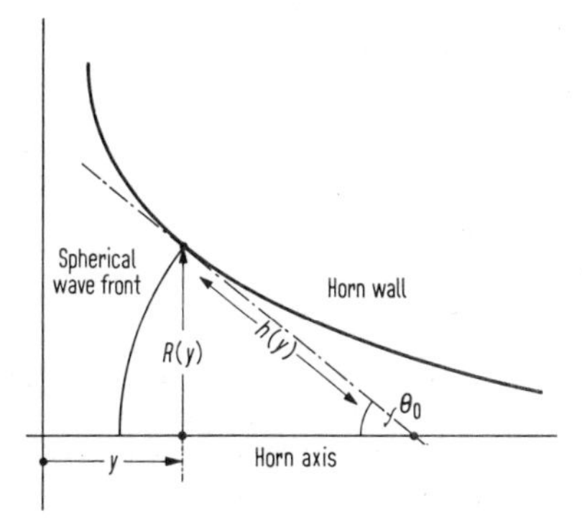


Fig. 1. Geometry of a flaring horn as related to that of a locally defined cone.

with $y$. Let $\alpha = 0.63$ and $B = 12.8$, so that $R = 9.9$ cm at a distance of 1.5 cm from the origin. Such a horn is quite similar to trombone bell. At a given point in the larger part of the horn (where the conical approximation is reasonable), the equivalent cone angle $\theta_0$, and corresponding radius $h$ of the wave front curvature, are calculated from eqs. (10) and (11) (see Fig. 1).

$$\tan \theta_0 = -\,\mathrm{d}R/\mathrm{d}y\,, \qquad (10)$$

$$h = R/\sin \theta_0\,. \qquad (11)$$

We choose the order $\mu_p$ of the Legendre function $P_\mu(\cos\theta)$ to give p-waves in a cone of local angle $\theta_0$ as explained in connection with eqs. (6) and (7) [9].

Inspection of the set of Legendre polynomials shows that the values of $\mu$ that make $P_\mu(\cos\theta)$ vanish at a particular angle $\theta_0$, are inversely proportional to $\theta_0$. Similar consideration of $(\mathrm{d}P/\mathrm{d}\theta)$ shows however that the values of $\mu$ which cause the vanishing of this function at $\theta_0$ (as is required in the problem at hand) are only approximately proportional to $1/\theta_0$. Empirically we find a very useful formula giving $\mu_p$ in terms of the half-angle $\theta_0$ as follows:

$$\mu_p(\theta_0) = \frac{219.55}{\theta_0[1 + 0.00244\,\theta_0]}\,. \qquad (12)$$

Here $\theta_0$ is expressed in degrees. The formula is normalized at $\mu_p = 2$ ($\theta_0 = 90°$); and at $\mu_p = 333.23$ ($\theta_0 = 0.6578°$). One finds that between these limits $\mu$ is always slightly underestimated. The worst discrepancy is found in the mid-range of $\theta_0$. For example where $\mu_p = 5$ ($\theta_0 = 40.09°$), the formula is in error by 0.3 percent. The cut-off value $k_p$ for p-waves assuming the horn to be conelike at any given point $y$ along it may be calculated from eq. (13) (see also eqs. (5b), (7), and (8)), remembering that $h$ and $\mu_p$ are functions of $y$.

$$k_p(\text{cone}) = (1/h)\,[\mu_p(\mu_p + 1)]^{1/2}\,. \qquad (13)$$

In the parts of the horn where it is basically cylindrical, the p-wave cut-off wave number $k_p$ may also be found from eq. (14) (see discussion following eq. (4)).

$$k_p(\text{cylinder}) = 3.832/R(y)\,. \qquad (14)$$

Fig. 2 shows the calculated variation of the cut-off wave number $k_p$ along the horn. It is clear from the figure that in the smaller, less tapered part of the horn, its properties as calculated on the basis of locally defined cones (in the manner indicated in Fig. 1) are consistent with those calculated on the assumption that the horn is basically cylindrical. In the more rapidly tapering parts, the cylindrical approximation loses its validity. At the present level of sophistication we have seen that there is a cut-off frequency associated with p-waves, and that this (and for waves of higher order) rises smoothly but very rapidly in going from the large to the small end of the horn. As was pointed out earlier the higher order Legendre functions approach the zero order Bessel function. The present discussion and diagrams are intended to show that (a) there is a considerable region of approximate overlap between the spherical and cylindrical representations, where one might safely use either notation; and that (b) the domain of appropriateness of the conical approximation includes that of the cylindrical approximation. We may anticipate therefore that more detailed analyses based on cylindrical pipe (plane wave) theories for horns, such as the ordinary Webster equation, can be adapted with only minor modifications when a spherical-wave form of the theory is constructed.

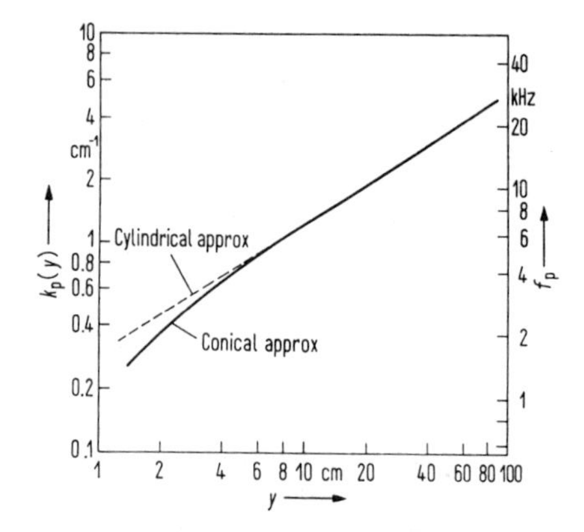


Fig. 2. Cut-off values $k_p$ and $f_p$ computed for a trombone-like Bessel horn $R(y) = B/y^\alpha$ ($B = 12.8$, $\alpha = 0.63$) on the basis of a literal application of cylindrical duct and conical horn theory. Note convergence of the results in the low-taper part of the horn.

### 2.4. *Summarizing remarks*

So far we have not committed ourselves to any special form for the wave fronts of disturbances in real horns. It has been customary to calculate as though these are plane (in the spirit of what we earlier called the cylindrical, or plane-wave approximation to horn theory), and qualifying statements are usually made which restrict the validity of the results to cases where the horn taper is small. Stevenson [10] has however given a very interesting (though laborious) method for finding "exact" s-wave solutions by expanding them in a series of p- and higher order waves, these also being calculated in cylindrical (plane wave) approximation.

Our discussion of the nature of p-waves in the cylinder-conical limit of real horn theory is intended to lay the foundation for allusions to p-wave effects later on in this theoretical report and in the subsequent experimental discussion of Part II. We will show that spherical s-wave theory fits experiment quite well in its own domain of validity, but that higher order corrections of p-wave type are clearly called for. The nature of the mode-conversion process is currently under study, so we will confine ourselves below to the shortest of outlines.

### 3. Derivation of the horn equation

We present now a derivation of the wave equation for axially symmetric waves (of s-wave type) in a flaring horn. This derivation is not dependent on any particular assumptions about the exact shape of the iso-phase surfaces, since the axial coordinate is taken to be $z$ as defined above, and the horn cross-sectional area is taken to be that of the iso-phase surfaces themselves. Furthermore, our interest in musical horns requires that we leave visible within our equation the effects of an axially varying bulk modulus and density for the contained gas. Although this derivation is closely related to the one presented by Morse [11] it does not restrict itself ultimately to a description of what Morse refers to as "good" horns (those with constant phase velocity along the horn). We should like to point out however that while these "good" horns, which are also known as Salmon horns, may have special utility for loudspeaker application, the theory is neither more tractable nor more accurate for them than it is for a much wider class of horns.

We have seen already that the normal component of velocity must be zero at the horn wall, and hence that the normal gradient of the pressure must vanish there. Because of this, the surfaces of equal phase within the horn will bulge in the direction in increasing horn size, in order to meet the wall perpendicularly. Consider a horn whose geometrical radius at the point $x$ is given by $R(x)$ (see Fig. 3). We denote the position of a given phase surface $S(z)$, by the position $z$ at which it cuts the horn axis. For definiteness we assume that the $x$-coordinate axis serves as the horn axis, so that ultimately we may calculate the position and shape of $S(z)$ in terms of the horn radius $R(x)$ and its derivatives, $x$ being evaluated at the place where $S(z)$ intersects the horn wall.

We now proceed to find the equation of motion of a curved shell of gas between the two neighboring equal-phase surfaces $S(z)$ and $S(z+\mathrm{d}z)$ under the initial assumption that the properties of the gas itself are functions of $z$. The volume of gas in this shell is well approximated by $S\,\mathrm{d}z$. As a sound wave progresses down the horn, the bounding surface of the shell which was at $z$ is moved a distance $\zeta$, and the other bounding surface is moved

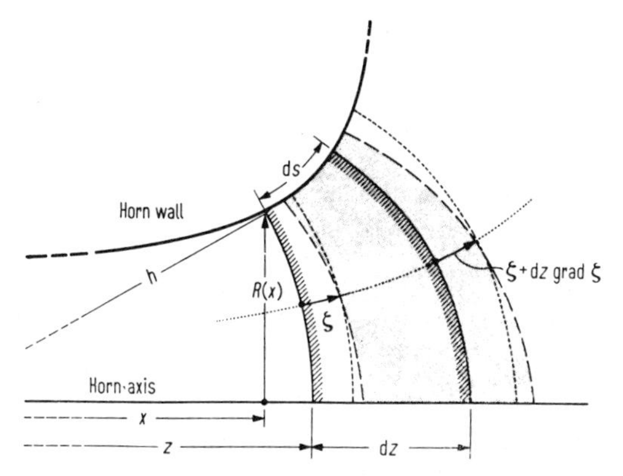


Fig. 3. Motion of a curved shell of gas within a flaring horn. $R(x)$ is the geometrical radius of the horn at the point where a wave front cuts the horn wall. This same wave front crosses the horn axis at the coordinate $z$.

a related amount $\zeta + \mathrm{d}z\,\mathrm{grad}\,\zeta$. Fig. 3 shows that a flaring horn wall makes for a progressively more bulging wave front for a disturbance which propagates along the horn. For this reason we find that an element of gas that lies near the horn axis has a larger displacement than does another element that lies near the horn wall, which therefore moves in a path that is approximately parallel to this boundary. In other words any single displacement-coordinate $\zeta$ gives only a one-dimensional first approximation to a description of the motion of gas in the shell. We must settle upon a consistent interpretation for $\zeta$: We shall take the symbol to connote a motion averaged over the surface of the shell, and for definiteness associate $\zeta$ with the displacement of gas along a horn-shaped surface lying within the horn, part way out from the horn axis to the boundary wall, as indicated in Fig. 3. We notice explicitly that the gas on the inside of this hypothetical horn-shaped surface moves a different (greater) distance than does the gas outside it. Such differences in the longitudinal gas motion in the horn require an accompanying small transverse flow for reasons that are exactly of the type given earlier in connection with our description of simple p-wave propagation. Thus we see that in horns of non-constant angle there is necessarily a small amount of p-type motion associated with disturbances that are predominantly of s-wave type. In a later section of this paper we will return to this subject, and make an estimate of the amount of mode conversions of s-wave into p-wave in a horn whose flare rate is specified.

We may temporarily set aside any consideration of transverse gas flow, by noticing that our definition of the displacement coordinate $\zeta$ puts it exactly on the nodal surface which belongs to p-waves in the horn. We deduce then that the simplified (s-wave) motions $\zeta$ and $(\zeta + \mathrm{d}z \operatorname{grad} \zeta)$ of the shell boundaries cause a fractional change in the shell volume that is given by eq. (15).

$$(\mathrm{d}V/V) = (1/S)(\mathrm{d}/\mathrm{d}z)(S\zeta). \tag{15}$$

The instantaneous (gauge) pressure $p(z)$ produced by this change within the shell is given in terms of the bulk modulus $B(z)$ of the contained gas

$$p(z) = -(B/S)(\mathrm{d}/\mathrm{d}z)(S\zeta). \tag{16}$$

Newton's second law for the acceleration $\partial^2\zeta/\partial t^2$ of the mass contained within the shell may be written in terms of the local gas density $\varrho(z)$ and the pressure gradient across it as follows:

$$S\varrho\,\mathrm{d}z(z^2\zeta/\partial t^2) = -(\partial p/\partial z)S\,\mathrm{d}z. \tag{17}$$

The desired wave equation for $p(z, t)$ may then be obtained by eliminating $\zeta$ between eqs. (16) and (17):

$$(\varrho/B)(\partial^2 p/\partial t^2) = (\partial^2 p/\partial z^2) + (\partial p/\partial z)(\varrho/S)(\mathrm{d}/\mathrm{d}z)(S/\varrho). \tag{18}$$

### *3.1. Discussion of the pressure equation*

The form of the wave equation presented here is not particularly new, although our derivation of it contains by implication the seeds of the next approximation, since we have segregated out of it the necessarily present admixture of transverse („radial") motion for later consideration. Furthermore it contains a somewhat unfamiliar generalization to the case of non-uniform gas mixtures. In addition we notice that the viscous and thermal effects taking place at the horn walls may be taken into account to first approximation in our theory in a rather straightforward way: one simply replaces the density $\varrho$ and bulk modulus by the complex expressions given here in terms of the angular frequency $\omega$ of interest.

$$\varrho \rightarrow \varrho[1 + (\beta_\mathrm{v}/r)],$$
$$B \rightarrow B[1 - (\beta_\mathrm{t}/r)].$$

In these expressions $\pi r^2 = S$,

$$\beta_\mathrm{v} = (1 - \mathrm{j})(2\eta/\omega\varrho)^{1/2},$$
$$\beta_\mathrm{t} = (1 - \mathrm{j})(\gamma - 1)(2\varkappa/\omega\varrho C_p)^{1/2}.$$

Here $\eta$ is the viscosity, and $\varkappa$ is the thermal conductivity of the gas, $C_p$ its specific heat at constant pressure, and $\gamma$ the ratio of principal specific heats [12], [13]. The v and t subscripts on the boundary layer corrections $\beta$ indicate the viscous and thermal origins of these corrections.

For present purposes we would like to set aside the complications caused by the variation of material properties along the horn, and lay our emphasis on two important aspects of eq. (18). The equation was derived without recourse to any special assumptions about the shape of the iso-phase surfaces $S(z)$. If these can be found, or plausible assumptions made about them, then the solutions for $p(z, t)$ are straightforward.

It is important to notice that the properties $B$ and $\varrho$ of the gas within the horn do not appear symmetrically in the equation. On the one hand the time derivative of $p$ is multiplied by the ratio $(\varrho/B)$. The square root of this is identifiable as being the reciprocal of the phase velocity of sound in an open region filled with gas of the type found at the position $z$, and this part of the boundary layer correction is recognizable as that worked out by Rayleigh and Kirchhoff for uniform tubes. The spatial derivatives of the pressure wave are on the other hand independent of the bulk modulus, being controlled by the function $(S/\varrho)$. One could therefore say that the horn has a local "effective cross section" $(S/\varrho)$ that depends on the local horn geometry, the gas density, and the viscous correction taken together.

In a musical horn, the presence of a temperature variation gives rise to an axially varying density and bulk modulus not only by way of the ordinary temperature dependencies of these parameters for an ideal gas, but also because of the extreme temperature sensitivity of the water vapor content of the air. One of us has reported on the effect of thermal gradients in wind instruments [14]. The theory suggested at that time correctly dealt with the temperature variation of $(\varrho/B)$ along the axis, but incorrectly assumed that the effective cross-section was $S/(\varrho B)^{1/2}$ rather than the stronger dependence $(S/\varrho)$ implied by eq. (18). Much more recently Shaw [15] has studied the interesting properties of horns in which $\varrho$ and $B$ are the dominant variables, rather than perturbations of $S$ as they are considered in this report.

In our second article, dealing with an experimental study of waves in rapidly flaring horns, we will have occasion to deal with boundary layer corrections as well as the effects of unavoidable thermal perturbations and other irregularities. However at present we will focus our attention on the way in which $S(x)$ controls the nature of $p(z, t)$, and so will consider $\varrho$ and $B$ to be constant. With these restrictions eq. (18) is given a simplified appearance

$$(1/c^2)(\partial^2 p/\partial t^2) = (\partial^2 p/\partial z^2) + (1/S)(\mathrm{d}S/\mathrm{d}z)(\partial p/\partial z). \tag{19}$$

This form of eq. (18) is commonly known as Webster's equation although as Eisner has pointed out [16] it had previously been derived many times in the years going back to Euler and Bernoulli. We would like to emphasize however that while the form of this equation is familiar, its content has been broadened, since it now applies to s-wave isophase surfaces of a horn with only very weak restrictions on the horn angle and on its rate of flare.

The reader will find interesting the elegant three-line derivation of eq. (19) given in 1927 by Bouasse [17]. He makes very few special assumptions, beyond the correctness of the general wave equation. While Bouasse restricts his argument to narrow horns of small taper, it is clear from the nature of his analysis that our results are implied by his formulation.

### *3.2. The reduced equation*

For machine computation eq. (19) is very convenient. However, for physical discussion, it is useful to rewrite the equation in a reduced form which has the virtue of eliminating the dependence of $p$ on $z$ to the extent that this is determined by the "obvious" requirement that the amplitude of a wave decreases as the wave-front area grows. Without making any assumptions about the exact physical meaning of this transformation (one learns eventually that no simple meaning can, in fact, be attached to it, except in an asymptotic sense) we define a „reduced" pressure wave function $\psi = p S^{1/2}$, and investigate the differential equation belonging to it. This reduced pressure wave function $\psi$ has a much simpler differential equation than does $p$, since most of the variations due directly to changes in $S$ are removed, leaving mainly those functional dependencies which are associated with changes in phase velocity. We have already noted a familiar example of this simplifying technique, which is to be found in eq. (5) above.

In the especially interesting case of a wave which varies sinusoidally in time with the angular frequency $\omega$, so that the free space wave number is $k = \omega/c$, the reduced wave equation for $\psi$ has the form given in eq. (20).

$$\psi'' + (k^2 - U)\,\psi = 0\,. \qquad (20)$$

Here primes indicate differentiations with respect to $z$, and $U(z)$, which we shall call the horn function, contains complete information about the shape of the horn. This horn function is most conveniently defined in terms of a sort of radius $r(z)$ chosen so that $\pi r^2 = S$, whence

$$U = r''/r\,. \qquad (21)$$

Let us pause here to extend eq. (20) before commenting briefly upon its general nature. Comparison of eq. (5b) with eq. (20) shows a close correspondence. We may deduce from this correspondence that for p- and higher order waves ($\mu \neq 0$) eq. (20) takes on an altered appearance.

$$\psi'' + [k^2 - U - \mu(\mu+1)/h^2]\,\psi = 0\,. \qquad (20\text{b})$$

Here $\mu$ and $h$ depend on the local radius and taper in the horn in a manner already discussed in connection with eqs. (10) and (11). We notice that both eq. (20) and its higher-mode adaptation (eq. (20b)) are quite simple-appearing. In addition eq. (20) is mathematically identical with the one-dimensional Schroedinger equation of quantum mechanics. Note in particular that our horn function $U$ plays the same role in horn theory as does the potential energy function in quantum theory. We are fortunate in being able to take over, largely intact, the large stock of physical and mathematical insight that has developed concerning this intensively-studied equation. See for example the classic papers of Salmon [18] and also the report by Pinkney and Basso [19].

### *3.3. Interpretation of the horn function*

We return now to an examination of the reduced wave equation (eq. (20)) and of the horn function $U(z)$ which characterizes it. To begin with we note that if the horn angle $\theta_0$ is small at some place, the surface $S(z)$ at that point is fairly flat and approaches the horn's geometrical cross-sectional area $\pi R^2(x)$, and also we find that $x \to z$. In this limit, a rather interesting property of $U$ becomes apparent. The ordinary mathematical definition for the curvature of a surface gives $(1/R)$ as the curvature of the horn as measured in a plane normal to the horn axis, while $(\mathrm{d}^2 R/\mathrm{d}x^2)$ represents the curvature in a plane which is normal to the first and which contains the horn axis. Thus $U(x)$ appears to be equal to the product of these two curvatures. Analysis of the geometry of horns where $\theta_0$ is not small shows that $U(z)$ is always well-approximated by the product of the longitudinal and transverse geometrical curvatures of the horn, at the axial position $x$ corresponding to $z$. If we assume that the shape of $S(z)$ is spherical, then $U(z)$ estimated in this way is quite accurate over the whole length of a trumpet or trombone bell.

We have seen that $U$, being the product of two curvatures, is a measure of the rate of flare of the horn wall. It is therefore easy to make "eyeball" estimates of $U$ on a real horn as follows. At any point $x$ along the horn, measure the ordinary geometrical radius $R(x)$ as well as the radius of the best-fitting circle that is locally tangent to the generating curve of the horn profile. We may refer to these two radii as the transverse and longitudinal radii of $R_T(x)$ and $R_L(x)$ of the horn. Then

$$U \cong 1/R_T R_L,$$

and we associate it with the value of $z$ that belongs to $x$ (as shown in Fig. 3).

Comparison of eq. (20) with eqs. (2b) and (5b) shows that once again we have a locally defined propagation constant $q = (k^2 - U)^{1/2}$ which is purely real above a minimum (cut-off) value for $k$, so that waves of sinusoidal type are possible. Below cut-off, $q$ is a pure imaginary, implying that the disturbance is of exponential (non-propagating) type. In other words eq. (20) shows that a flaring horn of any description is a high-pass structure for s-waves as well as for p and higher-order waves. A rapidly flaring horn (one with large $U$) has a high cut-off frequency, and furthermore, if $U(z)$ is not constant along the horn, then at a given frequency running waves can exist only in parts of the horn. For p-waves, and the other higher order waves we find that the presence of a flare has raised the cut-off value of $k^2$ by an amount $U$ above the values implied in Fig. 2. Inspection of the boundary layer corrections for viscous and thermal effects on $\varrho$ and $\beta$ (following eq. (18)) show that they both contain imaginary components. Under these conditions $q$ is found to have a small imaginary component for $k$ above cut-off, and a small real component below cut-off. Following standard techniques, we recognize that above cut-off $\mathrm{Im}(q) = \alpha$, the amplitude attenuation coefficient for a running wave whose propagation constant is $\mathrm{Re}(q)$.

## 4. Basis of a spherical wave approximation

Our considerations so far suggest that it is plausible ab initio to make calculations that assume spherical rather than plane iso-phase surfaces. It is certain that such an assumption will inherently give a better approximation in horns of wide angle than will a plane-wave calculation. Presumably, methods similar to those of Stevenson may then be adapted to the task of refining the spherical surfaces into better representations of the true state of affairs.

A more formal indication of the correctness of the spherical wave formulation (in fact it was our original hint), is to be found in a paper by Weibel [20]. He shows, in connection with a variational calculation, that for low frequencies the wave front shape is well approximated by the velocity equipotentials belonging to steady (DC) flow through the horn. We may say that Weibel's low frequency limitation restricts the discussion to a region below the p-wave cut-off frequency discussed in connection with Fig. 2 and eqs. (13) and (14) above. If then the steady flow equipotentials can be shown to be very nearly spherical, then we are in a position to proceed with confidence.

### *4.1. Preliminary experimental check: DC flow*

Helmholtz' equation for the velocity potential $\Phi$ of an acoustic wave is

$$\nabla^2 \Phi = (1/c^2)(\partial^2 \Phi / \partial t^2). \tag{22}$$

Here $c$ is the phase velocity of sound in free air. The time dependent electrical potential $V$ obeys exactly the same differential equation, except that $c$ now represents the velocity of light in free space. In the steady state, the right-hand sides of these equations both vanish, leading to the equations

$$\nabla^2 \Phi = 0 \quad \text{and} \quad \nabla^2 V = 0. \tag{23}$$

If we arrange an electrolytic tank experiment to have the same steady-state boundary conditions for the electric current as we have in a horn for the motion of air (no flow normal to the boundary), then the easily observable electrical distribution [21] may be used to define the equivalent distribution of velocity potential for steady air flow in the horn. The connection between the pressure wave fronts that are of interest to us and the measured electrical potential distribution may be made via the isomorphism of $\Phi$ and $V$: since the flow of air in a horn is proportional to grad $p$ and also to grad $\Phi$, we deduce that (to within an additive constant) $p$ is proportional to $\Phi$, and thence to $V$.

Fig. 4 illustrates a typical field plotting experiment made by us on a wedge-shaped body of water

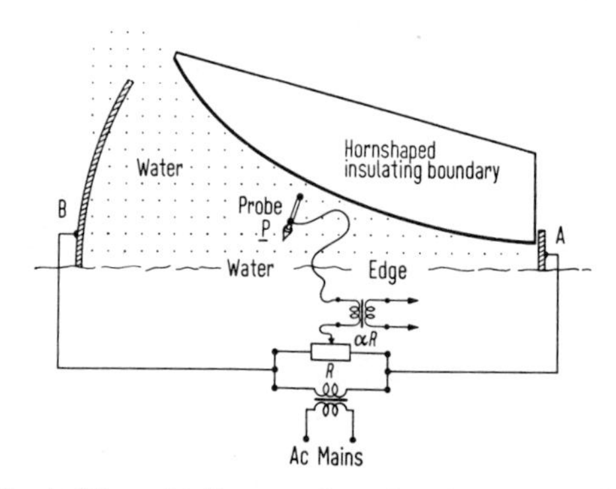


Fig. 4. Schematic diagram of an electrolytic tank field-plotting apparatus provided with a wedge-shaped volume of water. The equipotentials of the electric field are analogous to the low frequency flow equipotentials in an air filled horn.

whose thin edge represented the horn axis, and whose thick edge was bounded by a horn-shaped insulator. A 6.3 V transformer was used to set up a potential difference $V$ between electrodes A and B, which represent the small end of the horn and the outer region beyond its open larger end. A multi-turn potentiometer across the transformer secondary was used to select some fraction $\alpha$ of the total potential difference, and the probe P was moved about in the water to produce a potentiometric null indication on the oscilloscope. The path of P that traces out the null condition can be recognized as a tracing of the $\alpha V$ equipotential line. These experiments were done using a boundary shape identical with that of a trombone bell whose acoustical behavior we have studied extensively. We found that as long the outer electrode was far enough away, the equipotentials within the "horn" were indeed quite circular.

### 4.2. *Acoustical verification*

Additional acoustical experiments were made to verify the essential sphericity of the iso-phase surfaces for a standing wave sound in the trombone bell referred to above. A $^1/_2$ inch B and K microphone was moved in an arc across the bell on an arm of adjustable radius, arranged so that the motion followed the surface of a sphere that cuts the horn wall perpendicularly. At frequencies below that corresponding to the peak of the horn function (see below), the observed wave front shape was indeed found spherical to a good accuracy. We did not make an extensive study of the wave front shapes once their general nature was established, chiefly because E. L. Kent very kindly provided us with the results of a series of careful measurements made in his laboratory at C. G. Conn Ltd. which confirmed the nature of our conclusions.

## 5. Bessel horn in plane and spherical wave representation

The mathematically tractable Bessel horns make good examples of waveguides whose flare rate changes drastically from one end to the other. The fact that the musically useful horns are all very nearly of Bessel type makes these horns all the more interesting, because many of their properties are familiar (at least in a practical sense).

Before we take up the study of a particular horn, it will be necessary to obtain certain geometrical relations between the horn profile, the local radius, and the values of $z$ and $U(z)$. Reference to Fig. 3 shows that the area $S$ of a spherical cap which cuts the horn walls at the axial position $z$, is given by the integral

$$S = 2\pi \int_0^{\theta_0} h^2 \sin\theta \, d\theta \tag{24}$$

so that the equivalent radius $r$ defined following eq (20) is given by

$$r^2 = 2h^2(1 - \cos\theta_0) = 2h(z - x). \tag{25}$$

Here the distance between $x$ and the point where the cap cuts the axis is

$$(z - x) = h - R/(dR/dx) \tag{26}$$

and the radius of curvature $h$ of the cap is given by

$$h = R[1 + (dR/dx)^{-2}]^{1/2}. \tag{27}$$

Let us look at the qualitative behavior of the horn function $U$ for the Bessel horn whose geometrical radius ($R = B/y^{\alpha}$) becomes essentially infinite as $y \to 0$, and approaches zero as $y$ becomes large. We have reverted here for convenience to the reversed coordinate system shown in Fig. 1. In the limit of large $y$, $h$ becomes very large, and $z \to y$ as the wave fronts become more and more plane. From this we see that at the small end of the horn, $U$ is small, and takes the limiting form

$$U = \alpha(\alpha + 1)/y^2. \tag{28}$$

For the rapidly flaring part of the horn near the positive side of the $y$ coordinate origin we find that for any horn $h \to R$; $z$ reverses its sign and approaches $-R$; while $r \to R\sqrt{2}$. In this region of negative $z$ (outside the horn), $z$ becomes more and more closely equal to $-R$, and the wave fronts become almost exactly hemi-spherical. A calculation of $U$ in this region for the horn given above is lengthy, but elementary. The result given in eq. (29), shows that $U$ falls very rapidly to zero where the wave fronts bulge out of the horn.

$$U = (1/\sqrt{2})(\alpha + 1)^2 B^{1/\alpha}(-z)^{-(3+1/\alpha)}. \tag{29}$$

Fig. 5 shows (among other things) the geometrical profile of a Bessel horn that is very similar in shape to the trombone bell which was used in the field plotting experiments (for this horn, $B = 12.8$, $\alpha = 0.63$). Also shown in Fig. 5 are the spherical wave and plane-wave versions of the horn function $U$. The former is calculated using eqs. (25), (26) and (27). The plane wave form for $U$ is based on the assumption that the wave front area $S$ at any point is the geometrical cross section $\pi R^2$ of the horn at that point, and eq. (28) is used to calculate $U$ over the whole range of $y$. One additional thing is shown for reference in Fig. 5: the relation between the spherical wave axial coordinate $z$, and the corresponding plane wave coordinate $y$.

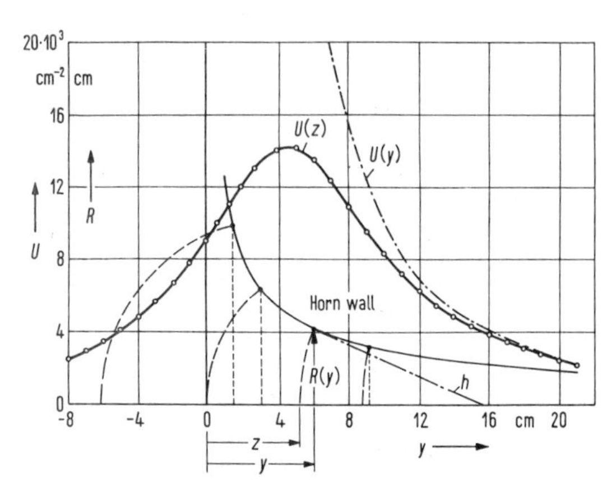


Fig. 5. Relation between the horn function $U(y)$ calculated for plane waves and $U(z)$ calculated assuming spherical waves, in a trombone-like Bessel horn. For reference the horn profile is also shown. The coordinate origins $y = 0$, $z = 0$ are chosen at the position where the horn radius $R(y) = B/y^{\alpha}$ becomes singular.

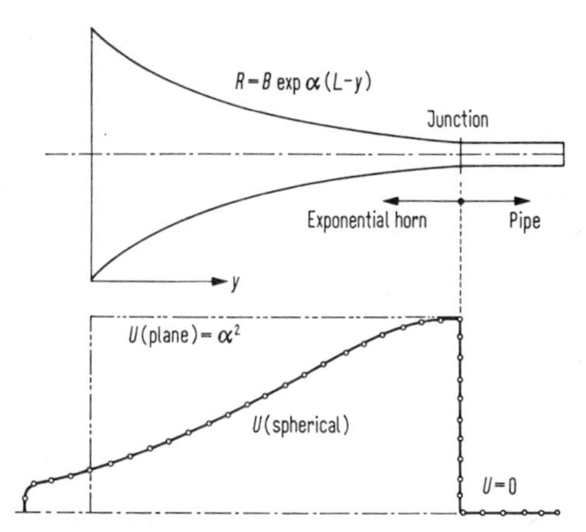


Fig. 6. Top: Exponential horn of length $L$ and flare parameter $\alpha$ attached to a cylindrical pipe. Bottom: Comparison of horn function $U(y)$ calculated assuming plane waves with $U(z)$ calculated for spherical waves in an exponential horn.

We notice that in our trombone-like horn, as $z$ increases, $U(z)$ approaches $U(y)$, as it should. Near the origin of coordinates, $U(z)$ goes through a maximum and then falls smoothly, whereas $U(y)$ has a quadratic singularity at the open end which (as is well known) causes severe problems in the mathematical treatment of radiation from the horn. In summary, we find that in those parts of the horn where there is small taper, the spherical and plane wave approximations are essentially equivalent, but where there is an increasingly large horn angle, the plane wave version progressively overestimates the magnitude of the horn function $U$. This conclusion also applies to horns whose geometrical radius remains finite at the origin. For example, Fig. 6 shows the behavior of an exponential horn of length $L$ joined to a cylindrical pipe at its small end. Using the $y$ coordinate system again, the geometrical horn radius $R(y)$ can be written

$$R(y) = B\exp[\alpha(L-y)].$$

The geometrical radius $R(y)$ is plotted along with the corresponding $U(z) = U$(spherical) (see eqs. (25), (26), (27)), and also the plane wave approximation $U(y) = U$(plane) calculated from eq. (28). It is interesting to notice that $U$(plane) for the related hyperbolic horn of length $L$,

$$R(y) = B\cosh[\alpha(L-y)],$$

is identical with that for an exponential horn, although $U$(spherical) falls below $\alpha^2$ slightly more slowly than is the case when the horn is exponential.

## 6. Radiation in plane and spherical approximation

We are now in a position to draw some general conclusions about the relation between the radiation behavior of a particular horn when calculated using spherical iso-phase surfaces and that calculated assuming these to be plane surfaces which coincide with the cross-sections of the horn. Fig. 7

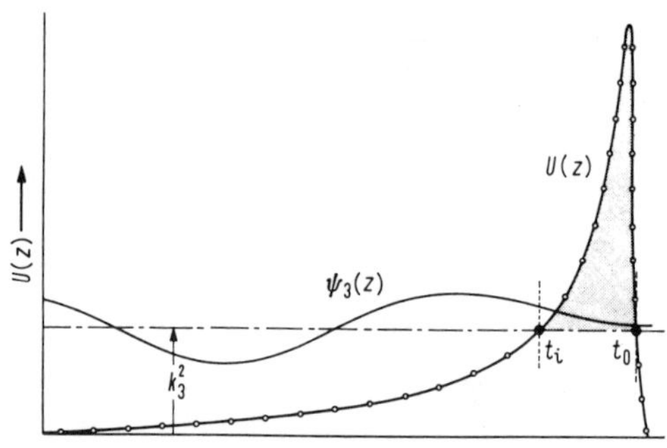


Fig. 7. Schematic diagram of a hypothetical horn function $U(z)$ superposed on the corresponding reduced wave function $\psi(z)$. The axis about which $\psi$ is drawn is located at the height $k_3^2$, so that the intersections of this line with $U(z)$ show the positions of the inner and outer turning points $t_i$ and $t_0$.

shows a hypothetical horn function along with the reduced-pressure wave function $\psi_3$ belonging to the third vibrational mode of the horn, assuming the small end to be closed ($\partial p/\partial y = 0$ at this end).

Inspection of the basic differential equation (eq. (20)) shows that every $\psi$ eigenfunction has an inflection at the inner turning point $t_i$, defined as the point inside the horn where the coefficient of $\psi$ vanishes in eq. (20). The outer turning point $t_0$ is defined in similar fashion outside the horn and again there is an inflection point ($\psi'' = 0$). Beginning at the small end of the horn and extending to turning point $t_i$, the solution is of sinusoidal (oscillatory) type, as is expected for a standing wave. In the barrier region between $t_i$ and $t_0$ (where $k^2 < U$), the solution is of exponential type. Here $\psi$ falls away more rapidly when the magnitude of $(k^2 - U)$ is large than when it is small, so that the amount of radiation that leaks out of the standing wave to outer space is a sensitive function of both the thickness of the barrier and its height above the value of $k^2$. The exact calculation of radiation is difficult unless the analytical form of the barrier function is simple; however for present purposes it is sufficient to illustrate the case where $k^2$ is well below the top of the barrier. Use can then be made of the WKB approximation [22] to find the transmission coefficient for power through the barrier. This transmission coefficient is proportional to the penetration factor $P(k)$.

$$P(k) \cong \exp\left[-2 \int_{t_i}^{t_0} (U - k^2)^{1/2} \, dz\right]. \qquad (30)$$

The integrand of eq. (30) is conveniently visualized with the help of its close relationship with the shaded part of $U$ indicated in Fig. 7.

The illustrative result shown in eq. (30) is sufficient to demonstrate that the s-wave energy loss rate from resonant vibrational states is always underestimated when calculated upon the plane wave assumption. For example, in the plane wave approximation, a long exponential horn

$$R = B \exp(-\alpha y)$$

has almost no transmission of energy for frequencies below cut-off ($k^2 < \alpha^2$). However it is clear from Fig. 6 that even in a long exponential or hyperbolic horn there will be considerable transmission (because the barrier is of limited extent) if the horn angle becomes large enough to produce bulging wave fronts.

The situation becomes yet more extreme in the case of a Bessel horn. Here the plane wave version of the horn function approaches infinity near the origin (see eq. (28)), and the solutions to eq. (20) are of the form [23].

$$\psi(y) = y^{1/2} J_{\alpha+1/2}(k y). \qquad (31)$$

If one takes the plane wave approximation seriously, the radiation from the large end of a complete horn (which extends from $y = 0$ to some length $y = L$) is identically zero; this is because $\psi(y)$ vanishes at the origin as a result of the infinite value of $U(0)$. If the horn is not complete to the origin, $U$(plane) stays finite at the open end. Although the WKB approximation is not valid in this case, we may gloss over the difficulties of connecting the internal plane wave with the external wave, and make a brute-force estimate of the radiation as follows. Inside the horn, the amplitude $\psi$(inside) may be normalized to unity, and if the physical horn is of Bessel shape up to the point $y_0$ at its rim, we may approximate the size of $\psi$ immediately outside the bell by evaluating $\psi(y_0)$. If $(k y_0)$ is very small, we get the following estimate for the penetration factor $P$:

$$P(k) \cong [\psi(y_0)/\psi(\text{inside})]^2 \cong (k y_0)^{2\alpha+1}. \qquad (32)$$

In other words, under the plane wave assumption, the radiation contribution to the half-power bandwidths of the various resonances should rise as the $(2\alpha + 1)$ power of the frequency. As we will see, this is inconsistent with the experimental measurement of the radiation loss. Similarly, we would expect the radiation to be a sensitive function of the truncation length $y_0$ in the plane wave approximation, where the spherical wave approach suggests that the radiation is not strongly controlled by $y_0$ as long as it lies beyond the peak of the horn function $U(z)$.

While the foregoing discussion can elucidate the analytical relations between the radiation losses predicted by the two forms of horn theory, it is not easy to make general statements about the relative numerical values of the two results. Eq. (30) shows the reason: the plane wave theory gives a thin but very high barrier against radiation, whereas the spherical wave version gives a lower, but thicker barrier.

## 7. Natural frequencies in plane and spherical approximation

We turn now to an elementary examination of the natural frequencies of a horn as calculated by the spherical and plane wave approximations. In the spirit of the WKB (phase integral) approximation to the solutions of our wave equation [24] we find that the natural frequencies of a horn closed at the small end are those for which the total phase accumulated from one end of the horn to the inner turning point $t_i$ should be an odd multiple of $\pi/2$ (including a phase correction $\Phi_t$ associated with the turning point boundary). That is, for the $n$-th mode of vibration

$$(2n-1)(\pi/2) = \int_{t_i}^{L} [k_n^2 - U]^{1/2}\,dz + \Phi_t(n)\,. \tag{33}$$

Eq. (33) shows that extending the length of the "allowed" region of the horn between $z = t_i$ and $z = L$ lowers the values of $k_n$ which approximate the solution. This arises partly because of the increased range of integration (as is illustrated by the familiar fact that a longer pipe always gives lower natural frequencies). The effect is enhanced because the lowering of $U$ everywhere in the range of integration (as is required to produce the shift of $t_i$) increases the magnitude of the integrand itself, and hence the resulting integral. We may usefully notice that the integrand in eq. (33) is the (spatially varying) wave number $q_n$ for $\psi$ within the horn. Comparison of $U$(plane) with $U$(spherical) in Fig. 5 shows that the plane wave form of our theory will always give a higher estimate of the normal mode frequencies of a horn than will the spherical approximation. In practice the difference is small but significant.

## 8. Mode conversion from s- to p-waves

Mention has been made several times already of the fact that in a flaring horn it is not possible for a given mode to propagate without the eventual admixture of small amounts of other modes. Mathematically this is a consequence or (or rather, evidence for) the nonseparability of the wave equation into purely longitudinal and transverse parts (see eqs. (2a) and (2b), or eqs. (5a) and (5b) for examples of the separability in non flaring horns). The kinematical reasons for the necessary admixture of a p-wave component in what is a primarily s-wave disturbance were indicated in Section 3, and are illustrated in Fig. 3. It is the purpose of the present section to provide a rough estimate of the p-wave admixture at various parts of a horn, and to sketch out some of the experimentally observable consequences of this admixture.

### *8.1 Kinematics of the wave-front motion*

Reference to Fig. 3 shows that if an iso-phase surface is to maintain its quasi-spherical shape as it oscillates within a flaring horn, then an element of the gas near the horn axis must move farther than does an element near the horn wall. For instance, if the axial element moves a distance $dz$, the element at the wall moves an amount $ds$, as indicated in the diagram. In Section 3 we defined a mean displacement coordinate which could be written in terms of a certain $dz$ and its corresponding $ds$. For definiteness here we will label the coordinate with the subscript s to emphasize that it refers to a purely s-wave type of motion.

$$\zeta_s = (dz + ds)/2\,. \tag{34a}$$

In the same spirit, we can define a new p-wave displacement co-ordinate $\zeta_p$

$$\zeta_p = (dz - ds)/2\,. \tag{34b}$$

This coordinate gives the amplitude of the p-type excursion of the gas on either side of the mean displacement $\zeta_s$.

We can now obtain an expression for the displacement amplitude ratio $C = (\zeta_p/\zeta_s)$ at any point $x$ in a horn of given geometrical shape $R(x)$. This may be done by differentiation of eqs. (26) and (27) with respect to $x$, making use also of the fact that

$$ds = dx/\cos\theta_0 = dx[1 + (R')^2]^{1/2}\,. \tag{35}$$

As before, primes indicate differentiation with respect to $x$, and $\theta_0$ (= arctan $R'$) is the half angle of the locally defined cone. The calculation of $C(x)$ is straightforward, with the following result.

$$C(x) = \frac{RR''[(1/s') - (1/RR')(s'-1)]}{2s' + RR''[(1/s') - (1/RR')(s'-1)]}\,. \tag{36}$$

Here we have written $s'$ as an abbreviation for $[1 + (R')^2]^{1/2}$. The amplitude ratio $C(x)$ given in eq. (36) has the expected form in that it is proportional to the rate of flare $R''$ of the horn.

At progressively higher frequencies we expect that the inertia of the gas in our horn will increasingly militate against the sort of radial flow (across the p-wave nodal surface) which is required to produce the postulated difference in displacement at the horn wall and on its axis. This expectation is consistent with our empirical knowledge that at the higher frequencies the wave keeps the relatively flattened wave front it had in the narrow part of the horn, as it propagates out of the wider and more flaring part of the horn (this phenomenon is familiarly associated with the increasing directivity of the horn at high frequencies). Because of this observed flattening of the wave fronts, the true gas motion must be represented by our "spherical" s-wave (whose bulginess increases in the flaring parts of the horn) plus a wave of p type whose phase is such as to subtract from the s-wave particle motion on the axis, and add to it at the horn wall. As a rough estimate of the size of this p-wave contribution to the particle displacement that is necessary at the point $x$, we might consider using $C(x)$

as given in eq. (36). The sign of $C(x)$ would however be reversed in order to produce the correct relative phase. The propriety of such employment of $C(x)$ is not yet clear, and we must turn our attention briefly to the behavior at low frequencies.

At low frequencies we expect to have no mode conversion at all. In other words, the s-wave representation becomes essentially exact (this assertion is in fact merely a rephrasing of Weibel's result, as discussed in Section 4). As the frequency rises, however, we expect an increasing amount of p-wave generation, but an amount which is always less than that implied by a naive use of $C(x)$. Thus we find it instructive to calculate the amount of disturbance of p type that is associated with an s-wave using $C(x)$, with the clear understanding that our result is in the nature of an upper bound to the actual amount of the contribution.

### *8.2. Calculation of the pressure amplitude ratio*

In the preceding section we have made an upper limit estimate of the amount of p-wave displacement that is to be expected in a flaring horn. All of our discussion heretofore has, however, dealt with pressure wave function, so that it is now necessary to convert the displacement result into an estimate of the pressure amplitude of the p-wave relative to the locally dominant s-wave at any point in the horn. Double integration of Newton's second law for the acceleration of a lamina of gas (see eq. (17)) gives the following relation between a particle displacement $\zeta$ and the corresponding local pressure gradient.

$$\zeta_s = (1/\varrho\,\omega^2)\,\mathrm{grad}\,p_s\,, \tag{37a}$$

$$\zeta_p = (1/\varrho\,\omega^2)\,\mathrm{grad}\,p_p\,. \tag{37b}$$

If we use $C(x)$ for our estimated upper bound for the displacement amplitude ratio, then

$$\mathrm{grad}\,p_p \lesssim C\,\mathrm{grad}\,p_s\,. \tag{38}$$

Inspection of Fig. 3 in conjunction with an examination of eqs. (5b) and (20b) shows that the p-wave cut-off frequency is well above any frequency that is of experimental interest to us in connection with our trombone-like horn. If we interpret $x$ in eq. (5b) once again to be the length $h$ of a locally defined cone at some point within a flaring horn, it is then apparent from eq. (5b) that $(kh)$ is always much less than the value that produces the first inflection point of the function $\Phi(h)$. This allows the use of a small-argument representation of the $p_p(kh)$ that is given exactly in eq. (6b). Morse [25] shows that this small-argument form is

$$p_p(kh) = \frac{(kh)\,\mu_p}{1\cdot 3\cdot 5\cdots(2\,\mu_p+1)} \tag{39}$$

whence

$$\mathrm{grad}\,p_p = (\mu_p/h)\,p_p\,. \tag{40}$$

The expressions given here hold only for those points along the horn where $\mu_p$ happens to be integral (as determined by the local cone angle), but the behavior at other points is continuous, so that we may properly use eq. (40) in our survey. At any given point in the horn, the horn radius and angle determine $h$, and $\mu_p$; the added presence of flare determines $C$, and also the basic s-wave solution $p_s$. Eq. (38) may then be rewritten as follows:

$$p_p \lesssim (h/\mu_p)\,C\,\mathrm{grad}\,p_s\,. \tag{41}$$

We have already seen that in the larger, more rapidly flaring parts of the horn $\mu_p$ decreases, $C$ increases, and $h$ also increases ($h \to R$) in this region). All of these tend to enlarge the importance of the p-wave admixture in the flaring part of the horn.

Let us go one step further in our evaluation of the size of $p_p$. In the WKB limit for the s-wave, we find that (apart from a phase shift close to $\pi/2$ radians in the case of a disturbance of sinusoidal type) the gradient of $p_s$ may be written thus:

$$|\mathrm{grad}\,p_s| = |q_s|\,|p_s| \tag{42}$$

whereas before, $q^2 = (k^2 - U)$. Note that eq. (42) also holds in regions where $q$ is pure imaginary, which is the reason for the use of absolute magnitude signs on $q$ in this expression. The combination of eq. (42) with eq. (41) gives a particularly simple means for estimating $p_s/p_p$ at any point in a horn.

$$|p_p/p_s| = (q\,h/\mu_p)\,C\,. \tag{43}$$

Let us put some numbers into eq. (43), in order to gain insight into its practical meaning. The ratio $p_p/p_s$ is calculated for various points in a trombone-like Bessel horn ($R(y) = B/y^\alpha$, $B = 12.8$, $\alpha = 0.63$) at three different frequencies, as tabulated below.

| $y$ cm | 500 Hz | 750 Hz | 1000 Hz |
|---|---|---|---|
| 1.50 | 0.1430 | 0.1248 | 0.2580 |
| 2.35 | 0.0968 | 0.0845 | 0.1747 |
| 3.29 | 0.0600 | 0.0523 | 0.1082 |
| 5.12 | 0.0228 | 0.0199 | 0.0411 |

It is clear from these results that there is only a very small amount of mode conversion taking place in parts of the horn which are more than a few centimeters from the large end of the horn. It is also clear that there is a significant amount of conversion to be expected in the most rapidly flaring part of the horn, particularly at frequencies that lie above the s-wave cut-off frequency

$$(c/2\pi)(U_{\max})^{1/2} \simeq 653 \text{ Hz}.$$

*8.3. Experimental implications of mode conversion*

The fact that any wave system that can be set up in a flaring horn has a certain admixture of p-type wave along with the main s-wave disturbance, has a number of experimentally observable consequences: all of these consequences ultimately depend on the fact that a certain amount of the energy is diverted from the main wave into a nonpropagating type of local storage.

At frequencies such that the "tunneling" of s-wave energy through the horn function barrier $U(z)$ is relatively small (i.e. when the radiation damping is not large), one observes well defined normal mode behavior. If we consider the net wave to be the sum of an outward wave toward the open end plus a return wave whose amplitude is diminished by radiation losses, the fact that some of the outward wave is diverted into a nonpropagating reactive form means that a smaller amount of the total energy becomes "eligible" for radiation by reaching the open end. Thus we expect that the observed radiation loss will be unambiguously less if mode conversion is present than if it is not present. Furthermore, the locally reacting connection between the s-wave system and its perturbing p-waves is formally of the nature of an alteration of the local bulk modulus, or density, (since it involves changes in the local kinetic and potential energy storage). This means that mode conversion alters the normal mode frequencies of the horn.

The magnitude of the changes produced by mode conversion in the eigenfrequencies and their radiation bandwidths depend on mode number in a particularly simple way. We have already noticed that mode conversion is only appreciable at the large end of a horn. The lower frequency standing wave modes in a horn have turning points well back from the open end, because of the rise in $U$. In other words they do not "visit" the region in which appreciable conversion takes place. To be more specific, modes with frequencies less than about 500 Hz have almost no s-wave amplitude within 5 cm of the end of our trombone-like Bessel horn, since Fig. 5 shows that $U$ has its maximum value (corresponding to 653 Hz) located at about 3.5 cm from the end of the horn. As a result, all low frequency standing waves have their turning points farther than 3.5 cm from the end, making the s-wave amplitude very small indeed in the region of appreciable mode conversion. We expect then, that the major changes due to mode conversion in a trombone bell are to be looked for above 500 Hz.

We have so far confined our discussion to frequencies low enough that relatively little energy is radiated, so that standing wave behavior is well established. Let us now turn our attention to frequencies that are above that corresponding to $U_{\max}$, so that increasing amounts of the outward bound s-wave energy is radiated. Because the s-wave amplitude is now becoming large in the strong conversion region we must enquire into the efficiency of radiation at the horn end by p-waves as compared with s-waves.

Radiation from an s-wave source into space is obviously fairly efficient, since all parts of the wave move in phase so that they act together as a simple (though extended) source. A p-wave on the other hand radiates much more weakly, since the inner portion of the source is moving in opposition to the outer portion. In other words, it has the qualitative nature of a coaxial doublet. Let us borrow from Morse [26] to find the ratio of energy radiated by a hemispherical s-wave with that of a corresponding p-wave source. This corresponds to radiation from the end of a horn which has flared abruptly so that $R \to \infty$ with $R' \to \infty$. The horn mouth has therefore opened into an infinite plane. In Morse's notation, $\Pi_m$ represents the power carried off by the wave whose angular dependence is the Legendre polynomial $P_m(\cos\theta)$. What we have called s-waves are to be identified with $m = 0$, while our p-wave belongs to $m = 2$ since the horn angle $\theta_0 = \pi/2$ (see eq. (12) and the accompanying explanation). We find that if displacement amplitudes are equal, then

$$\Pi_p/\Pi_s = (1/5)(D_0/D_2)^2$$

where the $D$'s are tabulated functions of $ka$, $a$ being the sphere's radius. If we take the radiating sphere to have a radius of about 10 cm (to agree roughly with the radius $h$ of waves at the end of our trombone-like horn), then at 1000 Hz $kh \simeq 1.8$, whence the power radiation ratio is found to have the value 0.072 and a corresponding radiated amplitude ratio of 0.27. At higher frequencies the power ratio quickly approaches 0.20 (amplitude ratio 0.45), since the $D$'s all approach $(1/kh)$. These results confirm that whatever p-waves may be generated are very poorly radiated indeed, so that our previous conclusion regarding radiation damping is further strengthened. To recapitulate, mode conversion reduces the radiation damping in a horn in two ways: (a) diversion of energy into the nonpropagating p-mode reduces the s-wave amplitude at the radiating end of the horn; (b) the mode conversion takes place chiefly at the end of the horn (where radiation is facilitated), but we find that the generated p-wave in this region radiates very weakly.

## 9. Corrections and perturbations

Because laboratory apparatus is seldom more than approximately similar to the idealized abstraction with which one initially deals in theory, we must provide ourselves with a few corrections and look into the major causes of change in the behavior of actual physical horns, as compared with the behavior of the simpler systems we have discussed so far.

When a flaring horn is attached to a long cylindrical pipe, there are several effects which shift the normal mode frequencies away from the values belonging to a complete horn whose total length is the same as that of the composite.

### *9.1. Discontinuity of taper at a junction*

There is in general a discontinuity of angle in the walls of the air column at the point where one segment of a horn meets another segment having different taper. The equations for continuity require that the logarithmic derivative of the pressure be constant across the junction (if the diameter is the same on both sides of the junction. When this is written in terms of $\psi$ we find

$$(r'/r)_{\mathrm{left}} - (r'/r)_{\mathrm{right}} = (\psi'/\psi)_{\mathrm{left}} - (\psi'/\psi)_{\mathrm{right}}. \quad (44)$$

Consider now the simple but illustrative case where a horn of length $L_{\mathrm{h}}$ joins a cylindrical pipe of length $L_{\mathrm{p}}$. Assuming that the pipe is closed at $z=0$, and that $k_n^2 \gg U$ in the part of the horn nearest the junction, this standing wave in the neighborhood of the junction may be written

$$\psi_{\mathrm{pipe}} = \cos k_n L_{\mathrm{p}}, \quad (45\mathrm{a})$$

$$\psi_{\mathrm{horn}} \cong A \cos(k_n L_{\mathrm{p}} + \varepsilon_n). \quad (45\mathrm{b})$$

Application of eq. (44) shows for example that if the flaring part of the horn has a length $L_{\mathrm{h}}$ and the radius is given by $r = B[L_{\mathrm{h}} + L_{\mathrm{p}} - z]^{-\alpha}$ in the neighborhood of the junction, then

$$\varepsilon_n \cong (\alpha/k_n L_{\mathrm{h}}) \cos^2 k_n L_{\mathrm{p}}. \quad (46)$$

The effect of this phase shift is always to raise the frequencies of the composite horn relative to those of a simple horn. This is true regardless of the position of the discontinuity of taper along the horn. However the magnitude of the alteration is very sensitive to its position relative to the standing wave, so that a segmentally constructed horn inherently has irregularities in its sequence of natural frequencies. The fact that $A$ differs from unity in eq. (45b) implies that a running wave incident on the junction will suffer partial reflection, as has been discussed by Frank [27] in connection with the closely related problem of the junction of two electromagnetic waveguides.

### *9.2. Horn perturbations in phase integral approximation*

We turn our attention now in a preliminary way to the experimentally important question of how much difference there is between the $k_n$'s belonging to a flaring horn that continues smoothly to its small end, and those associated with a horn in which a certain fraction of the small end of the horn is replaced by a cylindrical pipe. We will set aside here the correction just described, which deals with taper changes at the junction itself, and devote our analysis to the effect of making the horn taper vanish. We have already noted that in the spirit of the WKB approximation, the eigenvalues $k_n$ may be found from the total phase accumulated by integrating $q(z)\,\mathrm{d}z$ from one end of the air column to the other. For consistency with the desired boundary conditions (closed at one end, open at the other), this accumulated phase is equal to an odd multiple of $\pi/2$ plus a phase term $\Phi_n$ that is determined by the details of the horn taper at the closed end, and the rate of taper at the open end (eq. (33)).

If we reshape the horn, so that in some region between $z_1$ and $z_2$ the horn function $U(z)$ is changed by an amount $V(z)$, the total phase integral for the $n$-th solution will be altered by an amount $\Delta\Phi_n$.

$$\Delta\Phi_n = \int_{z_1}^{z_2} \{[k_n^2 - (U+V)]^{1/2} - [k_n^2 - U]^{1/2}\}\,\mathrm{d}z. \quad (47)$$

While this phase integral is not very accurate in rapidly flaring parts of the horn, we may use it to estimate the effect of small changes in regions of small flare (where $k_n^2 \gg U$). In such regions $\Delta\Phi$ is well approximated by

$$\Delta\Phi_n \cong -[1/(2k_n)] \int_{z_1}^{z_2} V(z)\,\mathrm{d}z. \quad (48)$$

From this result we deduce that the change $\Delta k_n$ produced by our perturbation $V$ is

$$\Delta k_n \cong [1/(2k_n L)] \int_{z_1}^{z_2} V(z)\,\mathrm{d}z. \quad (49)$$

Here $L$ is the total length of the horn from its closed end to the turning point (where $k_n^2 = U$).

Replacement of the small end of a flaring horn (in the region where the horn function $U_h$ is small) by a cylindrical pipe (for which $U=0$) constitutes a perturbation of the original horn in which $V=-U_h$. Eq. (49) shows that such replacement has the effect of lowering all of the resonance frequencies, the alteration being greatest for $n=1$, with the change becoming less important for the higher solutions. The more detailed analysis given in the next section shows that the general nature of our result is correct (compare eqs. (49) and (56)). However details are missing, such as the position of the perturbation relative to the standing wave, and the fact that perturbations of $U$ located at the nodes of $\psi$ produce no effect.

### *9.3. Perturbation theory for the horn equation*

In the preceding section a simple phase-integral procedure was outlined for use in regions of a horn where the taper (or more exactly, the flare) is small. In actual practice one often meets horns of more general shape, and the work of analyzing such horns is often reduced if they can be related to air columns of some analytically soluble type, or to a sequence of such types. It is important therefore to have methods available for adapting the analytically-available solutions to real situations over the whole range of the flare. Furthermore in the practical adjustment of musical horns it is useful to have an easily-applicable theory to guide the adjustment of a pre-existing horn by small perturbations of the bore that are chosen to produce a desired result. Most important of all for our present purposes, is the need for analytical tools by means of which we can conveniently assess the effect of various measurement errors and computational approximations on the results of our comparisons between horn theory and experiment. Perturbation techniques are highly developed [28] so that we will present only the briefest and most direct account, in a manner which is directly related to the work at hand.

Suppose that we have the complete set of orthogonal solutions for the wave equation belonging to a particular horn, with specified end-conditions. It is our desire to find a way to modify these solutions (or rather, to combine them) in a manner which will give the wave functions and eigenvalues for a horn of very similar shape, and identical end-conditions. The mathematical simplicity of the pressure ("Webster") wave equation (eq. (19)) suggests that we use it as an illustration of the perturbation technique. However it is to be emphasized that the reduced wave equation (eq. (20)) can be dealt with in exactly the same way.

We write $D(z)$ for the function $(S'/S) \equiv (2r'/r)$ which describes the original air column, while a set of $p_n$'s and $k_n$'s represent the associated wave solutions and their eigenvalues. The closely related (perturbed) horn will be described in terms of $D(z)$ plus a small added term $E(z)$. We will write $\Phi_n$'s for the solutions of this modified wave equation, and denote the new eigenvalues by

$$K_n = (k_n^2 + \delta_n)^{1/2}.$$

The wave equation (eq. (19)) may then be written down for each horn.

$$p_n'' + D p_n' + k_n^2 p_n = 0, \tag{50a}$$

$$\Phi_n'' + (D+E)\Phi_n' + K_n^2 \Phi_n = 0. \tag{50b}$$

Because of the presumed similarity of each $\Phi_n$ to its corresponding $p_n$, we are led to write $\Phi_n$ in a way that shows this similarity explicitly

$$\Phi_n = p_n + \sum a_{nm} p_m, \quad (n \neq m). \tag{51}$$

Here it is presumed that the summation of correction terms is small in its aggregate, as well as part by part. When $\Phi$ from eq. (51) is substituted in eq. (50b), we find

$$\delta_n p_n + E p_n' + \sum a_{nm} E p_m' + \\ + \sum a_{nm}(K_n^2 - k_n^2) p_m = 0. \tag{52}$$

To find the difference between the modified eigenvalue $K_n$ and the original $k_n$ we multiply eq. (52) by $(S/B)p_n$ and integrate over the length of the horn. Because of the orthogonality of the $p$'s with a weight factor $(S/B)$, as demonstrated in the Appendix, we obtain

$$N_n \delta_n = -\{\int (S/B) p_n E p_n' \mathrm{d}z + \\ + \sum a_{nm} \int (S/B) p_n E p_m' \mathrm{d}z\}. \tag{53}$$

Here

$$N_n = \int (S/B) p_n^2 \mathrm{d}z.$$

We may neglect the aggregate of terms following the summation sign, since they will prove to be of second order in the perturbation $E(z)$, as shown in the next paragraph.

The magnitudes of the $a_{nm}$ coefficients in our expansion may be obtained by multiplying eq. (52) by $(S/B)p_m$, $m \neq n$, and integrating as before.

$$N_n a_{nm} = \{\int (S/B) p_m E p_n' \mathrm{d}z + \\ + \sum (\ )\}/(k_m^2 - k_n^2). \tag{54}$$

The summation sign in eq. (54) represents higher-order terms similar to those found in eq. (53). We note that because of the "resonance denominator" in eq. (54) the dominant contribution of the $p_m$'s to a given $\Phi_n$ comes from those $p$'s for which $k_m$ is close to $k_n$.

Let us return to eq. (53) and rewrite it in a form that is useful for the practical calculation of a change $\Delta k_n$ produced by a perturbation of the horn radius. If the perturbation in $r$ is written $e(z)$, then the first-order nature of $E(z)$ is

$$E(z) = [(e'/r) - (e/r)D]. \tag{55}$$

We see here that $E(z)$ is made up of two parts, the first having to do with a change of taper of the horn, and the second having to do with a change of radius. Finally we note that since $\delta_n = 2k_n \Delta k_n$ (to first order),

$$\Delta k_n = [-1/(2k_n N_n)] \int (S/B)\, p_n E p_n' \,\mathrm{d}z. \tag{56a}$$

If the gas is uniform everywhere in the horn ($B=$ const.), then $B$ may be omitted from eq. (56a) and from the integral which defines $N_n$.

There is a similar perturbation integral based on the reduced wave functions $\psi_n$, as follows

$$\Delta k_n = [+1/(2k_n M_n)] \int (1/B)\, \psi_n V \psi_n \,\mathrm{d}z \tag{56b}$$

where

$$M_n = \int (1/B)\, \psi_n^2 \,\mathrm{d}z$$

and

$$V(z) = [(e''/r) - (e/r)U]. \tag{57}$$

The integral of eq. (56b) is however less easily used in many cases since it involves the second derivative of the radius perturbation $e(z)$. Also this integral will give wrong results if $e' \neq 0$ at the ends of the horn, unless proper correction is made for the alteration made by $e'$ on the boundary conditions imposed on $\psi$. Recall that one specifies physical conditions on $p$ and $p'$, where $\psi/r = p$ so, that $p' = \psi'/r - (r'/r^2)\psi$.

One final comment is in order concerning the perturbation formula of eqs. (56a) and (56b). Following eq. (18) it was pointed out that the presence of boundary layer effects at the horn wall give rise to small correction terms to the gas density $\varrho$ and bulk modulus $B$. Each of these correction terms has a real and an imaginary part, and the question arises as to the interpretation of eq. (56) when the boundary layer corrections are treated as perturbations. The real parts of the corrections pose no problems, the magnitudes of the eigenvalues $k_n$ being altered in a straightforward way. The imaginary part of $\Delta k_n$ on the other hand represents the introduction of damping into the system. Since the time variation of a standing wave solution is given by $\exp(\mathrm{j}\omega_n t)$, and $\omega_n = k_n c$ we recognize that

$$\mathrm{Im}(k_n c) = 1/\tau_n$$

where $\tau_n$ is the time required for the amplitude of the $n$-th standing wave to die down by a factor $(1/e)$. Upon the basis of this result we can relate the boundary layer coefficients to the familiar expressions that connect damping time to resonance bandwidth.

## Appendix

### Orthogonality of the solutions

In order that perturbation calculations can be carried out meaningfully, it is necessary that the various solutions to our wave equation be orthogonal. In any practical case, one finds that there are subtleties associated with the boundary conditions imposed on the two ends of our horn which must be dealt with if orthogonality is to be assured. It is the purpose of this appendix to sketch out a (familiar) technique for investigating the orthogonality of the solutions to a differential equation, in order to illustrate these subtleties; and then to show how they may be resolved. Because of its greater mathematical generality, we will discuss the "unreduced" form of the horn pressure wave equation (eq. (18)) which includes the effects of variable gas density and bulk modulus. The general procedure and the conclusions may however be adapted readily to the Webster form (eq. (19)), or to the "reduced" form of eq. (20).

We begin by writing down the wave equation (eq. (18)) twice in slightly modified form for a pair of solutions $p_a$ and $p_b$.

$$(S/B)\,\omega_a^2 p_a + (\mathrm{d}/\mathrm{d}z)[(S/\varrho)(\mathrm{d}p_a/\mathrm{d}z)] = 0, \tag{A.1}$$

$$(S/B)\,\omega_b^2 p_b + (\mathrm{d}/\mathrm{d}z)[(S/\varrho)(\mathrm{d}p_b/\mathrm{d}z)] = 0. \tag{A.2}$$

Here $\omega_a$ and $\omega_b$ are the eigenfrequencies associated with a particular set of boundary conditions imposed on the ends of the horn. Multiply eq. (A.1) by $p_b$ and eq. (A.2) by $p_a$, and integrate each equation over the length occupied by the horn. Subtracting one of these integrated equations from the other gives

$$(\omega_a^2 - \omega_b^2) \int_{z_1}^{z_2} (S/B)\, p_a p_b \,\mathrm{d}z + \tag{A.3}$$

$$+ \int_{z_1}^{z_2} \left[ p_b \frac{\mathrm{d}}{\mathrm{d}z}\left(\frac{S}{\varrho}\frac{\mathrm{d}p_a}{\mathrm{d}z}\right) - p_a \frac{\mathrm{d}}{\mathrm{d}z}\left(\frac{S}{\varrho}\frac{\mathrm{d}p_a}{\mathrm{d}z}\right)\right] \mathrm{d}z = 0.$$

The second integral in eq. (A.3) may be integrated by parts, leaving

$$(\omega_a^2 - \omega_b^2) \int_{z_1}^{z_2} (S/B)\, p_a p_b \,\mathrm{d}z =$$

$$= [(S/\varrho)(p_b p_a' - p_a p_b')]\Big|_{z_1}^{z_2}. \tag{A.4}$$

If the desired end conditions are such as to make $p$ (or $p'$) zero at $z_1$ and $z_2$ (so that the right hand side of eq. (A.4) vanishes), then orthogonality is at once proved. That is

$$\int_{z_1}^{z_2} (S/B)\, p_a\, p_b\, \mathrm{d}z = \begin{cases} N_a\,, & a = b \\ 0\,, & a \neq b\,. \end{cases} \tag{A.5}$$

So far the result is perfectly familiar. As remarked earlier, in many physical problems the end conditions are not simple. One finds that there are essentially arbitrary admittance requirements imposed on the solutions at the ends of the horn, which may be translated to be requirements laid on the logarithmic derivative $p'/p$ [29]. It is convenient to write these derivatives as $Y(\omega, z)$, defined at $z = z_1$ or $z_2$, and at $\omega = \omega_a$ or $\omega_b$. Using this notation, the right side of eq. (A.4) becomes

$$\Big\{(S/B)\, p_a\, p_b\big[Y(z, \omega_a) - Y(z, \omega_b)\big]\Big\}\Big|_{z_1}^{z_2}. \tag{A.6}$$

Since the $Y$'s are externally imposed, and arbitrary, it is clear that this expression will not in general vanish. There is however an artifice by means of which we can escape from the difficulty. It is always possible to devise an additional *terminating* segment of air column whose shape is such that it has a specified input admittance $Y(z, \omega)$ at one end, when its other end has $p$ or $p'$ identically zero. We can then construct a pair of such terminating segments for the two ends of our real horn, to provide a composite air column which *does* meet the orthogonality requirement (vanishing of eq. (A.6)) when the limits of the integration are widened to include the two extensions.

(Received September 14th, 1973.)

References

[1] Eisner, E., Complete solutions of the "Webster" horn equation. J. Acoust. Soc. Amer. **41** [1967], 1126.
[2] Benade, A. H., Brass instrument design and the theory of horns (abstract). J. Acoust. Soc. Amer. **52** [1972], 138.
[3] Benade, A. H. and Jansson, E. V., Spherical-wave approximation in horns: measured and calculated (abstract). J. Acoust. Soc. Amer. **44** [1968], 367.
[4] Jahnke, E. and Emde, F., Tables of functions, 4th ed. Dover, New York 1945, p. 166.
[5] Morse, P. M., Vibration and sound, 2nd ed. McGraw-Hill Book Co., New York 1948, p. 316.
[6] Morse, P. M. and Ingard, K. U., Theoretical acoustics. McGraw-Hill Book Co., New York 1968, p. 332.
[7] Morse, P. M. and Feshbach, H., Methods of theoretical physics. McGraw-Hill Book Co., New York 1953, p. 548.
[8] Hoersch, V. A., Non-radial harmonic vibrations within a conical horn. Phys. Rev. **25** [1925], 218.
[9] Jahnke, E. and Emde, F., Tables of functions, 4th ed. Dover, New York 1945. See p. 121 for angles which give integral values of $\mu$.
[10] Stevenson, A. F., Exact and approximate equations for wave propagation in acoustic horns. J. Appl. Phys. **22** [1951], 1461. See also Stevenson, A. F., General Theory of electromagnet horns on pp. 1447–1460 of the same issue.
[11] Morse, P. M., Vibration and sound, 2nd ed. Mc Graw-Hill Book Co., New York 1948, p. 265ff.
[12] Benade, A. H., On the propagation of sound waves in a cylindrical conduit. J. Acoust. Soc. Amer. **44** [1968], 616.
[13] Nederveen, C. J., Acoustical aspects of woodwinds. Frits Knuf, Amsterdam 1969, Chap. 2.
[14] Benade, A. H., Thermal pertubations in woodwind bores (abstract). J. Acoust. Soc. Amer. **35** [1963], 1901.
[15] Shaw, E. A. G., Impedance transforming wave systems with spatially varying density and elasticity (abstract). J. Acoust. Soc. Amer. **52** [1972], 138.
[16] Eisner, E., see ref. [1].
[17] Bouasse, H., Tuyaux et résonateurs. Librairie Delagrave, Paris 1929, pp. 383–384.
[18] Salmon, V., Generalized plane wave horn theory. J. Acoust. Soc. Amer. **17** [1946], 199, and Salmon, V., A new family of horns. J. Acoust. Soc. Amer. **17** [1946], 212.
[19] Pinkney, H. F. L. and Basso, G., On the classification of families of shapes for rods of axially varying cross-section in longitudinal vibration. Nat. Res. Council Canada, Ottawa, Mech. Eng. Rept. MS-109 [1963].
[20] Weibel, E. S., On Webster's horn equation. J. Acoust. Soc. Amer. **27** [1955], 726.
[21] Mason, M. and Weaver, W., The electromagnetic field. Univ. of Chicago Press, Chicago 1929. Reprint, Dover Publications, Inc., New York, n. d., p. 236ff.
[22] Morse, P. M. and Feshbach, H., Methods of theoretical physics. McGraw-Hill Book Co., New York 1953, p. 1099.
[23] Jahnke, E. and Emde, F., Tables of functions, 4th ed. Dover, New York 1945, p. 146.
[24] Morse, P. M. and Feshbach, H., Methods of theoretical physics. McGraw Hill Book Co., New York 1953, p. 1100.
[25] Morse, P. M., Vibration and sound, 2nd ed. McGraw Hill Book Co., New York 1948, p. 317, eq. 27.11.
[26] Morse, P. M., Vibration and sound, 2nd ed. McGraw-Hill Book Co., New York 1948, p. 321, eq. 27.18.
[27] Moreno, T., Microwave transmission design data. Sperry Gyroscope Co., 1948. Reprint, Dover Publications, Inc., New York 1958, pp. 53–54.
[28] Morse, P. M. and Feshbach, H., Methods of theoretical physics. McGraw-Hill Book Co., New York 1953, Chap. 9.
[29] Morse, P. M. and Feshbach, H., Methods of theoretical physics. McGraw-Hill Book Co., New York 1953, Chap. 6, Sec. 1, Sec. 3.

# 19B

*Copyright © 1974 by S. Hirzel Verlag, Stuttgart*

Reprinted from *Acustica*, **31**(4), 185–202 (1974)

# On Plane and Spherical Waves in Horns with Non-Uniform Flare II. Prediction and Measurements of Resonance Frequencies and Radiation Losses

by E. V. Jansson

The Department of Speech Communication, The Royal Institute of Technology (KTH), S-100 44 Stockholm 70, Sweden

and A. H. Benade

Case Western Reserve University, Cleveland, Ohio 44106, USA

[*Editor's Note:* Summaries in English, German, and French have been deleted because of limitations of space.]

## 1. Introduction

Two main questions lie behind our work; what are the acoustical properties of horns of considerable varying flare, as for instance bells of musical horns, and; how well are these properties predicted by means of simple models of the wave propagation? These questions were theoretically investigated in our previous paper, to which we shall refer as Part I in the future. In accordance with the theory presented in Part I, two models are tested in this its experimental companion; the first order approximation, plane wavefronts, and the second order approximation, spherical wavefronts. We chose to test the theory on representative horns of practical importance. Such horns are found in the bells of brass instruments. To be able to find answers to our questions we collected empirical data on acoustical properties and geometrical dimensions of representative horn bells. Our primary ambition was to collect data accurate enough for testing the models of wave propagation. Furthermore we wanted the data to be accurate enough to give relevant hints to a third order approximation if possible. Therefore we decided to make as accurate measurements as possible with a reasonable amount of work using the laboratory apparatus at hand. In order to obtain several measuring point (resonances and antiresonances) in the musically useful, and acoustically interesting frequency range of each bell, the bells were lengthened by cylindrical tubings at their small ends. We measured the input impedance at the far end of the cylincrical tube. It should be noticed that such measurements give data similar to that obtained from measurements of real musical instruments, except that we have simplified the system by cutting-off the acoustically complex mouthpiece and its tapering extension the mouthpipe.

In this paper we shall present the properties of our "horns" in terms of their eigenfrequencies and the corresponding power-reflexion coefficients. These power-reflexion coefficients are direct measures of how much of the injected excitation energy is reflected at the flaring bell section back into the cylindrical section. Thus the power-reflexion coefficients give direct measures of the energy storage in the air column and of the radiated power, as a function of frequency, i.e. a physically more easily interpreted parameter than the halfpower bandwidths. We give careful attention to the accuracy of measurement and machine computation in order to guide the drawing of conclusions.

Before starting the detailed description of our work we shall give two references slightly outside the boundaries of our investigation but of general interest in the field. Recently we have got to know that the spherical wave approximation has been suggested and examined by Lieber [1]. Parallel in time with our work a detailed investigation of the acoustics of a complete brass instrument, the trombone, has been conducted by Wogram [2].

## 2. Test objects

We decided to test bells of the three most common types of horns in the symphony orchestra. Furthermore we chose to test three different bells of one of these types of horns. Thus one French horn bell, one trombone bell and three trumpet bells were chosen as test objects. By an investigation of this sort we would gain knowledge about the properties of horn bells, about how the properties vary from one type of horn to another and about how the properties from one bell to another vary between different bells of the same type.

Our test bells had been taken out of production before they were joined to the cylindrical part and bent. Each of these bells was joined smoothly at its small end to one end of a length of cylindrical precision-bore brass tubing. The other end of the tubing was closed by a condensor microphone in a carefully fitted adapter. The airtightness of this adapter is most critical. Therefore each adapter was furnished with greased O-rings.

The dimensions of the tubes and the bells are given in Tables I and II, along with the estimated accuracies of the various measurements. The French horn bell is of the type used on Conn 8-D instruments, the trombone bell and one of the trumpet bells (II) are made by Rangarsons, New Dehli, and are closely similar to the bells used by Boosey and Hawkes on their Imperial instruments. Trumpet bell I is a C. G. Conn experimental bell and trumpet bell III is a bell designed for a H. N. White student instrument.

Table I.
Measures of tubes.
Length I = geometrical length of tube before the adding of the correction for open-end-radiation
Length II = geometrical length of tube when joined to bell.

| Tube to | Radius cm | Radius ± % | Length I cm | Length II cm | Length ± % |
|---|---|---|---|---|---|
| French horn | 0.78 | 0.3 | 181.9 | 180.7 | 0.06 |
| Trombone | 1.00 | 0.3 | 183.6 | 184.3 | 0.06 |
| Trumpets | 0.57 | 0.5 | 148.1 | 148.5 | 0.06 |

## 3. Experiments

### 3.1. Experimental apparatus

Our experimental apparatus is based on a GR Model 1900 A Wave Analyzer which provides us not only with a beat frequency oscillator but also with a narrow band tuned voltmeter tracking the oscillator frequency exactly. High accuracy fre-

Table II.
Measures of bells. $R$ is measured geometrical radius at $x$ cm from the small end. Estimated uncertainty $R \pm 1\%$.

| French hornbell $x$ cm | $R$ cm | Trombone bell $x$ cm | $R$ cm | Trumpet bell I $x$ cm | $R$ cm | Trumpet bell II $x$ cm | $R$ cm | Trumpet bell III $x$ cm | $R$ cm |
|---|---|---|---|---|---|---|---|---|---|
| 0.0 | 0.78 | 0.0 | 1.00 | 0.0 | 0.56 | 0.0 | 0.58 | 0.0 | 0.57 |
| 26.2 | 1.00 | 4.0 | 1.00 | 18.1 | 0.65 | 12.0 | 0.60 | 12.9 | 0.60 |
| 39.7 | 1.25 | 18.6 | 1.25 | 28.8 | 0.75 | 20.6 | 0.65 | 20.9 | 0.65 |
| 49.4 | 1.50 | 27.0 | 1.50 | 43.3 | 1.00 | 28.3 | 0.75 | 30.0 | 0.75 |
| 56.1 | 1.75 | 37.2 | 2.00 | 50.4 | 1.25 | 42.1 | 1.00 | 43.9 | 1.00 |
| 61.0 | 2.00 | 42.7 | 2.50 | 54.6 | 1.50 | 50.6 | 1.25 | 51.9 | 1.25 |
| 65.0 | 2.25 | 44.3 | 2.73 | 57.5 | 1.75 | 55.0 | 1.50 | 55.7 | 1.50 |
| 68.3 | 2.50 | 48.7 | 3.75 | 59.4 | 2.00 | 57.8 | 1.75 | 58.4 | 1.75 |
| 70.5 | 2.73 | 51.2 | 5.00 | 61.0 | 2.25 | 60.4 | 2.25 | 59.9 | 2.00 |
| 76.3 | 3.75 | 52.6 | 6.25 | 63.9 | 3.00 | 62.3 | 3.00 | 60.9 | 2.25 |
| 80.5 | 5.00 | 53.7 | 7.50 | 65.6 | 3.75 | 63.4 | 3.75 | 62.7 | 3.00 |
| 83.2 | 6.25 | 54.4 | 8.42* | 67.1 | 5.00 | 64.5 | 5.00 | 63.7 | 3.75 |
| 86.1 | 8.75 | | | 68.8 | 7.43* | 64.6 | 5.14* | 64.7 | 5.00 |
| 87.0 | 10.00 | | | | | | | 65.1 | 5.63* |
| 88.4 | 12.50 | | | | | | | | |
| 89.5 | 15.14* | | | | | | | | |

* marks extrapolated value.

quency measurements were made by use of a stroboscopic frequency meter (Stroboconn). The experimental arrangement may be considered to be made in three major parts: a closely controlled excitation part, a detection and measuring part, and a temperature monitoring part. The excitation part provides the horn with a sound source of constant flow amplitude. A microphone within the horn at the excited end detects the response of the horn, the microphone signal being measured by the tuned voltmeter. Because the velocity of sound within the horn (and thus its natural frequencies) are functions of the temperature, the temperature distribution along the horn must be well known.

A schematic diagram of our experimental arrangement is shown in Fig. 1. The excitation part consists of a constant pressure-amplitude acoustical source "in series" with a high impedance capillary tube, so that the combination functions as an almost ideal volume velocity source of constant strength. The source works in the following manners: a signal from the beat-frequency oscillator (part of the wave analyzer) is fed via a specially constructed voltage-controlled attenuator to a power amplifier (Bogen MO 100) and thence to a driver of a horn loudspeaker (100 or 75 W). The driver unit is screwed onto one end of a pipe about 50 cm long and 2 cm in diameter. The pipe is filled with fiberglass damping material to provide a partially non-reflecting acoustical load on the driver with fairly good acoustical damping. This load tube ensures good energy transfer from the driver to the air column at all frequencies of interest. The nonresonant nature of this coupling also reduces the dynamic range demanded of the servo-controller which is described next. The far end of this load tube is closed by a control microphone (B & K 4134) that is inserted through an airtight fitting. The signal from the microphone is amplified and fed to the signal attenuator. Here the control microphone signal is rectified and smoothed before being compared with a DC reference voltage. If the rectified signal voltage should become greater than the reference voltage, then a rapid-increasing progressive attenuation is inserted in the line between the oscillator and the power amplifier. If the rectified control microphone output is less than the reference value, there is essentially no insertion loss in the attenuator. As a result of voltage-controlled attenuator action, the acoustic pressure amplitude produced by the loudspeaker driver at the position of the control microphone is maintained constant within a fraction of a decibel over a wide range of frequencies. The desired constant flow amplitude excitation for the horn under the test is then achieved by feeding the horn from the servo-controlled constant pressure source by way of a length of capillary tubing. It runs from a point very near the control microphone in the source to a point close to the measuring microphone, which closes the small end of the horn and the tube combination. The capillary has a length of about 2.5 cm and an inside diameter of 0.06 cm.

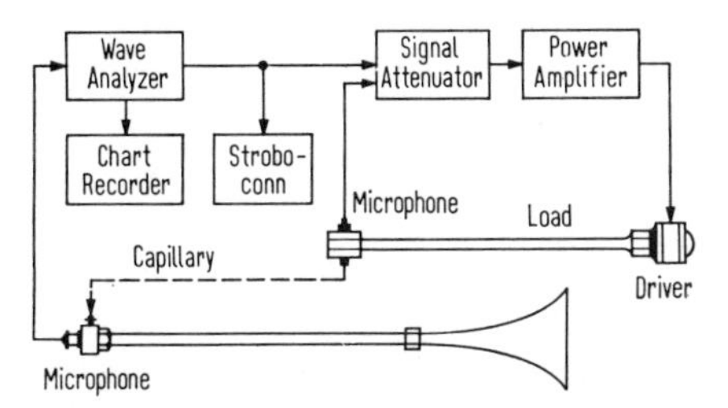


Fig. 1. Schematic diagram of experimental arrangement. The signal from a wave-analyzer oscillator is fed through a signal attenuator and a power amplifier to the driver of a horn loudspeaker. The driver is screwed on to a loading pipe containing damping material and a control microphone. Constant sound pressure is maintained in the pipe by the microphone and the attenuator. A constant flow velocity is obtained from a capillary tube and is injected into the cylindrical horn. The response of the horn is recorded via a measuring microphone, the wave analyzer and a chart recorder.

The measuring part of the apparatus employs a microphone (B & K 4134 or 4136) with amplifier and the tuned voltmeter of the wave analyzer. The output of the tuned voltmeter is fed to a General Radio 1521 A level recorder. A chain drive couples the motion of the recorder chart paper with the frequency dial of the wave analyzer. The oscillator and its associated voltmeter frequency setting can be measured at any time by means of the stroboscopic frequency meter. As mentioned above, the capillary tube (which functions as a constant flow source) is inserted into the horn's air column close to the measuring microphone and thus the pressure signal in this microphone is proportional to the acoustical input impedance at this end.

The temperature measuring part of the apparatus employs a high quality mercury thermometer, as primary reference, along with a pair of thermistors located at chosen points along the air column. These thermistors could alternatively be connected to a temperature measuring bridge. An important source of possible inaccuracy could be the cathode follower in the microphone-housing, heat being conducted to the horn under test. To reduce effects due to cathode follower heating, a cooling fan was placed close to the microphone. To monitor the temperature at this end one of the thermistors was plased close to the microphone adapter. The other thermistor was placed at the fitting that coupled the tubing to the bell. It was found that this junction was always at room temperature during the experiments.

### 3.2. *Measuring procedure*

The measurements were made in the following way: First we recorded a frequency response curve using the measuring microphone signal under the condition of constant input flow amplitude. For the bell-tubing combinations we also recorded the sound pressure at the control microphone as a check of the functioning of the control servo. Thereafter room temperature, temperature at the microphone adapter and the joint tubing bell, and the frequency of the lowest (first mode) resonance peak was carefully measured. We measured the frequency by returning the oscillator for maximum horn response three separate times; the readings then were averaged. This procedure was thereafter repeated for higher frequency peaks. Finally the thermistor at the joint tubing bell was moved and the temperature distribution along the pipe was measured. In this way basic acoustical properties of the tubes alone, and of the five bells with their proper tubes were measured under well known temperature conditions.

### 3.3. *Test of measurement method and calculation procedure*

In order to test the reliability of data derived from the measurements we made some preliminary tests of the experimental apparatus. We made sure that standing waves in the room did not influence on our measurements. Furthermore we made sure that the cylindrical tubing was so long that stray sound emitted by the driver housing and transmitted via the room into bell was not detectable.

The acoustical properties of cylindrical tubes are well known. Therefore we could use measurements on the cylindrical tubings to test the reliability of all our experimental procedures. The chart recorded response (input impedance) curve itself gives only a coarse measure of the resonance-peak frequencies and the bandwidths of these resonance peaks. Therefore the peak frequencies were measured separately as explained earlier. The response curve can, however, be used to calculate the losses accurately by means of measurements of what we call the peak-to-dip ratio. This is the ratio of the input impedance at maximum response (the "peak") to that at an adjacent response minimum (the "dip"). Because our level recorder plotted the resonance curve on a decibel scale, the peak-to-dip ratio was displayed in terms of an easily read linear vertical distance between the heights of the trace at the peaks and the dips. The actual measurement of the ratio was accomplished by drawing the envelope of the peaks and the envelope of the dips of the response curve. The ratio of the numerical values between the two envelopes at the same frequency represents the peak-to-dip ratio. Because the radiation losses at the open end of our pipe were negligible, this ratio can be thought of as the ratio between a maximum input impedance and a minimum input impedance obtained at the same frequency by opposite and lossless external boundary conditions. By doing so the wall losses of our experimental pipe can be calculated by means of standard transmission line theory.

For the frequencies of interest, the input impedance of a pipe of radius $a$, and length $L$, open at its far end is given by

$$Z_{\mathrm{in}} = \frac{\varrho c}{\pi a^2} \left[ \frac{\tanh \alpha L + \mathrm{j} \tan k L}{1 + \mathrm{j} \tanh \alpha L \tan k L} \right]. \tag{1}$$

Here $\alpha$ is the (relatively small) amplitude attenuation coefficient for a running wave whose wave number $k$ is $(\omega/c)$, where $\omega/2\pi$ is the frequency and $c$ is the velocity of sound. The maxima and minima of $Z_{\mathrm{in}}$ are found where $kL$ is an integral multiple of $(\pi/2)$. If $kL = \nu\pi/2$, $\nu = 1, 2, 3, \ldots$

$$Z_{\mathrm{dip}} = (\varrho c/\pi a^2) \tanh \alpha L \quad \nu \text{ even}$$
$$Z_{\mathrm{peak}} = (\varrho c/\pi a^2)/\tanh \alpha L \quad \nu \text{ odd}.$$

It is not at all difficult to generalize procedures based on peak-to-dip ratio measurements to the case where the terminating impedance of the pipe is not negligible, in particular the contribution associated with radiation damping.

We decided to adjust all measures to a temperature of 26.9 °C (300 °K) for convenience in making the various corrections. It was desired to keep the uncertainties because of temperature fluctuations less than 0.06% (1 musical cent) for the frequency measurements. We may adapt the perturbation theory equation (eq. (56a)) from Part I to guide us in an estimate of the temperature sensitivity of the experiment. It is shown in Part I that the bulk modulus $B$ and the density $\varrho$ of the gas do not appear symmetrically in the wave equation (see eq. (18), Part I) so that the perturbation to the horn's natural frequencies due to thermal effects is made up of two parts, (a) a change due to the integrated perturbation of the "speed of sound" $(B/\varrho)^{1/2}$ along the length of the horn, and (b) a change due to the thermal alteration of the "effective" cross sectional area $(S/\varrho)$. Suppose that the temperature $T(z)$ along the horn differs from the choosen 300 °K reference value $T_0$ by way of the function

$$T(z) = T_0[1 + \tau(z)].$$

It then follows that the perturbation formula for the fractional change $\Delta k_n/k_n$ of the $n$th resonance peak frequency takes the form

$$\Delta k_n/k_n = \frac{1}{2N_n} \times \times \left\{ \int_0^L \tau\, p_n^2 (S/B)\, \mathrm{d}z - \int_0^L p_n \tau' p_n' (S/B)\, \mathrm{d}z \right\} \quad (2)$$

where

$$N_n = \int p_n^2 (S/B)\, \mathrm{d}z .$$

Here $S(z) = \pi r^2$ is the cross sectional area of the spherical wave front at $z$, and $B(z)$ is the bulk modulus of the gas. The primes indicate differentiation with respect to $z$. The first integral in eq. (2) may be recognized as being the speed of sound correction, while the second term represents the changes in $(S/\varrho)$.

Our present interest is focused on the properties of a cylindrical pipe for which $S = \text{constant} = \pi a^2$ and $p_n = \cos k_n z$ with $k_n L = (2n-1)\,\pi/2$, whence $N_n = L/2$. Let us suppose now that the fractional temperature perturbation varies as $\tau = \tau_0 \exp(-\gamma z)$, as is plausible since heat from the detecting microphone's cathode follower can raise the temperature of the closed end of the pipe.

If $\gamma \to 0$, so that the temperature perturbation is uniform from one end to the other $(\Delta k_n/k_n)$ given by eq. (2) becomes

$$\Delta k_n/k_n = +\tau_0/2 \quad (3)$$

as is expected, since the velocity of sound is known to rise in proportion to the square root of the absolute temperature.

For those values of $k_n^2 \ll \gamma^2$ we find that the temperature effect is such as to reduce the natural frequencies

$$\Delta k_n/k_n \cong -(\tau_0/(\gamma L))\, \mathrm{e}^{-\gamma L} . \quad (4)$$

On the other hand, when $k_n^2 \gg \gamma^2$ the frequency shift is once again upward

$$\Delta k_n/k_n \cong +(\tau_0/4)\, \gamma L . \quad (5)$$

Consider now the case where $\gamma = 3/L$ so that the perturbation at the cold end of the pipe is only five percent of the value $\tau_0$ at the warm end. The lowest mode has $k_1 = \pi/(2L)$ so that $(k_1/\gamma)^2 = 0.27$. Eq. (4) is therefore applicable and we find

$$\Delta k_1/k_1 = -0.016\, \tau_0 . \quad (4\mathrm{a})$$

Already by the third mode $(k_n/\gamma)^2 = 6.8$ so that eq. (5) must be used.

$$\Delta k_5/k_5 = +0.75\, \tau_0 .$$

Comparison of eqs. (3), (4a) and (5a) shows that a very considerable error, of variable sign, and depending on the mode number can arise as a result of uncontrolled temperatures and temperature gradients.

Eq. (3) shows that the mean temperature of the air column must be known within ± 0.35 °C if the specified accuracy is to be maintained. Eqs. (4a) and (5a) show that thermal variations along the length of the horn must be held to somewhat closer limits. In a similar vein, we wished to have the (viscous and thermal) boundary corrections accurate within 1 percent in so far as they are temperature dependent. This requires a much looser temperature control, the tolerance being 8.2 °C.

By measurement, along with the temperature distribution along the tubes, it was possible to keep the effective temperature uncertainty down to a very satisfactory 0.2 °C. It may be pointed out that at no time did the room temperature vary more than 1 °C so that no temperature normalization was required in making the wall effect calculations.

From our frequency measurements on the various cylindrical tubes the velocity of sound was calculated. This calculated sound velocity, assuming the value of the attenuation constant according to Rayleigh's large tube approximation (as discussed in Benade [3]) radiation reactance corrections according to Benade and Murday [4] and corrections of temperature conditions to 26.9 °C, agreed with value given by Benade [5] within the uncertainty limits of measurements[1]. These results serve as a first confirmation of the validity of our measurement techniques, and also provide directly measured velocity data for each of the pipes which were later joined to the various bells in the main part of the experiment.

The attenuation constant $\alpha$ for the tubes calculated from the peak-to-dip ratios of the response curves, after small corrections for the finite (though large) impedance of the capillary, and for radiation at the open end, was found to agree within the

[1] The estimated outer bounds of sound velocities are a) of measurements ± 0.15% and b) of discrepancies between experimentally observed and theoretically derived are ± 0.10%.

uncertainty limits for the tubing used for the trumpet bells, but it was about 10% too high for the other two tubings as compared to Rayleigh's large tube approximation. A plausible explanation for the discrepancy is that sharp edges at the fittings gave higher losses for tubings a and b[2].

Thus we find that the frequencies are very close to the expected ones, i.e. the experimental data should be very reliable in this respect. The comparison of theoretically derived and experimentally measured losses in cylindrical pipes were found not to agree quite so well. The losses are higher for two of the tubings, which are likely to stem from losses at edges. In the calculation of radiation losses from peak-to-dip measurements on the bells, it was decided to use a wall dissipation constant chosen to represent the actual losses measured in the cylindrical pipes, rather than to use some theoretical value. In this way we avoid systematic errors arising from omission of energy losses which take place at the corners and in the fittings.

### 3.4. *Calculation of losses in tubes with bells*

The measured peak frequencies were normalized by being corrected to a temperature of $26.9 \pm 0.2$ °C. The normalization included corrections for the temperature variations along the tubing. In Fig. 2 the normalized experimentally obtained peak frequencies are displayed as deviations from a harmonic series with estimated uncertainties of $\pm 0.2\%$.

From the peak-to-dip ratios of the response curves we calculated the power reflection coefficients according to the following procedure. The tubing with bell is regarded as a uniform transmission line terminated by a terminating impedance. The internal boundary layer losses of the tube plus the bell are included in the description of the homogeneous transmission line. The imaginary part of this terminating impedance contains all parts of the bell acoustics which determine the departure of the observed peak and dip frequencies from the integer sequence that is characteristic of the idealized transmission line. The radiation losses through the bell are taken as constituting the real part of the terminating impedance.

An exact calculation of the boundary layer losses and sound velocity corrections in the bell is complex, but we may obtain useful estimates with the help

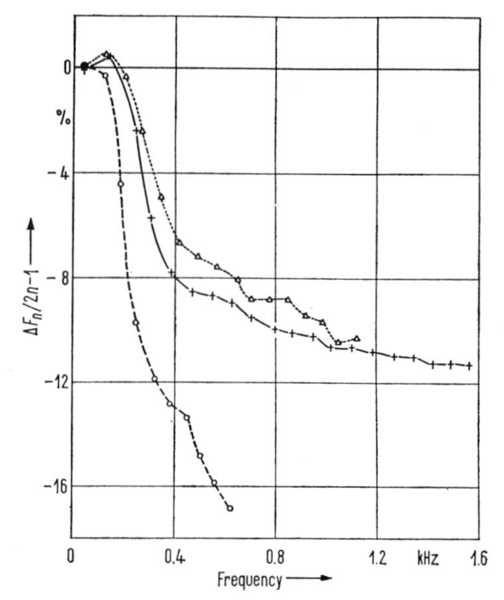


Fig. 2. Measured resonance frequencies of bells plus cylindrical tubes — French horn (○--○), trombone (△---△) and trumpet no. II (+—+). The frequencies are displayed as deviations from the odd numbered harmonic series with the first resonance (at 38.75, 40.02 and 45.62 Hz resp.) as fundamental.

once more of perturbation theory. In Section 3.1 of Part I we indicated that the thermal and viscous boundary layer effect may be assimilated into the wave equation by means of a modification of the density and bulk modulus coefficients of the gas. We reproduce the modified expressions here for ready reference

$$\varrho \to \varrho_0[1 + \beta_v/r] \qquad (6a)$$

$$B \to B_0[1 - \beta_t/r]. \qquad (6b)$$

Here $\beta_v$ and $\beta_t$ are related to the Rayleigh-Kirchhoff corrections for viscosity and thermal conduction at the horn walls. The radius $r$ is to be taken from the relation $S(z) = \pi r^2$ which defines the cross-sectional area of the bulging wave front which cuts the horn axis at the point $z$.

$$\beta_v = (1 - j)[2\eta/(\omega\varrho)]^{1/2} \qquad (7a)$$

$$\beta_t = (1 - j)(\gamma - 1)[2\varkappa/(\omega\varrho C_p)]^{1/2}. \qquad (7b)$$

In these expressions $\eta$ is the shear viscosity of the gas, $\varkappa$ its thermal conductivity, $C_p$ its specific heat at constant pressure, and $\gamma$ the ratio of specific heats $C_p/C_v$. It is pointed out at the end of Section 9.3 of Part I that the complex nature of the $\beta$'s merely means that a perturbation calculation gives both the frequency change and the damping change produced by the boundary layer.

[2] This matter has recently been restudied by Cuddeback and Benade (May 1972). While it is not possible to go back and correct the data discussed here, the nature of the discrepancies and their magnitudes are found to be entirely in agreement with the more detailed later observations.

The boundary layer perturbation integral (analogous to eq. (2) above) is

$$\Delta k_n/k_n = \frac{-1}{2N_n}\left\{\int_0^L \left(\frac{\beta_\mathrm{v}+\beta_\mathrm{t}}{r}\right)\left(\frac{S}{B}\right)p_n^2\,\mathrm{d}z + \right.$$

$$\left. + \int_0^L \left(\frac{r'}{r}\right)\left(\frac{\beta_\mathrm{v}}{r}\right)\left(\frac{S}{B}\right)p_n\,p_n'\,\mathrm{d}z\right\}. \quad (8)$$

Here the primes indicate differentiation with respect to $z$, and $N_n$ is the normalization constant defined as

$$N_n = \int (S/B)\,p_n^2\,\mathrm{d}z\,.$$

The second integral in eq. (8) is clearly recognizable as arising from the effects of horn taper. The first integral is associated with the more familiar Rayleigh-Kirchhoff corrections as will be demonstrated next.

If the horn is merely a cylindrical pipe of constant radius $r$ closed at $z=0$, then $p_n = \cos k_n z$ so that the first integral immediately gives the Rayliegh-Kirchhoff correction (which is inversely proportional to $r$), while the second integral vanishes identically. Let us now consider what happens in the more realistic case, where $r$ is not a constant. First we must notice that $p_n^2 S = \psi_n^2$, where $\psi_n$ is the "reduced" pressure wave function belonging to the wave equation

$$\psi_n'' + (k_n^2 - U(z))\,\psi_n = 0 \quad (9)$$

where the horn function $U(z) = (r''/r)$. The nature of this equation is discussed in Section 3.2 and 3.3 of Part I. As long as we are not looking at $\psi_n$ in the immediate neighbourhood of the turning point $z_\mathrm{t}$ (where $k_n^2 = U(z_\mathrm{t})$), or if we are dealing with frequencies high anough that is well above cut-off ($k_n^2 \gg U_\mathrm{max}$), $\psi_n$ has a WKB approximation representation

$$\psi_n \cong (q)^{-1/2} \cos \int_0^z q\,\mathrm{d}z\,. \quad (10)$$

Here

$$q^2 = (k_n^2 - U)\,,$$

and we have assumed that the horn has zero taper at the closed and, located at $z=0$. We recall that $U=0$ in the cylindrical part of our composite pipe-plus-bell, and that $U$ is small where the bell has small rate of flare. See Figs. 5 and 7 of Part I. To this approximation we recognize that the amplitude of $\psi_n$ varies only slightly, since $q^{-1/2}$ is extremely insensitive to the value of $z$ as long as $U \lesssim k_n^2/2$. This brings the WKB approximation to the following simple functional form

$$\mathrm{const} \int (\psi_n^2/r)\,\mathrm{d}z \cong \int \frac{1}{r}\,(\mathrm{cosinusoid})^2\,\mathrm{d}z. \quad (11)$$

Comparison of eq. (11) with the cylindrical pipe Rayleigh-Kirchhoff correction shows that we may use the harmonic mean radius of the horn in the standard formulas, in sofar as the WKB approximation is reasonable. In other words the use of this mean radius is satisfactory at high frequencies throughout the horn. At low frequencies it may be used in the small taper parts of the horn where $z < z_\mathrm{t}$. Beyond $z_\mathrm{t}$, in the cut-off region of the horn, the magnitude of $\psi_n$ rapidly falls to zero in exponential fashion. The contribution of the first integral of eq. (8) is therefore small in this region, and so may be neglected.

Till now we have set aside consideration of the second integral in eq. (8). Changing this second integral to $\psi$ form leads to an expression of the form given on the left side of eq. (12)

$$\mathrm{const} \int \left[\left(\frac{r'}{r}\right)\psi_n\,\psi_n' - \psi_n^2\left(\frac{r'}{r}\right)^2\right]\left(\frac{1}{r}\right)\mathrm{d}z \cong$$

$$\cong \mathrm{const} \int \left[\left(\frac{r'}{r}\right) - \left(\frac{r'}{r}\right)^2\right]\left(\frac{1}{r}\right)\mathrm{d}z. \quad (12)$$

The spatial variation of the magnitude of $\psi_n'$ is similar to that of $\psi_n$ (they are roughly constant to WKB approximation), which is the justification for writing the right-hand side of eq. (12). At low frequencies the main part of the standing wave is in regions where $(r'/r) \ll 1$, so that the contribution of this integral is small. At high frequencies well above cut-off, there may be an appreciable contribution to the boundary layer correction in the most rapidly flaring part of the horn. In practice we do not, however, need to be concerned about omitting this contribution for various reasons. In all of our experimental horns, the region of the bell in which $(R'/R)_\mathrm{geometrical} \gtrsim 1$ extends only a few centimeters out of an entire horn length which is of the order of 2 m. The fact that the wave fronts in the horn bulge more or less spherically makes $r'/r$ always less than the corresponding $R'/R$, especially in the rapidly flaring part of the horn. Thus the contribution in question can never amount to more than a few per cent of the main Rayleigh-Kirchhoff correction. Furthermore, as remarked earlier, this contribution from the second integral appears only at high frequencies. Here the radiation damping is so large that the boundary layer effects are hardly to be considered at all, and so their accuracy is not of crucial importance.

Our final conclusion from this perturbation theory examination of the boundary layer corrections is the following. We have made formal justification of a procedure originally proposed some years ago (Benade [6]) where Rayleigh-Kirchhoff corrections may be made for a horn of varying cross section by the use of standard formulas [7] where the effective radius is taken to be harmonic mean radius of the horn. This harmonic mean is to be calculated by integration over an effective length a) from the closed end of the horn to the turning point $z_t$ in the bell, for frequencies below cut-off, and b) over the whole length of the horn for frequencies above cut-off. Thus the boundary losses can be calculated as the losses of a pipe of just defined effective radius and effective length. For calculation convenience, however, we transformed this imaginary pipe into another hypothetical pipe. The radius of this later pipe was set equal to that of the small end of the bell and thus also equal to that of the joined cylindrical tubing. The length of the pipe, the effective loss length, was chosen to match the calculated boundary losses of the bell.

At the terminating impedance (the effect of flaring of the bell) a certain amount of the energy is transmitted out of the system and the rest of the energy reflected giving rise to a standing wave. By means of standard transmission line theory and the defined effective loss length we calculated from measurements how much of the inserted energy was dissipated in internal losses in the tube bell combinations. By subtracting this energy from the total energy losses, the energy reflected at the terminating impedance could be calculated.

### 3.5. *Experimentally obtained frequencies and losses*

Regarding the resonance frequencies the following observations can immediately be made. All resonance frequencies beyond the first fall below the frequencies which would be calculated as a 1, 3, 5 ... sequence of odd harmonics based in the first-mode frequency (see Figs. 2 and 3). This shows that the presence of a bell systematically narrows the normal mode frequency ratios of the pipe bell as compared with the expected sequence belonging to the pipe alone. There is an apparent exception to this remark. The "hump" shown at the second mode frequency in Figs. 2 and 3 may be understood in terms of the shift of the standing waves nodal system relative to the angular discontinuity produced by the junction of a bell with its pipe. We find that except for the French horn bell, all of our horns join their respective pipes with a significant angular discontinuity, so that there is a phase

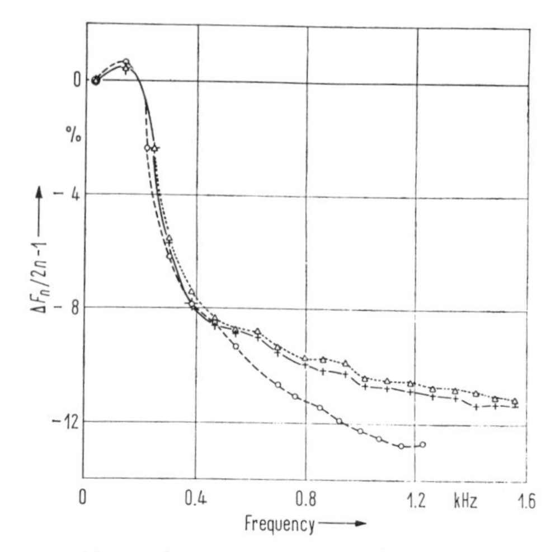


Fig. 3. Measured resonance frequencies of trumpet bells plus tubes. The frequencies are displayed as deviations from the odd numbered harmonic series with the first resonance (at 45.50, 45.39 and 45.62 Hz resp.) as fundamental.
○---○ No. I,
+——+ no. II,
△---△ no. III.

jump at the junction of the sort discussed in Section 9.1 of Part I. We discover also that the first two resonance modes of these bells fall at frequencies that are well below the value of the horn cut-off at the junction (200 Hz to 300 Hz). Because of this, the reduced pressure wave $\psi$ in the bell is of exponential rather than of the sinusoidal type dealt with in Part I. However, the final result of calculating the correction turns out to have the same form as before, so that we may base our discussion upon this result. When a Bessel-like horn of length $L_h$ and flare exponent $\alpha$ is joined to a pipe of length $L_p$, we found that the phase jump $\varepsilon_n$ at the junction was (see Part I, eq. (46))

$$\varepsilon_n \cong [\alpha/(k_n L_n)] \cos^2 k_n L_p \,. \quad (13)$$

We recall that $\varepsilon_n$ is of such a sense as always to raise the natural frequencies of the composit air column. For the first mode, the frequency correction for the experimental bells referred to above is relatively small due to the smallness of the cosine factor. The next two frequencies approach, or surpass the cut-off frequency at the junction. This has the effect of increasing the magnitude of the cosine factor toward, or just past its maximum value. This behaviour joins with the influence of the $k_n (= \omega/c)$ factor in the denominator to maximize the upward frequency shift of these modes which lie near, but somewhat below the local cut-off frequency, after which the phase jump has a rapidly decreasing influence on the observed frequencies. All of these phenomena are clearly observable in Figs. 2 and 3. Let us now turn briefly to an examination of the French horn bell to see why its measured frequency ratios do not show a "hump" like the other bells. Due to the great length of French horn bells, as compared with the others, the taper at the small end is very slight, and the rate of flare is even smaller. The first of these differences automatically reduces the magnitude of any phase jump which might be present. Furthermore, as a consequence of its small flare, the cut-off frequency is very low (of the order of 60 Hz) at the small end of the French horn bell, so that the frequency dependent part of eq. (13) is already near its maximum at the first mode frequency, and is falling toward zero by the second mode.

One final remark is called for in connection with the curves shown in Fig. 3. The three trumpet bells show the same sort of curve to about 500 Hz, then the resonance frequencies are lower for bell I. This bell was originally made for experimental purposes at C. G. Conn Ltd, and has a shape which makes it useless on a musical instrument. The curves shown here give a clear contrast between the musically useful trumpet bells (II and III) and the anomalous one.

Examination of Figs. 4 and 5 shows that the measured power reflection coefficients for the various bells have quite similar behaviour as a function of frequency. The power reflexion coefficients are close to unity for low frequencies and drop at higher. The coefficient for the French horn bell drops first and the trumpet bells last. Furthermore some of the curves show a second maximum at about 500 Hz, which stems from energy trapping in the

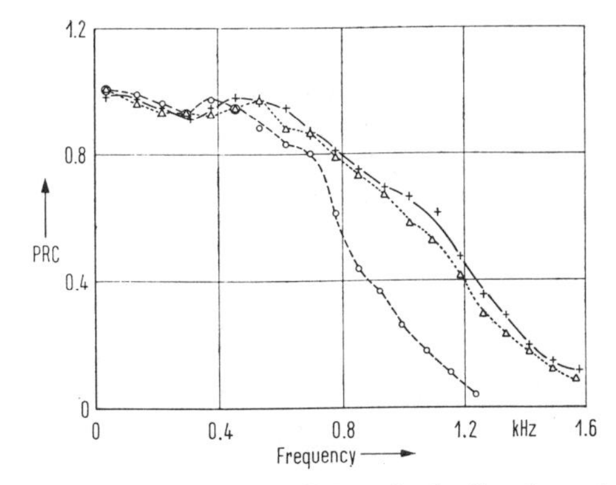


Fig. 5. Power reflection coefficients for the three trumpet bells calculated from experimentally observed losses.
o---o no. I,
+——+ no. II,
△---△ no. III.

bells due to mode conversion between the bell joint and the open end as will be discussed later. A comparison of the three trumpet bells shows that the reflexion coefficients of trumpet bell I fall below those of the other two bells above 500 Hz, which is one more example of the difference between this bell and the musically useful ones.

A detailed discussion of the relationships between the theoretically expected and the measured properties of these bells will be presented in the concluding sections of this report. Such discussion cannot be meaningful unless the details of the data reduction process, and the numerical integration of the wave equation are made clear.

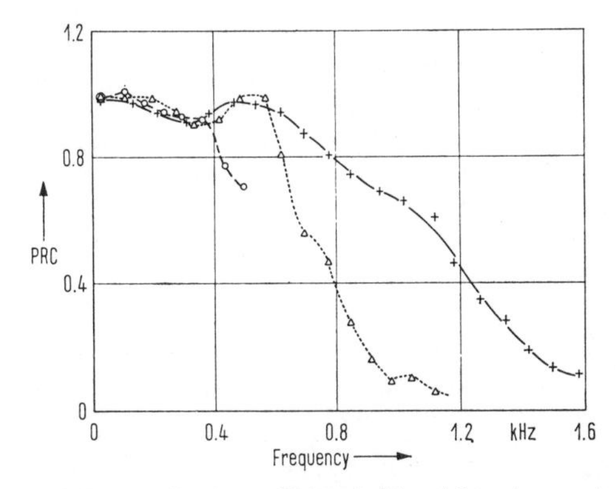


Fig. 4. Power reflection coefficient for French horn (o---o), trombone (△---△) and trumpet no. 2 (+——+) bells calculated from experimentally observed losses.

## 4. Calculations of resonance frequencies and losses

### 4.1. General

Calculations of resonance frequencies and losses in musical horns is a complex procedure. The horn bells are neither exponential nor catenoidal. The bells are well described by so-called bessel horns

$$R = B X^{-\alpha} \tag{14}$$

where $R$ is the radius as function of position $X$, $B$ is a scaling constant and $\alpha$ is the flare-rate constant. Eq. (14) is, however, still only an approximate description of the bell shape.

Wave propagation in horns is described by a differential equation, which for simple harmonic sound pressure wave can be written (c.f. eq. (19) Part I slightly modified)

$$\frac{d^2 p}{d X^2} = -k^2 p - \frac{2}{R} \frac{dR}{dX} \frac{dp}{dX} \tag{15}$$

where $k = \omega/v$, $\omega$ is the angular frequency and $v$ the phase velocity of the sound. No complete analytical solution is known to eq. (15) with boundary conditions given by the first approximation, finite and radiating Bessel horns eq. (14). This remark applies to both plane and spherical waves. The differential equation can, however, be numerically solved for any reasonable horn shape by integration step for step. When integration step for step is employed, the mathematical representation of the horn shape $R(X)$ can be divided into several separate regions in each of which we can adjust the parameters of $R(X)$ to fit some experimentally measured horn profile. In this way an arbitrarily close fit can be made to any reasonably shaped horn. Therefore we decided to employ the step by step numerical integration of the horn equation with the representation of the horn shapes divided into several separate regions. Although the calculation procedure is extremely simple, it is tedious to carry out by hand. It is, however, very well suited to a computer, for which programs were written.

The programs consist of mainly two subprograms: one for handling of the geometrical data, i.e. the geometrical boundary conditions, and one for calculating the pressure wave satisfying the wave equation under given geometrical boundary conditions. Both resonance frequencies and losses were calculated employing the same subprograms. The calculations are, however, done according to different physical processes: frequencies by means of standing waves and the losses by means of travelling waves.

### 4.2. *First subprogram — geometrical parameters*

The first subprogram calculates the geometrical parameter $\frac{2}{R}\frac{\mathrm{d}R}{\mathrm{d}X}$, which derives from the geometrical boundaries and is later needed in the numerical integration. The subprogram is written in two parts. In the first part the measured geometrical radius $R(X)$ is entered and the transformed radius representation $r(z)$ is calculated for use with assumed spherical wave fronts whose areas are given by $S(z) = \pi r^2(z)$. This first part is omitted, when the integrations are done for plane waves. In the second part the geometrical parameter $\frac{2}{R}\frac{\mathrm{d}R}{\mathrm{d}X}$ is calculated at every needed position $X$ and is stored.

As remarked earlier, the shapes of our real horns do not have any simple mathematical representation. The shapes are only approximately described by eq. (14). Therefore, the mathematical representation necessary for the use of the computer is provided by writing the horn flare in terms of third order polynomials. The polynomials are locally fitted to measured geometrical radii. For an introduction and a more extensive discussion of the used and more advanced methods of linear algebra, the interested reader is referred to Faddeeva [8].

The fitting procedure employs the following equations here written in matrix form

$$\begin{bmatrix} 1 & X_j & X_j^2 & X_j^3 \\ 1 & X_{j+1} & X_{j+1}^2 & X_{j+1}^3 \\ 1 & X_{j+2} & X_{j+2}^2 & X_{j+2}^3 \\ 1 & X_{j+3} & X_{j+3}^2 & X_{j+3}^3 \end{bmatrix} \begin{bmatrix} a_j \\ b_j \\ c_j \\ d_j \end{bmatrix} = \begin{bmatrix} R_j \\ R_{j+1} \\ R_{j+2} \\ R_{j+3} \end{bmatrix} \tag{16a—d}$$

where $j = 1, 2, 3, \ldots, n-3$; $n$ equals the total number of measured geometrical data points. Subtract the first row from the second, third and fourth rows, and the equation system can be split into two systems

$$a_j + X_j b_j + X_j^2 c_j + X_j^3 d_j = R_j , \tag{17}$$

$$\begin{bmatrix} X_{j+1} - X_j & X_{j+1}^2 - X_j^2 & X_{j+1}^3 - X_j^3 \\ X_{j+2} - X_j & X_{j+2}^2 - X_j^2 & X_{j+2}^3 - X_j^3 \\ X_{j+3} - X_j & X_{j+3}^2 - X_j^2 & X_{j+3}^3 - X_j^3 \end{bmatrix} \times \begin{bmatrix} b_j \\ c_j \\ d_j \end{bmatrix} = \begin{bmatrix} R_{j+1} - R_j \\ R_{j+2} - R_j \\ R_{j+3} - R_j \end{bmatrix} . \tag{18a—c}$$

By employing Cramer's rule a conveniently written set of solutions are obtained for computation of $b_j$, $c_j$, and $d_j$

$$b_j = \frac{\Delta_1}{\Delta}, \quad c_j = \frac{\Delta_2}{\Delta}, \quad d_j = \frac{\Delta_3}{\Delta} \tag{19a—c}$$

where $\Delta$ is the determinant corresponding to the $3 \times 3$ matrix of eqs. (19a—c), and $\Delta_k$ is the same determinant except from the $k$th column, which is substituted by $R$ matrix column. With $b_j$, $c_j$ and $d_j$ known $a_j$ is calculated by means of eq. (17). By means of eq. (19a—c) and (17) polynomials are locally fitted. For

1) $j = 1$; $l = 1$,
2) $1 < j < n-3$; $l = j + 1$ and
3) $j = n - 3$; $l = j + 1, j + 2, j + 3$

the following parameters are calculated (c.f. eqs. (24) to (27) in Part I)

$$\left[\frac{\mathrm{d}R(x_l)}{\mathrm{d}x}\right]_j = b_j + 2 c_j x_l + 3 d_j x_l^2 \tag{20}$$

$$[h(x_l)]_j = [R(x_l)]_j \left[1 + \left[\frac{\mathrm{d}R(x_l)}{\mathrm{d}x}\right]_j^{-2}\right]^{1/2} \quad (21)$$

$$[z(x_l)]_j = x_l - [R(x_l)]_j \left[\frac{\mathrm{d}R(x_l)}{\mathrm{d}x_l}\right]_j^{-1} + [h(x_l)]_j \quad (22)$$

$$[r(z_l)]_j = \{[2[h(x_l)]_j][[z(x_l)]_j - x_l]\}^{1/2}. \quad (23)$$

Thus the measured geometrical boundaries $R_l(x_l)$ are transformed into equivalent spherical wave boundaries $r_l(z_l)$.

In the second part of the first subprogram the same fitting procedure of third order polynomials to $r(z)$ is carried out. From these polynomials the geometrical parameter is calculated as

$$\left[\frac{2}{r(z_l)}\frac{\mathrm{d}r(z_l)}{\mathrm{d}z}\right]_j = b_j + 2c_j z_l + 3d_j z_l^2. \quad (24)$$

At points where two branches of different polynomials are overlapping the geometrical parameter is modified as

$$\left[\frac{2}{r(z_l)}\frac{\mathrm{d}r(z_l)}{\mathrm{d}z}\right] = \frac{1}{2}\left\{\left[\frac{2}{r(z_l)}\frac{\mathrm{d}r(z_l)}{\mathrm{d}z}\right]_{j-1} + \left[\frac{2}{r(z_l)}\frac{\mathrm{d}r(z_l)}{\mathrm{d}z}\right]_j\right\} \quad (25)$$

i.e. the mean value is used to smooth the function of the geometrical boundary. To these points, finally, the third order polynomial fitting procedure is carried out once more and $\frac{2}{r(z)}\frac{\mathrm{d}r(z)}{\mathrm{d}z)}$ is calculated at every axial position $\Delta z = 0.1$ cm apart. The calculation is done between the second and third point of the polynomial except from the polynomials at the ends of the bells, where the calculation is started from the first and ended at the last points respectively.

*4.3. Second subprogram — numerical integration*

In the second subprogram sound pressure waves are calculated satisfying the geometrical boundary conditions, and standing wave or travelling wave conditions. The calculations are done by numerical integration step for step of the wave equation.

The relations that our integration procedure uses are the differential equation describing the sound pressure wave $p(X)$, sinusoidally varying in time with the angular frequency, and Taylor expansions of the sound pressure and its first derivative, $\frac{\mathrm{d}p(X)}{\mathrm{d}X}$, i.e.

$$\frac{\mathrm{d}^2p(X)}{\mathrm{d}X^2} = -k^2p(X) - \frac{2}{R(X)} \times \frac{\mathrm{d}R(X)}{\mathrm{d}X}\frac{\mathrm{d}p(X)}{\mathrm{d}X} \quad (26)$$

$$p(X+\Delta X) = p(X) + \frac{\mathrm{d}p(X)}{\mathrm{d}X}\Delta X \quad (27)$$

$$\frac{\mathrm{d}p(X+\Delta X)}{\mathrm{d}X} = \frac{\mathrm{d}p(X)}{\mathrm{d}X} + \frac{\mathrm{d}^2p(X)}{\mathrm{d}X^2}\Delta X \quad (28)$$

where $k = \omega/v$ and $v$ the phase velocity of the sound.

The integration is started at a position $X$ where $p(X)$ and $\frac{\mathrm{d}p(X)}{\mathrm{d}X}$ are known. For an ascribed frequency, a given geometrical parameter

$$\frac{2}{R(X)}\frac{\mathrm{d}R(X)}{\mathrm{d}X},$$

and known $p(X)$ and $\frac{\mathrm{d}p(X)}{\mathrm{d}X}$ the second derivative $\frac{\mathrm{d}^2p(X)}{\mathrm{d}X^2}$ is calculated by means of eq. (26). $p(X+\Delta X)$ is calculated at a position $X+\Delta X$ by means of eq. (27). With the second derivative $\frac{\mathrm{d}^2p(X)}{\mathrm{d}X^2}$ known at $X$, the first derivative

$$\frac{\mathrm{d}p(X+\Delta X)}{\mathrm{d}X}$$

at $X+\Delta X$ is calculated by means of eq. (27).

Thus the sound pressure $p$ and its first derivative $\mathrm{d}p/\mathrm{d}X$ are obtained at the position $X+\Delta X$. By inserting $p(X+\Delta X)$,

$$\frac{\mathrm{d}p(X+\Delta X)}{\mathrm{d}X}$$

and $$\frac{2}{R(X+\Delta X)}\frac{\mathrm{d}R(X+\Delta X)}{\mathrm{d}X}$$

in eqs. (26), (27), and (28) respectively, $p$ and $\mathrm{d}p/\mathrm{d}X$ are obtained at the position $X+2\Delta X$. The procedure is repeated over and over again through the whole horn and we obtain the pressure wave through the complete horn. The procedure used is the so-called Euler's method, which will give a smooth wave solution through the bell for small steps $\Delta X$. For discussion of this and more advanced numerical integration methods, we refer to Henrici [9].

At far end of the bell a wave is smoothly fitted to the wave obtained by the numerical integration of the wave equation. This is done by continuing the integration a few steps into assumed cones smoothly joined to the bells. By assuming spherical waves in the cones the sound pressure amplitude can be normalized with respect to the effective radius of the wavefronts. The ratio between this normalized pressure and the correspondingly normalized pressure inside the cylindrical tubing gives measures of the energy storage relations. Maximum energy storage in the bell plus tube i.e. minimum in the assumed cone, occurs at resonance frequencies.

### *4.4. Resonance-frequency calculations*

In the calculations of the resonance frequencies the system tubing bell was assumed to consist of a cylindrical tube that is joined to the bell, the large end of the bell is fitted smoothly on to a cone of wide angle (equal to the terminal angle of the bell flare). The cone is assumed to be of very great (but finite) length, terminated by a spherical cap. This cone-plus-cap may be thought of as representing the room in which the instrument is "played", and constitutes a way to avoid computer difficulties with complex eigenvalues, which arise if the horn is allowed to radiate into infinite space.

A standing wave is assumed set up in the enclosed system with chosen frequency and the enclosing cap positioned at a sound pressure maximum. The ratio amplitudes between the wave function in the conical section and the wave function in the cylindrical section gives a measure of the fractional storage of energy in the two sections. At frequencies which are normally thought of as being the natural frequencies of the horn plus pipe, we find that the sound field energy density is particularly large within the horn, and also that the input impedance at the small end of the horn is a maximum. Frequencies corresponding to input impedance minima are those for which the wave energy density is particularly small within the pipe and horn. Thus a suitably normalized comparison of the pressure amplitude within the horn, with that in the outer space (cone) can be used as a means for finding normal mode (resonance) frequencies of the horn plus pipe. Such a suitable normalization is obtained by multiplying the sound pressure with the radius of the pressure surface i.e. $R(x)$ or $r(z)$ respectively.

The computer calculates the normalized ratio of the standing wave amplitude outside the pipe and horn in the cone, and that found inside the horn plus pipe. A parabola is fitted to the three amplitude ratios calculated at three adjacent frequencies and the frequency at the minimum of this parabola was extracted, i.e. a measure of the resonance frequency. In this way a set of calculated normal mode frequencies are obtained for the horn and pipe under study.

The frequency-determination integrations were started by giving the computer the lowest experimentally observed resonance frequency, then a slightly higher, and finally a slightly lower frequency. The (external/internal) pressure ratios defined above were calculated and a resonance response parabola was fitted to the three resulting points and the best estimate of the calculated first mode was calculated by finding the location of the minimum of the parabola. A similar procedure was carried out for each normal mode upon the basis of three closely spaced assumed frequencies for this mode. The center frequency assumed in each case was the experimentally observed resonance frequency in order to assure good accuracy in the fitting procedure. The whole procedure was then repeated, with the first approximation calculated resonance frequencies being used as a basis instead of the experimentally observed frequencies. Finally the procedure was carried out a third time using the previously found resonance frequencies as starting value, with the upper and lower frequencies in the trial sets being spaced only 1.7% above and below the basis frequencies.

A numerical estimation of the uncertainty of the frequency calculations is difficult. However, the step size is not critical; for the trombone bell the frequency shifts obtained with a doubling of the step size were negligible (approx. 0.01 and 0.05% for frequencies below and above $U_{max}$ resp.). Furthermore the numbers describe a smooth function. The frequencies do not always converge to a finite value. The convergence is not guaranteed for very small discrepancies between measured and calculated frequencies or for high frequencies which is outside the range of validity for our assumptions of the wave forms.

### *4.5. Calculation of radiation losses*

In the calculation of the power reflection coefficients we applied a different theoretical approach. The flaring section is regarded as a hindrance through which the penetration of running waves is calculated. The tubing plus bell are assumed to consist the same boundaries as in the frequency calculations, with two exceptions only: the boundaries set by 1) the closure of the cylindrical tubing and 2) the spherical cap terminating the cone are removed. Thus the system is regarded to consist of an infinitely long cylindrical tubing connected to an infinitely long cone by means of a transition region which is the bell. A running wave is assumed travelling from the cylindrical tubing into the bell and being split up into one reflected wave and one transmitted wave. Initial conditions are arbitrarily set, and the real and imaginary parts of the wave solution through the bell section are integrated separately. To the wave solution in the cylindrical section thus obtained one incident wave and one reflected wave are fitted, and in the conical section a transmitted wave is fitted. The energy content of the three waves are proportional to the squared sound pressure normalized with respect to the area of the iso-phase surface. Thus the power reflection coefficients can be calculated from the energy content of the three different waves (c.f. Section 6 in Part I). In this procedure no difficulties are encountered because of phase relations at the tubing-bell joint as with standing wave calculations. Furthermore the power reflection coefficients can be calculated at any frequency.

The power reflection coefficients were calculated at the measured frequencies. They were thereafter adjusted to the theoretically calculated frequencies. Because of the small discrepancies between measured and calculated frequencies this adjustment was generally not needed. The integration steps were as before chosen to 0.1 cm. Test calculations for one bell varying the step length and the initial conditions gave that the power reflection coefficients obtained by the integration procedure are significant to two figures below the cut-off corresponding to the horn function $U$ (eq. (21) Part I) and slightly less accurate above. Thus the power reflection coefficients are obtained with high accuracy and the discrepancies displayed in the plots are indeed significant.

## 5. Comparison of theoretical and experimental data

The resonance frequencies and the power reflection coefficients obtained from measurements and from calculations with different theoretical assumptions are displayed in Figs. 6, 7, and 8. The frequencies are displayed as differences between calculated and measured frequencies in order to make readings with high accuracy possible. The discrepancies are displayed in the upper diagram of the figures. In the lower diagram the power reflection coefficients are shown for readily comparison in absolute measures.

From the acoustical measurements we have found the following for the real horn bells. The frequencies become "flatter" for higher modes. The reflection coefficients drop with increasing frequency except for a shallow maximum, a hump, at about

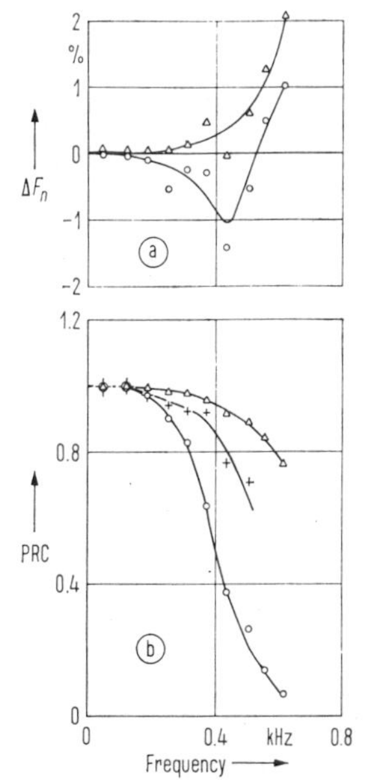


Fig. 6. French horn bell plus tube.
(a) Deviations between theoretically calculated frequencies and measured frequencies,
(b) Power reflection coefficients calculated from measurements and theoretical assumptions.
+—+ Measurements,
△—△ plane waves and
○—○ spherical waves.

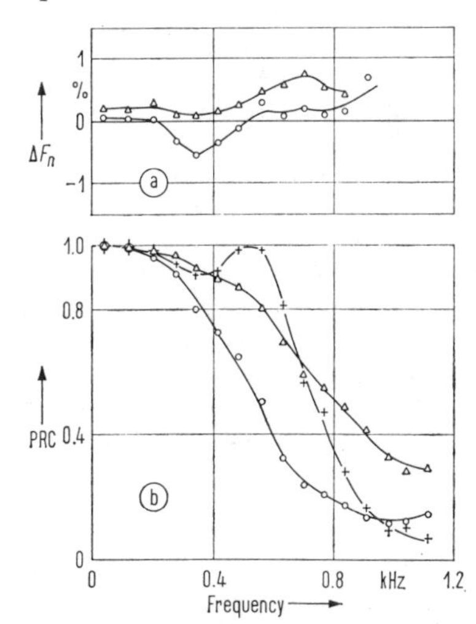


Fig. 7. Trombone bell plus tube.
(a) Deviations between theoretical calculated frequencies and measured frequencies,
(b) Power reflection coefficients calculated from measurements and theoretical assumptions.
+—+ Measurements,
△—△ plane waves and
○—○ spherical waves.

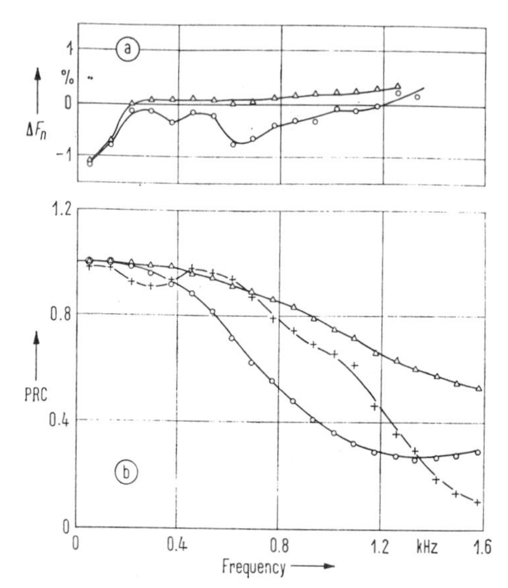


Fig. 8. Trumpet bell no. II plus tube.
(a) Deviations between theoretically calculated frequencies and measured frequencies.
(b) Power reflection coefficients calculated from measurements and theoretical assumptions.
+—+ Measurements,
△—△ plane waves and
○—○ spherical waves.

600 Hz. The hump is typical for the horns that have been investigated.

We find that the resonance frequencies calculated in either spherical or plane wave approximation lie extremely close to the measured frequencies. The discrepancies are generally less than 0.5%, and it is possible to draw smooth curves connecting the various calculated points in Fig. 6. This smoothness of the frequency dependence of the discrepancy curve indicates first of all that the two calculation procedures, and also the measurement techniques, were of very high dependability with random fluctuations which are seldom more than 0.1%. As a result we are justified in making a detailed examination of the relations between theory and experiments even though the total discrepancies are small.

We observe that the frequencies calculated in plane wave approximation lie above the values calculated in spherical wave approximation, and also those obtained by experiment. Both of these relations are expected upon the basis of the theoretical discussion found in Section 7 of Part I. The fact that the "spherical wave frequencies" generally lie below the measured values is not predicted in this section of Part I. However, when we examine the implications of Section 8.1 of Part I we realize that it is a general tendency of the s- to p-wave mode conversion phenomenon to produce wave front shapes which are slightly flatter than the postulated spherical s-waves. Thus we recognize that calculations based on perfectly plane, and on exactly spherical wave fronts should give normal mode frequencies that bracket the experimental values.

The question arises as to why the curves which compare the experimental frequencies with those computed using spherical waves, should show so much more variation than that associated with the plane wave calculation. Discrepancies that are associated with mode conversion and with computation to correctly include the small mass reactance which is present at the bell-to-pipe junction [10] should be common to both forms of calculation. We must therefore examine the difference in the way in which the horn's geometrical data are handled in the two computations. Fitting of the measured horn profile by means of a succession of overlapping polynomials inevitably gives rise to small discontinuities in the calculated horn wave functions. The plane wave calculation works directly from the polynomials, whereas there is an additional step involved when spherical waves are assumed; it is necessary to compute the locally defined spherical geometry in each part of the horn. This is a process which involves the finding of slopes of the horn profile and hence brings in additional variability of the overall computation.

In conclusion, we may say that for most practical purposes (if it is sufficient to obtain resonances with 0.5% accuracy), a plane wave calculation is considerably simpler, and in any event we have definite knowledge that it consistently overestimates the resonance frequencies by a small amount.

Let us turn our attention now to the power reflection coefficients (PRC). Setting aside temporarily the hump which appears in the PRCs for all bells except the French horn, we observe that overall the spherical wave calculation predominantly underestimates the reflecting ability of the bell as compared with experiment. On the other hand we see that the plane wave calculation systematically overestimates the PRC.

The differences in the s-wave barrier behaviour in the horn under the two assumptions for wave front shape are not expected to produce any marked differences in the reflection (or transmission) behaviour of a horn. Section 6 of Part I gives a careful discussion of these matters, and we may usefully reproduce here the concluding paragraph of that section: "While the foregoing discussion can elucidate the analytical relations between the radiation losses predicted by the two forms of horn theory, it is not easy to make general statements about the relative numerical values of the two results. Eq. (30) shows the reason: The plane wave theory gives a thin but very high barrier against radiation, whereas the spherical wave version gives a lower, but thicker barrier."

The presence of mode conversion in the most flaring part of the bell, provides us with a clear understanding of the relation between the radiation predictions of the two theoretical calculations and the experimentally observed PRC. As remarked above, in connection with our discussion of the resonance frequency results, plane wave theory is in essence an extreme form of a theory in which spherical s-waves are partially converted into p-waves. As explained in Section 8.3 of Part I, mode conversion reduces the radiation damping (increases the PRC) (a) because of the diversion of wave energy into a non-propagating p-wave mode, and (b) because the p and higher modes radiate inefficiently at the open end of the bell. Since some mode conversion is bound to exist in a real horn, we may conclude that it must have a PRC that lies intermediate between that calculated on the assumption of zero conversion and that based on a model with unrealistically large amounts of conversion.

We may present one further piece of evidence for the correctness of the mode-conversion interpretation of the relation between our calculations and experimental results. An additional set of resonance measurements was made with the trombone bell, but fitted with a pair of inner bell sections so shaped and located as to lie fairly well along the flow lines which would be associated to exact spherical wave propagation near the large end of the horn. Since the equal-phase pressure wave fronts must be orthogonal to any impenetrable surface which may be placed in the sound field, these inner bells serve to constrain the waves strongly into spherical s-wave type. In agreement with the interpretation given above, a significant decrease in PRC was observed. The additional boundary layer damping produced by these inner bells was much too small to produce the observed change in the PRC. It may be remarked in conclusion, that the practice of using cellular divisions within a loudspeaker horn is a well-recognized method of forcing the radiated waves to "follow the horn contours", and so to give efficient radiation from what we have called s-waves within the horn.

With the basic radiation behaviour of our horns clarified reasonably well, we are in a position in inquiring about the nature of the PRC "hump" which is observed in the experimental data for all bells besides that from the French horn. It is to be emphasized that this hump of anomalously efficient reflection was observed in the data from the three trumpet bells and the trombone bell of the present study.

Later measurements on actual trumpets (of modern and Baroque type) of the relation between the sound pressure within the mouth piece and that found outside the bell were carried out by one of us (AHB) in conjunction with C. Schlueter. These measurements were done both with excitation of the mouthpiece via a high impedance acoustical source, and under actual playing conditions with a normally produced musical tone providing the signals under study. In all cases the results imply a hump in the PRC of the type reported here. The absence of a hump in the French horn data suggests that this phenomenon has something to do with the properties of the pipe-to-bell junction. There can be a certain amount of reflection produced at this point due to the taper discontinuity and to the jog in the horn function. These matters have already been referred to in connection with the observed rise in the second mode resonance frequencies for all bells besides that of the French horn. The computer program was written to take this effect into account in calculating the PRC, but upon the assumption that mode conversion was not taking place; i.e. no reflections were assumed except those belonging to the main wave. If however there is some sort of back scattering produced via the p-wave conversion, it might be possible to understand the presence of the hump as being due to interaction of the conversion and the junction discontinuity. The fact the hump is not observed for the French horn bell is probably significant in this regard, since it is already recognized that this bell joins its pipe with unusual smoothness. A set of additional experiments was recently carried out by AHB with J. Sedlak and G. Bilbro using a null technique devised by JS to measure the conversion of s-waves to p-waves or in the reverse direction. Using a trombone bell, and cylindrical tubing as before we found that (a) there is significant mode conversion, (b) it is quite markedly frequency dependent, (c) it interacts (in ways that are not yet clarified) with secondary waves which arise at the pipe-to-bell junction. We hope to extend this work, which was of preliminary nature. In the later experiments as in the ones reported in the present paper, the anomalities are always located at frequencies that are closely equal to the resonance frequencies of the bells taken by themselves. Note: it is a property of short, widely flaring bells of musical type to have the first one or two mode frequencies very little changed whether the small end is closed or left open. As a result it is not a straight forward matter to deduce the relative phase relations of the scattered waves, which are presumably causing the hump.

## 6. Conclusions

The combined implications of our theoretical and experimental investigations into the acoustical properties of horns whose flare changes drastically along the horn may be summed up quite briefly as follows.

We find that the plane wave and spherical wave representations of horn acoustics both give excellent results in the calculation of resonance frequencies. These representations also are quite successful in accounting for the overall radiation behaviour. We find that both forms of the theory give these good results under conditions of rapid and changing flare, even when the horn angle is very large. In other words we find that the horn equation is valid in a domain which extends far beyond that to which it has been traditionally limited.

Let us now consider these conclusions in somewhat more detail, in order to illustrate the reasons why two representations which at first appear widely divergent, can both give close agreement with experiment. Consider first the question of resonance frequencies. We find that the traditional "plane wave" approach to horn theory gives excellent overall agreement with experiment as regards the predicted natural frequencies. There are, however, small systematic errors. For normal modes whose frequencies lie below the maximum cut-off frequency ($U^{1/2}_{\max}/c$) of the horn, the calculated frequencies are a few tenths of a percent higher than the measured frequencies, as discussed in Section 5 above. On the other hand, we find that calculations based on the assumption of spherical wave fronts within the horn underestimate these natural frequencies by a few tenths of a percent. We have already discussed this also in Section 5. In brief, one finds that the inevitable presence of s-to-p wave mode conversion leads directly to this ranking of natural frequencies (spherical $\leqq$ experimental $\leqq$ plane). In the language of the mode-conversion discussion in Section 8 of Part I, we find it necessary to add a small amount of p-wave to the strictly spherical s-wave to give rise to a slightly flattened wave front. Or, conversely, we must add a certain amount of p-wave (of opposite sign) to the plane wave to give it a certain amount of curvature. A less formal way to say this is to remark that the actual wave-front shape within the horn is neither plane nor spherical, but has an intermediate sort of curvature. The observed frequencies are then expected to lie between the limiting forms of the calculation. A point of considerable practical importance is that our results show that (the relatively easy) plane wave calculations may safely be employed for the estimation of frequencies even for horns of extremely rapid taper and sharply varying flare. That is, such calculations are trustworthy quite beyond the bounds of validity customarily attributed to plane wave theory.

It is not difficult to understand the close agreement between experiment and both forms of theory for the lower modes of the horn, since these modes have turning points well in front of the bell. As a result the standing waves hardly "visit" the region where the two theories differ appreciably. We should like to emphasize, however, that the agreement between plane and spherical forms of the theory also holds for the (heavily damped) modes lying well above the highest cut-off frequency of the horn, even though both theoretical approximations overestimate the resonance frequencies here as compared with experiment. The high frequency agreement between the two predictions may easily be understood by treating $U$(spherical) $-$ $U$(plane) $= V$ as a perturbation. We note that inside the bell, $V$ is negative and slowly varying (except at the bell end) whereas outside the bell $V$ is positive. We quote the perturbation integral (eq. (56b) of Part I) as a basis for our discussion:

$$\Delta k_n = [1/(2 k_n M_n)] \int (1/B)\, \psi_n^2\, V \,\mathrm{d}z\,. \tag{29}$$

For modes well above cut-off, $\psi_n$ is more or less sinusoidal, so that $\psi_n^2$ is made up of a constant part plus a rapidly oscillating part. The constant part gives a relatively small integrated result because of the reversal in sign of $V$ inside and outside the bell. The oscillatory part gives only a minute contribution because of cancellations arising from its rapidly alternating sign plus the effect of the reversal of $V$. Finally we see that the $(1/k_n)$ factor in front of the integral further reduces the effect of any perturbation $V$ on the predicted frequency change for the higher modes.

It is not perfectly clear why both forms of calculation overestimate the mode frequencies which lie above cut-off. In the case of the French horn bell, it may simply be a mathematical consequence of our replacement of complex eigenvalues by real ones, or a consequence of the computational difficulty of identifying the eigenvalues in a heavily damped system. In the case of the other bells where the computational results are relatively stable, the error could be the result of our having used a straight-sided cone smoothly fitted to the bell end to represent the room in which the horn is sounded. As has been remarked earlier, any discontinuity of taper or cross-section gives rise to a mass-like impedance [11]. The presence of such a discontinuity at the bell end in the experiments and its absence in the computations, would therefore be expected to give overestimated resonance frequencies for the highest modes, where the wavefunctions are reasonably large at the horn end. There is an important point to be noticed in this connection: we have seen already that for the lower modes of the horn, there is no need to devise any sort of "open end" or "flange" correction for the bell. For modes well above cut-off the small discontinuity-effect just described is only another name for an end-correction, and we have seen that it is small in any event.

The radiation behaviour of horns may also be usefully compared with theory. At frequencies well below cut-off we find that both plane- and spherical wave calculations give reasonably accurate estimates of the reflected power for reasons which have already been described in Section 5 above and Section 6 of Part I. As in the case of the resonance frequencies, the plane and spherical wave calculations of the PRC tend to bracket the experimental value (see Fig. 6 for a particularly clear example). This computational bracketing of the experimental result may be expected simply from the fact that the curvature of the real wavefronts is intermediate between limiting theoretical forms. In the neighbourhood of cut-off, we find that all of the bells except the French horn show marked discrepancy between the measured and calculated PRC. The interpretation of the discrepancy is made difficult by what appears to be interference effects between reflections arising at the pipe-to-bell junction and the waves returned by the bell flare and open end. In bells where the discontinuity is marked (so that one expects a few percent amplitude reflections at the junction) one finds a marked rise in PRC at a frequency where the phase of the bell reflection crudely matches that of the joint reflection. The French horn bell joint has on the other hand a very small discontinuity, and shows no anomalous behaviour. This is a point which deserves further study, both in the laboratory and on the computer.

In conclusion we may remark that for design purposes of musical horns, either form of horn theory is entirely adequate to calculate resonance frequencies of musical relevance. The physical insight provided by a study of both forms of theory may be put to good use in conjunction with the various perturbation techniques we have described, for the design or correction of musical horns. One of us (AHB) has already made practical use of these ideas for individual musicians, and for the commericial purposes of manufacturers.

Acknowledgements

The experimental work and the major bulk of computer calculations were made at Case Western Reserve University in 1967—1968. This was made possible by a generous stipend for one of us, Erik Jansson, from Case Western Reserve University, which we gratefully acknowledge. In our work we were greatly helped by technical suggestions and horn bells for study that were provided by Dr. Earle L. Kent of CG Conn Ltd, Elkhart Indiana, and by George McCracken at King Musical Instruments Company, Cleveland Ohio. In the earlier stages of this work we were much helped by searching conversations with our colleague Erwin Shrader, as well as by correspondence with Robert Pyle Jr. of Bolt Beranek and Newman, Boston Massachusetts, and with William Cardwell Jr., California Research Laboratories, Whittier, California.

(Received September 14th, 1973.)

References

[1] Wogram, K., Ein Beitrag zur Ermittlung der Stimmung von Blechblasinstrumenten, Dr. Thesis, Technische Universität Carolo-Wilhelmina, Braunschweig 1972.

[2] Lieber, E., Ermittlung der Naturtonlagen bei Metallblasinstrumenten. Hochfrequenztech. Elektroakust. **69** [1960], 29.

[3] Benade, A. H., On the propagation of sound waves in a cylindrical conduit. J. Acoust. Soc. Amer. **44** [1968], 616.

[4] Benade, A. H. and Murday, J. S., Measured end corrections for woodwind tone holes (Abstract). J. Acoust. Soc. Amer. **41** [1967], 1609.

[5] Benade, see ref. [3].

[6] Benade, A. H., On woodwind instrument bores. J. Acoust. Soc. Amer. **31** [1959], 137.

[7] Benade, see ref. [3].

[8] Faddeeva, V. N., Computational methods of linear algebra (translated by C. D. Benster). Dover, New York 1959.

[9] Henrici, P., Discrete variable methods in ordinary differential equations. John Wiley and Sons, New York 1962.

[10] Karal, F. C., The analogous impedance for discontinuities and constrictions of circular cross section. J. Acoust. Soc. Amer. **25** [1953], 327.

[11] Karal, see ref. [10].

# 20

Copyright © 1975 by the Acoustical Society of America

Reprinted from *J. Acoust. Soc. Am.*, **57**(6), Pt. 1, 1309–1317 (1975)

## Effective length of horns

Robert W. Pyle Jr.

*Bolt Beranek and Newman Incorporated, Cambridge, Massachusetts 02138*
(Received 30 April 1973)

Some authors writing about brass musical instruments have used the term "effective length," usually meaning the length of a cylindrical tube having the same resonance frequencies as a given horn, but possibly with different end conditions. In this paper, alternative definitions of effective length are considered, and one definition is chosen and generalized to all frequencies, not just discrete resonance frequencies. Within the framework of lossless plane-wave horn theory, a nonlinear first-order differential equation is derived that yields effective length as a function of frequency and horn contour. Effective length has been calculated for some horn contours resembling French horns and trumpets. The solutions are qualitatively consistent with the experience of instrument makers and players, and with the effective lengths of actual instruments, determined from measured resonance frequencies.

Subject Classification: 85.60; 75.40.

### INTRODUCTION

Brass wind musical instruments such as trumpets and trombones produce, for a given fingering or slide position, a series of notes whose fundamental frequencies closely approximate integer multiples of some "pedal" note. The pedal note itself is not used in all instruments. With the exception of the pedal note, the air-column resonances of the instrument with the mouthpiece closed and the bell open are essentially the same as the playing frequencies. It is important to realize, however, that resonances near harmonics of the note played have a considerable influence on the oscillation of the lip as well as on the tone color produced. It is this "privileged-tone" phenomenon[1,2] that allows the player to produce a more-or-less "in tune" pedal note when the lowest air-column resonance lies from two to seven semitones below the frequency of the pedal note.

Because the playing frequencies of a brass instrument very nearly coincide with the resonances of a doubly open cylindrical tube of the same nominal length, there has in the past been some confusion as to the boundary condition at the mouthpiece. Consideration of the regeneration mechanism at the lips[2] has demonstrated conclusively that the proper boundary condition for determining the air-column resonances is with the mouthpiece *closed.*

One can argue naively that an "ideal" brass instrument should have its air-column resonances in exact integer multiples of the lowest resonance; in practice, the lowest one to three resonances (depending on the type of instrument) are substantially lower than their "ideal" values, based on the middle- and upper-range resonances. Tones in the lowest part of the playing range make heavy use of the "privileged-tone" phenomenon, and it seems likely that an "ideal" instrument would not produce traditional tone quality in this range. It is thus questionable whether the "ideal" resonance pattern is even a desirable design criterion. Nevertheless, the degree of conformity to this "ideal" resonance pattern provides a convenient yardstick for comparing different instrument designs.

Some previous workers[3–5] have described the resonance patterns of actual instruments in terms of a frequency-dependent "effective length," the length of an equivalent cylindrical resonator whose resonances are adjusted to match those of the instrument by varying its length as a function of frequency. Depending on the choice of boundary conditions for the equivalent cylinder, two definitions of effective length are open to us. First, we can match the boundary conditions of the instrument: one end open, the other closed. This leads to

$$l=\frac{(2n-1)c}{4f_n}, \tag{1}$$

where $l$ is the effective length, $f_n$ the resonance frequency of the $n$th mode, and $c$ the speed of sound. Although $l$ as defined in Eq. 1 does have an approximate physical interpretation in terms of the turning point of the "Schrödinger" form of the horn equation,[6] it suffers from the fact that the effective length of an "ideal" instrument (where $f_n = nf_1$) is not constant but is proportional to $1-(1/2n)$. It is thus difficult to assess at a glance the degree of "nonidealness" of the effective length of some actual instrument. However, this is the definition adopted by Long.[7]

A second possible definition results if we choose to make the equivalent cylinder doubly open:

$$l=\frac{nc}{2f_n}. \tag{2}$$

This could also be construed as the length of an equivalent *conical* resonator, complete to the vertex, if one wishes to preserve the boundary conditions of the instrument. This second definition offers the advantage that the "ideal" effective length is constant. Since the whole purpose of defining effective length is to provide a ready interpretation of the air-column resonances of an instrument, this writer opts for the second definition. The confusion about equivalent resonators can be avoided by the following definition: The effective length of the $n$th mode of a brass instrument is $n$ half-wavelengths of a plane wave of the same frequency propagating in free air. This is simply an alternative description of Eq. 2.

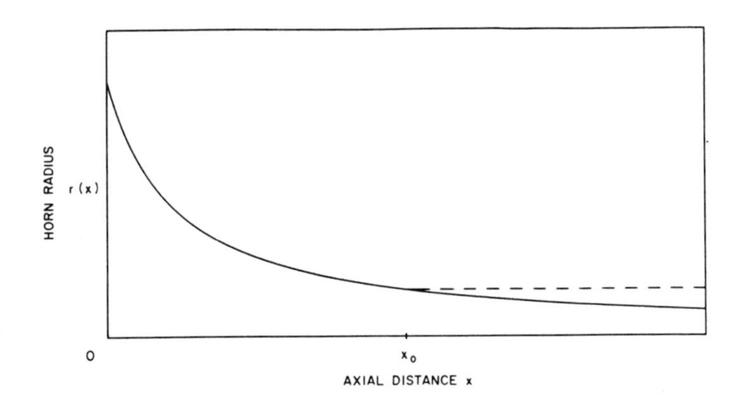


FIG. 1. Geometry for the reflection coefficient of Eq. 4. A cylinder of radius $r(x_0)$ replaces the horn for $x > x_0$. A pressure wave arrives from the right to be reflected at $x_0$.

## I. A DIFFERENTIAL EQUATION FOR EFFECTIVE LENGTH

In this section we extend the definition of effective length of all frequencies, not just discrete resonance frequencies. We also derive a differential equation yielding effective length as a function of frequency and horn contour. Our starting point is the so-called Webster horn equation,[8] actually dating from the work of Bernoulli, Euler, and Lagrange in the eighteenth century.[9] We write this as two coupled first-order differential equations, the telegrapher's transmission line equations

$$p' = ik \frac{\rho c}{S(x)} U , \tag{3a}$$

$$U' = ik \frac{S(x)}{\rho c} p , \tag{3b}$$

where $e^{-i\omega t}$ time dependence is assumed, $k = \omega/c$ = wavenumber, $p$ is the sound pressure, $U$ is the volume velocity (positive in the $+x$ direction), $S(x)$ is the cross section of the horn as a function of the distance $x$ along the horn axis, primes indicate derivatives with respect to $x$, and $\rho c$ is the characteristic impedance of air. Some musically significant second-order effects are ignored here, such as internal losses in the horn, nonuniform temperature distribution along the horn,[10] and the fact that Eqs. 3 do not accurately describe wave motion in a horn flaring as rapidly as most brass instruments do near the large end of the bell.

Now suppose we have the acoustical system shown in Fig. 1. A horn of radius $r(x)$ is cut at $x_0$ and a cylindrical pipe of radius $r(x_0)$ is joined to it there. We ask what the reflection coefficient is for a pressure wave impinging on the junction at $x_0$ from the right. It is

$$R = \frac{Z_L - Z_0}{Z_L + Z_0} , \tag{4}$$

where $Z_L$ is the acoustic impedance looking into the horn to the left at $x_0$, and $Z_0$ is the characteristic impedance of the cylindrical tube, in this case $\rho c/S(x_0)$. Now if we solve Eq. 4 for $Z_L = -p/U$ (the minus sign because $U$ is positive to the right), differentiate with respect to $x$, and eliminate derivatives of $p$ and $U$ using Eqs. 3, we get a Riccati equation for $R$ as a function of position:

$$R' = \frac{S'}{2S}(1 - R^2) + 2ikR . \tag{5}$$

One can similarly derive Riccati equations for impedance or admittance along a horn[11]; the present formulation has the advantage for numerical calculations that $R$ is a bounded function, while impedance and admittance are not.

We assume a lossless termination at $x=0$ and specialize for the moment to a cylinder ($S'=0$). Equation 5 then reduces to

$$R' = 2ikR , \tag{6}$$

whose solution is

$$R(x) = R(0)\, e^{2ikx} \tag{7a}$$

$$= e^{i[\phi(0)+2kx]} . \tag{7b}$$

Since $x$ is just the physical length of the cylindrical tube from 0 to $x$, and plane-wave propagation is nondispersive, we reason that $x$ should be exactly the *effective* length. We are then led by this simple example to a more general definition of effective length of an arbitrary horn in terms of $R(x)$:

$$R(x) = e^{2ikl(x)} . \tag{8}$$

We can now rewrite Eq. 5 with $l(x)$ as the dependent variable:

$$l' = 1 - \frac{S'}{S}\frac{\sin 2kl}{2k} . \tag{9}$$

Equation 9 can now presumably be integrated from the horn termination at $x=0$ to the other end of the horn. Note that the boundary condition at $x=0$ is now expressed as the initial value $l(0)$ with which we must start the integration. If we model the open bell end at $x=0$ as a pressure-release termination ($p=0$), then it follows from Eqs. 4 and 7b that

$$2kl(0) = \pi . \tag{10}$$

Consequently, the effective length of any brass instrument bore open at the bell will eventually increase as

$k^{-1}$ in the low-frequency limit ($k \to 0$). If $S$ is continuous, it follows from the Sturm–Liouville theory[12] that in the high-frequency limit ($k \to \infty$) $l$ can differ from the physical length of the horn at most by $O(k^{-1})$.

Let us now qualitatively consider the effect of a localized change in $S(x)$, a "dent" in our hypothetical instrument. Referring to Eq. 9, we see that the effect on $l$ will depend on the sign and magnitude of $\sin 2kl$. Dents a quarter wavelength apart (whose $kl$ differ by $\pi/2$) will have opposite effects, since the sine will have reversed phase. This is in accord with the Sturm–Liouville theory[12] and with instrument makers' experience that a change in bore at an antinode has the opposite effect from the same change at a node.

There are many horn contours for which the pressure distribution within the horn is known (i.e., solutions of Eq. 3). We can easily express the effective length in terms of the sound pressure. Let

$$y = -\frac{\rho c}{S(x)}\frac{U}{p} \tag{11}$$

be the normalized admittance looking *left* (hence the minus sign) at $x$. Then, from Eq. 4, we have

$$R(x) = \frac{1-y}{1+y}. \tag{12}$$

From Eq. 3, it follows easily that

$$y = i\frac{p'}{kp}, \tag{13}$$

and, therefore, from Eqs. 8 and 12, that

$$l(x) = -\frac{1}{k}\arctan\left(\frac{p'}{kp}\right), \tag{14}$$

provided the entire system be lossless, so that $p'/(kp)$ is real. If $L$ is the physical length of the horn, using the standard trigonometric identities we can rewrite Eq. 14 as

$$l(x) = L + \frac{1}{k}\arctan\left(\frac{p'\cos kL + kp\sin kL}{p'\sin kL - kp\cos kL}\right). \tag{15}$$

Equation 15 is preferable to Eq. 14 for numerical calculations because the arctangent in Eq. 15 normally stays within two quadrants, thus making it unnecessary to decide what branch of the arctangent to use.

## II. SOLUTIONS FOR SOME TYPICAL CONTOURS

Figure 2 shows schematically the contour of a typical brass instrument, which for purposes of analysis is divided into four parts: the mouthpiece (modeled as a Helmholtz resonator), a tapered mouthpipe, a cylindrical valve section (or slide, in the case of the trombone), and a flaring bell. (For instruments like the trumpet, whose mouthpiece has a relatively long backbore, the backbore should be considered a part of the mouthpipe rather than the mouthpiece.)

It would be helpful in understanding the influence of changes in the various parts of the instrument if the effective lengths of the various parts were additive, i.e., if we could calculate the effective length of each part independently and obtain the total effective length merely by adding the effective lengths of the individual components. Long[3] implicitly assumed that this was possible; we shall now show that this is not strictly true.

Consider the instrument shown in Fig. 2. Suppose we integrate Eq. 9 starting at the large end of the bell with the appropriate boundary condition there ($p = 0$). We integrate as far as the juncture between the valves and the mouthpipe, note the effective length $l$ accumulated to this point, and then continue the integration to the mouthpiece end of the instrument. The increment in effective length between the valves and the mouthpiece end is presumably the effective length of the mouthpipe–mouthpiece combination. What value this takes depends, however, on the value of $l$ at the valve–mouthpipe juncture, since this can be considered the initial value for an integration through mouthpipe and mouthpiece alone. This value, in turn, clearly depends on the particular bell used and on the length of the valve section. Hence, the effective length of mouthpipe and mouthpiece is not independent of the remaining parts of the instruments.

However, the instrument will be used at or near resonance (except for privileged tones). We can consider the valve section to function as a nondispersive (i.e., constant time delay) delay line joining bell and mouthpipe–mouthpiece, adjusted in length (time delay) to pro-

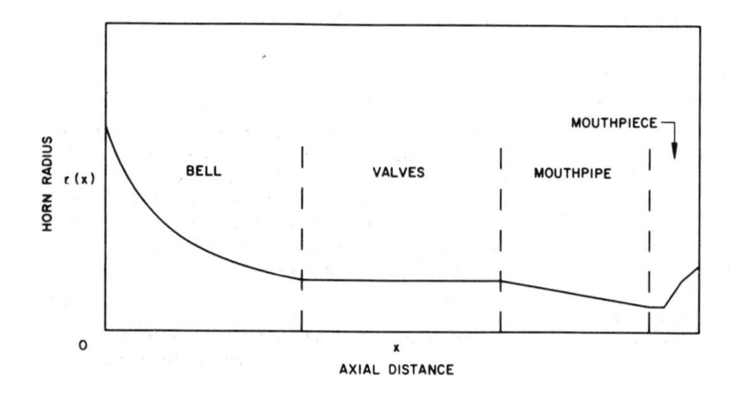


FIG. 2. Schematic representation of the contour of a typical brass instrument. A cylindrical valve section of variable length joins a flaring bell to a tapered mouthpipe and mouthpiece.

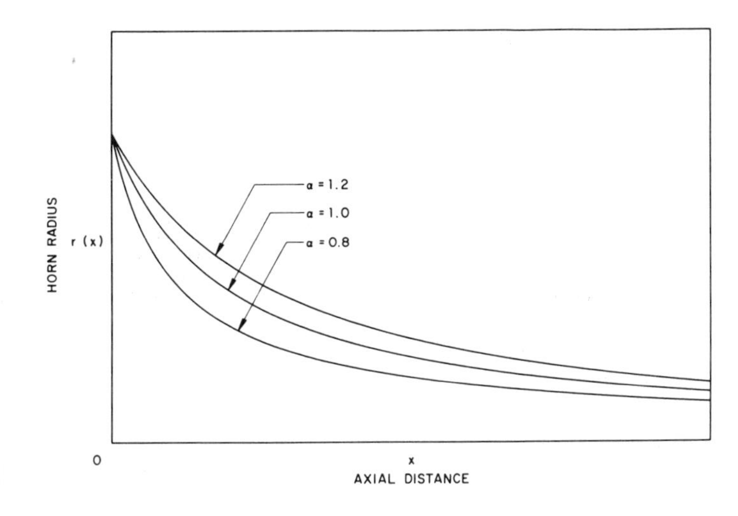


FIG. 3. "French-horn-like" bell contours. The proportions shown are for a maximum diameter of 30.5 cm, a minimum diameter of 1.20 cm, and a length $L$ of 142 cm. In Eq. 16, $D = 0$. The first 30 cm are shown.

duce resonance in combination with these elements. Let us integrate Eq. 9 from both ends of the instrument toward the middle, starting with the resonance boundary conditions $p = 0$ at the bell and $U = 0$ at the mouthpiece, and then adjust the length of the valves so that $p$ and $U$ match satisfactorily where the two solutions meet. If we use effective length primarily as a recipe for computing in this way how much length is needed in the valves for resonance, then we *can* add the independently computed effective lengths of bell and mouthpipe–mouthpiece. It is clear that, for additivity in this sense, any dispersive section must have one end terminated in a fixed boundary condition that determines the behavior of that section. Thus, mouthpipe and mouthpiece must be treated as a single unit. The sum of the effective lengths of the component parts of the instrument is not the same as the effective length of the total instrument defined by Eq. 8, but the two are equal at resonance. We can, therefore, usefully discuss the bell and the mouthpipe–mouthpiece combination separately.

### A. The bell

We can solve Eqs. 3 or 9 for a horn whose contour is of the form

$$r(x) = Cx^{-\alpha} + Dx^{\alpha+1}, \quad x > 0 , \qquad (16)$$

where $r(x)$ is the radius of the horn cross section ($S = \pi r^2$) and $C$ and $D$ are constants, arbitrary except for the requirement that $r$ not vanish. For $0.6 \le \alpha \le 1.4$ and appropriate choice of $C$ and $D$, $r(x)$ may be made to resemble strongly any of the common brass instrument bell shapes. Such horns are called "Bessel horns" because the solution of Eqs. 3 for the pressure can be expressed in terms of Bessel functions, viz,

$$p(x) = x^{1/2}[AJ_{\alpha+1/2}(kx) + BY_{\alpha+1/2}(kx)]/r(x) , \qquad (17)$$

where $A$ and $B$ are constants whose ratio is determined by a boundary condition and $J$ and $Y$ are Bessel functions of the first and second kinds, respectively. If $\alpha + 1/2$ is not an integer (as is the case here), $Y_{\alpha+1/2}$ may be replaced by $J_{-\alpha-1/2}$.

For $0.8 \le \alpha \le 1.2$ and $D = 0$, Eq. 16 is representative of many French horn bells. The value $\alpha = 0.8$ is typical of Viennese horns, 0.9 to 1.0 of traditional German instruments, and 1.1 to 1.2 of so-called "extra-large bore" horns that have increased in favor in the last two decades or so, especially in the United States. Figure 3 shows bell contours and Fig. 4 effective lengths for $\alpha = 0.8$, 1.0, and 1.2. Note that the large end of the bells is *not* at the point $x = 0$ in Eq. 16. The contours are drawn with vertical and horizontal scales proportioned as though for French horn bells of maximum diameter 30.5 cm, minimum diameter 1.20 cm, and length 142 cm. Effective length was calculated using Eq. 15. To understand the musical implications of the effective length plots, we note that the playing range is approximately $\pi/2 \le kL \le 6\pi$ and that one major division of the ordinate ($0.1\ L$) corresponds to a pitch change of about a semitone for a B-flat horn, somewhat less for an F horn. At the low-frequency end of the playing range, the horn clearly operates in the privileged-tone regime; the effective length is quite large thanks to the boundary condition, Eq. 10.

All three bells display some ripples in effective length at low frequency that die out as frequency increases. These ripples are caused by a partial reflection at the juncture of bell and valves due to the discontinuity in contour slope there. In practice, horn makers smooth out this juncture to varying degrees, reducing the magnitude of the ripples somewhat. The effective lengths plotted in Fig. 3 do not appear to be approaching $l = L$ asymptotically at high frequencies as they should. In fact, they would if the calculation were carried out to sufficiently high frequency; in the frequency range plotted they level off at a length that approximately equals the physical length of the bell if it is continued to $x = 0$ in Eq. 16. They will remain near this level until the frequency becomes high enough that the axial distance from $x = 0$ to the large end of the bell becomes

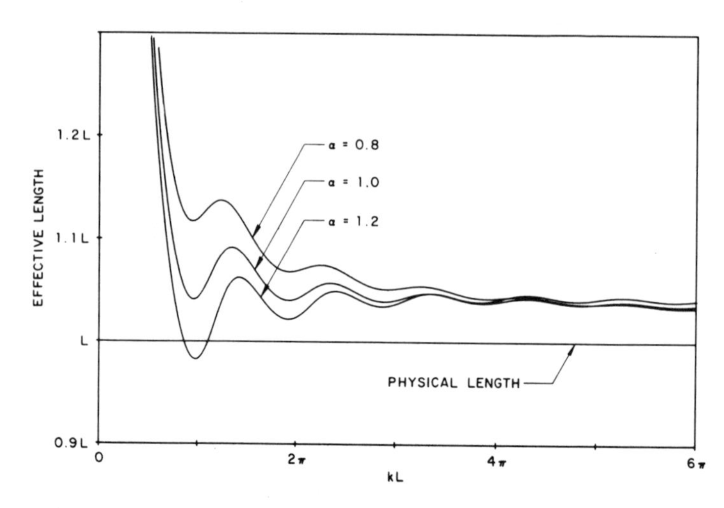


FIG. 4. Effective length as a function of dimensionless frequency $kL$ for the three "French-horn" bells of Fig. 3. $L$ is the physical length of the bell.

an appreciable fraction of a wavelength.

Of more interest is the general trend in each curve. For $\alpha=0.8$, the effective length generally continues to decrease throughout the playing range, whereas at the other extreme, $\alpha=1.2$, it increases. It would appear, then, that there is a general tendency as $\alpha$ increases for the instrument to run progressively flatter with increasing frequency. This is borne out in practice. Many horns with large-throated bells run slightly flat as the player ascends the scale. The player can offset this tendency to some extent by a judicious choice of mouthpiece; there are, in fact, consistent differences in the mouthpieces commonly used with the three different styles of horn. This will receive further attention in the discussion of mouthpieces below.

If in Eq. 16 we choose $\alpha=0.6$ and pick the ratio of $C$ and $D$ to make the slope of the contour vanish at the small end of the bell, we have quite a reasonable-looking B-flat or C trumpet bell, whose contour and effective length are shown in Figs. 5 and 6. The proportions of the contour are those of a trumpet bell of maximum diameter 12 cm, minimum diameter 1.17 cm, and length 66 cm. The trumpet's playing range in Fig. 6 is approximately $3\pi/4 \leq kL \leq 4\pi$. The ripples in effective length at low frequencies have been essentially removed by removing the discontinuity in contour slope at the bell–valve juncture. Due to the small value of $\alpha$, the effective length changes significantly through the playing range. For a 66-cm-long bell, the effective length changes by some 20 cm over the playing range, a large fractional change that must be compensated for by the action of the mouthpipe–mouthpiece combination.

### B. The mouthpiece and mouthpipe

First let us consider the mouthpiece alone, as though it were joined directly to the cylindrical valve section without any intermediate tapered mouthpipe. The mouthpiece is modeled as a Helmholtz resonator and hence is characterized by two parameters; these are here taken as two lengths defined through

$$L_0 S_0 = \text{volume of mouthpiece cup,} \tag{18}$$

where $S_0$ is the cross-sectional area of the valve tubing, and a "resonant length" $L_1$ defined by

$$kL_1 = \frac{\pi}{2} \tag{19}$$

at the mouthpiece natural frequency. The length $L_0$ is thus the length of valve tubing equal in volume to the mouthpiece cup, and is inversely proportional to the characteristic impedance of the resonator. The length $L_1$ equals a quarter-wavelength at the natural frequency of the resonator, and is thus the length of cylindrical tubing whose lowest resonance (with one end closed) equals the mouthpiece resonance.

The effective length of the mouthpiece is readily cal-

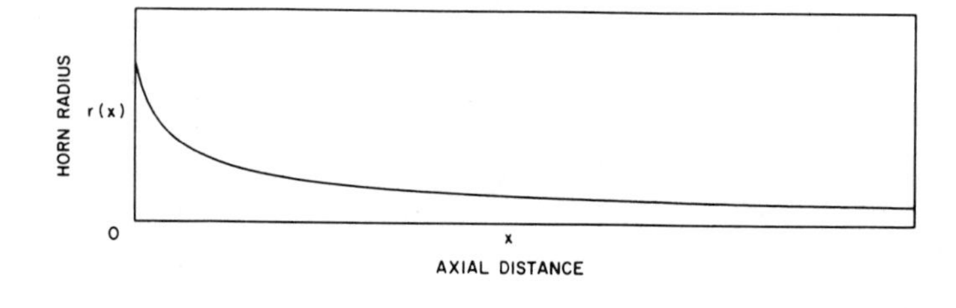


FIG. 5. A "trumpet-like" bell contour. The proportions shown are for a maximum diameter of 12 cm, a minimum diameter of 1.17 cm, and a length $L$ of 66 cm. In Eq. 16, the exponent $\alpha$ $=0.6$ and $C$ and $D$ are chosen to make the contour slope vanish at the small end. The first 30 cm are shown.

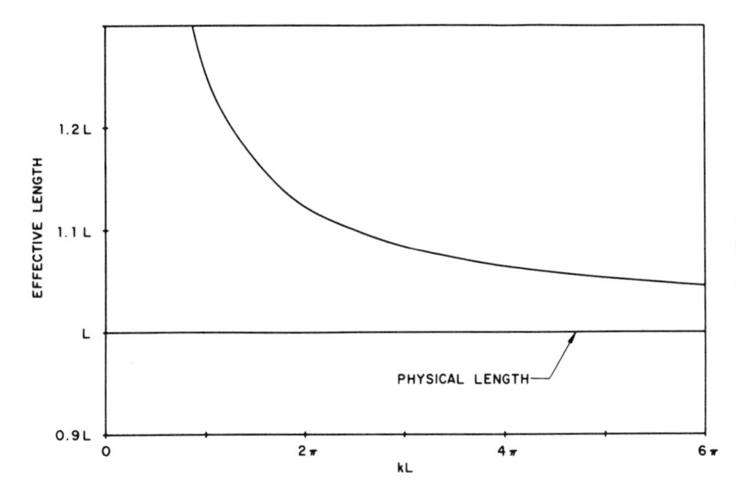


FIG. 6. Effective length as a function of dimensionless frequency $kL$ for the "trumpet" bell of Fig. 5. $L$ is the physical length of the bell.

culated using Eqs. 8 and 12:

$$l=(1/k)\arctan\{kL_0/[1-(2kL_1/\pi)^2]\} . \quad (20)$$

At low frequencies, $l$ approaches $L_0$; at the resonance, $l=L_1$. If the frequency is normalized to the resonance frequency, the curve of $l$ versus frequency depends only on the ratio $L_0/L_1$.

Figure 7 displays Eq. 20 for several values of $L_0/L_1$. For typical French horn mouthpieces, $L_0/L_1\approx 0.2$; for trumpet mouthpieces the value is smaller. French horn and trumpet mouthpieces do not differ markedly in $L_1$. The important difference is that the horn's playing range rarely extends above the mouthpiece resonance $kL_1=\pi/2$, while the trumpet is expected to play at least half an octave above the resonance. Horn players who choose "extra-large bore" instruments, perhaps similar to the $\alpha=1.2$ bell of Figs. 3 and 4, usually choose a mouthpiece with a "normal" cup but a large bore. The large bore shortens $L_1$ (raises the resonance frequency) and thus also increases the ratio $L_0/L_1$. Both factors mean the player is operating on a flatter portion of the curve of mouthpiece effective length, thereby offsetting to some extent the tendency of the larger bell to go flat at the top of the playing range.

The trumpet, by placing the mouthpiece resonance within the playing range, utilizes the entire variation in effective length of the mouthpiece. If we take $L_0=1$ cm and $L_1=10$ cm, this variation is about 13 cm, a large fraction of the variation in effective length of the hypothetical bell of Figs. 5 and 6. Unfortunately, the change in $l$ with frequency is concentrated near the resonance and not distributed over the playing range, so the mouthpiece alone will not compensate very well for the characteristics of the bell.

Next we add a tapered mouthpipe to the mouthpiece and examine the effective length of the combination. Using the principle of duality[13] we can use the Bessel bell analysis to solve for the effective length of a "Bessel mouthpipe" whose shape is given by

$$r(x)=(Cx^{-\alpha}+Dx^{\alpha+1})^{-1} . \quad (21)$$

Note that $x=0$ is now outside the *mouthpiece* end of the instrument and $x$ increases toward the valves (toward the left in Fig. 2). The volume velocity in such a mouthpipe is of the form

$$U(x)=r(x)\,x^{1/2}[AJ_{\alpha+1/2}(kx)+BY_{\alpha+1/2}(kx)] , \quad (22)$$

where the ratio $A/B$ must be chosen to satisfy a boundary condition, in this case the resonant impedance presented by the mouthpiece at the smaller end of the mouthpipe. Straightforward but tedious algebraic manipulations allow evaluation of $l$ through Eq. 15. Some results are presented in Figs. 8 and 9 for a "trumpet-like" choice of parameters.

The mouthpipe shapes shown in Fig. 8 are not based as closely on real instruments as the bells dealt with

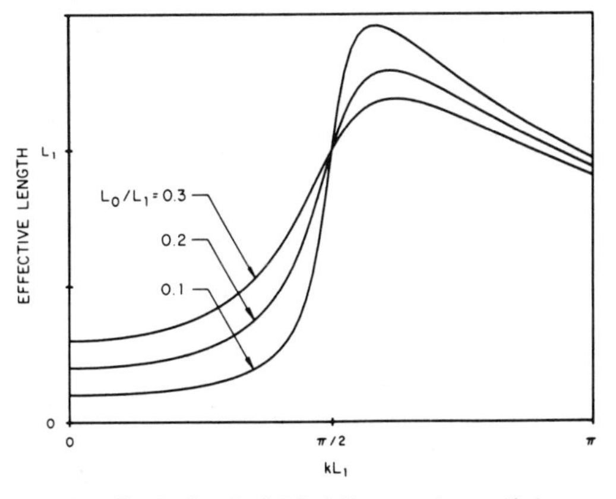


FIG. 7. Effective length of Helmholtz resonator mouthpieces as a function of dimensionless frequency $kL_1$. $L_0$ and $L_1$ are defined in the text.

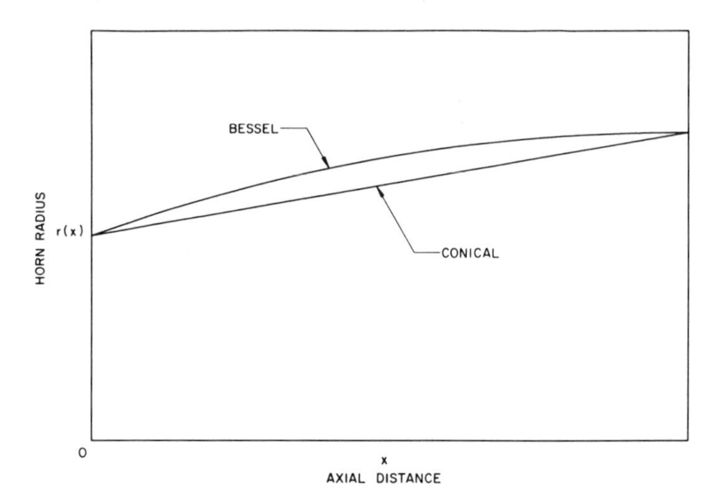


FIG. 8. Two mouthpipe contours. The Bessel mouthpipe is obtained from Eq. 21 with $\alpha = 0.9$ and $C$ and $D$ are chosen to make the contour slope vanish at the large end. The vertical scale is greatly exaggerated relative to the horizontal for clarity. For the "trumpet" calculations, the maximum diameter was taken to be 1.17 cm and the length 30 cm.

above. In fact the simple cone ($D=0$, $\alpha=1$ in Eq. 21) would never be used on a real instrument. It provides some idea of the variability introduced by what the player would term a radical change of mouthpipe. The second mouthpipe has $\alpha=0.9$ and $C$ and $D$ chosen to make the contour slope continuous at the mouthpipe–valve juncture. This sort of shape, which instrument makers would call "paraboloidal," is more representative of real instruments. Figure 9 shows the effective lengths of the two mouthpipes with mouthpieces; the length of each mouthpipe is taken to be 30 cm, and the minimum diameter is two-thirds of the maximum. The same mouthpiece parameters were used with each mouthpipe: $L_0=1$ cm and $L_1=10$ cm. This places the mouthpiece resonance at $kL=3\pi/2$ and the top of the normal trumpet playing range somewhere between $2\pi$ and $5\pi/2$. The mouthpipe serves to amplify and to "spread out" the change in $l$ of the mouthpiece alone. With the Bessel mouthpipe, the effective length changes by some 17 cm over the playing range for the parameter values chosen. The shape is not quite the desired mirror image of Fig. 6, but it is much closer than for the mouthpiece alone. The conical mouthpipe displays some "ripples," as might be expected, due to the discontinuity in contour slope at its large end.

Above the mouthpiece resonance, the two curves of Fig. 9 pass a maximum and coalesce, approaching the sum of the physical length of the mouthpipe and the effective length of the mouthpiece. Since the effective length of the bell (Fig. 6) continues to decrease in this range, our hypothetical trumpet will presumably go sharp at the top of the playing range, as many real trumpets do.

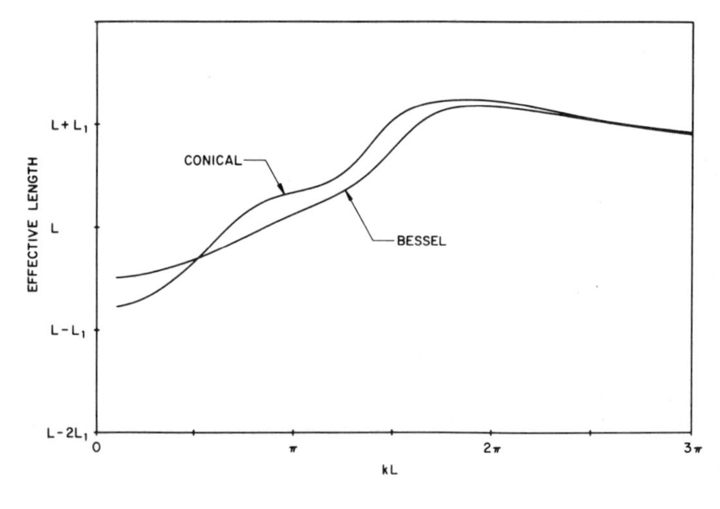


FIG. 9. Effective length of the two mouthpipes of Fig. 8 combined with a mouthpiece for which $L_0=1$ cm and $L_1=10$ cm. The frequency is normalized to the 30-cm length $L$ of the mouthpipes. The mouthpiece resonance is thus at $kL=3\pi/2$.

## III. EXPERIMENTAL RESULTS

Figure 10 shows the effective lengths of two French horns determined experimentally from measured resonance frequencies by using Eq. 2 (a sound speed of 345 m/sec was assumed). Both horns are of good quality and have been used professionally. Horn A has a large-throated bell, intermediate between $\alpha = 1$ and $\alpha = 1.2$ in Fig. 3. Horn B is termed "medium-bore" by its maker and lies between the $\alpha = 0.8$ and $\alpha = 1$ bells of Fig. 3. Horn A was tuned slightly flatter than horn B, accounting for the overall greater effective length. The resonance frequencies were measured with the bell open and the mouthpiece closed by a flat plate flush with the mouthpiece rim. In normal playing, the lips protrude into the mouthpiece cup, somewhat reducing the cup volume (in terms of our mouthpiece parameters, $L_0$ would be reduced and the ratio $L_0/L_1$ reduced by a somewhat lesser amount, proportionately). The bell is normally partially closed by the player's right hand. Without the hand in the bell, radiation damping became so severe above about 650 Hz that it was impossible to measure resonance frequencies in this experiment, although the normal playing range extends to about 700 Hz.

Note that from about 120 to 500 Hz the effective length of horn A increases while that of horn B remains reasonably constant, except for some ups and downs reminiscent of the ripples in Fig. 4. The progressive flattening of horn A with increasing frequency is readily apparent to the player. The difference between horns A and B is consistent with the results displayed in Fig. 4. Above 500 Hz, the mouthpiece resonance causes both horns to increase in effective length. Reducing the mouthpiece cup volume would tend to make the effective length level in this region. The hand in the bell lowers all resonance frequencies, the lower ones proportionately more than the higher. Thus the effects of lip and hand under playing conditions would combine to make the effective length more nearly constant above 120 Hz than the experimental measurements shown here indicate.

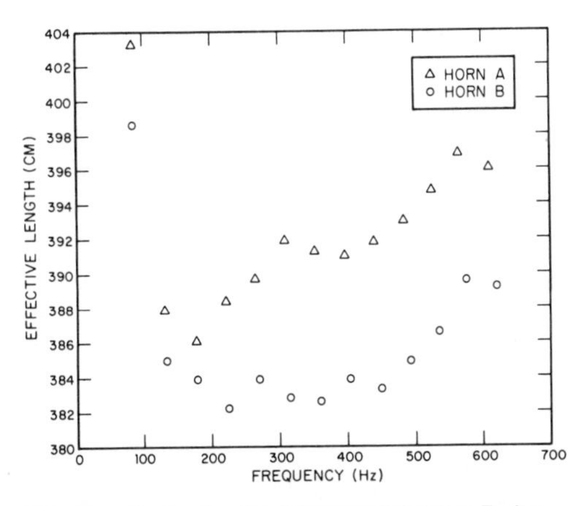


FIG. 10. Effective lengths of two French horns in $F$, determined from measured resonance frequencies through Eq. 2. Horn A is "large-bore" and horn B is "medium-bore" by current standards.

## IV. SUMMARY AND CONCLUSIONS

The effective length $l$ has been defined as the solution of a nonlinear first-order differential equation (Eq. 9) derived from plane-wave lossless horn theory and having frequency and horn shape as parameters. This equation can be readily integrated numerically for any continuous horn contour using any of the standard numerical methods. Alternatively, if the behavior of the horn is already known, either in terms of solutions for sound pressure or input impedance or admittance, other formulas (Eqs. 11–15) may be used to compute $l$ directly from these known solutions. For an instrument of conventional configuration (Fig. 2), the present formulation allows separate consideration of the effects of the bell and the mouthpipe–mouthpiece combination. Examples computed for "trumpet-like" and "French-horn-like" choices of parameters differ considerably in the way in which the various components contribute to the correct placement of resonance frequencies. In the French horn, the bulk of the tuning is the responsibility of the bell; the mouthpipe and mouthpiece make small (but important) corrections for the idiosyncrasies of the bell. The relatively small influence of the mouthpipe and mouthpiece is due to the placement of the mouthpiece resonance frequency at or above the top of the playing range. In the trumpet, on the other hand, the characteristic bell shape has an effective length that varies markedly over the playing range of the instrument. This is offset by placing the mouthpiece resonance within the playing range, using a more heavily choked, smaller-cupped mouthpiece than the French horn, and "adjusting" the effective length of the mouthpiece with a suitably tapered mouthpipe. It is consistent with instrument makers' experience that mouthpipe and mouthpiece design for the trumpet is more "finicky" than for the French horn. Experimental results presented for two French horns display qualitative differences similar to those suggested by the theoretical examples.

Effective length, as defined here, appears to offer the instrument designer a useful tool for assessing the effects of a bore change upon an existing instrument. In the past, some designers have occasionally attempted to correct "just one note" by a change of bore. Because effective length is now defined as a continuous function of frequency rather than at discrete resonance frequencies only, the effects of such a change upon other notes would be more readily apparent to the designer through a calculation of effective length. Due to idealizations in the analysis (e.g., lossless horn and termination, plane-wave propagation) and important effects not quantitatively considered (e.g., "privileged-tone" interaction of several air-column resonances), it is clear that consideration of effective length alone is insufficient for the design of a new instrument.

## APPENDIX A: NOTES ON THE COMPUTATIONS

The theoretical examples worked out require the evaluation of Bessel functions of the first kind $J_\nu(z)$, for arbitrary (real) order $\nu$. For $z < 20$, these were computed using an expansion in terms of integer-order Bessel functions:

$$\Gamma(\nu)\, J_\nu(z) = \sum_{n=0}^{\infty} (z/2)^{\nu+n} J_n(z)/[(\nu+n)n!]\ . \qquad \text{(A1)}$$

This is a specialization of a more general formula given by Erdélyi.[A1] For $z > 20$, Hankel's asymptotic formula was used.[A2] Calculations were carried out on a Digital Equipment PDP-10 computer (floating point, 27-bit mantissa). The $J_n$ required by Eq. A1 were computed using recurrence in the direction of decreasing order.[A3] Comparison of the values computed using Eq. A1 with tabulated values (integer or half-integer $\nu$) showed best results at small $z$, deteriorating to about four significant figures at $z = 20$. Hankel's asymptotic formula is at its best for large $z$, and deteriorates to about four significant figures, as implemented in our program, at $z = 20$. Hence, the crossover was put at $z = 20$.


[1] H. P. M. Bouasse, *Instruments â Vent* (Delagrave, Paris, 1929).

[2] A. H. Benade, *Horns, Strings, and Harmony* (Doubleday-Anchor, New York, 1960).

[3] T. H. Long, "The Performance of Cup Mouthpiece Instruments," J. Acoust. Soc. Am. **19**, 892–901 (1947).

[4] E. L. Kent, "System for Measuring the Effective Length of Wind Instruments or Portions of Instruments," J. Acoust. Soc. Am. **35**, 1902(A) (1963).

[5] E. L. Kent, "Comparison of a Mathematically Derived Effective Length of a Cornet Bell with Experimental Data," J. Acoust. Soc. Am. **35**, 1902(A) (1963).

[6] A. H. Benade, "Formulation of the Brass-Instrument Bore Problem," J. Acoust. Soc. Am. **39**, 1220(A) (1966).

[7] Long's paper suffers from an unusual definition of mode number and some ambiguity about experimental boundary conditions. Some clarification resulted from ensuing letters; see R. W. Young, J. Acoust. Soc. Am. **20**, 345–346 (1948) and T. H. Long, J. Acoust. Soc. Am. **20**, 875–876 (1948).

[8] A. G. Webster, "Acoustical Impedance and the Theory of Horns and the Phonograph," Proc. Natl. Acad. Sci. (U.S.) **5**, 275–282 (1919).

[9] E. Eisner, "Complete Solutions of the 'Webster' Horn Equation," J. Acoust. Soc. Am. **41**, 1126–1146 (1967).

[10] A. H. Benade, "Thermal Perturbations in Woodwind Bores," J. Acoust. Soc. Am. **35**, 1901(A) (1963).

[11] O. K. Mawardi, "Generalized Solutions of Webster's Horn Theory," J. Acoust. Soc. Am. **21**, 323–330 (1949).

[12] R. Courant and D. Hilbert, *Methods of Mathematical Physics* (Interscience, New York, 1953), Vol. I, Chap. VI.

[13] R. W. Pyle Jr., "Duality Principle for Horns," J. Acoust. Soc. Am. **37**, 1178(A) (1965).

[A1] A. Erdélyi, Ed., *Higher Transcendental Functions* (McGraw-Hill, New York, 1953), Vol. II, see Eq. 7.15 (10).

[A2] M. Abramowitz and I. A. Stegun, Eds., *Handbook of Mathematical Functions* (Natl. Bur. Stand. Washington, 1964); see Eq. 9.2.5.

[A3] See Ref. A2, Sec. 9.12.

Part III

# ACOUSTICS OF WOODWINDS

# Editor's Comments on Papers 21 Through 28



Paper 21 presents a brief review of some musical instrument history and a general overview of the woodwinds. Though written for general readership it lays some groundwork for the more technical papers that follow it. Except for this paper, the papers in this group on reed instruments are in chronological order.

The commonly used terminology in musical instruments may seem a bit strange to some. The cup-mouthpiece instruments usually are grouped as brass instruments even though they may not always be made of brass. The reed instruments are grouped as woodwinds though some may not be made of wood. Further, there is no visable reed on a flute or piccolo; but they are in the reed instrument group. As Benade explains, in flutes, the function of the reed is served by a thin jet of air blown across the embouchure hole of the instrument.

Papers 22 and 23 are by Benade also. Paper 22 deals primarily with a study of the bore shape in woodwinds apart from the reed system as an exciter. Paper 23 is a companion paper dealing primarily with the size and location of finger holes. The erratum for paper 22 was provided by Benade February 1963. The minor revisions, Appendix, and Table of Open-Hole Length Correction in paper 23 were provided by Benade July 1966, all through private communication.

Paper 24 examines the vibrating reed as the sound energizer in the clarinet and outlines a theory of the interaction of the reed and the air column in the case where the amplitude of vibration is very small and the system operates linearly. Backus indicates the importance of the damping of the reed, as had Helmholtz and Bouasse. Morse, Das, and Ghosh considered the reed undamped. Backus includes many more numerical data to support his theory than do the papers by earlier workers and he retains a physical reality which was missing in some earlier theories.

Walter E. Worman has carried the study further in his Ph.D. Thesis, *Self-Sustained Nonlinear Oscillations of Medium Amplitude in Clarinet-Like Systems,* Department of Physics, Case Western Reserve University, January 27, 1971. His 154-page thesis is an unfolding and intensification of the theory of nonlinear musical wind instrument oscillations outlined by Benade and Gans in Paper 13. Space does not permit reprinting Worman's paper here but it is recommended as useful to a reader interested in going into the nonlinear behavior in clarinet-like systems.

John Backus [B.A. (1932), Reed College; M.A. (physics, 1936) and Ph.D. (physics, 1940) University of California, Berkeley; and Master of Music (with major in orchestral conducting, 1959), University of Southern California] served Lawrence Radiation Laboratory 1940–1945 and joined the University of Southern California in 1945 where he is Professor of Physics.

Backus became a member of the Technical Committee on Musical Acoustics, Acoustical Society of America, in 1961 and served as its chairman 1964–1967. He was Chairman, Los Angeles Chapter of the Acoustical Society of America, 1963–1964.

He is a bassoonist and is the author of numerous papers on the acoustics of wind instruments. He is also the author of *The Acoustical Foundations of Music,* New York: W. W. Norton, 1969.

Paper 25 discusses the sound energizer in the flute and the organ flue pipe in a classic manner and presents an elegant measuring technique. Coltman, along with the Cremer and Ising paper cited by Coltman, offers the first explanation of how the flute-type sound producer really works. They point out that the air reed is basically a correct oversimplification and that the edge-tone explanation is basically an incorrect oversimplification.

Paper 26 supplements Paper 25 and corrects some assumptions made earlier by Benade and French. Helpful quantitative evaluations and technique are given.

A biographical sketch about Coltman was given on page 22.

Papers 27 and 28 come to grips quantitatively with the nonlinear work done qualitatively by Benade and Worman, the work reported by Coltman in Paper 25, and by Cremer and Ising (Cited by Coltman).

Neville H. Fletcher (1930–      ) was born in Armidale, Australia. He received his B.Sc. with first class honors in mathematics and physics and the University Medal in Physics, at the University of Sidney in 1951; a M.A. (1953) and Ph.D. (1955), both in solid-state physics, at Harvard; and a D.Sc. (1973) at Sydney University.

Fletcher worked on semiconductors and cloud physics with the CSIRO Radiophysics Laboratory in Sidney, 1956–1960. In 1960, he joined the University of New England in Armidale, Australia, as Senior Lecturer in Physics and was appointed Professor of Physics in 1963. He has served as Dean of the Faculty of Science (1963–1965), Chairman of the Professional Board (1970–1972), and Pro Vice-Chancellor (1968–1972) in that University. He has also served as a Visiting Lecturer at Bristol University (1966) and as JSPS Visiting Professor at Hokkaido University (1974).

Most of his research has been in the field of solid-state physics (he holds patents on early high-power transistor designs) and on the physics of ice and water. He is the author of *Chemical Physics of Ice,* New York: Cambridge University Press, 1970; *Physics of Rain Clouds,* New York: Cambridge University Press, 1962; and more than 60 scientific papers.

His interest in musical acoustics is associated in part with his activities as a flute player.

# 21

*Copyright © 1960 by Scientific American, Inc. All rights reserved.*

Reprinted with permission from *Sci. Am.*, **203**(4), 145–154 (Oct. 1960)

# The Physics of Wood Winds

by Arthur H. Benade

[*Editor's Note:* Illustrations were rendered in color in original publication.]

There are, of course, hundreds of directions in which the mind of a physicist can stray while he sits in a concert hall, but one in particular unites his esthetic and scientific interests in a most fruitful manner. He can, if he likes, trace the history of much of his discipline in terms of the study of music and the instruments that make it. As far back as Pythagoras it was recognized that the most prominent pitch intervals are obtained by shortening a harp string so that some simple fraction (1/2, 1/3 and so on) of its length is left free to vibrate. Study of the vibration of strings by René Descartes' collaborator Marin Mersenne laid a foundation for the study of partial differential equations and their applications, a development whose roots are found in the work of such great mathematical physicists as Daniel Bernoulli and Jean le Rond d'Alembert in the 18th century. In the 19th century Hermann von Helmholtz devoted a large fraction of his enormous talents to the study of vibrating systems, as did Lord Rayleigh (who died in the 20th century, leaving his *Theory of Sound*, which is still a classic).

The rise of quantum mechanics has made the understanding of the underlying classical wave-theory even more important to physicists than it was in the days of Rayleigh. As a result every student of physics, whether he is interested in music or not, is faced daily with classroom problems that are variations on a theme born originally of music.

Since the mid-1920's, however, the engrossing new questions of quantum physics have diverted the energy of both theoreticians and experimenters from the more traditional lines of study, and so brought active musical research largely to an end. Still, the stage is set for a revival of musical physics. The techniques of measurement and calculation that have developed during the last 40 years in other areas of physics may now make it possible to solve problems in music that have withstood the best efforts of the past.

Some of the most stubborn questions are posed by the search for an orderly connection between the physical properties of instruments and the musical sounds that issue from them. The instruments are all of ancient descent, antedating Pythagoras and others who first felt the strong pull of music on the scientific as well as on the artistic imagination. The various winds and strings assumed their modern forms by a process akin to biological evolution. Trial and error, rule of thumb and traditions handed down from generation to generation of instrument makers account for the characteristic quality of the sound that each one generates, as well as for their peculiarly individual appearance and design. Yet much of the anatomy, and therefore of the performance, of an instrument is susceptible to analysis. One is led to ask if it is possible to create, with the help of theoretical considerations, new ways of constructing instruments whose performance is the same as those that have grown from empirical invention. Can we clarify the problems facing players and builders of these instruments in a way that suggests answers to hitherto unsolved problems? Can we invent entirely new musically useful instruments?

My own interest in these questions began with the playing of wood winds—the tubular horns that bristle with levers, buttons and rings, and are played by the musicians who sit in the middle background of the symphony orchestra. Most familiar are the clarinet, the oboe, the bassoon, the saxophone, the English horn and the flutes (including the recorder, the fife and the piccolo). But the family also includes the bagpipe and such less well-known instruments as the arghool and the chalumeau (relatives of the clarinet), the aulos, or Greek flute, and the shawm (a relative of the oboe).

All wood winds may be disassembled mentally into three essential parts: the reed, the bore and the side holes. Air blown into the instrument through the reed sets up vibrations in the column of air within the bore, and this vibrating air column produces the sound of the instrument. The frequency at which the air vibrates is determined chiefly by the dimensions of the bore. These dimensions are modified in turn by the side holes in both their open and closed positions, as will be seen.

The reed system acts as a valve. It replenishes the vibrational energy of the air in the bore by converting a steady flow of compressed air from the player's lungs into a series of puffs at the frequency dictated by the bore. This valving of the air supply is accomplished differently in the flutes than in the other wood winds, but the device that does it may nevertheless be called a reed. The reed valves of all wood winds except the flutes are pressure-operated. They consist either of a single blade of cane fitted to a mouthpiece (as on the clarinet and saxophone) or a double blade of cane (oboe and bassoon). Vibration of the reed opens or shuts the thin slit (between the reed and the mouthpiece or between the two reeds) through which

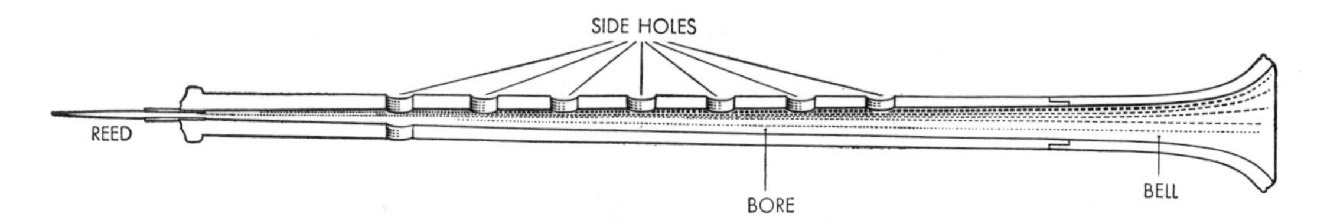


**MAIN PARTS** of a wood wind are the reed, the bore and the side holes. Oboe shown in this schematic cross section has fewer holes than actual instrument. Oboes, English horns and clarinets are equipped with bells; flutes, saxophones and bassoons are not.

the air is blown into the bore. The frequency of vibration is set by the cyclic changes in the pressure of the vibrating air in the bore. The mass and stiffness of the cane give the bore almost complete domination over the reed in determining the pitch. This domination of the reed by the bore is one of the distinguishing characteristics of wood winds. In contrast, the tube, or bore, of a brass instrument, such as the trumpet or trombone, strongly influences the "reed" (the vibrating lips of the player) but does not dominate it; the same is true of the relation between the pipes and reeds used in pipe organs.

In flutes the function of the reed is served by a thin jet, or "reed," of air blown across the mouth hole in the side of the instrument. The vibrations of an air-jet reed are controlled by cyclic changes not in the pressure but in the velocity of the air at the upper end of the bore. Rushing in and out of the bore at right angles to the reed, the vibrating air column drives the reed-jet upward and downward at the frequency fixed by the bore and side holes [*see illustration on pages 148 and 149*].

Because cane reeds are pressure-oper-

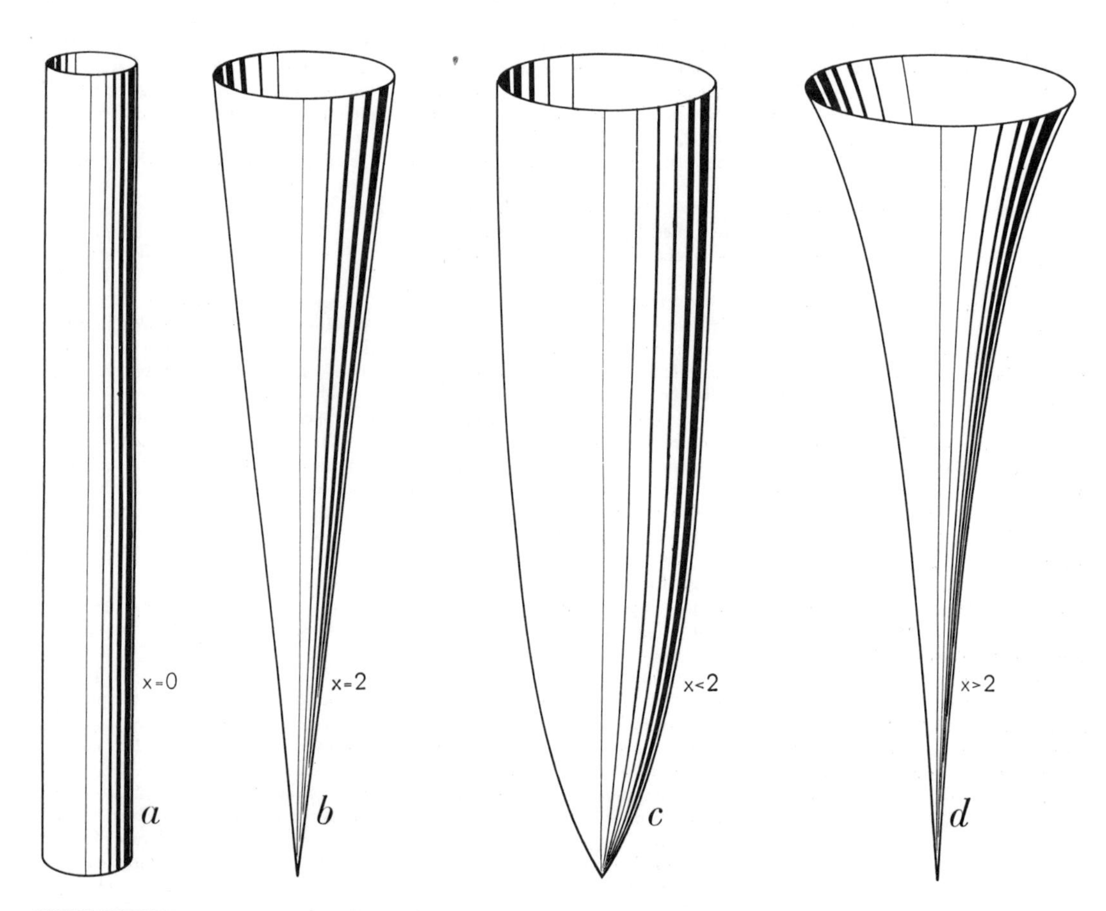


**BESSEL HORNS** increase in cross-sectional area according to some exponent ($x$) of the distance from the end of the horn. Bores of all practical wood winds are either cylindrical Bessel horns ($a$) or conical Bessel horns ($b$). Horns $c$ and $d$ are musically useless.

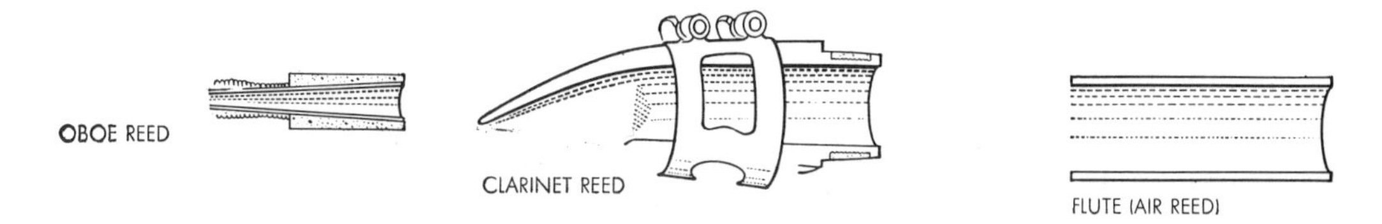


**REEDS** (*color*) **act as valves that control flow of air into a wood wind. Cane reeds of oboe and clarinet are opened and shut by changes in pressure of the vibrating air in the bore; air-jet "reed" of flute is controlled by changes in velocity of the air in the bore.**

ated, they will function only when the vibrations of the air column in the bore are such as to produce maximum variation in pressure at the mouthpiece end of the bore. The air-jet reed of the flute correspondingly requires vibrations that produce a maximum variation in velocity at the same end of the bore. Since the end of the bore away from the player's mouth is essentially open to the atmosphere, the variation in air pressure at that end can only be very small, and, with the air free to flow in and out, the variations in velocity will consequently be large. In short, the operation of a cane reed calls for those vibrations in the air column that produce maximum variation of pressure at the reed end of the bore, and essentially zero fluctuations at the lower end, while an air-jet reed will sustain only those vibrations that yield a maximum fluctuation in velocity at both ends. It is interesting that this specification of the "end conditions" for a bore is in precisely the same form as that which mathematicians use in solving problems of vibrating systems involving no reed at all. Theory and experiment agree that only a certain discrete set of vibrational frequen-

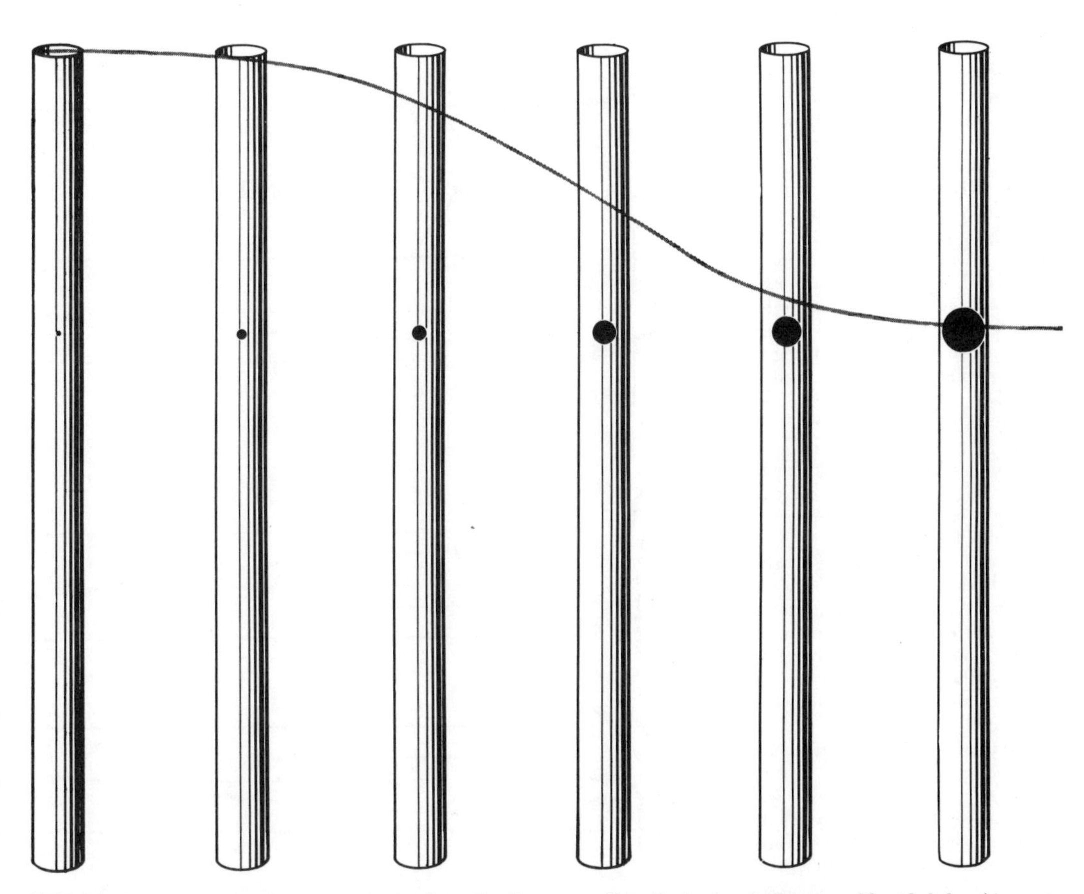

**SIDE HOLES decrease the effective length of a bore. In this schematic diagram full-length bore is shown in black; its corresponding effective length when pierced by side holes of increasing size is shown in color. Holes permit musician to play a scale.**

cies is possible for the air within a bore when it moves in a way that meets these conditions. These types of vibration (which are mathematically similar to the quantized states of motion of an electron in an atom) are called the "normal" or "natural" modes of vibration of the air in the bore.

The frequency and wavelength of these natural modes of vibration depend chiefly on the length and shape of the bore. For example, a cylindrical bore open at one end and blown at the other with a velocity-controlled air-jet reed (like that of a flute), or a conical bore blown at the small end with a pressure-controlled cane reed (as in the oboe), has a lowest, or fundamental, frequency of vibration whose sound has a wavelength twice the length of the bore; it can also vibrate in higher modes producing a sequence of notes that is often referred to as the harmonic series, with wavelengths that are integral fractions (1/2, 1/3, 1/4, 1/5 and so on) of the fundamental. A cylindrical bore blown by a pressure-controlled reed at one end vibrates in its lowest mode to produce a fundamental note whose wavelength is four times the length of the bore. The higher-frequency modes of vibration are those whose sound wavelengths are odd-numbered fractions (1/3, 1/5, 1/7 and so on) of the fundamental. Wood winds make extensive use of only the lowest three or four of their natural modes; the lowest mode corresponds to the so-called low register of the instrument, the second mode to the middle register, while the upper register uses one or another of the higher modes.

When a bugler plays reveille, he uses his lips as a pressure-controlled reed to excite one or another of the natural modes of vibration of a flaring brass pipe. It is the task of the bugle manufacturer to shape the instrument so that the frequencies of its natural modes are those desired for playing music. As everyone knows, the repertory of the bugle is rather limited: even a skilled bugler can sound only five or six widely spaced notes.

In contrast, wood winds can play a chromatic scale of more than 30 notes, because their makers have found ways to fill the gaps in pitch between the natural frequencies of the bore. This is accomplished by drilling a row of holes in the side of the bore. As intuition suggests, a hole just a few thousandths of an inch in diameter will cause little change in the pitch of a note played on

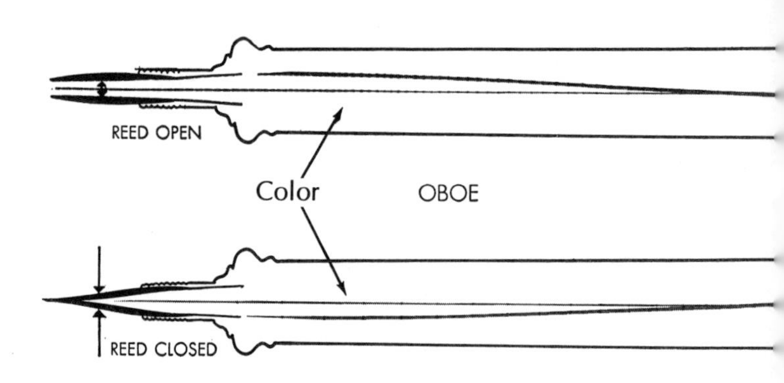


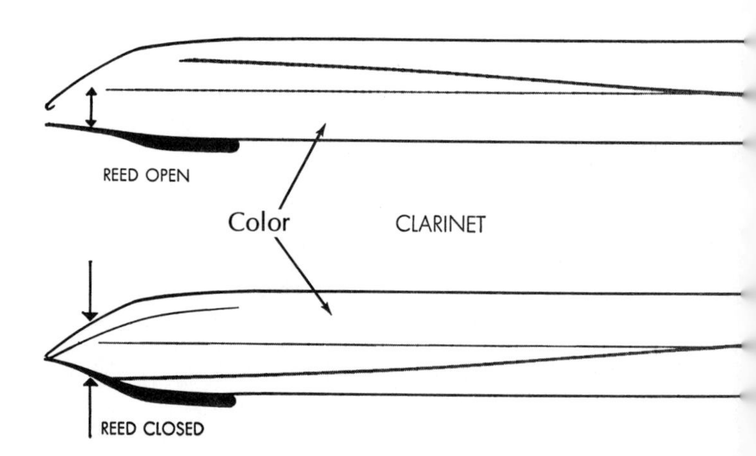


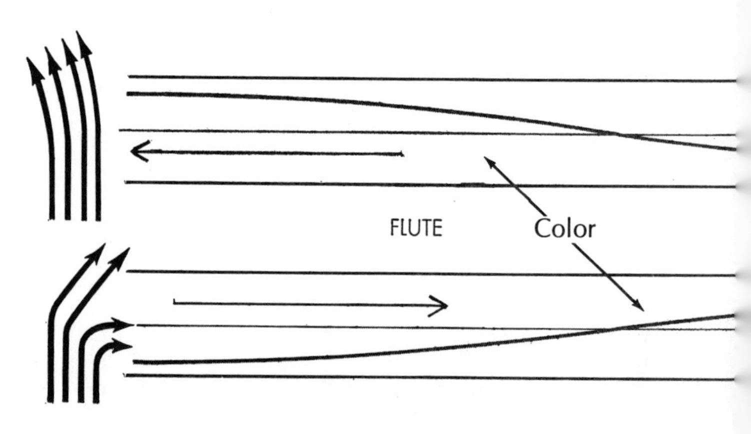


**BORE DOMINATES REED** in all wood winds. Pressure-operated reeds like those of oboe (*top*) and clarinet (*middle*) function only at frequencies at which bore produces maximum variation in pressure at the reed. Velocity-operated reed of flute (*bottom*) operates only at frequencies at which bore produces a maximum variation in velocity at the reed. Heavy

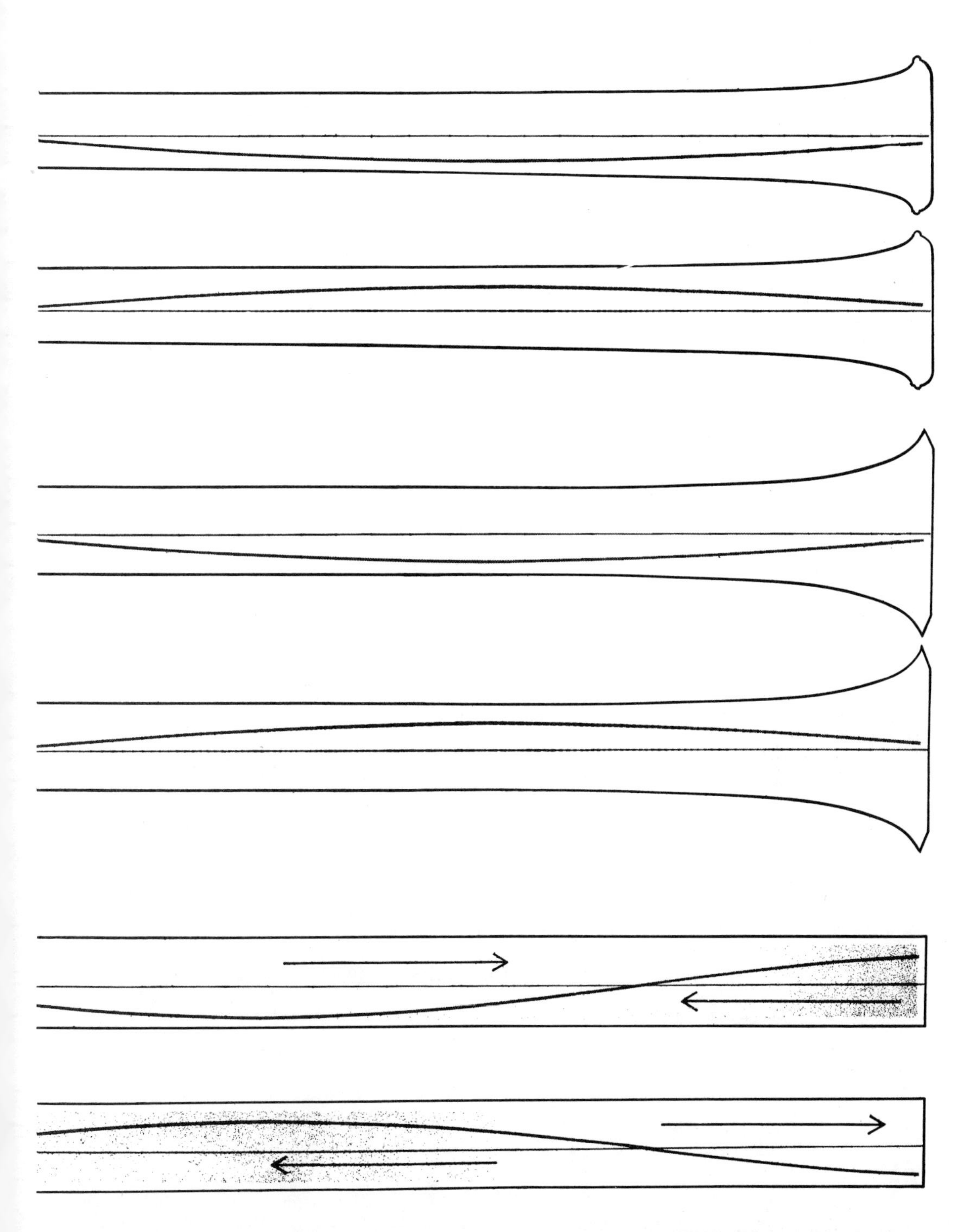

black lines represent reeds; gray lines show wave motion of vibrating air in bore. Heavy colored lines indicate high-pressure phases; lighter lines, low-pressure phases. In the flute heavy color indicates high-velocity motion in one direction; light color, motion in the opposite direction. Heavy black arrows show the vibrations of the air-jet reed. The instruments in this schematic diagram are shown playing in their second mode of vibration. The thickness of the bores and the relative size of the reeds are exaggerated.

the instrument. But if the hole is so large that the end of the bore is just about falling off, the pitch of the note will rise to that of a bore which extends only as far as the hole. There is no need to go to this extreme; a hole that can be covered by a fingertip will serve to raise the pitch. If a series of such holes is drilled in the bore, the bore behaves as though it were cut off at a point near the uppermost open hole. In effect the side holes give the instrument a set of alternative bore-lengths, each with its own natural modes of vibration. The player's fingers, aided by a more or less complicated mechanism, open and close these holes to get different notes on the scale.

An important point of distinction between wood winds and brasses appears at this point: brasses have no side holes to alter the effective length of the bore. Brass players achieve a scale by using a set of valves to insert short lengths of tubing into the bore. Thus if water is poured into the mouthpiece of a brass instrument, all of it will flow through the convolutions of the coiled tubing and pour out of the bell. But if one were to pour water through a wood wind (perish the thought), it would not all flow the whole length of the instrument; some of it would pour out of each open hole.

The lowest note in the musical range of a wood wind is the lowest of the natural frequencies of the complete bore. Higher notes are played by opening the holes one by one, starting at the lower end of the bore. The holes are spaced so that when all of them are open, the bore sounds a note that has the same pitch as the first overtone of the complete bore, that is, the second natural mode of vibration of the bore played with all the holes closed. To continue the scales the instrument may be shifted to play in its middle register, the holes are closed and the pitch altered upward in steps by again opening the holes in succession.

I had played various wood winds for years before it occurred to me that it might be possible to invent new wood winds by finding new kinds of bores that could be used in this way. After considerable thought I realized that in essence the problem is to find a class of horn shapes for which the ratios between the natural-mode frequencies will remain unchanged when the bore is cut off successively at the lower end, as by opening the side holes. This is a mathematical way of saying that the bore must be one in which the same set of holes may be reused in playing the scale in the middle and upper registers of the instrument. (Otherwise a set of holes that provided notes of proper pitch in the low register would be out of tune in the higher ones.) The only horns that fulfill these requirements and that can be used with pressure-controlled reeds are the so-called Bessel horns [*see illustration at bottom of page 146*]. They are named for the early 19th-century German astronomer F. W. Bessel, whose Bessel functions for the relation of variables in certain differential equations have been utilized in many areas of physics. One of these equations applies to waves in a series of horns that increase in cross section according to some exponent of the distance from the end of the bore. The exponent distinguishes one horn from another in the series. At first sight it would appear that one has available an infinity of useful shapes, one for each positive exponent. But practical and subtle considerations arising from the nature of our ears and the proper regeneration of sound-energy restrict the choice to those members of the family that possess whole-number ratios among the normal frequency-modes. A little study showed that this requirement is satisfied only by those shapes for which the exponent is either two or zero. It turns out that natural selection in musical instruments had long anticipated this finding of theory: Each of the wood winds has one or the other shape. The cylindrical clarinet is a representative of the zero-exponent class, in which the cross section remains constant along the length of the bore. The oboe, the saxophone and the bassoon, on the other hand, have conical bores and so belong to the class for which the exponent equals two. A bore that departs from these "ideal" forms does not enclose an air column with constant ratios among its natural modes of vibration from one open hole to the next. If the cross section increases slightly toward the open end, as compared with one or the other ideal bore, all the modes of vibration are raised somewhat in pitch, with the lowest mode being raised the most; if it decreases in cross section toward the open end, the modes of vibration are lowered in pitch, with the lowest mode being lowered the most.

The makers of wood winds not only discovered the ideal shapes generations ago; they have also empirically ex-

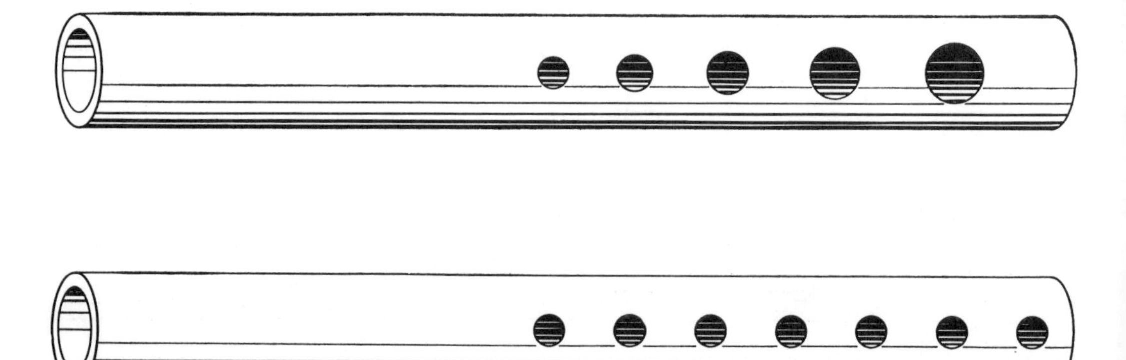

**OPEN HOLES of an actual wood wind (*top*) increase in size and spacing toward the open end of the bore. But the frequencies at which the air within the bore vibrates can be calculated by assuming that the holes are all of uniform size and spacing (*bottom*).**

ploited the effect of departures from the ideal. They judiciously alter the cross section of the bore by a few thousandths of an inch to compensate for various upsetting effects caused by the complex behavior of reeds and holes. As a result the bores of actual wood winds are not perfect cones or cylinders. Although the necessary modifications of a bore can in general be predicted quantitatively by proper mathematical analysis, to my knowledge such methods have almost never been employed by the manufacturers of wood winds. They make the final adjustments in the taper of each bore by a process of trial and error.

The size and position of the side holes are just as crucial as the shape of the bore in affecting the performance of an instrument. Not only do the side holes cut off the bore at a convenient spot for getting a scale; they also play a large role in setting the tone quality of the sound within the instrument. And when they are open, they influence the way in which this sound is ultimately radiated into the air for the listener to hear. A length of plastic tubing played with a clarinet mouthpiece gives a dull, plumbing kind of sound that few people can identify. When this same pipe is provided with a row of closed side-holes followed below by four or five open ones, the tone changes strikingly into the woody voice of a clarinet.

The "unused" closed holes convert the bore from a smooth-walled pipe into a lumpy duct that may be looked upon as a pipe with a series of swellings, as shown in the illustration below. Using a mathematical method devised by Lord Rayleigh, I was able to calculate that if the musical properties needed by the bore are to be preserved when it is supplied with closed finger holes, then the size of the holes must be related to their spacing in a certain definite way. One can say that the ratio of the volume of air contained in the closed hole divided by the volume of air in the length of bore between adjacent holes must be the same in all parts of the bore. I was able to verify this deduction from theory by a quick measurement of the hole sizes on present-day instruments. In all pressure-controlled reed instruments the holes must be larger and farther apart toward the lower end of the bore. This does not apply to the velocity-controlled flute family, which is much less sensitive to such perturbing effects, so that all the holes can be roughly the same size.

For generations craftsmen have used rules of thumb to determine where the holes should be placed in a wood wind. But a given set of rules applies only to a particular design, and must often be adjusted to correct vagaries in tuning between registers. The ability to make first-class oboes, clarinets and flutes is often a matter of highly prized family craftsmanship. Precision mass-production techniques must often be supplemented by painstaking handwork to maintain any sort of quality. Theoretically, of course, the positioning of the holes is determined by the physics of the musical scale, whether we understand it or not. Around 1930 the late E. G. Richardson of University College London, using electrical-analog techniques devised in 1919 by the late A. G. Webster of Clark University, calculated the behavior of a single open hole in the side of a tubular bore. Although this technique yielded a precise result and could in principle be extended to describe the musical case where there are several open holes, in practice it is too cumbersome to be usable. Since manufacturers of instruments were already able to make excellent wood winds without theoretical help, Richardson's work has lain largely neglected.

The difficulty with Richardson's approach is that each hole must first be treated separately, and then the mutual effects of the holes must be reconciled. A more practical approach is to study several adjacent holes simultaneously in a simplified way. A method for doing this in electrical systems was devised in 1927 by W. P. Mason of the Bell Telephone Laboratories. He worked out a set of equations to show the effect of regularly spaced loading coils on the vibrations in electrical transmission-lines. Because of the similarity of all vibrating systems, the equations can also be used for describing the sound vibrations in a bore with regularly spaced discontinuities such as holes. At first glance this does not seem useful because the holes along a wood-wind bore are not evenly spaced. But as all wood-wind players know, when their instrument plays a note in one of its lower two registers, only the two or three nearest open holes exert an appreciable effect on the sound produced; the size or position of the lower open holes makes essentially no difference. It

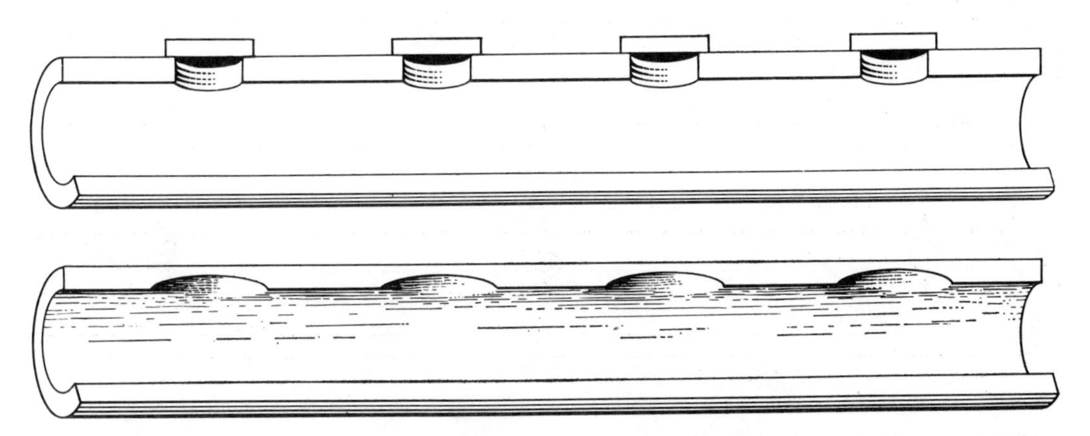

**CLOSED HOLES alter the vibrational properties of the bore. Side holes closed by player's fingers or by pads on key levers (*top*) convert the bore from a smooth-walled pipe to a lumpy duct that may be thought of as a pipe with a series of swellings (*bottom*).**

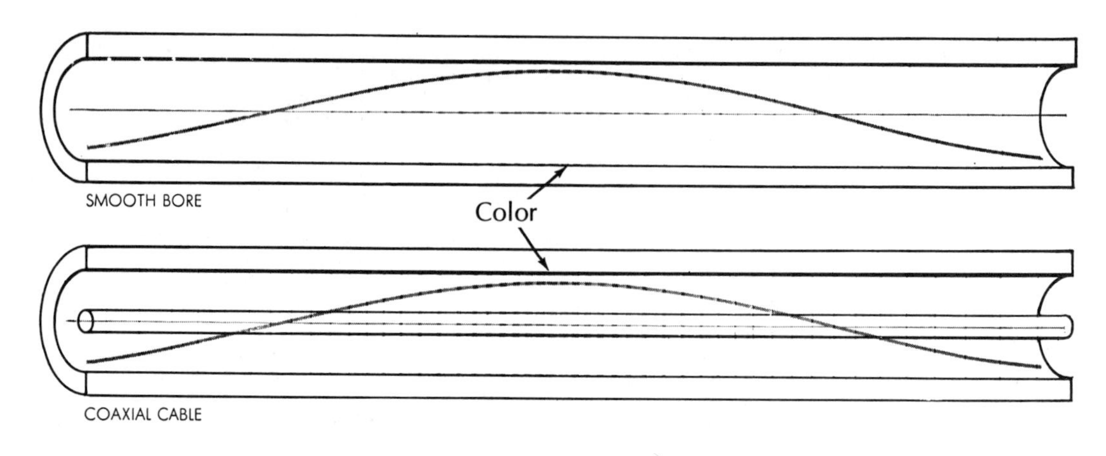


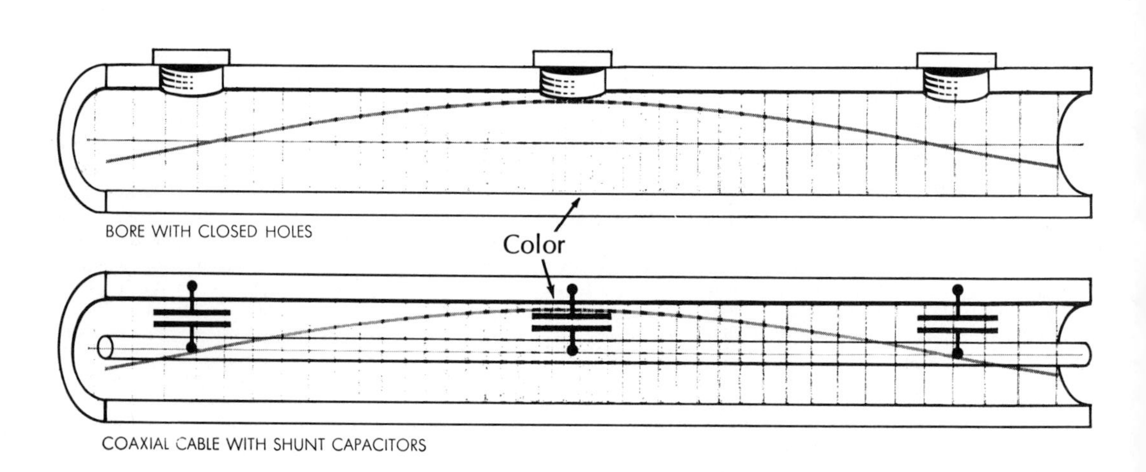


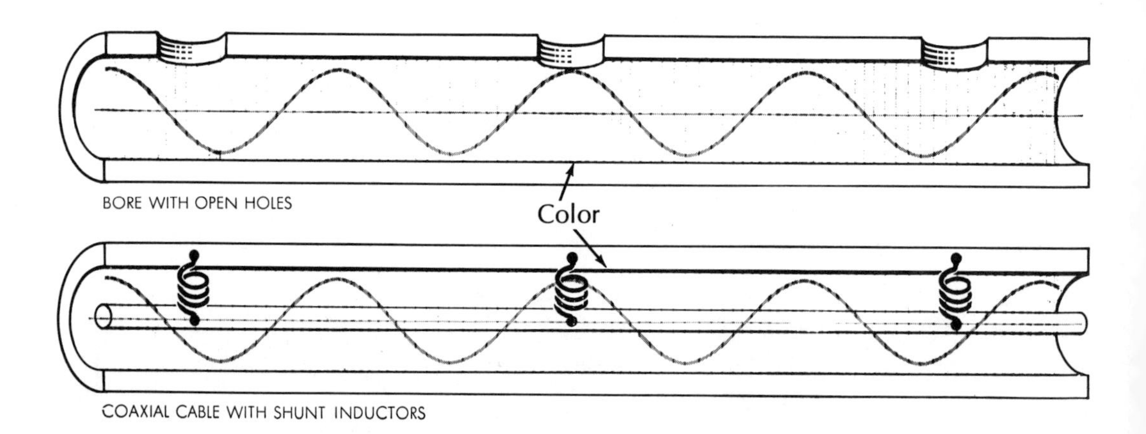


**ELECTRICAL ANALOGY depicts a wood-wind bore as a coaxial cable. The acoustical vibrations of the air within a smooth-walled bore are analogous to the electrical vibrations in the cable at top. Bore with closed side-holes behaves like cable with evenly spaced shunt capacitors connected across it (*middle*). Bore with open side-holes behaves like cable with evenly spaced inductors (*bottom*).**

occurred to me that one might learn something by pretending that the bore contains open holes of uniform size and spacing, the dimensions being fixed by the size and spacing of the two highest holes that are open for the note being played. The relation between this simplifying abstraction and the pattern of holes in a real instrument is shown in the illustration on page 150. To my delight, the trick succeeded in predicting the pitches of my own clarinet from measurements of its holes. After further experimental checks and a mathematical analysis as to why the whole informal scheme held together, I found that the main musical frequencies that give the pitch of a note are not able to travel very far in a bore with open holes; the larger, more widely spaced holes in the lower end of the bore send only weak "messages" back to the main bore.

William Dent has recently worked over this problem in a different way as a senior thesis project at Case Institute of Technology, using a mathematical approach that was originally suggested by Rayleigh, but was further developed for the purposes of quantum theory by Gregor Wentzel of the University of Chicago, H. A. Kramers of the University of Utrecht and Leon Brillouin. Dent found that in spite of the nonuniform arrangement of the open holes, they act almost as though they were of regular size and spacing, provided they are properly proportioned for their closed-hole duty. In short, although the lack of communication between the bore and the lower open holes makes the pitch relatively insensitive to their size and spacing, the messages that do get through from these holes make it seem as though they were uniformly spaced after all. Of course uniform spacing is not necessarily a musical virtue, but it is a convenience that makes it possible to use the mathematical methods that are at hand.

The relatively easy success of my first attempts encouraged me to re-examine the role of the closed holes in influencing the vibrations of the bore. It became clear that the closed holes act as a filter that discriminates strongly against the highest few components of the vibration spectrum produced by the reed. The "cut-off" frequency of this filter depends critically on the size and location of the closed holes. In flutes and saxophones the cut-off frequency is so high that it has little effect on the tone of the instrument, but in all the other wood winds (especially the oboe) the tone color is considerably altered by the filtering effect of the closed holes.

The next step was to try coaxing Mason's transmission-line equations into giving information about the way in which vibrations in the bore are coupled to the outside air. Any electrical or acoustical engineer looking at the equations for the row of open holes would instantly recognize them as describing a second sort of filter which transmits high-frequency vibrations, but attenuates those of lower frequencies. A wood wind thus emits the lower components of its tone into a room rather inefficiently, chiefly from the first one or two holes but symmetrically in all directions from the instrument. The higher components are radiated efficiently from all the open holes acting in concert, but in a highly directional manner. The size and spacing of the holes determine the frequency at which the "cross-over" in the mode of radiation takes place. In this complicated fashion the holes help determine the tone color of the sound that reaches the ears of the listener.

Listeners have come to associate wood winds with the type of sound that is emitted (by each of the two radiation mechanisms) from a row of open holes. The addition of the bell at the lower end of some wood winds reflects efforts over the years to provide the bore with a radiating system that approximates the behavior of a row of open holes even when all the holes are closed. It is a matter of long experience that this can never be done perfectly. (Of course an instrument maker might escape simultaneously from tradition and from the problem by simply providing a few extra open holes at the bottom of the bore which would be used only as emitters of sound.) In contrast to the clarinet and oboe, the flutes and saxophones are essentially bell-less because they radiate all components of their tones as if from a single hole.

This brief account of the interwoven complexities of wood-wind instruments has suggested some of the ways in which their structure affects their behavior. But it also suggests a more general observation. The curious weaving of familiar knowledge from various apparently unrelated fields, illuminated by flickers of intuition and analogy, is typical of the way in which most scientific knowledge develops. While many scientific efforts are shaped by esthetic considerations, the physics of music is particularly fortunate in being allied to an art from which it draws inspiration, and to which it often brings a deeper understanding.

# 22

*Copyright © 1959 by the Acoustical Society of America*

Reprinted from *J. Acoust. Soc. Am.*, **31**(2), 137–146 (1959)

## On Woodwind Instrument Bores

A. H. Benade
*Physics Department, Case Institute of Technology, Cleveland 6, Ohio*

(Received November 18, 1957)

The properties of horns that are suitable for use in woodwinds are deduced from first principles. The cylindrical pipe and complete cone are shown to be the only shapes which satisfy these requirements exactly. The behavior of nearly perfect cylinders and almost complete cones is described, the influence of closed finger holes on the effective bore of an instrument is discussed, and the effect of the mouthpiece cavity is analyzed. Damping of the normal modes by the walls of the bore is shown to play a dominant role in the playing behavior and tone color of woodwinds, and various consequences are deduced.

### I. INTRODUCTION

THE acoustic behavior of a woodwind instrument is complex, and a complete analysis would be hopelessly involved, and perhaps impossible to set up on the basis of present knowledge. It is however fruitful to use general physical principles together with the empirical knowledge of these instruments which is shown in their construction and use, to select significant aspects of the problem for study, and as guides in finding physically meaningful analytic approximations for their description. The problem divides itself into three reasonably distinct parts; one concerning the nature of the bore, one having to do with the action of the tone holes, and one dealing with the reed system as an exciter. Once these partial problems are clarified, it is not too difficult to bring them together in a discussion of the instrument as a whole. The present discussion will concern itself primarily with the requirements on, and behavior of, bores which are useful in woodwinds. The effects of open side holes will be taken up in a second paper.

In order to provide a basis for such an analysis it is worthwhile to review briefly the nature of a typical woodwind. Air contained in a tube with rigid walls is set in vibration by a beating reed, whose angular frequency of vibration $\omega_r$ is determined by the interaction of the reed with one of the normal modes of the air column. The blown reed is an aeroelastic device, so that, strictly speaking, the frequency produced cannot be predicted from an analysis of an air column that is coupled to an *unblown* reed. For this reason it is necessary to keep a clear distinction between the frequency of oscillation of an isolated blown reed, its free (unblown) natural frequency, the frequencies of the normal modes of the isolated air column, and the frequency of the combined reed-pipe system. However, it is an empirical fact that the general behavior of an instrument is sufficiently well defined, by the acoustical properties of the air column alone, that it is reasonable to study its properties apart from the reed, which may be shown to function in woodwinds very nearly as a closed end.[1] The small discrepancies arising from this simplification may be corrected later on when the instrument is considered as a whole.

[1] See Appendix I for a discussion of this point.

### II. REQUIREMENTS FOR A USEFUL BORE

As is well known, the lowest note on a given instrument is associated with the lowest normal mode of vibration of the complete air column. Successively higher notes of the chromatic scale are then produced by opening holes one by one along the tube, thus shortening its effective length, until a note is reached for which the fundamental frequency (lowest mode) of the shortened tube is the same as the frequency of the second mode of the complete tube. If the player causes the reed to vibrate at the frequency determined for it by the second normal mode of the air column, a repetition of this sequence of opening holes will continue the scale.[2] The tuning will of course be correct only if the frequency ratio (and therefore musical interval) between the first and second normal modes is the same for the complete horn as for one that is shortened by opening a few holes. This necessity for preserving a constant frequency ratio between the normal modes is essential in all woodwinds and provides a general limitation on the types of bore which are musically useful.

It is possible to show that if a row of reasonably large finger holes is opened in the side of a bore, the horn acts as though it were cut off a certain distance below the highest open hole, this distance being nearly constant with frequency. Variations in this distance will be ignored here, as it is easily taken care of by perturbation methods later on. Successively opened finger holes thus produce a sequence of shorter and shorter horns, and these must possess a certain acoustic similarity if they are all to have constant frequency ratios between their normal modes. Mathematically this implies that the ratios of the normal modes must be fixed by parameters of the horn, which are independent of its length. This requirement is satisfied by the so-called Bessel horns in which the cross-sectional area $S$ of the bore increases by some positive power $\epsilon$

[2] A similar, though more complex, procedure is used to extend further the range of the instrument by using the third normal mode.

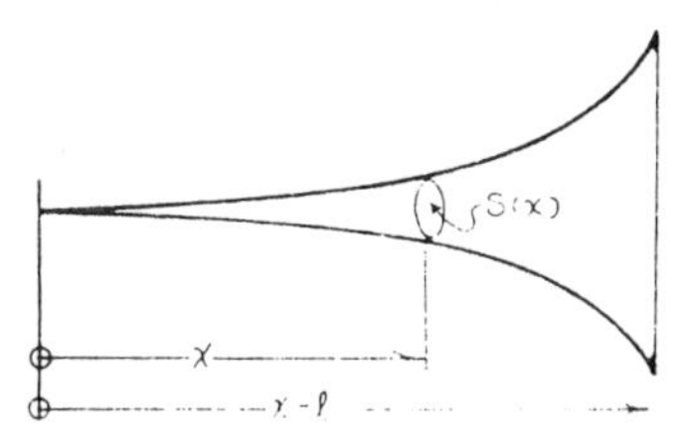


FIG. 1. General horn shape, showing dependence of cross-sectional area $S$ on distance from the apex. The over-all length of the horn is $l$.

of the distance $x$ measured from the vertex (see Fig. 1). Pressure disturbances in such horns obey the wave equation (1), in which $\omega$ is the angular frequency of the wave, and $c$ the velocity of sound[3];

$$\frac{d^2p}{dx^2}+\left(\frac{\epsilon}{x}\right)\frac{dp}{dx}+k^2p=0, \quad (1)$$

$$k=\omega/c.$$

Relevant solutions of this equation must satisfy the following two boundary conditions: (a) The volume flow $u(x)\cdot S(x)$ must be zero at the vertex. This is actually a specification of $dp/dx$ for small $x$ since the particle velocity is proportional to grad $p$. (b) The pressure variation must be zero at the open end located at $x=l$. Such solutions have the general form[4] shown in Eq. (2), and proper values of the wave number $k$ are found from the roots[5] of the Bessel function, as shown in Eq. (3);

$$p(x)=Ax^{\frac{1}{2}(1-\epsilon)}J_{-\frac{1}{2}(1-\epsilon)}(kx) \quad (2)$$

$$J_{-\frac{1}{2}(1-\epsilon)}(kl)=0, \quad \epsilon\geq 0. \quad (3)$$

Figure 2 shows the frequency ratios between the first and $n$th characteristic frequencies of these horns as a function of the flare exponent $\epsilon$. It is shown in Appendix II that Bessel horns are the only horns which satisfy the requirement that their normal mode frequency ratios be independent of horn length. This simplifies the subsequent analysis by making a great reduction in the number of special cases which must be considered.

While the preceding discussion has served to show that woodwind bores are restricted to being members of a particularly family, the restriction is necessary but not sufficient to give usable instruments. Consider a reed that is controlled by the lowest normal mode of an air column, so that it vibrates at an angular frequency $\omega_r \cong \omega_1$. Under these conditions puffs of air are periodically admitted into the pipe from the player's mouth, in synchronism with the motion of the reed, thus generating a Fourier spectrum made up of harmonic components having angular frequencies $n\omega_r$, ($n=1,2,3\cdots$). A general Bessel horn does not, however, have its characteristic frequencies spaced out in integral multiples of the fundamental frequency.[6] For this reason, when the reed is driving the column near its lowest mode, the higher modes of the pipe will not resonate with higher frequency components generated by the reed except in certain particular types of bore. The musically useful horn shapes from this point of view are those which possess normal modes with approximately integral frequency ratios, so that enough of the reed harmonics are reinforced by the horn as to produce a rich tone. Reference to Fig. 2 shows that there are two horns having exactly integral characteristic frequency ratios, the cylindrical tube ($\epsilon=0$) for which the ratios are 1, 3, 5, $\cdots$, and the straight-sided cone[7] ($\epsilon=2$) with frequency ratios 1, 2, 3 $\cdots$. A rapidly flaring horn with $\epsilon$ very slightly greater than 7 is also worth mentioning because in it the odd-numbered modes have frequencies which are almost precisely in the ratios 1, 2, 3, 4 $\cdots$, while the even-numbered modes fall between these frequencies and would not therefore be excited by the reed vibrating with the fundamental. Because it possesses integral normal mode frequencies, this last horn may theoretically be considered to be a member of the class of musically useful shapes. However, it has such a rapid flare that great mechanical

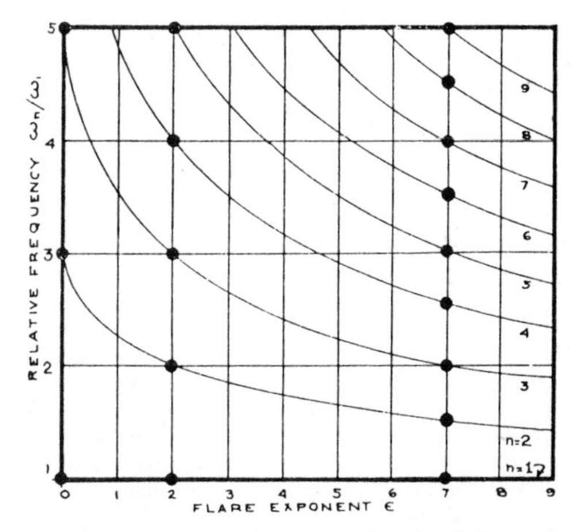


FIG. 2. Frequency of the $n$th normal mode relative to the fundamental ($n=1$) in Bessel horns, as a function of flare exponent $\epsilon$. The frequency ratios are integral only for $\epsilon=0$, 2, and 7. The normal modes of these particular horns are indicated by dots. Note that these frequency ratios depend only on the parameter $\epsilon$ and not upon the length of the horn (see also Appendix II).

[3] G. W. Stewart and R. B. Lindsay, *Acoustics* (D. Van Nostrand Company, Inc., New York, 1930), p. 133.

[4] E. Jahnke and F. Emde, *Tables of Functions* (Dover Publications, New York, 1945), fourth edition, p. 146.

[5] See reference 4, p. 153 and p. 168.

[6] The presence of improperly designed side holes may also produce this effect even in tubes where the frequency ratios would otherwise be integral.

[7] These two horns are exemplified in the orchestra by the cylindrical clarinets and by the conical saxophones, oboes, and bassoons, respectively.

difficulties would arise in constructing it for use with a reasonably sized reed. The disturbing effects of cutting off the horn near its apex, and the effects of the mouthpiece cavity, which are discussed in Secs. III and V, respectively, may be shown to grow rapidly with horn flare. For this reason any special properties theoretically available in the $\epsilon=7$ horn would be destroyed by the mouthpiece and reed combination. Furthermore, the heavy radiation damping produced by the large open end would practically obliterate the resonance peaks of the horn, so that the reed could not be controlled by the horn in any event.

## III. NEARLY PERFECT CYLINDERS AND CONES

Because no woodwind has an exactly cylindrical bore, nor a conical one which is continued to the apex, it is worthwhile to investigate the normal modes of pipes which are almost cylindrical, and cones which are almost complete.[8] Figure 3 shows the types of bore in question, together with the notation used to describe them. The physical length of the horn is $l$, $x_0$ being taken to be positive if the tube expands away from the closed end, and negative for a contracting tube. The sign convention for $x_0$ is perhaps best explained by means of an example. If a horn like that of Fig. 3(a) is made so that the distance between closed end and vertex is 10 cm, then $x_0$ has the value (+10 cm). On the other hand, for a horn like that of Fig. 3(b), a vertex-to-closed end distance of 10 cm is taken to mean that $x_0$ has a value of (−10 cm) in the formulas. The frequency of the $n$th normal mode of a nearly cylindrical pipe[9] is shown in Eq. (4);

$$\omega_n=(\pi c/2l)\{(2n-1)^2+(8/\pi^2)(l/x_0)\}^{\frac{1}{2}}$$
$$n=1,\ 2,\ 3\ \cdots \qquad (4)$$
$$(x_0/l)\gg(4/\pi^2)(2n-1)^{-2}.$$

Equation (4) shows, among other things, that a tube whose cross section decreases away from the closed end, has a lower fundamental frequency than a uniform pipe, and its normal mode frequencies are spaced more widely than the 1, 3, 5 ⋯ sequence of a uniform pipe. The reverse is true for a pipe which increases in cross section away from the closed end. The qualitative behavior is often exploited by instrument makers to adjust the intonation of clarinets by suitably chosen small departures from a simple cylindrical shape in the upper part of the bore. The bell of course has an appreciable effect only on notes for which most of the tone holes are closed.

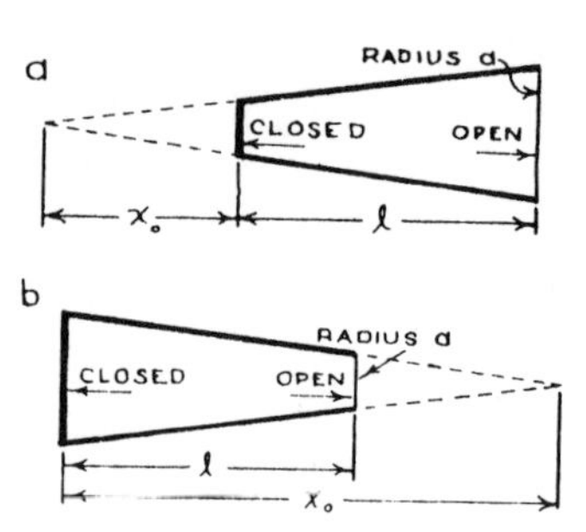


FIG. 3. (a) Diagram showing notation describing a conical pipe cut off and closed at the small end. The length $x_0$ is taken to be a positive quantity in pipes of this shape. (b) Diagram of a conical pipe, cut off and closed at the large end. The distance $x_0$ between the closed end and the vertex is considered to be a negative quantity.

The approximations made in obtaining Eq. (4) are invalid in the limit $(x_0/l)\to 0$, where the cone is almost complete. This case, which is applicable to instruments such as the saxophone and oboe for which $(x_0/l)\cong\frac{1}{3}$, requires a slight extension of a calculation due to Morse.[10] The result shows that the $n$th characteristic frequency of an almost complete cone is given by

$$\omega_n=n(\pi c/l)\{1+(x_0/l)(1/B)\}^{-1}$$
$$B\cong 1+(1/4)(l\omega/c)^2(a/l)^2(a/x_0)^2 \qquad (5)$$
$$n=1,\ 2,\ 3\ \cdots$$
$$a=\text{bore radius at open end.}$$

The value of $\omega_n$ may be obtained by an iteration procedure in which the $q$th approximation is calculated using the $(q-1)$th value for $\omega_n$ in the factor $B$. In the limit of small $x_0$ the normal modes are given[11] by Eq. (6);

$$\omega_n=n\pi c/(l+x_0). \qquad (6)$$

The iteration may be based on this last result, which will also be useful for other purposes later in this paper. In conical woodwinds the largeness of $(x_0/l)$ gives the factor $B$ an appreciable frequency dependence, whose qualitative nature may be seen in the first approximation of Eq. (5), where $B$ takes on the value given in Eq. (7);

$$B\cong 1+(\pi/2)^2(a/x_0)^2[a^2/(l+x_0)^2]n^2. \qquad (7)$$

SEE "ERRATUM" ON PAGE 146

This shows that real conical instrument bores have their normal modes spread more widely than the 1, 2, 3 ⋯ sequence of the simple cone. In the oboe this spreading

[8] See also H. Bouasse, *Tuyaux et Résonateurs* (Librairie Delagrave, Paris, 1929), Chap. 10.

[9] This expression is adapted from one obtained by P. M. Morse, *Vibration and Sound* (McGraw-Hill Book Company, Inc., New York, 1948), second edition, Eq. 24–23, p. 286. The predicted frequency ratios are in very good agreement with experiments conducted on an old taper-bore flute (for which $x_0/l=-2.4$) that was excited at the large end by a clarinet reed and mouthpiece. The mouthpiece cavity correction had a negligible effect on the normal mode frequency ratio, which was $\omega_2/\omega_1=3.6$.

[10] See reference 9, p. 287. Since $x_0$ is fixed and $l$ is varied by opening finger holes, $(x_0/l)$ varies over a factor of about two in woodwinds.

[11] Equation (6) shows that the effective length of a cutoff conical instrument is $(l+x_0)$ and not its physical length $l$. This has caused some confusion in the literature, since ignoring $x_0$ leads one to suppose the reed is far from acting like a closed end [J. Redfield, J. Acoust. Soc. Am. 6, 34 (1934)]. In actual instruments it is easily verified that the effective length is close to being $(l+x_0)$.

in the normal modes is partially offset in the notes below $G$ by a slight increase in the rate of taper in the lower part of the bore, which increases the effective flare parameter $\epsilon$ and so compresses the mode frequencies. Additional compensation can be introduced by a suitable choice of finger hole sizes, and by the nature of the cavity inside the reed, as shown in the following sections.

## IV. SIDE HOLES AND HORN FLARE

In playing a woodwind, the typical configuration is one in which several holes are closed by keys and fingertips, below which is a row of open holes which may be assumed (to the present approximation) to play no part in the behavior of the instrument. The effective cross-sectional area $S_{eff}$ of a horn with closed side holes is the sum of two parts, one being the area of the smooth-walled horn, while the other is the average volume per unit length enclosed within the side holes. Figure 4 illustrates the situation and defines the notation of Eq. (8);

$$S_{eff} = \pi a^2 + (\pi b^2 t)/2s. \tag{8}$$

In general, $a$, $b$, $t$, and $s$ are functions of $x$, the distance along the horn, and preceding arguments have shown that they should be chosen in such a way that $S_{eff}$ is either constant or varies as $x^2$ for the two families of instruments. Observation of typical woodwinds shows that their makers adhere to this requirement reasonably well.

In a somewhat idealized clarinet the interhole spacing $2s$ is roughly proportional to $x$, and in order to get a chromatic scale, $2s \cong 0.06x$. Both bore radius $a$, and wall thickness $t$, are essentially constant, so that in order to get an effective cross-sectional area which is independent of $x$, Eq. (9a) must hold;

$$b = x^{\frac{1}{2}} \cdot \text{const.} \tag{9a}$$

Because tone holes are not drilled into the bore all the way up the tube to the reed in a real instrument, there is a discontinuity in $S$ at the position of the top hole, the effective bore being larger below than above this hole. This would upset the intonation of the instrument if it were not compensated for by a slight increase in the

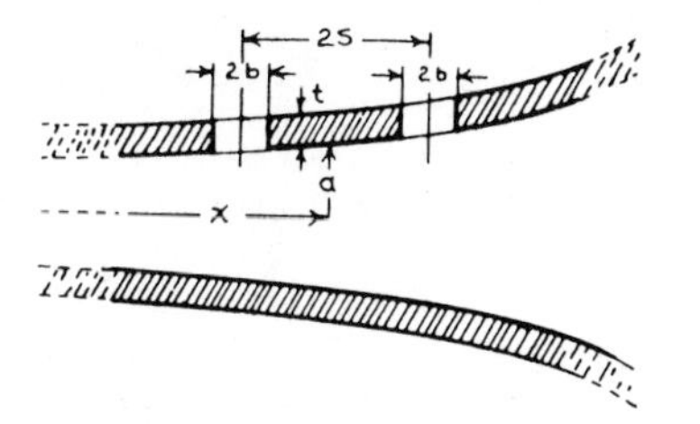


FIG. 4. Diagram of a woodwind bore of radius $a$, with side holes of radius $b$ and spacing $2s$ drilled through a wall of thickness $t$. These dimensions are generally functions of $x$, the distance along the horn from the closed end.

SEE JASA 32, 1591, (1960)

bore above the top hole, which may also be required for other reasons in many instruments.

In a similarly idealized oboe, the cross-sectional area of the bore will increase as $x^2$ in the proper way if the hole radius $b$ satisfies Eq. (9b);

$$b = x^{\frac{3}{2}} \cdot \text{const.} \tag{9b}$$

Actually the holes of an oboe do not follow this dependence,[12] but vary in radius with a higher power of $x$, and also, the wall thickness $t$ may decrease as $x$ increases, so that the effective bore flares more rapidly than does an ideal straight-sided cone. The result is that the normal mode frequencies are compressed slightly. This contribution to the effective flare produced in oboes by the side holes is of such order of magnitude as to complete approximately the compensation of the normal mode frequency ratios which are upset by the relatively large value of $(x_0/l)$.

## V. MOUTHPIECE CAVITY EFFECTS

In all woodwinds, particularly those having a tapered bore, the mouthpiece does not make a uniform continuation of the idealized bore discussed in the preceding section, so that the behavior of the instrument is not in accordance with calculation (even leaving aside the effects due to the reed's own dynamical behavior) unless corrections are made. In keeping with the rest of this paper, the effects of the mouthpiece cavity will be analyzed under the assumption that the reed merely serves to close up the end of the instrument. This is a good assumption for clarinets and saxophones which are provided with rigid mouthpieces, and in which no amount of biting down on the reed will change the cavity volume appreciably. For these instruments the following calculations have quantitative significance, which is easily checked. For the double-reed families of instruments, the mouthpiece cavity is a part of the reed structure, and the reed dynamics are so intimately mixed with the system that only qualitative information can be obtained for these instruments.

The present calculations will be carried out under the assumption that the mouthpiece cavity is a relatively small volume, whose linear dimensions are much smaller than the wavelength of any sound of interest. This permits the cavity to be treated as a lumped constant terminating impedance at the end of the horn. In certain special cases this approximation breaks down, but the general method is easily modified to take care of these cases, and in any event the qualitative conclusions are still valid. Morse[13] gives an expression for the acoustic admittance ratio at the throat of a family of horns, which when simplified by the

[12] It is essential to note in this connection that $x$ is measured from the vertex of the complete cone and not from the top of the instrument (which is located at $x_0$). The difference is approximately 15 cm on an ordinary oboe.

[13] See reference 9, Eq. 24–20, p. 285.

omission of the radiation damping terms (these turn out not to be important), leads to the following expression, when it is specialized to the case of an incomplete cone:

$$\rho c/z_0 = i\cot(\omega l/c) + ic/(\omega x_0). \tag{10}$$

The notation here is the same as that of the preceding section, the sign of $x_0$ being determined as before, except that it is measured from the throat of the horn, rather than from the closed end. If the throat of this horn is attached to a cavity of volume $V$, the resonances will be found at those frequencies for which $z_0$ is an "inductive" reactance equal in magnitude to the "capacitative" reactance $X_c$ of the cavity. This last[14] is found to be

$$X_c = i\rho c^2\pi a_0^2/\omega V$$
$$a_0 = a x_0/(l+x_0) \equiv \text{throat radius}. \tag{11}$$

Combining Eq. (10) with Eq. (11), so that the two reactances are related in the way just described, leads to the following eigenvalue equation:

$$\cot(\omega l/c) = (V/\pi a_0^2)(\omega/c) - (1/x_0)(c/\omega). \tag{12}$$

The limit $(x_0/l)\rightarrow\infty$, which corresponds to a cylindrical pipe closed at one end by a cavity, is represented musically by the clarinet, if the tube length $l$ is measured up to the base of the mouthpiece, whose cavity has the volume $V$. For clarinetlike systems, Eq. (12) reduces to

$$\cot(\omega l/c) = (V/\pi a_0^2)(\omega/c). \tag{13}$$

If (and this is the practical case) the right side of this equation is much less than unity, standard methods show that the normal modes of the system are well approximated by

$$\omega_n \doteq \frac{(2n-1)\pi c}{2[l+(V/\pi a_0^2)]} \tag{14}$$
$$n = 1, 2, 3 \cdots.$$

Examination of this relation shows that the system acts as though the pipe was increased in length by a fixed amount which may be called the length correction of the mouthpiece for use with that particular bore. This correction is equal to the length of a piece of the clarinet bore which contains the same volume as the mouthpiece cavity. The relation holds whether the mouthpiece bore is smaller or larger than that of the pipe, and is displayed explicitly in Eq. (15);

$$\Delta l = (V/\pi a_0^2). \tag{15}$$

This result is also obtained and discussed by Bouasse.[15]

Conical-bore instruments such as the saxophone, oboe, and bassoon are instruments for which $(x_0/l)$ is finite, so that both terms must be retained on the right side of Eq. (12). In order to give an appearance of simplicity, this equation may be rewritten in the form

$$\begin{aligned}\cot(\omega l/c) &= -(1/x_0)[1-(V/\pi a_0^2)(\omega/c)^2 x_0](c/\omega)\\ &= -(F/x_0)(c/\omega).\end{aligned} \tag{16}$$

The factor $F$ is defined here for convenience only, and has the advantage of allowing the direct use of Eqs. (5) and (6) to estimate the frequencies produced by a nearly complete conical pipe terminated at its small end by a cavity.[16] All that is required is to replace $x_0$ by $(x_0/F)$ in these equations. For most practical purposes it is sufficiently accurate to use an approximate value for $\omega$ in computing the magnitude of $F$. This value may be taken directly from the unmodified Eq. (6), or from the frequency of the written note which the instrument is intended to play.

Because of the complicated appearance of the algebraic expressions obtained here, the physical implications of the calculation are difficult to see. In order to display these more plainly it is worthwhile to look at the extreme case where $V$ is very small, making the factor $F$ very slightly different from unity. When this is done, use of Eq. (6) in evaluating $F$ permits one to show that the effective length of the horn is increased by an amount approximately given by Eq. (17);

$$\Delta l \cong (\pi V/a^2)n^2 \tag{17}$$
$$n = 1, 2, 3 \cdots$$

In this expression, the radius $a$ of the *open* end of the horn appears rather than the throat radius $a_0$. Because the mouthpiece correction is strongly dependent on frequency (by way of the mode number $n$) it is not possible to add a constant amount to the length of the bore of conical instruments as can be done for cylindrical ones. The presence of a mouthpiece cavity on conical instruments flattens all the notes, the higher modes being flattened considerably more than the lower ones, so that the normal mode frequency ratios are compressed. It will be recalled that truncation of the cone produces an opposite effect.

It is of interest to compare the relative magnitude of the cavity correction for the same mouthpiece of volume $V$ on a straight pipe and on a cutoff cone, both having the same throat radius. Examination of Eqs. (15) and (17) shows that even for the lowest mode ($n=1$), the correction for a conical pipe (for which $(x_0/l)=\frac{1}{3}$) is larger by a factor of $\pi^2/4$ than that for a cylindrical pipe. The discrepancy is of course even larger for the higher modes. The large magnitude of the cavity correction on conical instruments has a great deal to do with their somewhat slippery intonation, particularly

[14] See reference 9, pp. 235 and 237.

[15] See reference 8, p. 452.

[16] Equation (4), which applies to nearly perfect cylinders, also contains $x_0$, but the behavior of this type of resonator is so nearly like that of a straight pipe that only a negligible error is introduced by applying the much simpler result given in Eq. (15).

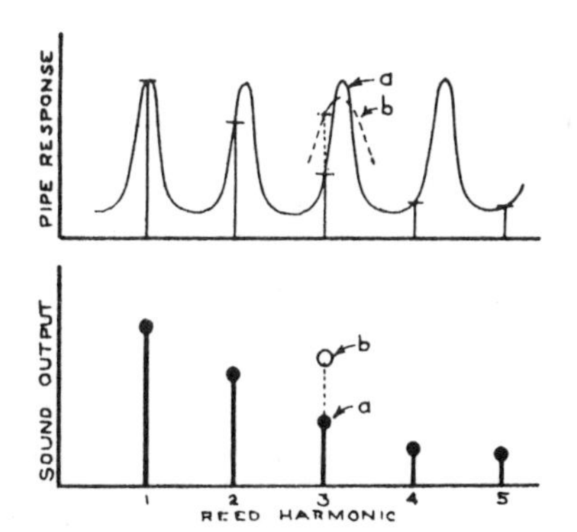


FIG. 5. Upper curve: Schematic representation of the resonance curve of a pipe with almost integral frequency ratios between its normal modes. The dotted curve *b* shows the effect of increased damping on the breadth of a resonance. Lower curve: Schematic representation of the sound output spectrum of such a pipe when driven by a reed which produces all harmonics with equal amplitude. The third harmonic shows how the output amplitude changes if the damping of a resonance is altered. The letters *a* and *b* indicate the behavior for low and high damping, respectively.

on oboes and bassoons where the reed provides a flexible cavity.[17]

A primary problem of the instrument maker is to insure that the frequency ratio of the second to the first normal mode is integral, so that the "overblown" middle register notes have acceptable intonation with respect to the low register. The acoustical complication of fork fingerings used in the upper register make the third mode less accessible to adjustment. For this reason the successive approximate means for compressing or extending the frequency ratios, discussed here and in the preceding sections, are traditionally adjusted by experiment to "fit" only the first two modes, letting the higher modes take their own course. As a result the tone quality, which depends on the response to *all* the reed harmonics, becomes a complicated function of the "system of fingering" upon which the holes are based. A later section will develop the implications of this in connection with the effect of wall material on tone color.

## VI. BAND WIDTH OF NORMAL MODES

When the effective bore of an instrument has been chosen so as to give approximately integral ratios between its characteristic frequencies, the sound output at any one of the reed harmonics is strongly affected by the band width of the nearest vibrational mode of the air column, together with the amount of mistuning that exists between the mode and the harmonic. For this reason any attempt at understanding the tone color of a woodwind must concern itself closely with the actual frequencies of the normal modes, and with the damping of these modes, since the latter controls the band width. Figure 5 shows schematically the effect on tone quality of band width and mistuning of the modes relative to the reed harmonics.

There are two means whereby a vibrating air column may lose energy. The dominant one is the frictional and thermal energy transfer to the walls of the horn. The second, which is the one for which the instrument is built, is the radiative transfer of sound energy to the air outside the horn by way of the open tone holes and bell. It is often suggested that the vibration of the wall material itself can give rise to energy absorption, and thus affect tone quality in a way separate from the damping arising from viscosity, surface roughness, etc. Similarly the differing thermal conductivities of various materials are considered to give rise to effects varying with material. Since the product of density and sound velocity ($\rho c$) is enormously greater than that of air for all ordinary wall materials, it seems very unlikely that the energy transfer between the sound waves in an ordinary woodwind pipe and its walls could play much of a role. Similarly the heat capacity and thermal conductivity of the walls is so large with respect to that of the air that the walls must be considered as isothermal boundaries for the wave, regardless of their material. The essential point, however, is not the detailed mechanism by which energy is lost by the standing wave, but the fact that it *is* lost.

### A. Wall Damping

For losses to the walls, the damping time constant $\tau_w$ of wave energy stored in a general horn of length $l$ is given by Eq. (18);

$$\tau_w = 1/(2\bar{\alpha}c). \quad (18)$$

Here $\bar{\alpha}$ stands for the averaged amplitude attenuation coefficient for waves travelling in one direction down the horn. At a point $x$ where the radius is $r(x)$, $\alpha$ takes the form shown in Eq. (19), where $A$ is a constant depending on the wall material and its surface condition;

$$\alpha(x) = A\omega^{\frac{1}{2}}/r(x). \quad (19)$$

The average value of $\alpha$ in a horn is thus determined by the reciprocal harmonic mean radius $(D/a)$ of the horn, expressed for convenience in terms of the radius $a$ at the open end of the horn. The factor $D$ stands for the ratio of the reciprocal harmonic mean radius to the reciprocal radius of the open end of the pipe, and is introduced here only for compactness in notation.

The half-power band width $g_w$ is related to $\tau_w$ by the ubiquitous complementarity relation $g\tau = 1$, so that the fractional band width $(g/\omega)$, which is also the reciprocal of $Q$, is found to be

$$(g/\omega)_w = (2ADc)/\omega^{\frac{1}{2}}a. \quad (20)$$

[17] An oboe fitted with small clarinet-type mouthpieces in which the cavity volume was altered by pieces of wax, displayed these phenomena very clearly. The reed effects here were kept constant (for a given mouthpiece) by the fixed lay and aperture in the table.

For a cylinder

$$D=1$$
$$\omega=(2n-1)\pi c/2l$$
$$n=1,\ 2,\ 3\ \cdots.$$

For an almost complete cone, use of Eq. (6) gives

$$D=(1+r)\log_e[(1+r)/r]$$
$$\omega=(n\pi c/l)(1+r)^{-1}$$
$$n=1,\ 2,\ 3\ \cdots.$$

The parameter $r=x_0/l$ describes the relative incompleteness of the cone. These expressions when substituted into Eq. (12) give explicit formulas for the fractional band widths of tubes and cones, respectively. For a cylinder

$$(g/\omega)_w=\{A(8c/\pi)^{\frac{1}{2}}\}(l^{\frac{1}{2}}/a)(2n-1)^{-\frac{1}{2}};\qquad(21a)$$

for a cone

$$(g/\omega)_w=\{A(4c/\pi)^{\frac{1}{2}}(1+r)^{\frac{1}{2}}\times\log_e[(1+r)/r]\}(l^{\frac{1}{2}}/a)n^{-\frac{1}{2}}.\qquad(21b)$$

The fractional band width of both horns *decreases* as the square root of the frequency, and falls directly as the radius $a$ in an instrument of fixed length. The term contained in braces is greater for a conical tube than for a cylinder by a factor of only about 1.5 in the case of an oboe, where $(x_0/l)\cong 0.3$, so that the essential features of the wall damping may be illustrated by considering the properties of the cylindrical pipe alone. The careful experiments of Fay[18] on smooth brass tubes give a value for $A$ of $1.12\times10^{-5}$ $(\mathrm{sec})^{\frac{1}{2}}$ (cgs units), while rough measurements on the band widths of resonant tubes show that $\frac{5}{8}$-in. diameter tubes of laminated phenolic plastic require an increase of 50 to 100% in $A$ over the value obtained by Fay. A series of $\frac{3}{8}$-in. holes spaced at $1\frac{1}{4}$-in. intervals along the tube and closed by heavy application of masking tape on the outside increases the coefficient by about 70% more. For these reasons it is not unreasonable to use a rounded off value $A=2.5\times10^{-5}$ $(\mathrm{sec})^{\frac{1}{2}}$ in estimates of band width due to the net wall losses in woodwinds.[19]

### B. Radiation Damping

Standard calculations of the radiation loss from an unflanged cylindrical pipe[20] may be used to obtain the expressions (22a) and (22b) for the fractional band widths arising from radiation damping. For a cylindrical pipe

$$(g/\omega)_{\mathrm{rad}}=(\pi/4)(a/l)^2(2n-1).\qquad(22a)$$

For a nearly complete cone

$$(g/\omega)_{\mathrm{rad}}=(\pi/2)(1+r)^{-1}(a/l)^2 n.\qquad(22b)$$

Once again the properties of the cone are close enough to those of the pipe for them to be considered together. The band width increases with frequency, and with the square of the open end radius for a given length. The radiation damping is very much less than the wall damping for all musically interesting values of the mode number.[21] For all practical purposes the resonance widths of the normal modes in most woodwinds may therefore be considered as being determined by energy transfer to the walls alone. The saxophone is an exception, in that its wider conical bore provides considerably greater radiation damping, and less wall damping, than do any of the other common woodwinds. Only the first three modes are dominated by wall damping, which may well account for the somewhat anomalous tone color and behavior of this instrument as compared with other woodwinds.

## VII. MUSICAL IMPLICATIONS OF WALL DAMPING

It is of interest to explore some of the implications of the dominance of wall damping from the point of view of the designer and player of woodwinds.

### A. Tone Color Relation between Modes

According to Eq. (21), the fundamental of a tube with heavy wall damping has the same $Q$ as does the $m$th mode of a tube $m$ times as long. This fortunate circumstance works to keep the tone color uniform when transition is made between the lower and middle registers of a woodwind. On the other hand, the rising $Q$ produced as $l$ is shortened (by the opening of finger holes) requires ever better accuracy in the integer relations between the normal modes if a full tone color is to be preserved. Certain ill-advised combinations of hole size and spacing can be shown to lead to wide departures from integral frequency ratios, so the decreasing hole diameter required by the intonation considerations of Sec. IV may lead to a worsening of the quality of the notes played through the holes nearest the reed. Furthermore, on conventional instruments where the upper part of the bore is not roughened by the presence of side holes, the effective value of the wall friction coefficient $A$ (see Sec. VI) is less for notes played with many open holes than for those requiring many to be closed. The result is a further increase of $Q$ for the higher notes as compared with the lower ones. These effects together provide a basis for explaining the "deadness" of the so-called bridge notes on a clarinet. A possible escape from the difficulty would be to construct an instrument with fairly constant side

[18] R. D. Fay, J. Acoust. Soc. Am. 12, 62–67 (1940). This work is in excellent accord with theoretical estimates of $A$ provided both thermal and viscous losses are taken into account.

[19] To fix ideas, a pipe 49 cm in length with a radius of 0.7 cm has a fractional band width of $(g/\omega)_w=7.5\times10^{-2}$ $(2n-1)^{-\frac{1}{2}}$. This is in fair agreement with actual measurement on a clarinet.

[20] H. Lamb, *Dynamical Theory of Sound* (Edward Arnold and Company, London, 1910), p. 269.

[21] The fractional band width due to wall losses is larger by a factor of 470 $(2n-1)^{-\frac{3}{2}}$ than the radiation width in the pipe referred to earlier. This means that the two types of damping have comparable effect when the frequency is around 60 times that of the fundamental ($n\cong30$).

hole diameter, compensating this in the manner previously outlined in Sec. IV by a suitably chosen taper of the bore itself. The sequence of the holes might well be continued all the way up to the mouthpiece, the unneeded ones being closed off by a cover plate.

### B. Choice of Bore Diameter

In a family of instruments of various pitches, which are to have similar tone quality, it is necessary to insure that their normal modes should have roughly the same $Q$'s for corresponding notes in their scales. Equations (21) and (22) show that for constant $Q$, one has two sets of criteria; (a) $(l/a^2)=\text{const}$ (if wall losses dominate), (b) $(l/a)=\text{const}$ (if radiation losses dominate). Examination of members of the flute, clarinet, and saxophone families of instruments shows that generally the radius lies within 15% of the value set by criterion (a), in agreement with the conclusions of the preceding section.[22]

### C. Effect of Wall Material on Tone

The much vexed question of the influence of wall material on tone color in woodwinds may be given a partial discussion in the present context. Reference to Fig. 5 shows clearly that altering the band width of any given normal mode (leaving its position unchanged) can have a marked effect on the amplitude of one or more of the Fourier components present in the sound output. Any woodwind whose over-all normal frequencies do not exactly match the corresponding reed harmonics will give rise to a tone color depending on the amount of damping which is present.

Woodwind instruments whose bores are neither perfectly cylindrical nor perfectly conical, those whose mouth-piece cavities give rise to nonconstant corrections, and those with side holes requiring frequency-dependent "end corrections," are therefore expected on theoretical grounds to be more or less sensitive to the material from which they are made, and to its surface conditions. The simple large bore organ pipe, which has been used occasionally in studies of the problem, is an instrument with almost rigorously exact integer relations between its normal modes, and furthermore, a large part of the damping is due to radiation. On theoretical grounds at least, it would appear that an instrument less sensitive to wall material could hardly be found. The very careful experimental work of Boner and Newman on large organ pipes bears this out in detail.[23,24] It should be emphasized that detailed calculations of the positions and band widths of the normal modes are required before definite theoretical statements can be made on the sensitivity of a given type of woodwind to its wall material. These calculations require methods of dealing with the side holes which will be described in a later paper. For this reason it is premature and incorrect to see a contradiction between the present discussion and (for example) the experimental results of Parker,[25] who found the tone color of clarinets to be essentially independent of their wall material.

## VIII. ACKNOWLEDGMENTS

The author would like to thank R. M. Haybron for measurements performed on band widths of the normal modes in pipes. J. C. Stavash, head of Educator's Music Service (Cleveland), a professional musician and repairman, has provided much helpful information and comment. The interest and assistance of H. B. Miller of the Clevite Research Laboratory (Cleveland) is also gratefully acknowledged.

## APPENDIX I

Experiments and calculations going back at least to the work of E. Weber in 1825 have shown that a reed-pipe combination, of the sort used in musical instruments, always emits a sound that is of lower frequency than the closed-end frequency of the pipe alone.[26,27] The over-all behavior of the reed-pipe combination is a study in itself. For the purposes of this paper on woodwind bores, it is important only to show that the effect of the reed is not so large as to prevent the usefulness of a study of isolated pipes with the reed replaced by a closed end. Figure 6 shows in summary form the behavior of the compound system as it is relevant to the present inquiry.[28] In this diagram, the normal mode frequencies of a cylindrical pipe closed at one end are shown as a function of tube length. For example, the curve $ABC$ represents the length dependence of the third mode of such a pipe. Also shown are the frequencies produced by a normal-sized reed coupled to this pipe, as in a clarinet. The curve $AB'C'$ shows the behavior of the third mode in this case. It will be observed that in a reed-driven pipe there is a limiting frequency above which the instrument cannot sound, even for arbitrarily short pipes and high mode

[22] It is worth commenting that criterion (b) is used by organ builders in designing sets of pipes. It is usually attributed to Cavillé-Coll [Compt. rend. 48, 176 (1860)], who obtained it from geometrical considerations governing the frequency alone. Most organ pipes are built with relatively large bores, however, so that radiation damping may well be dominant.

[23] C. P. Boner and R. B. Newman, J. Acoust. Soc. Am. 12, 83 (1940).

[24] The wooden bugle made by Mahillon, and the Tenite bugles manufactured during World War II, might also be cited in this connection as being instruments in which radiation damping dominates over the playing range so that the tone is not strongly influenced by the nature of the wall material.

[25] S. Parker, J. Acoust. Soc. Am. 19, 415 (1947).

[26] See reference 9, especially Chap. II, Vol. II.

[27] The experimental results of V. Aschoff on the clarinet [Akust. Z. 1, 77 (1936)] are, in the main, anticipated and explained in reference 26. The conditions of this later work are not sufficiently close to the way reeds are used by a clarinetist that they need be considered further in the present context. It may be noted however that if clarinets behaved in a player's hands as they did in Aschoff's experiments, the instrument would be musically useless. Experiments bearing on this are described later in the appendix.

[28] This diagram is adapted from *Instruments à Vent*. See reference 8, Fig. 24, Vol. II, p. 83.

numbers. For a free reed, this limiting frequency $\omega_{max}$ is essentially that of the free mechanical vibration of the reed, independent of wind pressure. This result can be obtained by elementary analysis of the phase relations required between the reed and air vibrations in a regenerative system. The behavior of a beating reed is more complicated, since $\omega_{max}$ is then determined jointly by the reed mass and stiffness, the type of table, blowing pressure and lip tension.

It is important for present purposes to show that under *playing conditions* the limiting frequency of the reed is high enough above the first two or three normal mode frequencies of the pipe that the notes obtained are in reasonably close agreement with the behavior of a simple closed pipe. A rough check is easily made by separating a clarinet at its middle joint, and measuring the frequency of the lowest mode as excited by the player. The instrument is taken apart to remove the complicated end correction produced by the finger holes, leaving only the mouthpiece cavity correction discussed in Sec. V. When the pipe is played as sharp as possible (this being the desired situation for simple analysis, as shown by Fig. 6), one finds that the flattening effect due to the reed is only a fraction of a semitone. This sort of experiment is not conclusive for the higher modes, however, because of disturbances arising at the register key, from variations in the bore, and from the closed-hole effects that are discussed in Sec. IV. It is better to use smooth-walled cylindrical tubes of various lengths, drilled at the ideal places for speaker holes to assist in the production of higher modes. These holes may generally be closed once the tone is stabilized, so that their presence cannot produce any complication. The present writer has studied an ordinary clarinet reed used with a standard mouthpiece and matching tubing. Measurements were made for tubes varying in length between 16 and 76 cm, a range greater than that used in clarinets. Over this range the frequencies produced were less than 5% lower than those expected from a pipe closed off at the reed aperture.[29] The frequency ratios between the normal modes of a given pipe were integral to an accuracy of two or three percent.[30] All of these measurements were made with the notes played as sharp as possible, so that they were well defined by the properties of the pipe (since $\omega_{max}$ has its highest possible value). Such simple measurements as were made are relevant to the present discussion of woodwind bores because as normally played, the reed is used well within a semitone of its sharpest possible frequency. They show that the chief effect of the reed system on a given piece of tubing is to increase its effective length by an amount which is nearly constant with frequency (as shown by the accurately integral normal mode frequency ratios). It is therefore worthwhile to consider the properties of pipes which are closed at one end, even though the effective acoustical pipe differs in its length from the physical pipe. The discrepancies between the reed-driven frequencies of a pipe and the normal modes of the same pipe closed at the reed end have been shown to be small in the mathematical sense, even though they cannot be ignored in the construction of instruments. The mathematical smallness of the effects makes it permissible to have separate analyses of the bores and tone holes of a woodwind, leaving the synthesis of these passive systems to the active reed system to a separate perturbation-theory type of calculation. In any event, at the present state of understanding of woodwinds, it is useful to have accounts of the properties of their various parts, for the qualitative help they can give to the musician and designer.

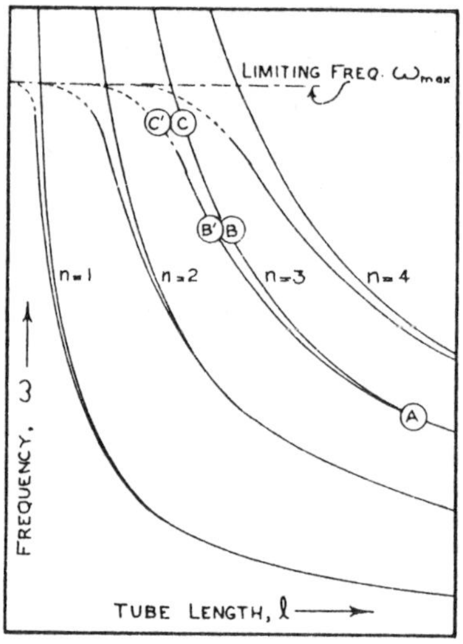

[29] The mouthpiece cavity itself was allowed for in the manner discussed in Sec. V, so that the figures quoted here refer to the flattening produced by the reed system alone.

[30] This inquiry was greatly aided by the Pruefer Clarinet Company of Providence, Rhode Island, who were kind enough to supply several barrels and sections of clarinet upper joints unpierced by finger holes. Later, C. G. Conn Ltd. of Elkhart, Indiana, provided soprano and bass clarinet mouthpieces modified so that they could be used, respectively, with tubes made from $\frac{1}{2}$- and $\frac{3}{4}$-in. thin wall electrical conduit. Experiments made with these different types of bore gave consistent results.

FIG. 6. Diagram showing the frequencies of the normal modes of a cylindrical pipe, closed at one end, as a function of tube length, together with frequencies produced by this pipe when driven by a reed. The curve *ABC* shows, for example, the length dependence of the third mode of the simple pipe, while *AB'C'* shows the third mode frequencies produced by a reed on the same pipe.

## APPENDIX II

It has been shown that the Bessel horn family satisfies a musically imposed requirement that the frequency ratios of the various normal modes be independent of the length of the horn. It remains to be shown that this property is possessed uniquely by the Bessel horns.

The cross-sectional area of a general horn, at a distance $x$ from the closed end, may always be represented by a suitably chosen polynomial in $x$. Let the degree of the polynomial be $N$, and the lowest power of $x$ be $M$, then

$$S(x)=\sum_{n=M}^{N} S_n x^n. \tag{23}$$

Consider the limiting behavior of this generalized horn for very long and very short horns, for the case of finite $N$. In an enormously long horn, the dominant term in the cross-sectional area expression is $S_N X^N$ over most of the length of the horn, so that the normal mode frequency ratios approach those of a Bessel horn with flare parameter $\epsilon=N$. On the other hand, in arbitrarily short horns the order of the area polynomial reduces to $M$. Thus any horn, when sufficiently shortened, possesses normal mode ratios which approach those of a Bessel horn having a flare parameter $\epsilon=M$. For horns of intermediate length, the normal mode frequency ratios will fall somewhere between those of the two limiting Bessel horns. The foregoing discussion shows that the general horn (of finite order $N$) will possess length-dependent frequency ratios except in the following three cases: (a) very long horns, where $S_N x^N \gg S_{N-1} x^{N-1}$, (b) very short horns, where $S_M x^M \gg S_{M+1} x^{M+1}$, (c) when $N=M$. The first two possibilities are essentially trivial, while the third case merely amounts to a redefinition of the Bessel horn family itself. Horns represented by *infinite* power series in $x$ (such as the exponential horn) require slightly different discussion to bring them within the framework of the preceding analysis. Very long horns of this type never approach the behavior of a limiting Bessel horn, due to the convergence properties of the terms in the infinite series. On the other hand a sufficiently short horn *will* approach a limiting Bessel horn in its frequency ratios, so that the length dependence of the frequency ratios is established for this class of horns.

The conclusion to be drawn from the foregoing set of arguments is that Bessel horns are the *only* horns which satisfy the primary requirement for instruments making use of side holes. They constitute the only family of bores in which the normal mode frequency ratios are independent of the length of the horn.

[*Editor's Note:* Inked corrections made and Erratum prepared by A. H. Benade in February 1963.]

ERRATUM

The n'th characteristic frequency of a cut-off cone is given by

$$\tan(\omega_n \ell/c) = -(\omega_n \ell/c)r \tag{5}$$
$$r = (x_0/\ell)$$

A useful algebraic approximation for $\omega_n$ is given in Eq. (5a).

$$\omega_n = (c/\ell)\left[n\pi - \arctan(n\pi r - yr\cos^2 y)\right] \tag{5a}$$
$$y = \arctan(n\pi r)$$

This is accurate to within a few hundredths of a semitone over the range of musical interest. In the limit of small $x_0$ the frequencies reduce to those given in Eq. (6). See reference 11 at the bottom of page 139.

$$\omega_n = (n\pi c)/(\ell + x_0) \tag{6}$$

The simple result given here will prove useful elsewhere in this paper.

In conical woodwinds with finite $(x_0/\ell)$, the actual frequencies are somewhat sharper than those given in Eq. (6). An exact calculation shows for example that if r = 0.2, the lowest mode is only about 0.07 semitones sharper than the simple result, while the modal frequency ratios are spread out so that the second, third, fourth, and fifth modes are sharp by about 0.5, 0.9, 1.3, and 1.5 semitones relative to a harmonic series based on the correctly-calculated lowest mode. Similar calculations using the unrealistically large value of r = 0.4 show on the other hand that the lowest mode is now raised by as much as 1.5 semitones, and the harmonic series is stretched by about 1.0, 1.5, 2.0, and 2.5 semitones.

# 23

Copyright © 1960 by the Acoustical Society of America

Reprinted from *J. Acoust. Soc. Am.*, **32**(12), 1591–1608 (1960)

## On the Mathematical Theory of Woodwind Finger Holes

A. H. BENADE
*Case Institute of Technology, Cleveland 6, Ohio*

(Received May 13, 1960)

The acoustical effects of open and closed finger holes on woodwind bores in the lower two playing registers are investigated in a mathematical formulation which permits a coherent and comprehensive understanding of the interaction of holes with the bore of a woodwind. Results are expressed in a way which permits accurate engineering calculation of all effects which are discussed. It is shown that when the holes are closed at their outer ends, the system is simply and accurately representable by an adaptation of standard transmission line theory for a tube with side branches. Interestingly, this representation is only possible for musically usable hole sizes and spacings. A related formulation is also possible for a sequence of open finger holes: once again the accuracy of the formulation is greatest for musically usable holes. The part of a woodwind bore that is provided with closed side holes functions as a low-pass filter. Similarly the open holes lower down on the bore function as a high-pass filter. The positions of both cutoff frequencies depend critically upon the hole sizes and spacings. Both fall at frequencies which allow them to play a role in the tone production. Methods are given for calculating "end corrections" for bores with some open and some closed holes as well as for bores with perturbations to the bore cross section. The effects of "misplaced" or "mis-sized" holes are investigated by these methods, and the position of the lowest open hole calculated. An estimate of the errors in these calculations shows them to be essentially exact for musical purposes. The radiation behavior of a row of open finger holes is analyzed. Frequencies below the "cutoff" of the open hole system are radiated essentially isotropically, while each of the higher components is emitted with its own pattern, all of which are roughly conical, in analogy with the shock wave produced by a supersonic projectile. The musical implications of this are discussed briefly. Light is shed on the function of the bell on woodwind instruments, and on the reason why a bell is not needed on certain of them. The dominant role of the "closed-hole" properties of a bore with finger holes is stressed throughout the paper.

### I. INTRODUCTION

MUSICAL wind instruments share in common an acoustical system made up of some sort of horn-like resonator together with a reed mechanism which converts the steady wind pressure supplied by the player into oscillatory variations of air pressure within the horn. The normal modes of vibration of this horn play an important part in determining the frequency of oscillation of the reed. If the instrument is to play a complete scale, some means must be provided for changing the normal-mode frequencies of the horn. Modern brass instruments are provided with valve-controlled crooks for this purpose, which introduce varying lengths of tubing into the horn. Woodwinds, on the other hand, have traditionally used finger holes drilled in the side of the horn to alter its normal mode frequencies, the size and spacing of these holes being chosen to give the desired scale.

An earlier paper on the properties of woodwind instruments[1] showed that as a consequence of the use of finger holes, the only musically useful bores for woodwinds are members of the Bessel horn family, in which the cross-sectional area $S(x)$ of the bore varies as some single positive power $\epsilon$ of the distance $x$ from the reed end. Various considerations further limit the bores to two members of this family. The straight cylindrical bore of the clarinet family is a representative of one of these remaining types ($\epsilon=0$), while the conical bore used in oboes, bassoons, and saxophones belongs to the other possibility ($\epsilon=2$). The previous discussion[1] was based on the assumption that opening a series of side holes in the lower part of a woodwind bore is equivalent to cutting off the tube at a point near the position of the highest open hole. This assumption will be examined in the present paper, and also the properties of a bore with many closed side holes will be discussed as an extension of certain remarks made on this topic in the earlier paper. Furthermore, methods will be outlined for the calculation of the effective length of a pipe having many open side holes, and several questions of intonation will be examined, insofar as they relate to the nature of the side holes, in the lower two registers of a woodwind instrument. The action of the register keys, and the acoustic behavior of cross-fingered pipes, will not be taken up in the present context, since a discussion of these matters involves a close examination of the properties of the reed system in addition to those of the bore and its side holes. A theory of the effects of hole size and spacing on the angular distribution of the radiated sound is easily developed once the intonation aspects of fingerhole theory are understood. Such effects, and the light they cast on the nature and use of the bell, will also be dealt with briefly.

The present paper, like its predecessor, is concerned with the theoretical foundations of woodwind instrument design. Once again no attempt is made to formulate a design procedure, since such a formulation can only be meaningful when it takes into account the nature of the excitory reed system as well as that of the bore and its side holes. However, such a formulation must rest upon a clear understanding of the various parts of the complex dynamical system, which are (fortunately for us) subject in large measure to separate analysis.

[1] A. H. Benade, J. Acoust. Soc. Am. **31**, 137 (1959). This paper will be referred to in future as "A".

## II. PIPES WITH MANY CLOSED SIDE HOLES

A woodwind instrument having all its finger holes closed, constitutes a tapered transmission line *with side branches*, whose characteristic impedance and wave velocity properties are affected by the size and spacing of the holes along it. On account of the nature of our musical scale, the spacing of these side branches is not uniform along the pipe, the distance between a given hole and its nearest neighbors being very nearly 6% of the length of the bore from the reed to that particular hole. The hole radius is also variable, as is the thickness of the wall through which it is drilled. Elementary consideration of the closed holes in paper A showed the existence of a necessary relation between the interhole spacing, and the radius of each hole, for a tube with given wall thickness. This matter will now be examined in more rigorous fashion for the simple case of a cylindrical pipe (the extension to conical pipes being more tedious than difficult). Not only will this clarify the relations between the wall thickness, hole size, and hole position, which are determined by the closed-hole properties of the bore, but it will also provide a basis for the calculation of the end correction produced by a series of opened holes below a row of closed ones.

Consider for the moment a long cylindrical pipe, having a bore radius $a$ and wall thickness $t$, pierced by a row of holes of radius $b$ spaced a uniform distance $2s$ apart. These holes are closed on the outer surface of the pipe as is shown in Fig. 1. Such a system of holes on a pipe constitutes a low-pass filter for sound waves traveling down its length, where the characteristic impedance $Z_c$ and propagation constant $\Gamma_c$ of the filter are given for an angular frequency $\omega$ by Eqs. (1) and (2), respectively[2,3] (damping is neglected).

$$Z_c=\left(\frac{\rho c}{\pi a^2}\right)\left(\frac{1-\frac{1}{2}(b/a)^2\tan(\omega t/c)\tan(\omega s/c)}{1+\frac{1}{2}(b/a)^2\tan(\omega t/c)\cot(\omega s/c)}\right)^{\frac{1}{2}} \quad (1)$$

$$\cosh(2\Gamma_c s)=[1-\tfrac{1}{2}(b/a)^2\tan(\omega t/c)\tan(2\omega s/c)]\times\cos(2\omega s/c). \quad (2)$$

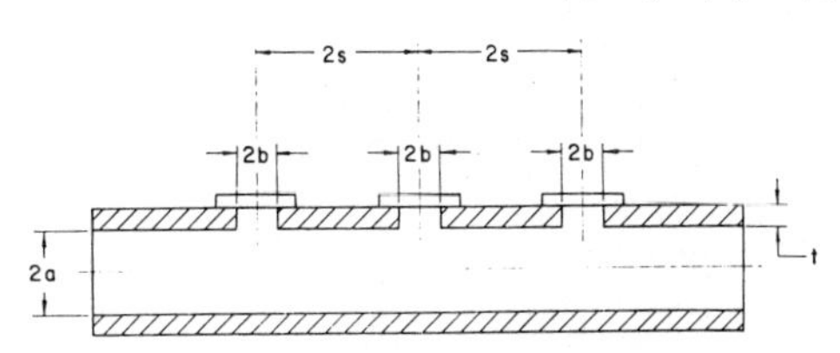


FIG. 1. Basic configuration of a woodwind bore having a radius $a$, and provided with side holes of radius $b$, drilled with a spacing $2s$ through a wall of thickness $t$. These holes are assumed closed at their outer ends by rigid covers.

[2] W. P. Mason, *Electromagnetic Transducers and Wave Filters* D. Van Nostrand Company, Inc., Princeton, New Jersey, 1948), 2nd ed., p. 73, Eq. 2.152.

[3] G. W. Stewart and R. B. Lindsay, *Acoustics* (D. Van Nostrand Company, Inc., Princeton, New Jersey, 1930), Appendix IV, p. 334.

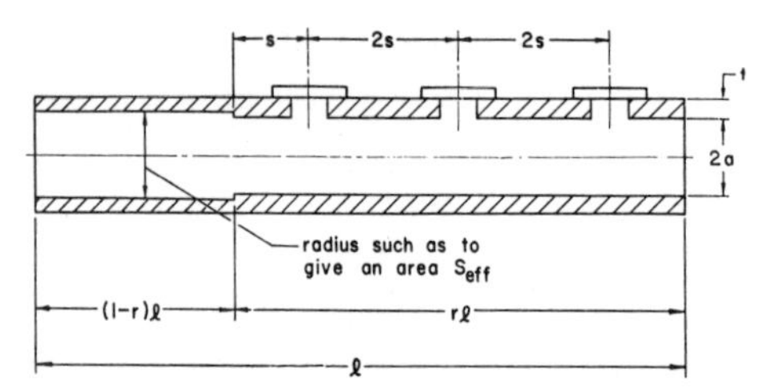


FIG. 2. Closed-hole woodwind bore joined to a smooth-walled tube having the same characteristic impedance. The phase velocity is not the same in the two parts.

In these equations, $c$ stands for the velocity of sound in the open air, and $\rho$ is the mass density of air at atmospheric pressure. Examination of these equations shows that there is free transmission of waves in the duct for all frequencies below a cutoff frequency at which $Z_c$ changes from real to imaginary. Below this cutoff frequency, the hyperbolic cosine in Eq. (2) may be replaced[4] by $\cos(2\omega s/v_c)$, where $v_c$ is the phase velocity of waves propagating in the duct at the frequency $\omega$. The musical implications of the cutoff frequency will not be discussed in this paper; suffice it to say that in woodwinds it lies well above the playing range, and so need not be considered in connection with intonation.

In the musical case, the interhole spacing $2s$ is considerably less than the free-space wavelength of the pipe fundamental, so that it is instructive to make a "low frequency" approximation to Eqs. (1) and (2) by letting $(\omega s/c)\rightarrow 0$, and $(\omega t/c)\rightarrow 0$, as shown in Eqs. (3) and (4).

$$\begin{aligned} Z_c &= (\rho c/\pi a^2)[1+D_c]^{-\frac{1}{2}} \\ D_c &= \tfrac{1}{2}(b/a)^2(t/s) \end{aligned} \tag{3}$$

$$v_c/c=[1+D_c]^{-\frac{1}{2}}. \tag{4}$$

It is interesting to note that due to the symmetry of the cosine, and antisymmetry of the tangent, these approximations are good to third order in $(\omega s/c)$ and $(\omega t/c)$. It is important to notice that both equations depend on the combination $(b/a)^2(t/s)$ of the hole variables. We are now in a position to make use of the fact that the characteristic impedance of a smooth duct is inversely proportional to its cross-sectional area, to find the "effective" cross section of a pipe with closed holes. Equation (3) shows that this effective cross-sectional area (in the sense of paper A, Sec. IV) is given by Eqs. (5a) and (5b).

$$S_{\mathrm{eff}}=\pi a^2[1+D_c]^{\frac{1}{2}} \tag{5a}$$

and if $D_c \ll 1$

$$S_{\mathrm{eff}}\cong\pi a^2[1+(D_c/2)]. \tag{5b}$$

Equation (8) of paper A gave a simple estimate for $S_{\mathrm{eff}}$ for a similar tube which may be cast in the same form as the present Eq. (5b), and differing from it only by a factor of two in the correction term. Thus, while the numerical value of the closed hole effect is now seen to be different, the important earlier conclusion remains unchanged that for proper overblowing the combination $2D_c=(b/a)^2(t/s)$ must remain constant along the tube so as to keep the sound velocity and effective diameter constant over the length of the bore.

Since transmission line theory is easily applicable to systems in which the propagation velocity and characteristic impedance are the same when evaluated anywhere along the line, the foregoing result shows that in the long wavelength limit it is indeed permissible to use such theory for the closed hole part of a woodwind bore, even though it does not constitute a periodic system. All that is required in the playing range of the instrument is that the parameter $D_c$ remain constant.[5]

In addition to the alteration of effective cross section by closed holes, the compressibility of air within the side hole cavities lowers the velocity of sound within the bore, as shown in Eq. (4). Numerically, this reduction of velocity is of the order of a few percent in most woodwinds, an amount which is far from negligible for the designer. While it might be desirable from several points of view to drill side holes into the bore all the way up to the mouth-piece, such a practice is never followed in practice, nor is it usual to avoid reflections by slightly expanding the bore above the highest hole in a manner which makes the actual cross section of the upper bore the same as the effective cross section of the part which has side holes. It is, however, worthwhile to examine the behavior of such a system because of its simplicity and instructiveness, in order to see that the tuning is affected differently for notes played with many closed holes and those using only a few. A closely related problem will be discussed in Sec. IV. Consider the composite pipe of over-all length $l$ shown in Fig. 2. A fraction r of this pipe has a geometrical cross-sectional area $\pi a^2$, and is provided with closed side holes as described in the foregoing; to this is joined a section of smooth-walled pipe with a cross-sectional area calculated with the help of Eq. (5a) using the dimensions of the holes in the other part of the pipe. There will be no reflections set up at the junction of the two parts, since the characteristic impedance is continuous across the boundary, even though the velocity in the smooth-walled section is $c$ while in the section with side holes the velocity is $v_c$ as found from Eq. (4). Direct calculation shows that the average phase velocity of sound in this composite pipe is that given by Eq. (6) in terms of the fractional length r occupied by side holes.

$$V_{\mathrm{av}}=c\{1-r[1-(v_c/c)]\}. \tag{6}$$

A somewhat more usual way in which to express this result is to find a "length correction" $\Delta l$, which is to be added to the geometrical length of the composite system

[4] See work cited in footnote 2, p. 31, for a discussion of the transmission function as it depends on frequency.

[5] This statement also applies to conical bore instruments.

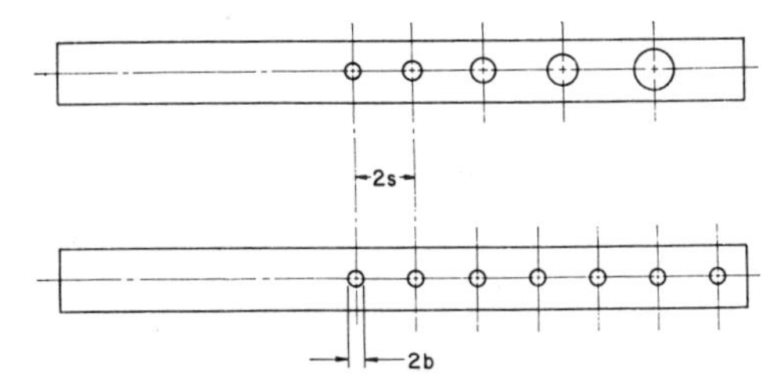


Fig. 3. Schematic representation of a woodwind provided with open holes whose size and spacing increase progressively (above); together with "equivalent" bore with evenly spaced holes of fixed size (below). The size and spacing of these holes is equal to that of the first two holes of the actual bore.

in order to find the acoustical length of a smooth walled tube with the same resonance frequencies. For a composite pipe of the sort diagrammed in Fig. 2, this length correction may be found with the help of Eq. (6) to be the value given by Eq. (7).

$$\Delta l = l\left\{\frac{r-[1-(v_c/c)]}{1-r[1-(v_c/c)]}\right\}. \tag{7}$$

Very similar considerations also apply to conical bore instruments, provided certain precautions are observed in the matching of the tapers and diameters of the unpierced sections of the bore.

### III. PIPES WITH MANY OPEN SIDE HOLES

The size and spacing of the finger holes of a woodwind are jointly determined by the twin necessities of having the correct effective bore in that part of the instrument where the holes are closed (as discussed in the preceding section) and of the need for obtaining a chromatic scale by successively opening the holes. Very fortunately for mathematical analysis, the interaction of these two requirements is small enough to permit a separate analysis of each at the beginning, after which it is possible to make a synthesis which permits accurate calculations of the over-all acoustic properties of the bore and its set of holes.

It has been 30 years since Richardson first applied impedance theory to the calculation of normal modes of a pipe with side holes,[6] but his formulation was only tractable when applied to the case of one or two open holes in a pipe, and was basically a graphical method from which it was difficult to draw any general conclusions. Attempts to apply transmission line theory to the open hole system of a woodwind were stalled (in the present author's mind at least) by the common knowledge that the equations governing a lumped-constant line with variable coefficients are very complicated, a complication which is aggravated by the fact that in musical instruments the coefficients may change very greatly in the distance of one (free-space) wavelength. These *ab initio* considerations overlook a familiar fact, known to musicians and designers alike, that the frequency and tone quality of a given played note are almost wholly independent of the size and position of the open holes beyond the first two or three.[7] This independence implies that a meaningful approximate theory might be constructed with the help of an assumed "equivalent" transmission line having its holes uniformly sized and spaced according to the dimensions and spacing of the *first two open holes alone* in the manner shown by Fig. 3. A study of the impedance and propagation properties of this equivalent uniform line will permit calculation of the acoustical behavior of several of the lowest vibrational modes of a real woodwind when account is taken of the composite nature of the system. That is, the actual instrument bore is treated as being in three major parts: (a) a smooth tube between mouthpiece and the first closed hole, (b) a lumped-constant uniform low-pass line created by the sequence of closed holes, and (c) a lumped constant line associated with the remaining holes which are open. The calculation of resonance frequencies, etc., must, of course, be made for the complete system.

The characteristic impedance $Z_0$ and propagation constant $\Gamma_0$ of a long cylindrical pipe of radius $a$ and wall thickness $t$, pierced by open holes of radius $b$ spaced a uniform distance $2s$ apart, may be shown[2,3] to take the form shown in Eqs. (8) and (9), where $t_e$ represents the "effective length" of the open side hole. As in the preceding section, damping is neglected.

$$Z_0 = \left(\frac{\rho c}{\pi a^2}\right)\left(\frac{1+\frac{1}{2}(b/a)^2\cot(\omega t_e/c)\tan(\omega s/c)}{1-\frac{1}{2}(b/a)^2\cot(\omega t_e/c)\cot(\omega s/c)}\right)^{\frac{1}{2}}. \tag{8}$$

$$\cosh(2\Gamma_0 s) = [1+\tfrac{1}{2}(b/a)^2\cot(\omega t_e/c)\tan(2\omega s/c)] \times\cos(2\omega s/c). \tag{9}$$

Since the interhole spacing $2s$, and the effective thickness $t_e$ are once again very much smaller than the wavelength of the played notes in a musical instrument, it is useful and instructive to find the "long-wave-length" approximations to these formulas, as shown in Eqs. (10) and (11).

$$Z_0 = j(\rho c/\pi a^2)\{(2t_e/s)[1+D_0]\}^{\frac{1}{2}}(a/b)(\omega s/c),\quad D_0=\tfrac{1}{2}(b/a)^2(s/t_e). \tag{10}$$

$$\cosh(2\Gamma_0 s) = [1+D_0]. \tag{11}$$

[6] E. G. Richardson, *Technical Aspects of Sound* (Elsevier Publishing Company, Inc., New York, 1953), Vol. 1, p. 488. The general subject is discussed (with references extending back to the work of Lambert in 1775) in H. Bouasse, *Instruments à Vent* (Librairie Delagrave, Paris, 1930), Vol. II, pp. 111–138. Dr. R. W. Young has recently called to my attention an earlier paper, by W. Steinhausen, Ann. Physik **48**, 693 (1915), in which basic tone hole theory is presented, with a graphical solution, but this was not an "impedance" calculation.

[7] This remark is not intended as a rigorously correct statement but rather as a strong hint on how an approximate theory may be constructed. The validity of the statement may then be re-evaluated in the light of the successes and failures of such a theory.

Inspection of Eq. (10) discloses that at low frequencies the characteristic impedance is a pure (masslike) imaginary quantity, so that a musical instrument ending with a row of open holes behaves very much like a pipe terminated by a tubular aperture. A detailed discussion of such a composite system appears as Sec. V of this paper. The hyperbolic cosine in Eq. (11) has a magnitude greater than unity in the low-frequency limit, which shows that the system operates like a high-pass filter below cutoff so that there is no wavelike propagation in the open-hole section of the bore; the pressure variations being in phase all down its length but damped exponentially with a linear attenuation coefficient $\alpha_0$ given by Eq. (12), where

$$\alpha_0=(1/2s)\cosh^{-1}[1+D_0]. \qquad (12)$$

As a result, the pressure amplitude at the $i$th hole is greater than that at the $(i+1)$st hole (a distance $2s$ below it on the bore) by an amount given in Eq. (13), where

$$p_i/p_{(i+1)}=\exp\{\cosh^{-1}[1+D_0]\}. \qquad (13)$$

The smaller holes on a clarinet or oboe are so spaced and proportioned that the pressure amplitude falls by about 0.75 from hole to hole, while the large holes of a flute or saxophone give rise to a very high attenuation (of the order of 0.06) between holes. The angular distribution and intensity of the radiated lower frequency components of a woodwind tone will among other things be controlled by the rate of attenuation calculated here (see Sec. VI of this paper). It should be emphasized at this point that not all of the sound output of a woodwind falls within the qualitative domain of validity of the approximations given in Eqs. (8)–(13). The fundamental assumption of the present analysis is that the lower open holes of a real woodwind do not determine the effective impedance presented to the closed-hole part of the bore by the open-hole part. Mathematically this represented by the fact that the open-hole system acts as a nonpropagating line, so that "messages" concerning the nonuniformity of the line are not carried back to the main bore. Those components of the tonal spectrum of an instrument which lie above the cutoff frequency implied by a sign change in the denominator of Eq. (8) will, at first thought, appear to propagate with very little reflection down the open-hole portion of the bore. This is not actually the case as may readily be verified. Once a wave is presumed to propagate freely in the open-hole part of the instrument, we have explicitly violated the initial assumption that the lower bore has no effect upon the impedance, and Eq. (8) must be replaced by a more realistic expression which has the qualitative nature of a formula for the impedance of some kind of flaring horn-like extension to the closed hole bore. To sum up, the present simple theory may be expected to be quite good for those components of the tonal spectrum which lie below cutoff, while those falling above this frequency will be affected in a different manner which depends upon the detailed arrangement of all of the open holes.

## IV. LENGTH CORRECTIONS FOR BORES WITH CLOSED HOLES

### A. General Discussion

For many years it has been customary to give the vibration frequency of a complex resonator in terms of the length of some closely related simple resonator. There is the familiar example of the cylindrical pipe of length $l$ and radius $a$ that is closed at one end by a cavity of volume $V$. Here the effective length of the resonator is easily shown[8] to be $[l+(V/\pi a^2)]$; in other words, a cylindrical pipe of this new length, but closed by a plug at one end, would have the same fundamental resonance frequency. A point which is sometimes neglected in regard to these end corrections is that they are almost always frequency dependent so that the higher modes of oscillation of the complex resonator do not in general coincide in frequency with the corresponding modes of the standard resonator. For the case of a small cavity on the end of a cylindrical pipe, the correction remains almost exactly constant with rising frequency until the linear dimensions of the cavity become comparable with the sound wavelength within it. On the other hand, it is shown in $A$ [Eq. (17)] that the length correction for the same cavity mounted on a conical bore varies drastically with frequency.

Because woodwind bores with open and closed holes constitute systems in which the velocity of sound may vary with frequency, and because both conical and cylindrical tubes are used, there can be considerable confusion as to whether the acoustical length used in a given calculation is based on the internal velocity of sound or on the external free-space velocity $c$. To avoid this ambiguity, and for other reasons which will become apparent, the length correction $\Delta l_k$ for a complex pipe system whose desired *lowest* mode frequency is $\omega_k$ will be given as a fraction $F_k$ of the freespace quarter wavelength of this frequency for a clarinet-like bore (cylinder closed at one end), and of the free space half wavelength for flute-like bores (cylinder open at both ends) and for oboelike bores (complete cones closed at the small end). $F_k=\Delta l_k/l_k$, where

$$l_k=\pi c/2\omega_k \text{ (clarinet)},$$
$$l_k=\pi c/\omega_k \text{ (flute, oboe, sax, etc.)}. \qquad (14)$$

The mechanical length $L_k$ of the actual bore is then given by Eq. (15), where

$$L_k=l_k(1-F_k). \qquad (15)$$

Usually it is important to know what the corrections are at frequencies that are integral multiples of $\omega_k$; for this reason, it is useful to define $F_k(m)$ as the value of $F$ at the $m$th harmonic of $\omega_k$. For example, one might

[8] See paper A, Eq. (15).

wish to use Eq. (15) with $m=1$ to calculate the proper length for a clarinet bore which is to play the (chalumeau register) frequency $\omega_k$, and then find it worthwhile to check up on the intonation of the $n$th modes by evaluating $F_k(m)$ for the odd integers $m=(2n-1)$. In general there are several end corrections to be considered simultaneously: the mouthpiece cavity produces one of these as already mentioned, as does the blown reed. In addition to these are the corrections resulting from the open and the closed side holes as well as to the irregularities in the bore, not to mention the results of damping. These several corrections are additive in first order, so that if each correction is labeled by a subscript $i$ the complete equation for the length $L_k$ of a bore which is to play the note $\omega_k$ is that shown as Eq. (16), where

$$L_k = l_k(1-\textstyle\sum_i F_{ik}). \quad (16)$$

There is one such equation for each note in the low register of the instrument, the subscript $k$ giving the serial number of the note beginning with the lowest in the scale. Once the various $F$'s have been found, the design of a woodwind is in principle straightforward. All that is required is to drill the holes for all the notes at the proper distances $L_k$ from the reference mark at the top of the bore, after which the mouthpiece is attached so that it also is at the proper position relative to this same mark.

### B. Effect of Small Variations in the Cross-Sectional Area

In a typical woodwind the bore is not precisely cylindrical (or conical), and small variations from these idealized shapes arise not only from irregularly spaced or duplicated finger holes but also from deliberate alterations introduced by the builder in an attempt to improve the tone, the "response," and the tuning of his instruments. For the present, we shall consider a bore to be "uniform" in its shape if the effective cross-sectional area [as defined by Eq. (5b)] remains constant in the case of "cylindrical" instruments (clarinet, flute), or if it grows as the squared distance from the apex of the cone in instruments such as the oboe, saxophone, and bassoon. The slowing down of waves in a pipe with closed side holes gives rise to a separate end-correction as already explained at the end of Sec. II so that here we will take the wave velocity within the bore to be simply $c$.

Let $S_0(x)$ represent the bore cross-sectional area at a distance $x$ from the upper end of the idealized pipe under consideration, so that $S_0=\pi a^2$ for cylindrical bores, and $S_0=\pi a^2(x/l)^2$ for conical pipes. In both cases the radius of the open lower end is $a$, and $l$ represents the idealized physical length. Let the variations of an actual bore from this idealized cross section be represented by a perturbing area $S_p(x)$ such that $(S_p/S_0)\ll 1$ at all points in the bore. The frequency of oscillation of the $n$th mode of such a perturbed system may be accurately calculated by Rayleigh's method which exploits the equality of the mean potential and kinetic energies of the vibrator and which makes use of wave functions belonging to the unperturbed bores.[9] A convenient place to begin is from the velocity potential $\Phi_n(x,t) = \phi_n(x)\cos\omega_n t$ which represents the vibrations appropriate to the $n$th mode of each type of idealized bore,[10] as shown in Eqs. (17a)–(17c). For a cylindrical tube closed at $x=0$ (clarinet-type bore),

$$\phi=\cos kx, \quad k=(2n-1)\pi/2l. \quad (17a)$$

For a cylindrical tube open at both ends (flute-type bore),

$$\phi=\sin kx, \quad k=n\pi/l. \quad (17b)$$

For a conical tube closed at a distance $x_0$ from the apex with a length $l$ between apex and open end (oboe, sax, etc., bore),

$$\begin{aligned}\phi &= (1/x)[\sin(kx)+B\cos(kx)],\\ B &= [kx_0-\tan(kx_0)][1+(kx_0)\tan(kx_0)]^{-1}, \quad (17c)\\ k &= n\pi/l \text{ (note } B\to 0 \text{ as } x_0\to 0).\end{aligned}$$

In these equations the propagation constant $k$ is the one appropriate to the unperturbed bore and is further limited for the conical bore to the musically useful case where $(x_0/l)\lesssim 1/4$.

The ratio of the mean kinetic to the mean potential energy may be written in terms of the space and time derivatives of $\Phi$ as shown in Eq. (18) which may then be solved for $\omega^2$ as shown in Eq. (18a),

$$1=\langle KE/PE\rangle_{\text{av}} = \frac{c^2\int_0^l (\partial\Phi/\partial x)^2\cdot(S_0+S_p)dx}{\int_0^l (\partial\Phi/\partial t)^2\cdot(S_0+S_p)dx}, \quad (18)$$

$$\omega^2 = \frac{c^2\int_0^l (\partial\phi/\partial x)^2\cdot(S_0+S_p)dx}{\int_0^l \phi^2\cdot(S_0+S_p)dx}. \quad (18a)$$

Each of the integrals appearing here may be separated into an unperturbed part proportional to $S_0$ and a much smaller perturbing part whose size is determined by $S_p$. A little juggling of terms, keeping only first powers of the perturbing integrals shows that the altered system vibrates so that its $n$th mode is equal in frequency to that of an idealized bore whose length is increased by

[9] G. Temple and W. G. Bickley, *Rayleigh's Principle* (Dover Publications, New York, 1956), pp. 1–24.

[10] See work cited in footnote 3, pp. 20–31.

the amount $\Delta l$ which is given by Eq. (19a)–(19c). For clarinet-type bores with $S_0=\pi a^2$,

$$\Delta l=+\int_0^l\left(\frac{S_p}{S_0}\right)\cos\left[\frac{(2n-1)\pi x}{l}\right]dx. \quad (19a)$$

For flute-type bores[11] with $S_0=\pi a^2$,

$$\Delta l=-\int_0\left(\frac{S_p}{S_0}\right)\cos\left[\frac{2n\pi x}{l}\right]dx. \quad (19b)$$

For a cone that is complete to the apex[12] with $S_0=\pi a^2(x/l)^2$,

$$\Delta l=-\int_0^l\left(\frac{S_p}{S_0}\right)\left\{\cos\left[\frac{2n\pi x}{l}\right]+\left(\frac{l}{n\pi x}\right)\sin\left[\frac{2n\pi x}{l}\right]+\left(\frac{l}{n\pi x}\right)^2\sin^2\left[\frac{n\pi x}{l}\right]\right\}dx. \quad (19c)$$

Examination of these expressions shows that an enlargement of the bore in the neighborhood of a pressure node of the standing wave always raises the vibrational frequency, while an enlargement near an antinode of pressure lowers the frequency. As a result, the effect of a given perturbation of the bore may sharpen or flatten a note, depending on the note being played and on the register which is in use, as will be shown by numerical examples in a later part of this section.

A glance at Fig. 2 shows that on instruments whose bore is *not* enlarged above the highest hole, there is an effective *contraction* of the upper (holeless) bore in the amount $S_p=-(\pi b^2 t/2s)$. The length correction for such an instrument is the sum of those given by Eq. (7) and Eq. (19).

### C. Effect of Duplicated, Missing, or Mis-Sized Closed Holes

The presence of a closed hole of volume $V=\pi b^2 t$ located at the position $x_i$ along the otherwise regular bore of an instrument may be represented mathematically by a delta-function perturbation to the cross-sectional area of the form given in Eq. (20), where

$$S_p(x)=V\delta(x-x_i). \quad (20)$$

This perturbation is to be used in the potential energy (denominator) term of Eqs. (18) and (18a), but *not in the numerator*, since physical considerations show that the compression of air in the cavity can very well alter the potential energy of the complete system, but the small extent of the hole in the axial direction of the bore precludes the possibility of much longitudinal motion and so eliminates the hole's contribution to the kinetic energy. A shallow hole whose diameter is comparable with that of the bore (as on a flute) is not very well represented by this formulation, nor is a smaller hole whose inner end has been "fraised" extensively. For these two cases it would be possible to use the complete Rayleigh expression with an experimentally determined coefficient multiplying the kinetic energy perturbation term. This coefficient would be zero for an ordinary small diameter hole and close to unity for a very shallow large one.

Another method of calculation (which is perhaps more fashionable nowadays), is based on impedance methods as follows: The part of a bore which extends a distance $l_i=(l-x_i)$ beyond the hole position $x_i$, together with hole cavity itself, may be thought of as forming an admittance which acts as a "load" for the upper part of the bore. The problem of finding a length correction $\Delta l$ consists of calculating the proper length $(l_i+\Delta l)$ of unperturbed bore which has precisely the same admittance as does the actual system. If $Y(l_1)$ represents the admittance at $x_i$ of the part of the bore which lies beyond the hole, and if $Y_h$ is the admittance of the closed hole, then the problem may be indicated schematically in the manner of Eq. (21), where

$$Y(l_i+\Delta l)=Y_h+Y(l_i). \quad (21)$$

If the hole admittance is sufficiently small (and this is a question which is easiest answered in the Rayleigh-method context), then one is led to replace $Y(l_i+\Delta l)$ by a two-term Taylor expansion $Y(l_i)+(dY/dl)\Delta l$, so that Eq. 21 can be solved directly for $\Delta l$. Let $Y(l_i) =-j(\pi a^2/\rho c)\cot(kl_i)$ and $Y_h=+j(\pi b^2/\rho c)\tan(kt)$ with $k$ set equal to $\omega/c$, or better yet with the value of $k$ given by the definitions appearing in Eq. (17). Then $\Delta l$ will be found to take the forms given in Eq. (22a) and (22b). For clarinet-type bores with $S_0=\pi a^2$,

$$\Delta l=\left(\frac{V_i}{S_0}\right)\cos^2\left[\frac{(2n-1)\pi x_i}{2l}\right]. \quad (22a)$$

For flute-type bores with $S_0=\pi a^2$, and for oboe-type bores with $(x_0/l)<0.25$ for which $S_0=\pi a^2(x_i/l)^2$,

$$\Delta l=\left(\frac{V_i}{S_0}\right)\sin^2\left[\frac{n\pi x_i}{l}\right]. \quad (22b)$$

Note that if $x_i\rightarrow 0$ the length corrections become the mouthpiece corrections given in Eqs. (15) and (16) of paper A.

While it is not particularly clear from the form of the impedance equations, an examination of Rayleigh's method of calculation in this same problem shows that the net length correction resulting from several closed holes located along the bore is accurately given by the sum of the separate corrections obtained for each hole by the use of Eq. (22a) or (22b). As a matter of fact,

[11] This case is given in Rayleigh, *Theory of Sound* (Dover Publications, New York, 1945), Vol. II, Sec. 265, p. 67.

[12] The exact expression for the frustum of a cone is not given here for reasons of simplicity and brevity; the general conclusions remain the same for the more complicated case.

the length correction given by Eq. (7) may be computed in a new way by the simultaneous application of Eq. (19) for the enlarged upper bore along with the sum of terms from Eq. (22) for all the closed holes in the lower part of the bore, whether or not they satisfy the regularity condition laid down in Sec. II.

We should notice at this point that impedance methods of the ordinary sort employed here can take correct account of vibrations along the axes of the side holes, but they do not give even a hint of the presence of effects which result from transverse motion in the holes. The direct physical approach of Rayleigh focuses attention on the actual motion of the air in a way which can be explained to anyone, and which readily suggests approximations that are useful and instructive.

Until now it has been assumed that the closed holes form perturbations in a smooth-walled bore of standard type, while the considerations of Sec. II show that a properly laid out set of closed holes gives an effective bore which is slightly larger than that of the original instrument before the side holes are drilled and that furthermore the velocity of sound in this enlarged bore is slightly reduced. In order to use the results of the present section for computations on an actual bore with closed side holes, one has merely to replace $S_0$ in all the formulas by the value $S_{\text{eff}}(x)$ given by Eq. (5b). This correction applies equally well to both cylindrical and conical bore instruments and is constant along the bore for instruments whose holes satisfy the regularity conditions mentioned in the foregoing. On instruments in which the hole size and spacing does not exactly follow the condition of constancy laid down on $D_c$, $S_0$ becomes $S_{\text{eff}}$ evaluated from the *average* value of this combination and $S_p(x)$ contains a term representing the local deviations from this average, in addition to the other perturbations which are considered more explicitly in the present section.

Many woodwinds have duplicated side holes for certain notes placed there for the purpose of easing the technical problems of the musician. The duplication of the G# hole on the Boehm flute is an example, as is the hole controlled by the right-hand cross key for playing low B on the Boehm clarinet. A more troublesome duplication appears on the upper joint of a clarinet, where not one, but two extra holes are provided for the playing of D# above middle C. These extra holes will give rise to frequency changes of varying sizes for all notes played with one or more holes closed below them in an amount determined by Eq. (22), and there is *no accurate means of eliminating the disturbance.* At first thought it would seem logical to put a projecting lug into the bore opposite to the hole to form a "negative volume" equal to the positive volume introduced by the extra closed hole. However, there is no possible way to do this without constricting the *flow* of air in the neighborhood of the hole and its correcting lug, so that there is a kinetic energy contribution to the Rayleigh integrals or a series inductance to be considered in the admittance equations. Put more briefly: unlike a closed hole, a projection into the bore behaves like a true constriction so that its effects must be calculated from Eq. (19) rather than from Eq. (22). Equation (19) shows that a given perturbation can raise or lower the frequencies of various notes affected by it, while Eq. (22) can only lower the frequency. As a result, it is impossible to find a way in which to ream the bore or to choose a projection which will compensate exactly for a duplicated hole.

### D. Effect of a Displaced Closed Finger Hole

It sometimes happens that one side hole is displaced from its "proper" position in the regular sequence of holes and moved down or up the bore a short distance $\delta$, so that it is located at the position $(x_i+\delta)$. In order to preserve the tuning of the note played with this particular hole open, the hole must be enlarged above its normal size if $\delta$ is positive and decreased if $\delta$ is negative.[13] The amount by which the size must be altered is determined by the open-hole properties of the instruments which are discussed in the next section. The effect of this altered hole on the tuning of all those notes of the scale which require the closing of holes below the altered one may be calculated upon the basis of Eq. (22) as follows.

A displaced hole may be considered as the combination of (a) a *negative* perturbing volume $V$ equal to the volume of the normal hole (located at $x_i$) which it replaces, together with (b) a positive perturbation $V'$ of the actual hole located at its displaced position $(x_i+\delta)$. If we represent both versions of Eq. (22) by the schematic form $\Delta l = Vf(x)$, where $f(x)$ is the trigonometric factor divided by $S_0$, then the correction arising from the displaced hole is given by Eq. (23), where

$$\Delta l = V'f(x_i+\delta) - Vf(x_i). \tag{23}$$

If the fractional displacement $(2n-1)\delta/l$ for clarinets, or $n\delta/l$ for flutes and conical instruments is much less than unity, as is almost always the case in practice, the length correction may be rewritten as a Taylor expansion whose leading terms are convenient for discussion and for computation as shown by

$$\Delta l = (V'-V)f(x_i) - V'\delta(df/dx). \tag{24}$$

The perturbation may be thought of as the consequence of two changes whose effects are additive: (a) the alteration $(V'-V)$ resulting from the changed hole volume at the point $x_i$ as given by the first term, and (b) the shift of the hole location by an amount $\delta$ to its new position, as given by the second term in Eq. (24). As a matter of practical convenience, we can often make use of the fact that no first-order error is

[13] A familiar example of this is found in the upwardly displaced hole of reduced size which is used to give C# above written middle C on a clarinet in order to avoid drilling the hole through the middle-joint tenon.

brought into the estimate of $\Delta l$ when the ideal hole position $x_i$ is replaced by the actual position $(x_i+\delta)$ in the arguments of the two trigonometric functions: $f$ and $df/dx$, Equations (25a) and (25b) give explicit formulas obtained from Eq. (24) for the various types of musical bore. Clarinet-type bore with $S_0=\pi a^2$,

$$\Delta l=\left(\frac{V'-V}{S_0}\right)\cos^2\left[\frac{(2n-1)\pi x_i}{2l}\right]-(2n-1)\left(\frac{\pi}{2}\right)\left(\frac{V}{S_0}\right)\left(\frac{\delta}{l}\right)\sin\left[\frac{(2n-1)\pi x_i}{l}\right]. \quad (25a)$$

Flute-type bores with $S_0=\pi a^2$ and oboe-type bores, where $S_0=\pi a^2(x_i/l)^2$,

$$\Delta l=\left(\frac{V'-V}{S_0}\right)\sin^2\left[\frac{n\pi x_i}{l}\right]+n\pi\left(\frac{V}{S_0}\right)\left(\frac{\delta}{l}\right)\cos\left[\frac{2n\pi x_i}{l}\right]. \quad (25b)$$

The first term in each of these equations has to do with the change in hole size, and (if $V'>V$), always contributes a flattening effect which varies sinusoidally as $n$ changes with an amplitude independent of $n$, while the second (displacement) term may be either sharpening or flattening in its effect with a magnitude which grows in importance linearly with the mode number $n$.

### E. Further Remarks on Closed Hole Effects

It is worth comment that for cylindrical instruments such as the flute and clarinet, the *fractional* length correction $(F=\Delta l/l)$, which results from each closed hole perturbation, is proportional to the ratio of the perturbing volume $V_p$ to that of the complete bore $(V_b=S_0 l)$. The exact magnitude of the correction is equal to this ratio multiplied by a simple trigonometric function of the hole position. As a result, the interval corresponding to the ***maximum*** (positive or negative) fractional frequency change which can possibly be caused by a hole is given in hundredths of a semitone by the following expression, where

$$\text{Maximum change}=1.66(V_p/V_b)\ 0.10^3 \text{ cents.} \quad (26)$$

For a conical bore an analogous relation holds, except that the relevant bore volume here is to be taken as the volume of a cylinder whose length $l$ is that of the complete cone and whose cross-sectional area is that of the cone *at the position of the hole.*

An examination of the approximations involved in all of the length corrections obtained in the present section is rather difficult to carry out in impedance language, but quite straightforward when the problem is studied from the point of view of Rayleigh. Fortunately, all the approximations turn out to have the same order of accuracy which may readily be estimated from the size of the length correction itself. The error in cents to be expected in the final corrected length $(l+\Delta l)$ for any single one of the several corrections may be shown to have a size of the order of $(m^2\times10^{-3})$ cents for a $(\Delta l/l)$ correction of $m$ cents. This sort of error is completely negligible from the musical point of view as will be shown in the examples later on.

While the error arising from a single correction is negligible, the question arises as to whether or not the superposition of many such corrections does not lead ultimately to errors which are serious in their consequences to the designer of musical instruments. A simple estimate of this net error may be based on the fact that the *signs* of the errors contributed by the various corrections are essentially random and not correlated with the sign of the correction itself. It is a well-known principle of statistical analysis that the resultant of such a set of random quantities is given by the square root of the sum of the squares of the various quantities. Thus, if the $j$th correction for a particular note has a magnitude $m_j$, and it has an error $(m_j)^2\times10^{-3}$, the resulting error for the complete set of corrections belonging to this note is given approximately by Eq. (27), where

$$\text{Resultant error}\cong10^{-3}[\textstyle\sum(m_j)^4]^{\frac{1}{2}} \text{ cents.} \quad (27)$$

### F. Numerical Magnitudes of Closed-Hole Effects

The formulas given so far for the calculation of length corrections are all straightforward when considered singly, but it is perhaps worthwhile to give a few numerical examples of certain selected effects in order to clarify the nature and practical magnitude of these corrections for a simplified but typical bore, that of a "clarinet" with a cylindrical bore 15mm in diam. For convenience all results will be given as a fractional correction $F=(\Delta l/l)$ and expressed in cents.

(1) Suppose that the diameter of the mouthpiece and barrel joint is increased in diameter by 1 mm above the 15-mm diam of the rest of the bore so that the cross-sectional area in the upper bore is increased by a perturbing amount $S_e$, and that this perturbation extends down to a point $x_e=10$ cm on a bore whose length $l$ is 40 cm (roughly equivalent to the low $B$ in the chalumeau register) and also for the case when $l$ is only 20 cm (which is at the top of the drilled hole system of a clarinet). Since the perturbation is constant from $x=0$ to $x=10$ cm, and zero beyond that, it is a simple matter to integrate Eq. (19a) to get the desired length correction[14]:

$$\frac{\Delta l}{l}=\frac{1}{(2n-1)\pi}\left(\frac{S_e}{S_0}\right)\sin\left[\frac{(2n-1)\pi x_e}{l}\right]. \quad (28)$$

For the 40-cm bore, we find by direct calculation from

[14] We find that the limiting expression for small $x_e$ obtained from this equation is identical with the mouthpiece cavity correction which was calculated as a special case in paper A.

Eq. (28) that the first mode is flattened by 50 cents, the second mode by 16 cents, while the third mode is sharpened by 10 cents. On the other hand, the 20-cm bore length is flattened by 70 cents in its lowest mode, sharpened 23 cents for $n=2$, and flattened again by 14 cents in the third mode.

Two important points are illustrated by these results: (a) the magnitude of the correction fluctuates greatly with mode number, (b) a short bore is much more strongly affected than is a long bore, and its fluctuations are *completely different* from those of a long bore. Since all the notes in the musical scale are played as one mode or another of a set of different bore lengths $l_K$, it is clear that the intonation of an instrument with a nonuniform bore is made quite ragged from note to note in the scale from this cause alone.[15]

(2) Many times when playing in an ensemble a musician has to tune to the other instruments by pulling out the mouthpiece and/or barrel joint. It is of interest to investigate this situation with the help of Eq. (22a) which gives the length correction produced by a cavity of volume $V$. Let us assume that the mouthpiece is pulled out a distance of 3 mm from the barrel joint, so that the perturbing volume $V_g$ in the gap is about 0.6 cm$^3$, located at a distance $x_g=7$ cm from the effective closed end of the instrument. The volume of the bore itself is about 70 cm$^3$ if its length is 40 cm so that the lowest mode of the system is flattened 13.4 cents, the second mode is lowered 6.5 cents and the third mode is pulled down only 0.6 cents. If, on the other hand, the instrument is lengthened by pulling it apart between the barrel joint and the upper joint, the flattening of the first three modes are 12.2, 2.1, and 2.1 cents.

Once again it is apparent that the intonation of the instrument is completely upset by relatively small perturbations and that these perturbations are irregular throughout the scale so that the musician has to learn to correct each note separately, treating it as a special case.

(3) The two extra side holes for the alternate fingering of D# − A# on a clarinet are each about 6 mm in diam and drilled through a wall that is about 7 mm thick at a position $x_i=27$ cm from the upper end of the instrument. Application of Eq. (22a) to this case for a bore whose length is 40 cm leads to the following alterations in the effective length produced by the cooperative effect of these extra holes: lowest mode two cents, second mode nine cents, third mode nine cents, all of these being flattenings.

The duplicated *G#* hole on a flute produces changes of the same general size as these, while the relatively large holes used on the narrow bore of an oboe lead to such large and erratic detunings that their makers have been forced to avoid duplicated holes almost entirely, at the expense of a complicated key mechanism.

[15] While tone color considerations are not within the scope of the present paper, it is not improper to point out that the tone is dependent in part on the tuning of the higher modes of the pipe.

## V. LENGTH CORRECTIONS FOR OPEN HOLE EFFECTS

### A. Preliminary Remarks

Historically speaking, the primary interest of the designers and builders of woodwinds has been directed toward the proper location of finger holes so as to provide the desired musical scale. In Sec. II we have seen a brief discussion of a possible formulation of the open-hole problem in the language of impedance theory, and we are now in a position to apply it to musical instruments.

The system of open holes at the lower end of a musically useful horn may be considered as forming a terminating impedance attached to the end of a bore of length $L_k$ which extends from the upper (mouthpiece) end to the position of termination. The effective length of this combination is $(L_k+\Delta l)$, a combined dimension chosen so as to give the desired lowest-mode frequency $\omega_k$. It is apparent that $\Delta l$ stands for the additional distance beyond $L_k$ to which the original bore should be extended if it is to have the same lowest mode of vibration. That is, the input impedance of the effective bore extension $\Delta l$ is identically equal to the input impedance of the system of open holes. Thus, for a closed-hole bore with characteristic impedance $Z_c$ and average propagation velocity $v_c$, used with a terminating impedance $Z_t$,

$$jZ_c \tan(\omega\Delta l/v_c)=Z_t, \tag{29}$$

which may be solved for $\Delta l$ as shown in Eq. (30), where

$$\Delta l=(v_c/\omega)\tan^{-1}(-jZ_t/Z_c). \tag{30}$$

In general, $\Delta l$ is a complicated function of the frequency $\omega$, but this causes little difficulty in the design of an instrument since the frequency is preassigned by the nature of the musical scale. Once again it is sometimes useful to employ Eq. (15) as a basis for discussion, where the fractional correction $F_k=l/l_k$ may be directly deduced from Eq. (30).

### B. Bore with Single Side Hole

The case of a bore pierced by a single side hole at a given distance from the lower end was solved by Richardson as has already been mentioned, and will serve us as a simple introductory problem. As a practical matter, the case where $L$ is very nearly equal to $l$ arises in the calculation of the position of the lowest hole of a bell-less woodwind such as the flute and refers also in a similar sense to the saxophone. The terminating impedance appearing at the bottom of the closed-hole part of the bore consists of the paralleled input impedance of two ducts: one of which is the hole itself, the other being the length of bore below the open hole (see Fig. 4).

Let the hole be of radius $b$, drilled a distance $M$ from the lower end of the instrument ($M_e=M+$open end correction at the bottom of the bore). As before the effective thickness of the wall is $t_e$, and the radius of the bore *at the hole* is $a$. Under these assumptions the input impedances $Z_h$ and $Z_M$ of the hole and the bore extension are the following:

For the hole,

$$Z_h = j(\rho c/\pi b^2)\tan(\omega t_e/c). \quad (31)$$

For cylindrical bores,

$$Z_M = j(\rho c/\pi a^2)\tan(\omega M_e/c). \quad (32a)$$

For conical bores where $x_1$ is the apex-to-hole distance,

$$Z_M = j(\rho c/\pi a^2)\tan(\omega M_e/c) \times[1+(c/\omega x_1)\tan(\omega M_e/c)]^{-1}. \quad (32b)$$

The length correction for cylindrical bore extensions is that given by Eq. (33).

$$\Delta l = (v_c/\omega)\tan^{-1}\left[\frac{\tan(\omega t_e/c)\tan(\omega M_e/c)}{(b/a_e)^2\tan(\omega M_e/c)+\tan(\omega t_e/c)}\right], \quad (33)$$

where $a_e^2 \cong a^2(1+D_c)^{\frac{1}{2}}$ and $v_c \cong c(1+D_c)^{-\frac{1}{2}}$ [see Eqs. (3) and (4)]. For conical bore extensions the same formula applies (even for the case of a cylindrical instrument with a conical bell beginning at the lowest hole) if it is modified by multiplying $\tan(\omega M_e/c)$ by $[1+(c/\omega x_1)\times\tan(\omega M_e/c)]^{-1}$ wherever it appears. These results are accurate for any length $M_e$ and $t_e$.

When the length $M_e$ is much shorter than the wavelength, as is the practical case when only the lowest hole is open, we can legitimately make use of the low-frequency limit of Eq. (33) which turns out to be independent of frequency, as shown (for cylindrical extensions below the hole) in Eq. (34), where

$$\Delta l = t_e(v_c/c)[(b/a_e)^2+(t_e/M_e)]^{-1}. \quad (34)$$

For conical extensions the equivalent formula is found by replacing the term $(t_e/M_e)$ by $(t_e/M_e)[1+(M_e/x_1)]$. Examination of the approximations involved shows that as the frequency rises from very low values, $\Delta l$ increases toward (but not *to*) an apparent asymptote in the neighborhood of $t_e$, but so slowly as to have almost no importance for musical purposes, as may readily be verified by comparison of the results of Eqs. (33) and (34) for the first two or three modes of vibration of the instrument.[16]

Equation (32) may be used as a means for finding the place to drill the first hole at the foot of an instrument that is to play a chromatic scale. Let us use the convention that $l_0$ is the desired effective length of the complete bore and $l_1$ that of the bore when the lowest hold is opened. From the nature of things we see that $l_0 = L_1 + M_e$ as a mechanical requirement on the bore, while musically we must require that $1.06\, l_1 = l_0$ if the first hole is to raise the frequency one semitone (the number 1.06 used here represents the frequency ratio for the even tempered semitone). By definition $l_1 = (L_1 + \Delta l)$, so that in the case of cylindrical bores Eqs. (34) and (35) may be combined and solved for $M_e$ as shown in Eq. (36), which assumes that $t_e(1-v_c/c) \ll 0.06(b/a_e)^2 l_0$:

$$0.06 l_0 + 1.06\Delta l = 1.06 M_e \quad (35)$$

$$M_e = (0.06 l_0/2)(1/1.06) \times\{1+[1+(4/0.06)(1.06)(a_e/b)^2(t_e/l_0)]^{\frac{1}{2}}\}. \quad (36)$$

An interesting feature of this expression is the freedom it gives the designer in the choice of the hole size $b$ and wall thickness $t$. Once these have been chosen from mechanical considerations and from the requirements laid down by the acoustical properties of the closed-hole part of the bore, one has only to drill the hole a distance $M$ up from the open end. The freedom referred to is not absolute, however, inasmuch as the calculation is based on a low-frequency approximation. No serious difficulty will be experienced with the failure of this approximation, however, if the value of $M_e$ satisfies the very conservative inequality appearing in Eq. (37), an inequality which is almost automatically satisfied in practice,

$$(\pi M_e/6 l_0)^2 \ll 1. \quad (37)$$

As a result of the more complicated algebraic form of the correction in the case of conical instruments, no such simple procedure is available. However, an iteration procedure for this case can be started from the simpler result.

While the analytical form of the solution for $M_e$ on an instrument having a true bell at the lower end is different from that given in the foregoing, the general approach to its calculation is exactly the same, and many of the qualitative results described here may be carried over unchanged to this more complex case.

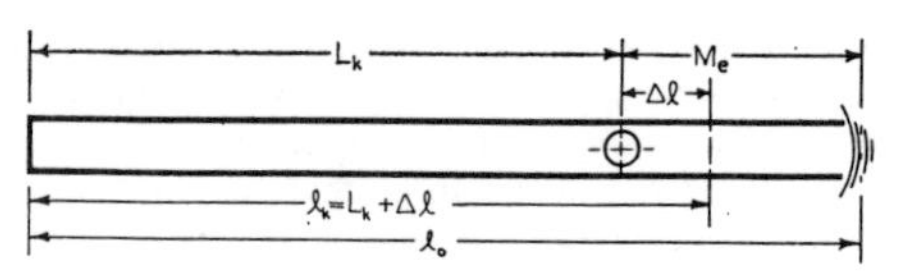


FIG. 4. Diagram showing the notation used to describe the behavior of a pipe with a single side hole near its lower end.

### C. Pipe with Many Open Holes

A problem of great significance in the theory of woodwinds is that of a bore ending in a section provided with

[16] The first maximum of $\Delta l$ in a practical musical instrument falls in the neighborhood of frequencies for which $M_e$ is a quarter wavelength, so that $\tan(\omega M_e/c)$ is large. Under this condition

$$\Delta l \cong (c/\omega)\tan^{-1}[(a/b)^2\tan(\omega t_e/c)],$$

which may be of the order of a few times $t_e$. For clarinets this occurs in the neighborhood of the 16th harmonic of the chalumeau note so that it is in the frequency region where the closed-hole part of the bore is beginning to cut off the propagation of waves. A similar result holds for the other families of instruments, where the maximum of $\Delta l$ occurs in the neighborhood of the 8th harmonic of the lowest mode note.

several open side holes. In Sec. III it was shown that in the musically interesting case where the interhole spacing is small compared with the wave length, a cylindrical pipe with open holes along it has an input impedance which is of a mass-like character [see Eq. (10)]. Since this impedance acts as the termination for the upper, closed-hole part of the bore, we may use $Z_0$ from Eq. (10 [or its more exact ancestor, Eq. (8)] to serve as $Z_t$ in the correction formula Eq. (30). There is, however, a serious trap concealed within this statement: it is fundamental to the nature of impedance equations for periodic lines, that the lines begin and end with "half-sections." The equations of Secs. II and III are based upon the assumption that each of the two types of line begins at a point *midway between the holes* so that the $\Delta l$ implied in the foregoing is to be measured from a point lying midway between the first open and the last closed hole! For practical purposes, we are not so interested in this quantity as in one which tells how far up the bore from the point $l_k$ to drill the first open hole, so that we must subtract the distance $s$ (half the inter-hole spacing) in order to obtain the desired correction. Equation (38) gives this altered result for practical use,

$$\Delta l=(v_c/\omega)\tan^{-1}\left\{\left[\frac{(1/2)(b/a)^2\cot(\omega t_e/c)\tan(\omega s/c)+1}{(1/2)(b/a)^2\cot(\omega t_e/c)\cot(\omega s/c)-1}\right]^{\frac{1}{2}}\times\left(\frac{a_e}{a}\right)^2\right\}-s. \quad (38)$$

Examination of this expression shows that the value of $\Delta l$ remains nearly constant over a frequency range which extends rather close to the critical frequency at which the lower bore begins to "conduct" waves, as signaled by the change of sign in the denominator of $Z_0$. A result of this approximate constancy of $\Delta l$ is that the lower normal mode frequency *ratios* of a pipe ending in a sequence of open holes of the sort used in musical instruments lie within a tenth of a semitone of those of a simple open-ended pipe of the same sort. Here we have an explicit mathematical justification for the assumptions made in paper A on the negligible effect of the open hole series on the results of that paper. One must recall at all times, however, that these remarks are only valid below the cutoff frequency of the open-hole system.[17] Since the assumptions underlying a calculation of the effective length of such a composite pipe not a part of the familiarly verified content of musical acoustics, a careful experimental verification of their validity has been made in an especially clear situation.[18]

[17] For frequencies above cutoff (and also for certain conditions below cutoff), the tapered line may be analyzed by means of the WKB approximation. A study of this aspect of the problem is being carried out by the author in collaboration with W. A. Dent.

[18] This experimental work, which was described briefly by the author at the October 1959 meeting of the Acoustical Society in Cleveland, will be discussed in detail in a later publication in this Journal.

A cruder but much more easily accessible verification may be carried out as follows: If one measures upward from the first open hole a distance equal to one-quarter wavelength reduced by the calculated $\Delta l$ for a particular note on a clarinet, a point near the tip of the mouthpiece is reached which is the nominal effective closed upper end of the bore for that note. If this procedure is carried out for several notes in the chalumeau register, all the nominal upper ends lie within 2 or 3 mm of each other. If a detailed analysis is made of the various perturbations to the bore caused by the irregularities in hole spacing and bore diameter, the effective closed end at the mouthpiece proves to be the same for all notes within a millimeter, and this discrepancy is at the limit of accuracy imposed on the calculation by the difficulty of getting accurate data concerning the bore and its holes.

There is one aspect of the present calculation which has particular interest for a designer. The open hole correction is measured from the hole in question and depends only upon the size of this hole and on the distance between it and its neighbors on either side. As a result there is no accumulation of error from hole to hole as the scale is laid out: each hole is displaced an amount $\Delta l$ above its "naive" quarter- (or half!) wavelength distance from the effective upper end of the instrument, and any reasonable initial choice of interhole spacing will give good results since the value of $\Delta l$ for the neighboring holes is roughly the same. As a matter of fact, the magnitude of $\Delta l$ is itself roughly constant over the scale of a cylindrical instrument of the clarinet type, even though the fractional correction $F+\Delta l/l$ increases as we go up the low-register scale. This comes about from the fact that the decreasing hole size is nearly compensated by the decreasing interhole spacing in the upper part of the bore. For normal sized holes used in woodwind bores it turns out that the numerator under the square root in Eq. (38) is close to unity, while the denominator is much greater than one in the playing range. As a result an approximate low-frequency limit for $\Delta l$ takes the general form $\Delta l=\text{constant}\ (sa^2/b^2)^{\frac{1}{2}}$ which is itself constant because of the closed-hole restrictions on $b$ and on $s$. If this constancy were strict, then the interhole spacing of the corrected positions would be exactly that of the naive set of holes even though they would all be moved up the bore a fixed amount $\Delta l$! In this way we see that the "Theoretical" hole position (in the sense of Theobald Boehm's endeavors) which are based on the assumption that $\Delta l=0$, is a very fine starting point for the design of a system of finger holes.

### D. Theoretical Discussion of Assumptions

In Sec. III it was assumed possible to treat the open-hole system of a woodwind as being approximately equivalent to a series of uniformly spaced open holes all of the same size as the highest one. This assumption was based on empirical grounds and was supported after the fact by the nonpropagating nature of the resulting transmission line at musical frequencies so that "messages" could not reach the main bore from the lower, nonuniform part of the system. The discussion immediately preceding these remarks has shown that as a practical matter, the hole spacings and sizes chosen to give an *exact* (low-frequency) uniformity to the closed-hole bore also turn out to produce an *almost* constant open-hole end correction $\Delta l$ throughout the low register scale. Since $\Delta l$ depends directly upon the characteristic impedance $Z_0$ of the open-hole system, we deduce from this that in the low-frequency (musically important) limit, the quantity $(Z_0/\omega)$ is nearly constant along the bore. That is, changes produced in $Z_0$ by the increasing hole size in going down the bore are roughly compensated by the changes due to the increasing interhole spacing, as already pointed out.

As a result, not only does the fact that the open-hole part of the bore operates as a filter below cutoff minimize the effects of nonuniformity in its properties, but we have also found that this nonuniformity is itself rather small. We may deduce then that our formulation of the intonation problem can confidently be expected to give accurate results, as is indeed shown by experiment.

## VI. SOME IMPLICATIONS

We have investigated the nature of the corrections which must be made to simple theory if it is to represent the behavior of bores provided with a row of side holes, and there have been repeated remarks made about the applicability of one formula or another to design purposes. Without attempting to make a complete study of the design process which is implied by the present formulation, it is perhaps worthwhile to give a brief outline of the way in which such a procedure might be laid out.

For simplicity, this outline will confine itself to the case of a cylindrical bore for a clarinet-type of instrument, and the reed end will be assumed to be closed completely. First the bore radius $a$ is chosen, and then the size of one of the side holes. Assuming that at first all the holes are to be drilled at their "naive" positions distant one-quarter wavelength from the closed end, we adjust the hole sizes throughout the scale to conform with the square root law described in paper A and analyzed in Sec. II of this paper. All the various perturbations and corrections can now be approximated making use of this preliminary set of hole sizes and spacings.[19] The positions of the holes may now be shifted to their approximately correct positions, which would give a playable but not commercially acceptable instrument. The second approximation may now be started by readjusting the hole sizes to fit the closed-hole uniformity requirements for their new positions, and a new set of effective length corrections computed for the hole positions. Drilling holes at these positions would lead to an instrument needing only the slightest alteration by a tuner so that the labor of a third approximation would not be justified (if we could ignore reed effects!).

Until now in this section the implicit assumption has been made that the side holes are cylindrical openings drilled through the wall into the bore of a woodwind. In practice many of the holes are made bell-mouthed at their inner ends by use of a milling cutter (the operation is usually called fraising). The custom of fraising originally started as a simple means of correcting the tuning of notes, but it was early recognized that a properly treated instrument is better in a number of ways than its untreated mate. It is not possible to give a complete account of the acoustical effects of fraising in this paper, since they involve the regenerative properties of the reed system and are largely concerned with the tone quality and with "responsiveness" rather than with the frequency behavior of woodwinds which concerns us here. However, a few qualitative remarks are appropriate and may stimulate further thought.

In the upper (closed-hole) part of a woodwind bore, fraising has the effect of increasing the volume enclosed by each altered hole. Examination of Eqs. (1)–(5) of Sec. II shows that such an increase has three results: (a) the effective bore cross section is increased, (b) the sound velocity $v_c$ is decreased so that the frequency is lowered, (c) the cutoff frequency is lowered so that a thoroughly fraised bore is one which eliminates a few more of the highest components in the radiated sound spectrum than is the case with an unfraised bore. The discussion of perturbations to the closed hole bore which appears in Sec. IV implies that an instrument with some of the holes unfraised and others fraised in varying amounts will have an irregular intonation that is not correctible by any other sort of alteration in the shape of the bore.

Fraising of the open holes has the effect of decreasing their impedance and is equivalent to drilling them through a thinner wall or to enlarging them, as is well known. The analysis of Sec. III implies the cutoff frequency of the open-hole bore is raised by fraising so that a larger part of the sound spectrum falls within the region of validity of the formulas obtained there. The falling-off in amplitude of the pressure disturbances from hole to hole is increased since $\alpha$ is increased by fraising. The chief consequences of this increase in $\alpha$ will become apparent in the next section.

The practice of leaving an opening through the pad of a finger hole on some Boehm flutes is acoustically equivalent to fraising in that it increases the volume enclosed in each closed hole and decreases the effective length of the open hole. However, the alteration in the

[19] The proper and consistent application of the full set of corrections is a matter of considerable subtlety and cannot be carried out without close attention to the inter-relations between various parts of the bore. These complications cannot be discussed in the present outline.

*open*-hole impedance produced by piercing the pad is negligible since the new aperture is almost completely "short-circuited" by the normal opening under the pad. We see that the chief effect of providing holes through several of the pads on a flute is to alter the *closed-hole* part of the bore, but to leave the open-hole part unchanged. While the distinction between different instruments often lies in the most subtle details of the bore, it would seem that the usual arguments in favor of the open-hole flute are essentially specious since they are based upon properties of the open holes.

On many oboes one sees a second type of alteration that is closely related to, but not identical with, fraising. Here the hole is counter-bored from the outside of the instrument so that the aperture closed by the pad is considerably larger than the hole through the wall. At low frequencies the behavior is identical with that of normal fraising and may be so considered for the purposes of adjusting the intonation. On the other hand, a counter-bored hole that is closed by a pad forms a minute Helmholtz resonator with a resonance frequency which may lie as low as a thousand cps. At frequencies well below this resonance, the hole acts in a qualitatively normal way, but above resonance it presents a masslike impedance rather than the normal elastic impedance and so behaves like an open hole! The implications of this are far reaching but chiefly in the domains of the upper register and of tonal color and so are quite outside the scope of our present investigation.

## VII. RADIATION FROM OPEN HOLES

### A. Formulation of the Problem

The sound we hear from a woodwind is radiated from the open holes at the lower end of the bore and from the open end or bell if there is one. The angular distribution and frequency dependence of this radiated sound is determined by the interference of the waves arising from each of the open holes whose size and location determine the amplitude and phase of each elementary wave. It is a fortunate circumstance that the radiation efficiency of these holes is small enough that we have been able to calculate the behavior of acoustic disturbance within a woodwind bore without taking radiation damping explicitly into account. Having studied the nature of vibrations set up within the bore, we can now consider them as drivers for the external air waves which interfere to give us the observable radiation pattern. The general problem of radiation from a bore of variable cross section pierced by open holes of variable size and spacing is long and cumbersome but not mathematically difficult once the description of the pressure wave within it is known. However, little insight is to be gained from the general solution which cannot also be gained more easily from a suitably chosen simple case.

Let us consider a uniform bore which lies along the $x$ coordinate axis and is proved with holes of radius $b$ drilled through a wall whose effective thickness is $t_e$. Suppose that the first of these holes is drilled at the coordinate origin and that the others lie along the positive axis for a distance $L$ (no assumption is made yet as to regularity of spacing or of size). Inside the bore there is a damped running wave of frequency $\omega$, velocity $v$, and amplitude attenuation coefficient $\alpha$. We may take its amplitude to be $p_0$ at the position $(x=0)$ of the first open hole. The amplitude of the wave set up outside the $m$th hole depends upon the "source strength" (maximum rate of volume flow) $Q_m$ of the oscillation in the hole. This source strength may be found from the pressure amplitude $p_m$ within the bore at the location of the $m$th hole with the help of the impedance $Z_m$ of the hole itself as shown in Eq. (39),

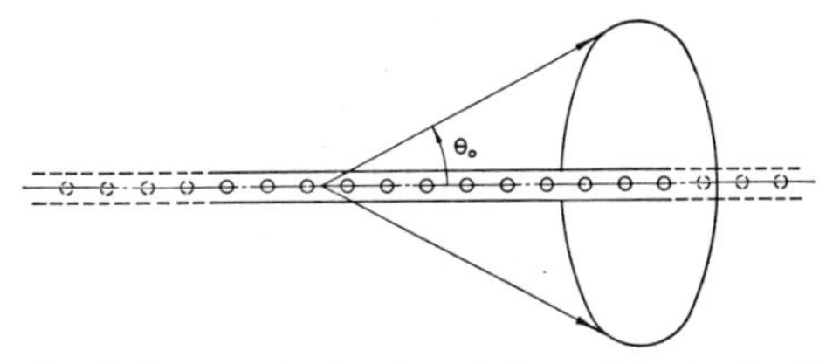


FIG. 5. Diagram showing the notation used to describe the radiation from a row of open holes. At low frequencies the radiation is almost isotropic, while the radiation pattern for the higher components is conical, with cylindrical symmetry about the bore axis. Maximum power is radiated in the direction $\Theta_0$.

$$Q_m=(p_m/Z_m)=(jp_0\pi b^2/\rho\omega t_e)e^{-\alpha x_m}. \qquad (39)$$

Here the hole impedance $Z_m=j(\rho c/\pi b^2)\tan(\omega t_e/c)$ has been replaced by its low-frequency limit for simplicity.

The pressure amplitude $P(\theta,R)$ produced at a long distance $R$ in a direction making the angle $\theta$ with the $x$ axis (see Fig. 5) will be

$$\begin{aligned} P(\theta,R)&=j(\omega\rho/4\pi R)\textstyle\sum Q_m\exp[(jA-\alpha)x_m], \\ A&=(\omega/c)[(c/v)-\cos\theta]. \end{aligned} \qquad (40)$$

The fundamental equations from which this is derived may be found in Morse[20] and Lamb[21] while closely related problems are discussed by Thiessen and Embleton,[22] Schiff,[23] and by Beverage, Rice, and Kellog.[24] While some physical interest attaches to the pressure amplitude defined here, our purposes are better served by finding the angular distribution and distance dependence of the radiated power. We may define a quantity $I(\theta,R)$ as being the intensity of the radiation traveling in the direction $\theta$ from the line of holes at the

[20] P. M. Morse, *Vibration and Sound* (McGraw-Hill Book Company, Inc., New York, 1948), 2nd ed., p. 313ff.

[21] H. Lamb, *Dynamical Theory of Sound* (Edward Arnold and Company, London, England, 1910), Chap. VIII.

[22] G. J. Thiessen and T. F. W. Embleton, J. Acoust. Soc. Am. **30**, 449 (1958). The angle $\Theta$ used in this paper is the complement of our present angle. Note also that the factors $A$ defined in the two papers refer to entirely different quantities.

[23] L. I. Schiff, *Quantum Mechanics* (McGraw-Hill Book Company, Inc., New York, 1949), 1st ed., pp. 261–265.

[24] H. H. Beverage, C. W. Rice, and E. W. Kellogg, Trans. AIEE **42**, 215 (1923).

long distance $R$, so that

$$I(\theta,R)=P(\theta,R)^2/2\rho c$$
$$=(1/32)(p_0^2/\rho c)(1/R^2)\,|\sum_m (b^2/t_e)_m \times\exp[(jA-\alpha)x_m]|^2. \quad (41)$$

It must be emphasized that this radiation goes out in a cylindrically symmetrical pattern whose axis is the bore itself, even though the holes may all be in a line along one side of the pipe. This is because the bore is always small in diameter as compared with the free-space wavelength so that the sound diffracts around it isotropically in the azimuthal direction.

Equation (41) is a formal solution to the problem at hand, but it is of a form which is more easily computed than interpreted (Thiessen *et al.* give a good description of many properties of this expression). For many musical purposes the holes may be considered as being closely spaced when compared with the relevant lengths $(v/\omega)$ and $(\alpha)^{-1}$ so that we are led to investigate a related expression which is obtained by replacing the summation by an integral with the further assumption that the holes are all of uniform size and spacing. This is physically equivalent to providing the bore with a uniform narrow slot along one side from which radiation may take place in the manner of certain microwave antennas,

$$I(\theta,R)=(1/32)(P_0^2/\rho c)(1/R^2)(\text{const}) \times\left|\int_0^L \exp[(jA-\alpha)x]dx\right|^2$$
$$\sim(e^{-\alpha L}[e^{-\alpha L}-2\cos(AL)]+1)(A^2+\alpha^2)^{-1}. \quad (42)$$

We are now in a position to discover some salient features of the radiation from open holes on a woodwind bore by means of examples chosen from various special cases of Eq. (42).

### B. Radiation When $\alpha$ Is Large

If the length $L$ of pipe that is provided with radiating apertures is such that $(\alpha L)\gg 1$, Eq. (42) reduces to a particularly simple form,

$$I(\theta,R)\sim 1/(A^2+\alpha^2)$$
$$A=(\omega/c)[(c/v)-\cos\theta]. \quad (43)$$

$I(\theta,R)$ has a maximum value when the angle $\theta$ is such as to make $A$ vanish. If this special angle is designated by $\theta_0$, and the "half-power angles" $\theta_w$ are defined to be those angles at which the radiated intensity is half that at the peak, we find[25]

$$\cos\theta_0=(c/v)$$
$$\cos\theta_w=\cos\theta_0[1\pm(\alpha v/\omega)]. \quad (44)$$

It is a familiar fact that no radiation takes place when $(v/c)<1$ as is indicated at once by the imaginary value for $\theta_0$ which appears for these lower velocities in Eq. (44). The question immediately arises as to whether or not the foregoing analysis has any relevance whatever to the musical case. That is, one is led to ask whether or not the wave velocity in the open-hole part of a woodwind bore is indeed larger than the free-space value $c$.

From the usual definition of the propagation constant $\Gamma$ for a transmission line, we find that the imaginary part represents the quantity $j(\omega/v)$ so that Eq. (9) of Sec. III may be solved for the desired velocity $v_0$ in the case of a bore provided with open holes. In Sec. III it has already been pointed out that at low frequencies [i.e., at frequencies which lie below a few hundreds of cycles per second so that the second term in the denominator of Eq. (8) is less than unity] such a bore is below cutoff and that there is only a damped isophase disturbance within it. Mathematically this is a consequence of the fact that $\Gamma_0$ has a real part only, so that $(\omega/v_0)$ is identically zero. This is just another way of saying that $v_0$ itself is *infinite* below the cutoff frequency. Any frequency that lies *above* the cutoff gives a pure imaginary value to $\Gamma_0$ so that there is free propagation of waves. Standard methods of analysis show that the propagation velocity $v_0$ of these waves is *always* greater than $c$ in the pass band of such a filter so that any sort of disturbance set up in the lower part of a woodwind bore is able to produce radiation.[26]

Comparison of Eqs. (42) to (44) shows that the sole frequency dependence of the radiated power lies in the dependence of $A$ and $\alpha$ on $\omega$ and that at the angle $\theta_0$ of maximum intensity, the radiated power depends upon the rather weak variation of $\alpha$ alone. This is in marked contrast to the way in which radiation is emitted from the open end of a simple pipe which radiates isotropically with an intensity that is proportional to the square of the frequency. In this simple contrast we find a qualitative explanation for the difference between the sound spectrum produced in the air by a woodwind reed attached to a simple pipe and that radiated from a row of open holes at the lower end of a pipe.

For those components of a woodwind instrument's tonal spectrum which lie below the cutoff frequency of the open holes, the wave velocity in the bore is infinite so that $\theta_0$ is $\pi/2$ radians, meaning that these sounds are radiated most strongly in a cylindrical pattern directly outward from the axis of the instrument. Under these conditions the half-power angles are given simply by $\cos\theta_w=(c\alpha/\omega)$. It has already been pointed out in Sec. III that at low frequencies in the clarinet and oboe

[25] The angle $\theta_0$ will be recognized as being analogous to the angle at which an electron of velocity $v$ emits Cerenkov radiation in a medium in which light travels with the velocity $c$. It is also related to the complement to the angle of the shock wave produced in air by a supersonic projectile moving with velocity $v$ in air where the normal sound velocity is $c$.

[26] It is interesting to note that a composite type of bore provided with a long uniform alternating sequence of closed cavities as well as small open holes is unable to radiate any sound from its holes at frequencies for which the slowing-down effect of the cavities on the wave velocity is greater than the speeding-up effect of the open holes so that $(v/c)<1$ within the passband of the system!

the pressure amplitude falls by a factor of about 0.75 from hole to hole so that $2s\alpha=\log_e(1/0.75)$. Furthermore, the interhole spacing is very nearly 6% of a quarter wavelength for the low range of a clarinet making $2s=(0.06\pi/2)(c/\omega)$. These two results may be combined in the manner indicated in Eq. (45),

$$\begin{aligned}(c\alpha/\omega)&=(2/0.06\pi)\log_e(1/0.75)\\&=2.4.\end{aligned}\qquad(45)$$

Clearly the cosine of any physical angle must have a magnitude less than or equal to unity so that the large value obtained here for $(c\alpha/\omega)$ implies that the intensity *never* falls to half maximum at any angle. The lower frequency components of a woodwind tone are, therefore, radiated in an *almost perfectly isotropic manner*. It is important to notice that this result is based only upon the assumption that there are enough open holes that the lowest one contributes negligibly to the radiation, so that we may apply it to all notes of the clarinet which are not complicated by the action of the bell. The only difference to be found in the case of the oboe arises from the fact that $\omega$ here is double that for a clarinet of the same length so that $(c\alpha/\omega)$ is halved. The qualitative conclusion still stands unchanged however, that the lower spectrum components are radiated isotropically. The large holes of a flute, and to a lesser extent the saxophone, give even larger values for $\alpha$ at low frequencies so that in an almost literal sense the whole radiated sound comes effectively from the first open hole, and we can predict that it is emitted isotropically. The first hole acts very much like an ordinary open end for the bore so that the frequency dependence of the radiation is characteristic of such an open end rather than that of a row of small holes as is the case for other instruments.

### C. Radiation When $\alpha$ Is Negligible

If the attenuation of waves in the open hole part of a bore is negligible, Eq. (42) may be simplified in a different way by setting $\alpha$ equal to zero as follows,

$$I(\theta,R)\sim[1-\cos(AL)]A^{-2}.\qquad(46)$$

It is a little hard to deduce the detailed shape of the radiated distribution by inspection of this expression because of the double trigonometrical dependence of $\cos(AL)$ upon $\theta$; however, the qualitative nature is easily recognized if physical comparisons are made with a related but more familiar problem. The radiation from the actual pipe may be thought of as arising from a series of Huyghens' wavelets arranged along a line of length $L$, each of which is delayed in phase a fixed amount relative to its neighbor.[27] The same situation holds exactly in the case of Fraunhofer diffraction by an aperture of width $L$ which is inclined at an angle such that the light from the source reaches successive elements of the aperture after traveling just the proper additional distance to produce the desired phase shift. A brief examination of the geometry involved shows that this angle is precisely the same as $\theta_0$ so that the distribution of radiated intensity has the qualitative shape of a single slit Fraunhofer pattern centered so that its maximum falls at $\theta_0$.

Once again the width of the radiation distribution is of some interest and may easily be found as a function of the length $L$ of radiating bore. For this purpose it is useful to make use of a standard trigonometrical identity to rewrite Eq. (46) in the form

$$I(\theta,R)\sim[2\sin^2(AL/2)]A^{-2}.\qquad(47)$$

This function obviously has a strong maximum at the angle which makes $A$ equal to zero so that $I_{\max}\sim(L^2/2)$. We may note that the peak power should indeed be proportional to the squared length of radiator since the total source strength has been assumed directly proportional to $L$. The half power angle may be found as follows: We can solve Eq. (48) for $A_w$ and then use the defining equation for $A$ to calculate $\theta_w$, as

$$(1/2)(L^2/2)=[2\sin^2(A_wL/2)]A^{-2}.\qquad(48)$$

This equation may be solved graphically if it is first arranged in the form $0.707y=\pm\sin y$ (where $y$ stands for $A_wL/2$), from which one finds that $|A_w|=1.39/L$. If use is made of the fact that $\theta_0=(c/v)$ and that $(v/\omega)=(\lambda/2\pi)$ where $\lambda$ is the wavelength of the disturbance *within* the radiating bore, it is possible to show that the half power angles $\theta_w$ are given by the following relation,

$$\cos\theta_w=(\cos\theta_0)[1\pm0.442(\lambda/L)].\qquad(49)$$

Here the familiar phenomenon of diffraction is clearly displayed; if the radiating source is many wavelengths long, the spread in the radiation pattern is small and decreases as $L$ grows.

Woodwinds radiate their higher spectral components (those components whose frequencies are above cutoff and which, therefore, travel "unattenuated" in the open-hole bore) in a manner which is approximately described by the low-attenuation equations just derived since the frictional losses to the walls and the radiation losses through the holes are so small as to reduce the pressure amplitude in the bore by only a few percent in several wave-lengths distance along it. If the wave velocity $v$ within the bore for one of these frequencies is about 10% higher than the free space velocity $c$, and if the open-hole bore extends for a not unreasonable length of $6\lambda$, the foregoing equations show that the radiation is projected most strongly along the surface of a cone whose half-angle is $\theta_0=26°$ with a smearing which extends about 10° on each side of the maximum (the two values of $\theta_w$ are about 15° and 34°). It must not be forgotten, however, that an actual open-hole bore is neither uniform nor provided with a smooth narrow

[27] This is the viewpoint which was taken in the earlier part of the present section and which is discussed in detail by Thiessen and Embleton. (See work cited in footnote 22.)

slit from which to radiate. If the holes were of uniform size and spacing, the angular pattern would contain many uniformly spaced dips and peaks, all of which lie within an "envelope" whose shape is exactly that which has been calculated here for the radiation pattern for a pipe with a slot along its length. Nonuniform hole sizes and spacings will in general increase the angular spread of the radiation pattern, not only because of the usual effect of irregularities upon interference patterns, but also because of the complicated dependence of the velocity $v$ upon these same dimensions.

### D. General Remarks on Radiation from Woodwinds

The analysis which has been outlined in the earlier parts of this section has many implications for the student of woodwinds, some of which have already been mentioned. On account of their importance these will be summarized here in brief as results without the distraction attendant upon their mathematical demonstration.

The sound which is radiated from the open holes at the lower end of a woodwind instrument forms an interference pattern which is formally similar to that of Fraunhofer diffraction from an aperture inclined at an angle $\theta_0 = c/v$. The spread in this pattern which is centered around the angle $\theta_0$ depends upon the length $L$ of the radiating portion of the bore and on the attenuation rate of the pressure wave within it. As we have seen everywhere else in the theory of finger-holes, the qualitative behavior of the system may be divided into two distinct parts which are associated with the pass and stop bands of the pipe and its side holes.

The lower components of the sound of a woodwind (this includes essentially all those of frequencies belonging directly to the written notes for the instrument together with some of their harmonics) lie within the "stop-band" of the open-hole bore. These components are radiated in an almost exactly isotropic fashion as from a small point source. Furthermore, all the woodwinds except the flute and saxophone radiate their lower spectral components with an efficiency which is *almost independent* of frequency and of the radiating length $L$, while the two exceptional instruments radiate isotropically in a manner analogous to that of an open ended bore so that their radiated power grows as the square of the frequency.[28]

The high-frequency components of the woodwind tonal spectrum which lie above the cutoff of the open-hole bore are, on the other hand, radiated in a very complicated pattern whose envelope is centered at the angle $\theta_0$. The half-power angles $\theta_w$ for this case depend in a simple way upon the ratio $(\lambda/L)$ of the wavelength inside the open-hole bore to its radiating length. A long section of bore which can radiate gives rise to a narrow envelope in the usual fashion. The radiated power of these high-frequency components is once more essentially independent of frequency, but it does grow as the square of $L$. This is true to the extent that it is possible to neglect the attenuation of the wave inside the bore. For woodwinds and the frequencies which they produce, any physically plausible value for $L$ is short enough, and the attenuation from wall losses and from radiation is small enough that its effects may be neglected in the present context.

A proper discussion of the relation of a bell to the open holes of a woodwind would require considerable space and falls chiefly in the realm of tone quality which is not a proper part of the present report. There are, however, a few comments on this relation which are appropriate at the present time. We have seen that the frequency dependence of the total energy radiated from a row of open holes is essentially different from that issuing from the open end of a bore, so that the tone quality of the notes played with all the holes closed on a bell-less woodwind would be jarringly different from the rest of the scale. An obvious way to eliminate this difficulty in an exact way would be to extend the bore for several inches, providing it with a continuation of the sequence of open holes which are then left open. Many musicians are aware of this fact as is evidenced by the frequently heard comment on the improvement which is produced in the tone of an instrument's normal scale when the lower joint is extended for the ostensible purpose of adding a few semitones to its lowest range. The traditional solution to the problem of uniformity for the closed-hole notes is an attempt to find a bell whose radiation properties are satisfactorily close to those of a sequence of open holes. In a very real sense, this is not a possibility, as even a cursory study of the frequency dependence of the real parts of horn impedances will show. The practical truth of this is also clearly shown, for example, by the blaring tone which an inexperienced player gets from even very fine clarinets when playing the second mode with all the holes closed (the written $B$ in the middle of the staff for most instruments).[29]

It is interesting to notice that while most of the woodwinds have been provided with bells so as to smooth out the discontinuity in timbre produced by closing all the holes, the flute and saxophone stand out as being

[28] The relation of wall damping to radiation damping which was discussed in paper A must be revised in the light of the present remarks. It was shown (see work cited in footnote 21 of paper A) that the ratio of wall loss to radiation loss from the open end of a bore varies inversely as the three-halves power of the mode number $n$. This conclusion and its consequences still apply to flutes and saxophones which have large holes but not to the other woodwinds where the approximate frequency independence of the radiation from open holes causes the ratio to become more nearly proportional to the square root of the mode number. This shows that wall losses are strongly influential in the behavior of woodwinds to considerably higher frequencies than was implied in the earlier paper.

[29] There are, of course, situations in which the discontinuity of tone is sought out and musically exploited, as is spectacularly the case with the bulbous bell of an English horn. In the present remarks we are concerned only with the *possibility* of obtaining a uniform scale and not with its universal desirability.

bell-less just as would be expected from our analysis. Their large holes already radiate in the manner of an open end and do not give rise to the interhole cooperative effects which appear in the other woodwinds.

## VIII. CONCLUDING REMARKS

In the present paper we have investigated the acoustical properties of ducts provided with side apertures, as they pertain to the finger holes of woodwind musical instruments. The analysis is confined to the relation of the bore to its finger holes and is chiefly concerned with finding methods for calculating the lowest few normal mode frequencies of such bores *apart from the perturbing effects of the reed mechanism*. As a result, predictions of behavior are made here and there in the paper which may not be borne out by simple experiments with reed-excited bores. Such discrepancies are to be expected since the reed and its regeneration mechanism plays an important part in the nature of a woodwind, and it is only upon a thorough understanding of the vibration properties of the bore and its holes that a proper theory of regeneration can be constructed. While a statement limiting the present discussion to reedless bores appears at the beginning of this paper, and at intervals through it, such limitation is not referred to at every place in the text where it might apply—chiefly for reasons of compactness, and to avoid monotony. On the other hand, our general discussion of the effective length correction problem may be used as a basis for designing real woodwinds if an empirical length correction may be ascribed to each condition of frequency and pressure (etc.) of the reed. Such corrections could be found experimentally by comparing the frequency of the normally-blown reed-excited note with that of the corresponding normal mode frequency of the pipe measured with a rigidly clamped reed. It is of course the calculation of the latter which makes up the main subject of the present paper as well as of its predecessor *A*. In brief we may say that the reed correction is a measure of the discrepancy between the blown-reed frequency of an instrument and the properly computed frequency belonging to the bore.

We have examined the nature of a cylindrical bore provided with a sequence of short side branches closed at the outer end (the closed finger holes), and found that a proper choice of hole dimensions permits the closed hole part of the bore to behave in all essentials like a smooth walled cylindrical bore of altered diameter in which waves propagate with slightly lowered but constant velocity. This demonstration, which applies also to conical bores with closed side holes, shows it is indeed possible to satisfy the musical requirements found in paper A for practical woodwinds. Everywhere in the present paper reference is made to this possibility, which opens the way to a calculation of many other properties of the system, since it provides a definite limitation on the choice of hole size and spacing which may be used to give a musical scale.[30]

A theoretical formulation of the acoustical nature of that part of a woodwind bore which is provided with open side branches (finger holes) is based initially upon the empirical recognition that (in the playing range) the input impedance of such a transmission line is roughly independent of the holes beyond the first two or three. Once the resulting simple equations are written down, it is easy to show that the hole sizes and spacings dictated by the necessities of the closed-hole bore lead to an almost constant characteristic impedance along a bore with open holes. As a consequence of this, we find that the simple equations for the resonance length of a bore provided with open holes at its lower end are, in fact, almost precisely exact as is borne out by experiment. It is at this point that we can begin to appreciate the importance of the closed holes on a woodwind. All of them play a part in determining the resonance frequency, while only one or two of the open ones do so. As a result, it is the closed holes which are the most stringently controlled by musical requirements. It is in a sense only a happy accident for the construction of theories, and for the manufacture of instruments that the rather loose limitations on the open holes are almost perfectly in accord with those already laid upon these holes by their effect when closed.

The radiation properties of the open holes are examined briefly in several physically interesting simple cases, and the observation made that each Fourier component of the sound spectrum is emitted with its own characteristic angular distribution and radiation efficiency. That these distributions may be divided into two main classes is associated with the fact that a duct with open holes constitutes a high-pass filter which propagates sounds in a qualitatively different manner for frequencies lying above and below the cutoff frequency. We also find simple reasons why the large holes on saxophones and flutes obviate the need for bells at the lower ends of these instruments, while most other instruments make use of bells in a partially successful effort to gain uniformity of tone.

In summary, we may describe the present report as being chiefly a demonstration of the possibility of using transmission line theory for woodwind bores with side holes, from which we find the crucial role of the closed holes. Everything else is merely a systematic exploration by standard methods of the practical implications of these two results, with close attention paid to the accuracy obtainable in the calculations.[31]

[30] Reference is made to the effects of closed holes on the intonation of the English flute by R. Herman, Am. J. Phys. **27**, 22 (1959), but there is no indication of the way in which such effects are calculated, nor are any general conclusions drawn.

[31] An informal and elementary discussion of the content of this paper and of paper A appears as part of the author's recently published book, *Horns, Strings and Harmony* (Doubleday-Anchor, Garden City, New York, 1960), Chap. 9, pp. 196–233.

## APPENDIX A

To guide the fine tuning of an already-existing woodwind, or to aid in investigating the effect of irregularities in hole size and placement, it is useful to have differential expressions for the change $d(\Delta l)$ produced by small alteration in bore and tone hole sizes, wall thickness, and hole spacing.

*A. Bore with Single Side Hole*

This case is dealt with in Section V-B, and the working formula for $\Delta l$ is given in Eq. (34). Under the assumption that $a \cong a_e$, $v_c \cong c$, differentiation of Eq. (34) gives:

$$
\begin{aligned}
d(\Delta l) = \; & da[2(b/a)^2(t_e/a)\,(\Delta/t_e)^2] \\
& - db[2(b/a)(t_e/a)(\Delta l/t_e)^2] \\
& + dM_e[(t_e/M_e)^2(\Delta l/t_e)^2] \\
& + dt_e\{[1 - (t_e/M_e)(\Delta l/t_e)](t_e/Me)\}
\end{aligned} \tag{1}
$$

*B. Pipe with Many Side Holes*

This case is taken up in Section V-C, and Eq. (38) gives the working formula. For many purposes it is convenient to ignore the rather slight frequency dependence of this expression in the lower playing range of the instrument, and use the $\omega \rightarrow 0$ limit of Eq. (38) as a simplified approximation. This limit is shown below as Eq. (2), and tabulated in Appendix B.

$$
\Delta l = s\{[1 + 2(a/b)^2(t_e/s)]^{1/2} - 1\} \tag{2}
$$

Differentiation of this expression gives:

$$
\begin{aligned}
d(\Delta l) = \; & da\{2(a/b)(s/b)(t_e/s)/[(\Delta l/s) + 1]\} \\
& - db\{2(a/b)^2(s/b)(t_e/s)/[(\Delta l/s) + 1]\} \\
& + ds\{(\Delta l/s) - [(a/b)^2(t_e/s)]/[(\Delta l/s) + 1]\} \\
& + dt_e\{(a/b)^2/[\Delta l/s) + 1]\}
\end{aligned} \tag{3}
$$

It is worth noting that if the bore is reamed, so that $da > 0$, and $dt,_e = -da$, the direct term in $da$ is considerably larger than the descendent $dt_e$ term (whose sign is opposite). As a result, *enlarging the bore flattens the note* from this cause, over and above any other effect such an enlargement might have on the tuning. Maintaining the ratio $(db/da)$ equal to $(b/a)$ as the bore is reamed will, however, make $d(\Delta l)$ zero.

## Appendix B

### Low Frequency Approximation to Open-Hole Length Correction

$C \equiv (\Delta l/s)$, $R \equiv (a/b)$, $C = (\sqrt{1 + 0.6\,R^2T} + 1)$, and
$T \equiv 3.333(t_e/s)$ so that $T = 1, 2, 3, \ldots$ corresp. $(t_e/s) = .3, .6, .9, \ldots$

| *T* | *R* | *C* | *T* | *R* | *C* | *T* | *R* | *C* |
|---|---|---|---|---|---|---|---|---|
| 1 | 1.0000 | 0.26491 | 2 | 1.0000 | 0.48324 | 3 | 1.0000 | 0.67332 |
| 1 | 1.5000 | 0.53297 | 2 | 1.5000 | 0.92354 | 3 | 1.5000 | 1.24722 |
| 1 | 2.0000 | 0.84391 | 2 | 2.0000 | 1.40831 | 3 | 2.0000 | 1.86356 |
| 1 | 2.5000 | 1.17944 | 2 | 2.5000 | 1.91547 | 3 | 2.5000 | 2.49999 |
| 1 | 3.0000 | 1.52982 | 2 | 3.0000 | 2.43511 | 3 | 3.0000 | 3.14728 |
| 1 | 3.5000 | 1.88963 | 2 | 3.5000 | 2.96232 | 3 | 3.5000 | 3.80104 |
| 1 | 4.0000 | 2.25576 | 2 | 4.0000 | 3.49444 | 3 | 4.0000 | 4.45893 |
| 1 | 4.5000 | 2.62629 | 2 | 4.5000 | 4.02991 | 3 | 4.5000 | 5.11964 |
| 1 | 5.0000 | 2.99999 | 2 | 5.0000 | 4.56776 | 3 | 5.0000 | 5.78232 |
| 1 | 5.5000 | 3.37607 | 2 | 5.5000 | 5.10737 | 3 | 5.5000 | 6.44647 |
| 1 | 6.0000 | 3.75394 | 2 | 6.0000 | 5.64830 | 3 | 6.0000 | 7.11171 |
| 1 | 6.5000 | 4.13322 | 2 | 6.5000 | 6.19027 | 3 | 6.5000 | 7.77781 |
| 1 | 7.0000 | 4.51361 | 2 | 7.0000 | 6.73304 | 3 | 7.0000 | 8.44457 |

| *T* | *R* | *C* | *T* | *R* | *C* |
|---|---|---|---|---|---|
| 4 | 1.0000 | 0.84391 | 5 | 1.0000 | 0.99999 |
| 4 | 1.5000 | 1.52982 | 5 | 1.5000 | 1.78388 |
| 4 | 2.0000 | 2.25576 | 5 | 2.0000 | 2.60555 |
| 4 | 2.5000 | 2.99999 | 5 | 2.5000 | 3.44409 |
| 4 | 3.0000 | 3.75394 | 5 | 3.0000 | 4.29150 |
| 4 | 3.5000 | 4.51361 | 5 | 3.5000 | 5.14410 |
| 4 | 4.0000 | 5.27694 | 5 | 4.0000 | 5.99999 |
| 4 | 4.5000 | 6.04272 | 5 | 4.5000 | 6.85811 |
| 4 | 5.0000 | 6.81024 | 5 | 5.0000 | 7.71779 |
| 4 | 5.5000 | 7.57904 | 5 | 5.5000 | 8.57862 |
| 4 | 6.0000 | 8.34879 | 5 | 6.0000 | 9.44030 |
| 4 | 6.5000 | 9.11928 | 5 | 6.5000 | 10.3026 |
| 4 | 7.0000 | 9.89036 | 5 | 7.0000 | 11.1655 |

### Errata

Page 1593, column 1, Eqs. (3) and (4). Author's note: See C. J. Nederveen and D. W. Wullften Palthe, *Acustica* **13,** 65 (1963).

Page 1594, column 1, Eq. (7) should read:

$$\text{"}\Delta l + l\left\{\frac{r \cdot [1 - (v_c/c)}{1 - r\,[1 - (V_c/c)}\right\}.$$

Author's note: When $V_c$ is variable, a better formula than that of Eq. (7) is

$$\Delta l = \int_0^l dx/(V_c/c) = \int_0^l \tfrac{1}{2}Dc(X)dx.$$

Page 1599, column 1, Eq. (26) should read:

"Maximum change = 1.66 $(V_p/V_b) \times 10^3$ cents."

Page 1600, column 1, paragraph (2). Author's note: These flattening effects due to the correction produced by a cavity produced when a joint is pulled are in addition to the flattening produced by mere elongation, which amounts to 12.5 cents.

Page 1601, column 1, Eq. (34). Author's note: See Appendix A, section A.

Page 1602, column 1, Eq. (38). Author's note: See Appendix A, section B and tabulation of the $\omega \rightarrow 0$ approximation to Eq. (38) in Appendix B.

# 24

*Copyright © 1963 by the Acoustical Society of America*

Reprinted from *J. Acoust. Soc. Am.*, **35**(3), 305–313 (1963)

# Small-Vibration Theory of the Clarinet

JOHN BACKUS

*University of Southern California, Los Angeles 7, California*

(Received 23 November 1962)

A theory of the clarinet is developed based on the experimental observation that for weak tones the reed and air-column vibrations are nearly sinusoidal. The clarinet is assumed to be a cylindrical air column open at one end and closed at the other by a diaphragm containing a slit of variable width, corresponding to the aperture between reed and mouthpiece. A velocity potential appropriate to a tube with wall friction is assumed. The impedance of the slit as a function of opening and pressure across it is evaluated experimentally and checked against theory. The volume flow through the slit is calculated from the velocity potential and equated to the flow calculated from the slit impedance. The flow and impedance both depend on the pressure, which in turn is again calculated from the velocity potential. Expressions for the operating frequency and threshold blowing pressure are obtained by assuming the flow to consist of a small alternating component superimposed on a steady component. The frequency is found to be below the resonance of the system considered as a tube closed at the reed end, the shift varying nearly linearly with the slit opening and depending on the reed damping. The threshold blowing pressure is found to be proportional to the opening and to the reed stiffness. Operating frequencies and pressures for the artificially blown clarinet were measured experimentally and found to be in very good agreement with values calculated from the theory.

## INTRODUCTION

MUSICAL instruments have developed into their present forms through empirical processes in which acoustical theory has played a negligible role. However, the development and application of adequate theory for the behavior of musical instruments are not only important for their own sake, but also will obviously be of great assistance in improving their practical performance. For the woodwind instruments, a considerable amount of theory is available to predict approximately the resonance frequencies of conical and cylindrical tubes containing side holes, expanded or contracted sections, and other deformities.[1–3] However, for those instruments employing a vibrating reed as the sound energizer, such as the clarinet, oboe, and bassoon, the interaction of the reed with the resonant system is obviously of great importance, and very little work has been done on this aspect of the wind instruments. Some calculations of reed behavior have been attempted by Das and others[4–6]; their main result is to demonstrate the probable origin of the even harmonics in the clarinet tone.

The purpose of this paper is to outline a theory of the interaction of the reed and the air column in the clarinet for the case where the amplitudes of the vibrations are small. It is based on the experimental observation that for soft tones the vibrations of the reed and air column are nearly sinusoidal.[7] The results of the theory will be used to explain two matters of practical importance to clarinet players: the slight but important control the player has over the frequency of his instrument, and the existence of a threshold blowing pressure.

## OBSERVATION

The playing frequency of a woodwind instrument depends, of course, primarily on the length of the vibrating air column as determined by the finger holes, and by the velocity of sound inside the instrument. However, the player can alter the frequency slightly by varying the pressure of the lip on the reed, increased pressure raising the frequency, and conversely. This

[1] E. G. Richardson, *Technical Aspects of Sound* (Elsevier Publishing Company, Amsterdam, 1953), Chap. 18.
[2] A. H. Benade, J. Acoust. Soc. Am. **31**, 137–146 (1959).
[3] A. H. Benade, J. Acoust. Soc. Am. **32**, 1591–1608 (1960).
[4] P. Das, Indian J. Phys. **6**, 227–232 (1931).
[5] R. G. Chatterji, Proc. Natl. Acad. Sci. India **A21**, 261–267 (1952).
[6] R. N. Ghosh, J. Acoust. Soc. Am. **9**, 255–264 (1938).
[7] John Backus, J. Acoust. Soc. Am. **33**, 806–809 (1961).

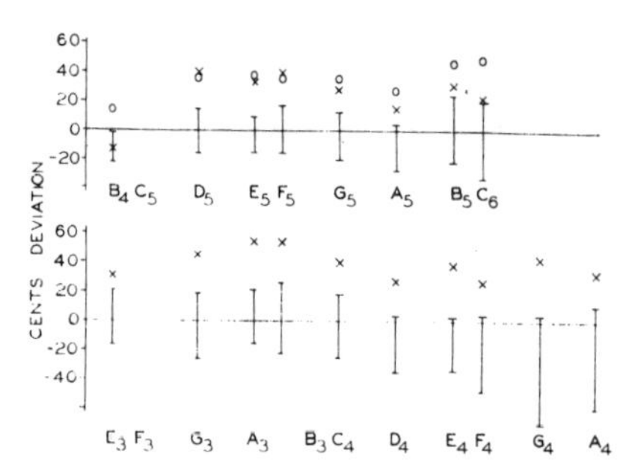


FIG. 1. Frequency ranges of several clarinet tones as normally played. Crosses and circles show resonance frequencies of instrument obtained by external excitation with reed aperture closed (see text).

effect is of great importance in maintaining good intonation in ensemble playing. The frequency of some tones of the bassoon, for example, can be varied by more than a semitone; since a great many of its tones are out of tune due to necessary compromises in the positions of finger holes, the bassoon player by long practice learns to compensate for the intonation defects of the instrument by applying the proper lip pressure for each tone.

The same effect exists in the clarinet but in lesser degree. Figure 1 gives the approximate ranges in playing frequencies of some tones on the clarinet, shown by vertical solid lines. These are to be compared with the resonance frequencies of the instrument considered as a tube closed at one end, which are measured as follows. An Altec 21BR microphone is mounted in the mouthpiece, as subsequently described. The reed is clamped tightly against the mouthpiece to close the air column of the instrument at that end. The air column is excited by means of a loudspeaker mounted near the instrument and fed from an oscillator and amplifier. The frequency of the oscillator is varied to get a maximum response from the microphone, and this frequency measured by means of a stroboscopic frequency meter (Stroboconn). The lower half of Fig. 1 shows tones produced by sounding the fundamental, together with the resonance frequencies measured as described and indicated by crosses. The upper half of the figure shows tones produced by sounding the next higher mode of vibration, together with the measured resonances for this mode. Since this mode is very nearly three times the frequency of the lowest mode, it is convenient to refer to it as the quasi-third harmonic. The crosses show the resonances measured with the left thumb key closed. The circles are with this key open, which is the usual playing condition; the function of this key is to open a hole so located as to facilitate the production of the quasi-third harmonic and thus produce tones in the upper register. It is to be noted that the playing frequencies are below the resonance frequencies by the order of half a semitone.

The fact that a certain minimum pressure is required to make the clarinet sound is of practical importance to the player; it means that considerable practice is necessary to be able to produce soft tones of even loudness that do not suddenly cease because of a momentary diminution of pressure below the threshold value. It can be easily observed qualitatively that this threshold depends on the reed, being higher with stiffer reeds; this will be quantitatively explained below.

## THEORY

Figure 2(a) shows a section through the operating portion of a clarinet, the playing frequency being determined primarily by the distance from the tip of the mouthpiece to the first open hole 0. The tip of the reed is separated from the mouthpiece by a distance $\xi$, which varies with the motion of the reed, and through which air is blown from the player's mouth at an excess pressure $p_0$ above atmospheric. We shall idealize this into the arrangement of Fig. 2(b), in which a tube of length $l$ and internal cross-sectional area $A_0$ is open at one end and terminates at the other in a diaphragm containing a slit of variable width $\xi$. This slit communicates with a reservoir maintained at the excess pressure $p_0$ by air entering as shown by the arrow. We shall consider the motion of the air in the tube to be one-dimensional, assuming that the air entering through the slit spreads out and acquires a uniform motion along the tube in a distance short enough to be negligible.

### The $Q$ of the Clarinet

The clarinet is a dissipative system, so we must take into account air friction at the internal walls. Taking $\phi$ as the velocity potential of a wave traveling in the direction $x$ along a tube with friction at the walls, the differential equation for $\phi$ is[8]

$$\partial^2\phi/\partial t^2+r(\partial\phi/\partial t)=c_1^2(\partial^2\phi/\partial x^2), \quad (1)$$

where $r$ is a friction term and $c_1$ is the velocity of sound in the tube. For the clarinet $c_1$ differs from $c$, the velocity of sound in free air, by about 1%, which may

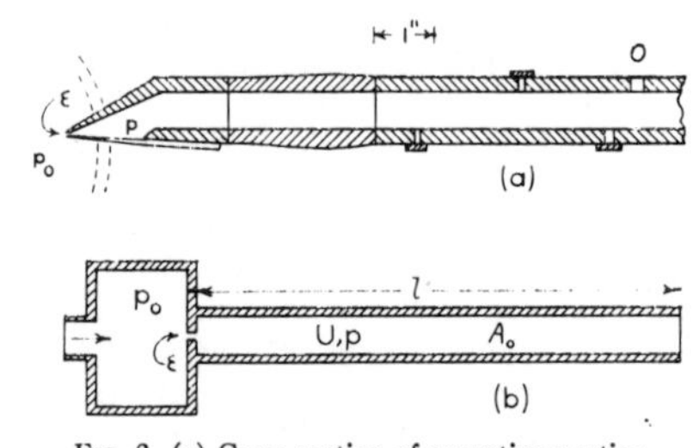


FIG. 2. (a) Cross section of operating portion of clarinet; (b) idealized version.

[8] Lord Rayleigh, *Theory of Sound* (Dover Publications, Inc., New York, 1945), Vol. II, p. 319.

be neglected. A solution of Eq. (1) is then

$$\phi = e^{j(\alpha t \pm Kx)}, \tag{2}$$

provided

$$\alpha^2 - jr\alpha = c^2K^2. \tag{3}$$

A damped oscillatory solution of (1) is obtained by setting $K=k=\omega/c$. Then we have

$$\phi = \exp\{-\tfrac{1}{2}rt + j[\omega t(1-r^2/4\omega^2)^{\frac{1}{2}} \pm kx]\}. \tag{4}$$

If we define the $Q$ of the system to be such that the logarithmic decrement is $\pi/Q$, we find the friction term to be

$$r = \omega/Q. \tag{5}$$

A periodic solution of Eq. (1) is obtained by setting $\alpha=\omega$. Then

$$K = k(1-jr/\omega)^{\frac{1}{2}} = k(1-j/Q)^{\frac{1}{2}}. \tag{6}$$

We shall find that $Q$ for the clarinet is at least 20, so to the accuracy in which we are interested

$$K = k(1-j/2Q) \tag{7}$$

and

$$\phi = \exp[j\omega t \pm jkx(1-j/2Q)]. \tag{8}$$

The volume velocity $U$ and the pressure $p$ in the tube are then given by

$$U = -A_0(\partial\phi/\partial x), \quad p = \rho(\partial\phi/\partial t), \tag{9}$$

where $A_0$ is the cross-sectional area of the tube and $\rho$ the density of air.

Let us apply these equations to a tube closed at $x=0$ and open at $x=l$, with a pressure $p=p_O e^{j\omega t}$ acting there. Then the appropriate form of Eq. (8) is

$$\phi = e^{j\omega t}(p_O/j\omega\rho)\cos[kx(1-j/2Q)]/\cos[kl(1-j/2Q)], \tag{10}$$

which gives the ratio of the pressure amplitude $p_{Cl}$ at the closed end to the pressure amplitude $p_O$ at the open end as

$$p_{Cl}/p_O = \cos[kl(1-j/2Q)]^{-1} = [\cos kl \cosh(kl/2Q) + j\sin kl \sinh(kl/2Q)]^{-1}. \tag{11}$$

The phase angle $\varphi$ between these pressures is given by

$$\tan\varphi = \tan kl \tanh(kl/2Q), \tag{12}$$

so that the phase shift is 90° if $kl=\frac{1}{2}n\pi$, with $n$ an odd integer. The magnitude of the pressure ratio is given by

$$|p_{Cl}/p_O|^2 = 2/[\cos 2kl + \cosh(2kl/2Q)], \tag{13}$$

which will be maximum at $kl=\frac{1}{2}n\pi(1-1/2Q^2)$, or the same as for the 90° phase shift if $Q$ is reasonably large. The value of this maximum is

$$|p_{Cl}/p_O| = 4Q/n\pi, \tag{14}$$

so that the $Q$ of the system can be measured by determining the pressure ratio. This can be done for the clarinet with the resonance-measuring arrangement described above. The output of the microphone in the mouthpiece is compared with the output of another microphone placed near the open end or the first open hole when the system is energized with an external speaker; this comparison is most easily done by putting the outputs on the two deflection plates of an oscilloscope. The frequency for the 90° phase shift can be set quite precisely and the pressure ratio then determined. We find for the clarinet that the $Q$ is approximately 20 to 25 for the fundamental and 40 to 45 for the quasi-third harmonic.

### The Vibrating Clarinet

To apply the above equations to the clarinet in vibration, we shall assume first, with Benade,[2] that the energy lost by radiation from the open end is negligible compared to that lost by friction at the walls. We thus assume that $p=\phi=0$ at the open end $x=l$, where $l$ will include any necessary end correction. Since air is blown into the instrument to make it sound, we also need a term in $\phi$ to give an average steady flow. The form of $\phi$ satisfying these requirements will be

$$\phi = Be^{j\omega t}\sin[k(x-l)(1-j/2Q)] - U_0(x-l)/A_0, \tag{15}$$

where $U_0$ is the steady volume flow and $B$ a constant. This will give, at $x=0$,

$$U = U_0 - BA_0e^{j\omega t}k(1-j/2Q)\cos[kl(1-j/2Q)], \tag{16}$$

$$p = -j\omega\rho Be^{j\omega t}\sin[kl(1-j/2Q)], \tag{17}$$

using Eq. (9). The flow given by Eq. (16) must now be matched to the conditions necessary to give this flow through the reed aperture $\xi$ at $x=0$. This will involve the impedance of the aperture and the pressure difference across it.

### Reed Aperture Impedance

Sivian[9] has given expressions for the acoustic resistance and reactance of small circular and rectangular orifices. For a rectangular aperture of width (long dimension) $w$, opening $\xi$, and length $l$ in the direction of air flow, the reactance is $X=\omega M$, where the acoustic mass $M$ is given by the expression

$$M = \frac{\rho}{w}\left[\frac{l}{\xi} + \frac{1}{\pi}\left(1 + 2\ln\frac{2w}{\xi}\right)\right], \tag{18}$$

provided $\xi/w \ll 1$. The derivation of Eq. (18) assumes the aperture to be situated in an infinite plate. The actual reed aperture in the clarinet mouthpiece is more complicated than this, as Fig. 2 shows, so we would expect Eq. (18) to apply only approximately. Experimental values of $M$ for the reed aperture were obtained by mounting the clarinet mouthpiece and reed on a small closed volume, this volume and the reed aperture

[9] L. J. Sivian, J. Acoust. Soc. Am. 7, 94–101 (1935).

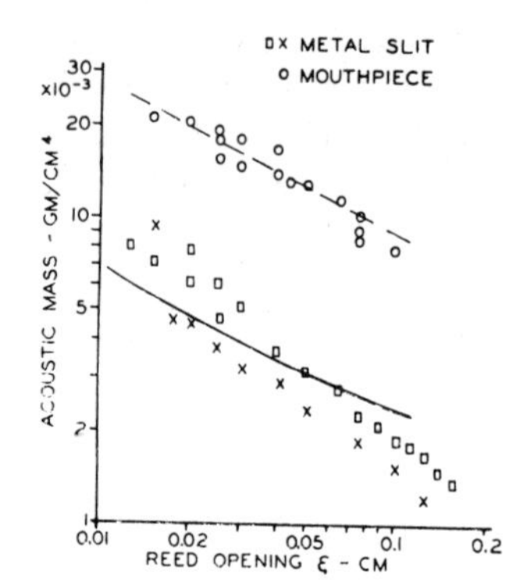


FIG. 3. Effective acoustic mass of reed aperture as a function of opening.

thus forming a Helmholtz resonator. It was excited by an external speaker and the resonance frequency observed by means of a microphone inserted into the volume. The aperture mass was then computed from the formula

$$\omega^2 = c^2\rho / M V_0, \tag{19}$$

$V_0$ being the total volume of the system including the mouthpiece. The mass was obtained for various values of the opening $\xi$, as measured with a traveling microscope; the results are plotted in Fig. 3. The solid line in the figure is the plot of Eq. (18) based on the assumption that $w = 1.5$ cm, $l = 0.05$ cm. Also shown for comparison are experimental results for a metal slit of these dimensions. It will be noted that the mass values for the clarinet reed aperture are some three times the theoretical, presumably due to the shape of the mouthpiece. The dashed line in the figure gives the values of acoustic mass vs $\xi$ used in subsequent calculations.

A more important quantity is the acoustic resistance of the reed aperture. Sivian[9] gives expressions for orifice resistance based on viscous flow, for which the volume flow is proportional to pressure difference so that the resistance is a constant. He also shows that as the flow is increased, the energy of the air flowing through the aperture becomes important, and the resistance increases. This is found to be the case for the clarinet, where the slit dimensions are such that viscosity has a negligible effect. For air flowing through an opening from a region at pressure $p_0$ to one at pressure $p_1$, the velocity $u$ in the opening is given in thermodynamics texts by the expression[10]

$$\tfrac{1}{2}\rho u^2 = p_0[\gamma/(\gamma-1)][(1-(p_1/p_0)^{(\gamma-1)/\gamma}]. \tag{20}$$

For a small pressure difference $p = p_0 - p_1$, Eq. (20) reduces to

$$\tfrac{1}{2}\rho u^2 = p, \tag{21}$$

giving, for the volume flow $U$ through an opening of area $A$,

$$U = A(2p/\rho)^{1/2}. \tag{22}$$

The resistance $R = p/U$ of the opening is thus not a constant, but increases with the square root of the pressure difference. However, it is still convenient to use this quantity for calculation.

Since the flow of air through the clarinet is a steady current on which is superimposed an alternating one, the resistance for steady flow needs to be determined. A Plexiglas tube $3\frac{1}{2}$ in. i.d. was fitted with a diaphragm that could be moved by a pressure difference of less than one-third inch of water. The air flow through the reed aperture at a known blowing pressure was obtained as a function of pressure difference and reed opening. The results for volume flow and resistance are shown in Fig. 4, with the experimental points indicated by crosses. Inaccuracies are mostly due to the irregular contour of the reed as seen under the microscope. Pressures are read on a commercial diaphragm gauge calibrated in inches of water, which is a convenient unit; 1 in. water $= 2.49 \times 10^3$ dyn/cm². For comparison, the graph of Eq. (22) is shown as a dashed line, calculated for a slit of width 1.5 cm and a pressure of 15 in., which gives $U = 1.3 \times 10^4 \xi$.

The experimental data are fitted quite well by the expression

$$U = 37 p^{2/3} \xi^{4/3}, \tag{23}$$

as shown in Fig. 4 by the solid lines calculated for three values of $p$. Equation (22) gives a linear dependence of $U$ on $\xi$ if $A = w\xi$. The faster variation of $U$ with $\xi$ is due to the detailed construction of the reed and mouthpiece assembly, as follows: As shown in Fig. 5, the "lay" of the mouthpiece—the area adjacent to the flat face of the reed—is flat over most of its area, but

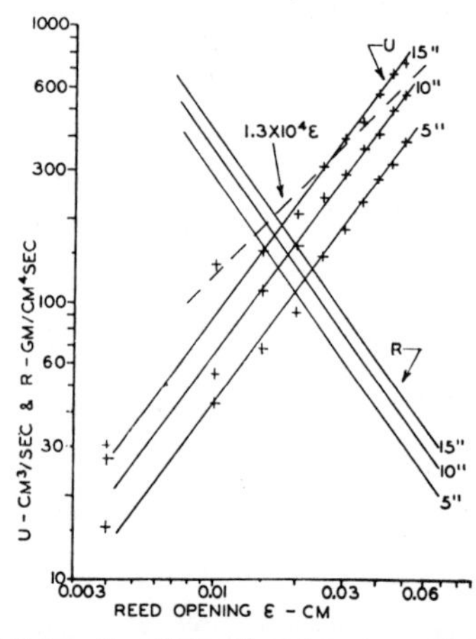


FIG. 4. Volume flow $U$ through reed aperture and aperture resistance $R$ as a function of opening.

[10] H. A. Sorensen, *Principles of Thermodynamics* (Holt, Rinehart, and Winston, New York, 1961), p. 266.

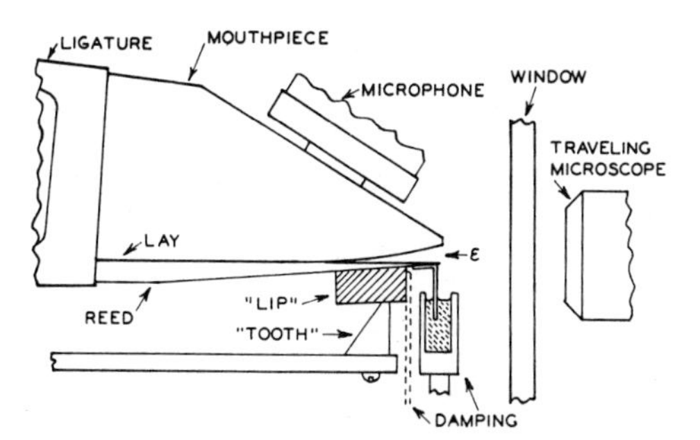


FIG. 5. Side view of tip of mouthpiece showing artificial embochure and reed-damping mechanism.

curved slightly for about 1.5 cm from the tip of the mouthpiece. The reed is clamped against the lay by means of the ligature, and, because of the curvature mentioned above, the tip of the reed is slightly more than 1 mm away from the tip of the mouthpiece. This separation is then reduced further by pressing the lower teeth cushioned by the lip against the reed about 5–10 mm back from the tip, the separation $\xi$ for playing being roughly in the range 0.02–0.06 cm. The area of the reed aperture then consists of an approximately rectangular opening of area $1.5\xi$ cm$^2$, plus the two wedge-shaped areas on the side of the reed. As the separation is reduced by increasing the lip pressure, the point of contact of the reed with the lay moves further out toward the tip of the mouthpiece. The area of the wedge-shaped portions thus varies somewhat as $\xi^2$, while that of the rectangular portion varies as $\xi$, so the result is the four-thirds power variation found experimentally.

The variation of $U$ with $p^{2/3}$ in Eq. (23), instead of with $p^{1/2}$ as in the theoretical Eq. (22), is due to the combination of the above effect with the flexibility of the reed. If the blowing pressure is increased, the flexible tip of the reed will be forced closer to the mouthpiece; the lip pressure must then be reduced to keep the separation constant. This results in enlarging the wedge-shaped areas described above, and a consequent increase in volume flow over the theoretical value. This was verified by using a stiff metal reed instead of a cane reed to measure the flow; the metal reed gave values of $U$ quite accurately proportional to $p^{1/2}$.

The resistance $R$ of the reed aperture is thus proportional to $p^{1/3}$. Values of $R$ for three values of pressure are shown in Fig. 4.

We may now write the conditions to be satisfied at the reed aperture. From Eq. (23) the pressure necessary to produce a given volume flow may be written

$$p = DU^{3/2}\xi^2. \tag{24}$$

To this must be added the pressure necessary to produce the volume acceleration through the aperture. Letting $p_0$ denote the constant blowing pressure and $p$ the mouthpiece pressure, we then have

$$M(\xi)(\partial U/\partial t) + D(U^{3/2}/\xi^2) = p_0 - p. \tag{25}$$

Now we assume that the flow is a steady term plus a small alternating component, and that the pressure inside the mouthpiece varies sinusoidally. The reed displacement will then be an average value $\xi_0$, plus a small sinusoidal variation proportional to the mouthpiece pressure, so we may write

$$U = U_0(1 + \mu e^{j\omega t}), \tag{26}$$

$$p = p_1 e^{j\omega t}, \tag{27}$$

$$\xi = \xi_0(1 + \kappa p_1 e^{j\omega t}), \tag{28}$$

where $\mu$ and $\kappa p_1$ are assumed to be small quantities. We note further that the mass term in Eq. (25) may be written

$$M(\xi) = M_0 + M_1 e^{j\omega t}, \tag{29}$$

where $M_0$ is the value for the average reed displacement $\xi_0$. These are now to be substituted in Eq. (25), the result expanded in powers of $e^{j\omega t}$, and only the constant and lowest frequency terms retained. We obtain

$$DU_0^{3/2}/\xi_0^2 = p_0 \tag{30}$$

equating constant terms, and

$$(j\omega M_0 U_0 + \tfrac{3}{2} p_0)\mu = p_1(2\kappa p_0 - 1) \tag{31}$$

from the $e^{j\omega t}$ terms, using Eq. (30).

The displacement of the reed about its average position due to the sinusoidal variation in mouthpiece pressure will be

$$\xi - \xi_0 = p_1 e^{j\omega i}/(S_r - M_r\omega^2 + j\omega R_r), \tag{32}$$

where $S_r$ is the stiffness of the reed in dyn/cm$^3$, $M_r$ the effective mass in g/cm$^2$, and $R_r$ the damping resistance in dyn sec/cm$^3$. The resonance frequency $\omega_r$ of the reed itself, for which $\omega_r^2 = S_r/M_r$, is at least ten to twenty times the playing frequency $\omega$, so the mass term in Eq. (32) may be neglected. The damping term, however, is very important. When playing the instrument, this term is supplied by the player's lower lip, and is necessary to keep the reed from vibrating at its own frequency instead of that of the air column. This can be demonstrated by trying to play the clarinet with the teeth instead of the lip pressing against the reed; very high-pitched squeals result.

We shall define a constant $\kappa_0$ by

$$\kappa_0 = 1/\xi_0 S_r, \tag{33}$$

and the tangent of the phase angle between mouthpiece pressure and reed displacement by

$$\eta = \omega R_r/S_r. \tag{34}$$

Using these, the constant $\kappa$ in Eq. (28) becomes

$$\kappa = \kappa_0/(1 + j\eta). \tag{35}$$

Now if we compare Eqs. (26) and (27) with Eqs. (16) and (17), we find

$$\mu = -(BA_0/U_0)k(1-j/2Q)\cos[kl(1-j/2Q)], \quad (36)$$

and

$$p_1 = -j\omega\rho B \sin[kl(1-j/2Q)]. \quad (37)$$

Next we substitute Eqs. (35)–(37) in Eq. (31) and expand the trigonometric functions. Letting $p_0/U_0 = R_0$, the aperture resistance, and defining parameters $\tau$ and $\zeta$ by

$$\tau = \rho c/\tfrac{3}{2}A_0R_0, \quad (38)$$

$$\zeta = kl/2Q, \quad (39)$$

we obtain

$$\left[1+\frac{\omega M_0}{3R_0Q}+j\left(\frac{3\omega M_0}{2R_0}-\frac{1}{2Q}\right)\right](1+j\eta)$$
$$\times(\cos kl \cosh\zeta + j \sin kl \sinh\zeta)$$
$$=\tau[\eta+j(2\kappa_0 p_0-1)]$$
$$\times(\sin kl \cosh\zeta - j\cos kl \sinh\zeta). \quad (40)$$

Some approximations are now necessary. The frequencies of the clarinet will be fairly close to those of a closed pipe of the same length, so that $kl \approx \frac{1}{2}n\pi$, with $n$ odd; for the present, we will only be concerned with the fundamental and quasi-third harmonic. Using $Q = 25$, we find $\zeta = kl/2Q \approx 0.1$ or less. Hence in Eq. (40) we may replace $\cosh\zeta$ by unity and $\sinh\zeta$ by its argument. In the range of reed apertures and frequencies of interest, the term $3\omega M_0/2R_0$ as evaluated from Figs. 3 and 4 is 0.4 at most, so the term $\omega M_0/3R_0Q$ is negligible. For convenience we take

$$b = 3\omega M_0/2R_0 - 1/2Q \quad (41)$$

and equate the real and imaginary parts of Eq. (40). The results are

$$\cos kl[1-\eta b-\tau\zeta(2\kappa_0 p_0-1)]$$
$$-\sin kl[\zeta(\eta+b)+\tau\eta]=0, \quad (42)$$
$$\cos kl(\eta+b+\eta\tau\zeta)$$
$$+\sin kl[\zeta(1-\eta b)-\tau(2\kappa_0 p_0-1)]=0. \quad (43)$$

The cross section $A_0$ of the clarinet is 1.75 cm². The parameter $\tau$ from Eq. (38) and Fig. 4 then has a value of 0.2 at most. We may then neglect the term $\eta\tau\zeta$ in Eq. (43) and obtain

$$\tau(2\kappa_0 p_0-1)=\zeta-\zeta\eta b+(\eta+b)\,\text{ctn}\,kl. \quad (44)$$

The last two terms on the right of Eq. (44) are small and approximately cancel in practice, so we may neglect them. We thus find for the threshold blowing pressure, using Eq. (33),

$$p_0 = \tfrac{1}{2}\xi_0 S_r(1+\zeta/\tau). \quad (45)$$

Substituting Eq. (44) in Eq. (42) and neglecting terms in $\zeta^2$ and smaller, we find

$$\text{ctn}\,kl = [\eta(\tau+\zeta)+\zeta b]/(1-\eta b). \quad (46)$$

We wish to find the small shift in frequency $\Delta f$ from the resonance value, for which $kl=\frac{1}{2}n\pi$, so we write

$$kl = \tfrac{1}{2}n\pi(1+\Delta f/f). \quad (47)$$

This gives

$$\text{ctn}\,kl = -\tfrac{1}{2}n\pi\Delta f/f, \quad (48)$$

and, using $\zeta = n\pi/4Q$, we find for the fractional frequency shift

$$\Delta f/f = -[2\eta\tau/n\pi+(\eta+b)/2Q]/(1-\eta b). \quad (49)$$

It is to be noted that the shift is always downward, in agreement with observation.

## EXPERIMENT

### Equipment

Data were taken to check experimentally the calculated threshold pressure and frequency shift given by Eqs. (45) and (49). The clarinet was sounded by blowing air through it from a household vacuum cleaner, using the artificial embochure sketched in Fig. 5. The reed opening $\xi$ could be varied from outside the blowing chamber (not shown) by changing the pressure of the brass "tooth" on the foam neoprene "lip." The opening could be measured by means of a traveling microscope sighting through a window in the blowing chamber. The position of the Altec 21-BR microphone used to measure the mouthpiece pressure is shown in the figure. The output of this microphone was applied to the Stroboconn, which measures frequencies to 0.01 semitone (0.05%).

The air from the vacuum cleaner warms up on continuous operation and changes the clarinet frequency slightly. This effect amounts to 2.9 cents rise per °C, and must be taken into account. A 2000-ohm thermistor was mounted on a cork and arranged to project just inside the air column of the clarinet. The thermistor was made one arm of a Wheatstone bridge. The unbalance current of the bridge, amounting to 0.2 $\mu$a per °C, was calibrated against measured air temperatures. The time constant of the system was sufficiently short, and the temperature could be read to within 0.2°C.

To measure the phase shift $\eta$ between reed displacement and mouthpiece pressure, the traveling microscope in Fig. 5 was replaced by the photocell arrangement previously described.[7] Light from an automobile headlight placed opposite the open end of the clarinet passed through the reed opening and into the photocell. It was found that the 6-V headlight could be conveniently operated from the 4-ohm tap of a Dynakit Mark III amplifier energized by an audio oscillator at 4000 cps; this eliminated any intensity modulation in the illumination. The photocell output was put on the horizontal deflection of a Dumont type 401 oscilloscope.

The output of the mouthpiece microphone was applied to the vertical deflection through a phase-shifting network consisting of a variable resistance $R$ in series and a variable capacity $C$ in parallel with the oscilloscope, General Radio resistance and condenser boxes being used. By varying $R$ and $C$, a phase shift is introduced in the microphone signal to compensate for the reed-phase shift $\eta$, so that a straight line is produced on the oscilloscope. Under these conditions it is easy to show that $\eta=\omega RC$. The air flowing through the reed aperture developes a considerable amount of noise which appears in the microphone output. This effect limits the accuracy of the phase-shift measurements, especially at low values. Calculations based on the calibration curve of the Altec microphone indicated that it would introduce negligible phase shift at the frequencies used.

The reed stiffness $S_r$ was determined simply by observing the reed displacement vs blowing pressure change at various openings; it is constant over the range of openings used.

### Measurements

Operating data for the clarinet were taken in the following manner: The reed aperture was closed and the resonance frequency and $Q$ of the clarinet measured for the particular note being observed, using the separate excitation method described above. The resonance frequency is somewhat inaccurate because of the relatively low $Q$, which gives a broad maximum in the mouthpiece-microphone response. The accuracy could be increased by opening the reed aperture slightly and applying blowing pressure; this puts the system closer to the self-oscillation condition and increases the $Q$. It is possible to go smoothly from the separately excited condition to the self-excited one.

The resonance frequency being determined, the reed opening was increased to a selected value and the blowing pressure increased to the point where the clarinet was barely sounding. The pressure $p_0$ was read on a calibrated diaphragm gauge. The reed could be seen under the microscope to be vibrating with a small amplitude, and its average distance $\xi_0$ from the tip of the mouthpiece was measured. The vibration frequency was obtained from the reading on the Stroboconn, which gives the frequency in terms of cents deviation above or below one of the standard frequencies of the musical scale; a shift of 17 cents corresponds to a fractional frequency shift of 0.01. The air temperature in the clarinet was observed by reading the thermistor-bridge unbalance current. The traveling microscope was then replaced by the photocell assembly and the values of $R$ and $C$ determined for the setting of the phase-shifting network to compensate for the reed phase shift. The process was then repeated for other reed openings. Measurements were made for reed openings up to about 0.04 cm. Above this value

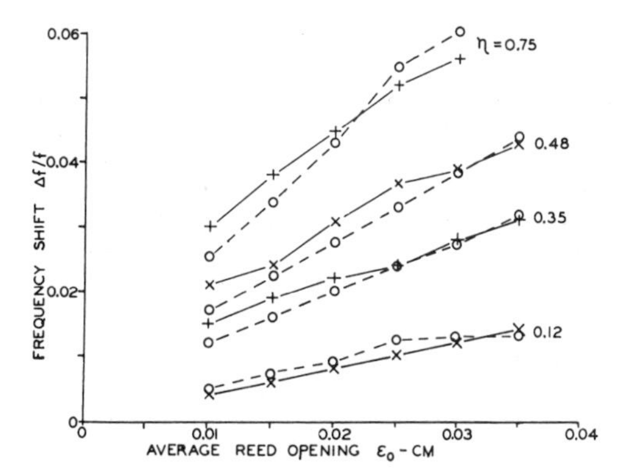


FIG. 6. Fractional frequency shift $\Delta f/f$ as a function of reed opening $\xi_0$ for different values of reed phase angle $\eta$. Measured shifts shown by crosses; calculated values by circles.

small vibrations were not stable; once started, the reed vibrations would increase in amplitude until the reed was striking the mouthpiece.

### Results

The first measurements taken were with reed damping provided by the rather crude arrangement of a metal strip pressing against the foam neoprene "lip" on the reed; this strip is indicated by the dotted lines in Fig. 5. The reed phase shifts given by this damping were small and not accurately measurable because of noise, as mentioned above. However, agreement with theory was encouraging enough to warrant a more quantitative control of reed damping. Some measurements were made with all tone holes closed and the bell or bell and first joint of the clarinet removed so that the experimental arrangement resembled as closely as possible the theoretical model. Other measurements were made with tone holes open in the usual manner. There does not appear to be any fundamental difference between the two arrangements.

A better damping arrangement used for the present measurements is shown in Fig. 5. A vane of 0.005-in. aluminum $\frac{3}{16}$ in. wide was fastened to the tip of the reed with Eastman 910 cement. This vane did not affect the playing quality of the reed, at least for the present application. It was arranged to dip into a small plastic trough containing 50 centistoke Silicone oil. The position of the trough could be varied from outside the blowing chamber. The reed damping could thus be changed over a considerable range. With this particular arrangement, the clarinet would vibrate only in the quasi-third harmonic.

A series of measurements were made with various values of reed damping and opening. In Fig. 6 is shown the fractional frequency shift $\Delta f/f$ as a function of reed opening $\xi$ for four different values of the reed phase shift $\eta$. The experimental values, obtained from the Stroboconn readings and corrected for temperature, are shown by crosses connected by solid lines. Values calculated from Eq. (49), using measured values of $\eta$ and other quantities calculated from Eqs. (38) and (41), with mass and resistance values taken from Figs. (3) and (4), are shown by circles connected by dotted lines. Figure 7 is a similar plot of another run made by varying the damping at set values of reed opening. The agreement of the experimental values with the theoretical expression is seen to be very good.

First results of this work reported earlier[11] gave the frequency shift as $\omega M_0/2R_0Q$. This expression was obtained by assuming no reed phase shift, so that $\eta=0$ in Eq. (49), and by assuming that the flow through the reed aperture was proportional to the pressure instead of its two-thirds power. First experimental results were encouraging, but subsequent work showed the expression to be obviously insufficient to account for observed shifts.

The experimental values of threshold blowing pressure vs reed opening are shown in Fig. 8. The values calculated from Eq. (45) using a measured stiffness $S_r$ for the particular reed used of $1.4\times10^{-6}$ dyn/cm³ are also shown. The agreement is again very good.

The playing frequency of the clarinet is thus seen to be below the air-column resonance by a small amount that varies nearly linearly with the reed opening and the reed damping. This explains quantitatively the slight but essential control the player is able to exert on the frequency of the instrument, as illustrated in Fig. 1; the rise in frequency with greater lip pressure on the reed is due to the resulting smaller reed opening, and not due to any change in the resonance frequency of the reed itself. The threshold blowing pressure is directly proportional to the reed opening and reed stiffness, and is modified somewhat by the $Q$ of the instrument. It does not vary with the reed damping, for example, and should therefore not depend on the condition of the player's lip.

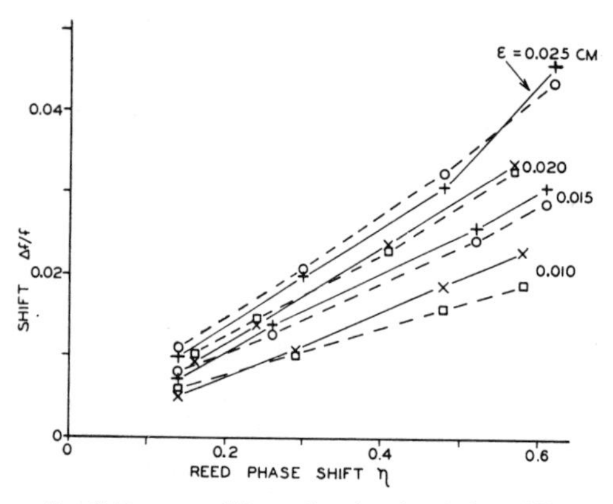


FIG. 7. Frequency shift as a function of reed phase shift. $\eta$ for different values of reed opening $\xi_0$.

[11] John Backus, J. Acoust. Soc. Am. **33**, 862 (1961).

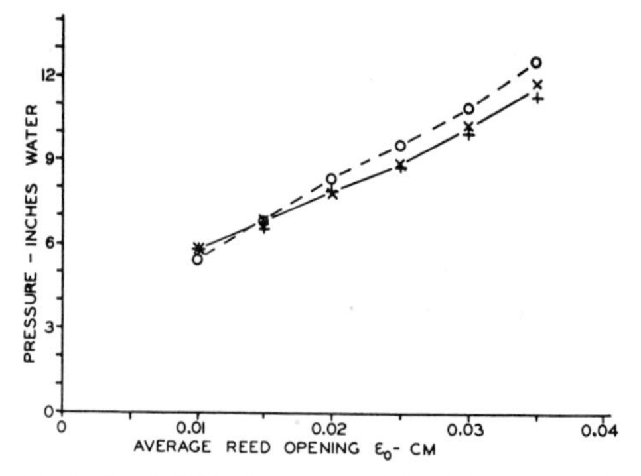


FIG. 8. Threshold blowing pressure of the clarinet as a function of reed opening. Measured pressures shown by crosses; calculated values by circles.

The agreement of the above theory with experiment is encouraging and gives some hope that perhaps its further development can explain other aspects of clarinet behavior, such as the harmonic structure of the louder tones and its dependence on reed properties and instrument construction. With the proper modification, it should also be applicable to the oboe and bassoon.

## ACKNOWLEDGMENT

This work was performed under a grant from the National Science Foundation, whose assistance is gratefully acknowledged.

## APPENDIX

Equation (1) in the text is valid for a tube in which the medium is at rest, and requires modification if there exists a steady flow along the tube, as is the case for the clarinet when sounded. For small oscillations superimposed on a steady flow of velocity $u_0$, Eq. (1) becomes

$$\left(\frac{\partial}{\partial t}+u_0\frac{\partial}{\partial x}\right)^2\phi+r\left(\frac{\partial}{\partial t}+u_0\frac{\partial}{\partial x}\right)\phi=c^2\frac{\partial^2\phi}{\partial x^2}, \quad (50)$$

with the excess pressure $p$ given by

$$p=\rho[(\partial/\partial t)+u_0(\partial/\partial x)]\phi. \quad (51)$$

To see how the vibration frequencies of a tube are affected by this steady flow, let us apply these equations to a frictionless tube of length $l$ open at both ends. Setting $r=0$ in Eq. (50) and trying $\phi=e^{i(\omega t-Kx)}$, we get the conditions for solution as

$$K=-k/(1+u_0/c), \quad +k/(1-u_0/c). \quad (52)$$

Putting this result into Eq. (51) and evaluating to get $p=0$ at $x=0$, we find

$$p=Ae^{j\omega t}[e^{-jkx/(1+u_0/c)}-e^{+jkx/(1-u_0/c)}]. \quad (53)$$

To get $p=0$ at $x=l$, Eq. (53) gives two conditions:

$$\cos[kl/(1+u_0/c)]-\cos[kl/(1-u_0/c)]=0,$$
$$\sin[kl/(1+u_0/c)]+\sin[kl(1-u_0/c)]=0. \quad (54)$$

These are satisfied by

$$kl=n\pi(1-u_0^2/c^2), \quad (55)$$

with $n$ an integer.

The resonance frequencies for the system thus differ from those of the tube with no flow by the fractional amount $u_0^2/c^2$. For the clarinet, $u_0/c$ is less than 1%, so the effect of the flow on the clarinet frequencies is negligible.

# 25

Copyright © 1968 by the Acoustical Society of America

Reprinted from *J. Acoust. Soc. Am.*, **44**(4), 983–992 (1968)

# Sounding Mechanism of the Flute and Organ Pipe

John W. Coltman*

*3319 Scathelocke Road, Pittsburgh, Pennsylvania 15235*

Measurements on an artificially blown and mechanically excited flute head joint provide values of the complex acoustic back pressure generated by the blowing jet. The magnitude of the acoustic back pressure is calculable from the jet momentum and is approximately twice the static blowing pressure times the ratio of the lip-aperture area to the tube cross-section area. The phase of the induced back pressure relative to the oscillation volume velocity is determined by the lip-to-edge distance and the velocity of propagation of a wave on the jet. Adjustment of this phase is demonstrated to be the major means by which the flutist selects the desired mode of oscillation of the instrument. The efficiency of conversion from jet power to acoustic oscillation power is low (2.4% at 440 Hz) and is about equal to the ratio of particle velocities in the air column and the jet. Nonlinear (turbulent) losses are measured and are substantial. Stroboscopic views of the jet motion under explicitly stated oscillation conditions show the large amplitude of the jet wave and its phase relative to the stimulating acoustic disturbance.

## INTRODUCTION

QUALITATIVE theories of the means by which acoustic oscillations are maintained in flutelike instruments have been available at least since that proposed by Sir John Herschel in 1830.[1] The intervening period has seen a certain amount of dissension as to the nature of the mechanism, accompanied by only a few controlled observations. Carrière[2] injected steam into the air jet of a very large organ pipe and observed stroboscopically the vortices formed in this stream. Brown[3] observed in detail the instabilities of a jet of air subjected to an acoustic disturbance, and Sato[4] has recently treated theoretically the mechanics of such a fluid stream. Cremer and Ising[5] treat the self-excited organ pipe as a resonant system coupled by a feedback mechanism to an oscillating jet.

The picture that is presented is briefly this: A thin flat jet of air, subjected to an alternating disturbance near its point of issuance, will develop a sinuousity in the form of a growing wave whose propagation velocity is roughly one-third to one-half the original jet velocity. The disturbances will eventually grow into a series of vortices. In the flute or organ, however, an edge or wedge upon which the jet plays interrupts the jet before these vortices are fully developed, and the result is to provide on each side of the wedge a set of air pulsations at the frequency of the initial disturbance. These pulsations can maintain acoustic oscillations in a resonator to which the wedge is properly affixed, and these oscillations in turn provide the initial disturbance for the jet. Subject to certain phase and loop-gain conditions, the entire system will then maintain itself in oscillation. In general, there are several modes of oscillation that can take place, both with respect to the number of acoustic wavelengths contained in the resonant pipe, and the number of undulant wavelengths of the jet stream, giving rise to a two-dimensional set of possible steady-state conditions that has been described (not entirely correctly) by Benade and French[6] and Bouasse.[7]

The present work inquires quantitatively into the processes involved in converting the direct current of the performer's breath into the alternating oscillations of the acoustic resonator, and how the oscillations depend on the parameters of the blowing mechanism. While the investigation has been limited to a single geometry and a relatively small range of frequencies, it has provided enough information to formulate a simple quantitative theory that appears adequate to

* This work was carried out privately. The author is at the Westinghouse Res. Labs., Pittsburgh, Pa. 15235

[1] R. S. Rockstro, *The Flute* (Rudall, Carte & Co., London, 1928), p. 34.

[2] M. Z. Carrière, J. Phys. **2**, 53–64 (1925).

[3] G. B. Brown, Proc. Phys. Soc. (London) **47**, 703–732 (1935).

[4] H. Sato, J. Fluid Mech. **7**, 53–80 (1960).

[5] L. Cremer and H. Ising, Acustica **19**, 143–153 (1963).

[6] A. H. Benade and J. W. French, J. Acoust. Soc. Amer. **37**, 679–691 (1965).

[7] H. Bouasse, *Tuyaux et Resonateure* (Librarie Delagrave, Paris, 1929).

explain many aspects of the behavior of the flute and organ pipe with reasonable accuracy.

## I. NATURE OF THE JET MOTION

Carrière's pictures[1] of jet streams were taken with an enormous (50-ft) organ pipe whose proportions were quite different from those of the flute. Moreover, he reported no measurements of the strength of oscillation. It seemed desirable then to obtain some visual information about the jet motion under conditions characteristic of the flute. Accordingly, a flute head joint, provided with acoustical driving and measuring mechanisms to be described later, was blown with an artificial air supply through an orifice closely resembling that of the flute player's lips. A small stream of cigarette smoke introduced into the jet, and a phase-locked stroboscope, permitted observation of the jet form. In Fig. 1 are sketches of the observed form of the jet. Each picture is for a specific phase relative to the acoustic current (volume velocity) at the mouthhole, as marked. A caution is raised about these and similar pictures: They are merely snapshots of the configuration of the smoke at a given instant. It must not be inferred that the smoke particles follow paths such as these in getting to that position, nor should it be assumed that air that does not contain smoke is not also in motion.

The conditions for these pictures are typical of the flute when playing A at 440 Hz moderately loud. Some features of the motion are worthy of comment. *First*, it can be seen that the jet does not instantly alter its form in response to the acoustic current. At 90°, the acoustic current has been moving out of the mouthhole during $\frac{1}{4}$ of a cycle, but the jet is just now blowing over the edge rather than into the hole. *Second*, the jet reacts strongly to moderate disturbances. Its own initial velocity in this case was 1320 cm/sec. The acoustic particle velocity (which acts roughly at right angles to the jet) was about 300 cm/sec. The acoustic particle amplitude of motion is about 1 mm; the jet, however, moves laterally at least 10 times this distance. A quite complete switching action thus occurs as opposed to the modulation that would obtain if the lateral jet motion were comparable to the jet thickness.

The experiments to be described were directed at measuring the acoustic pressure engendered in the resonator by such a switched jet.

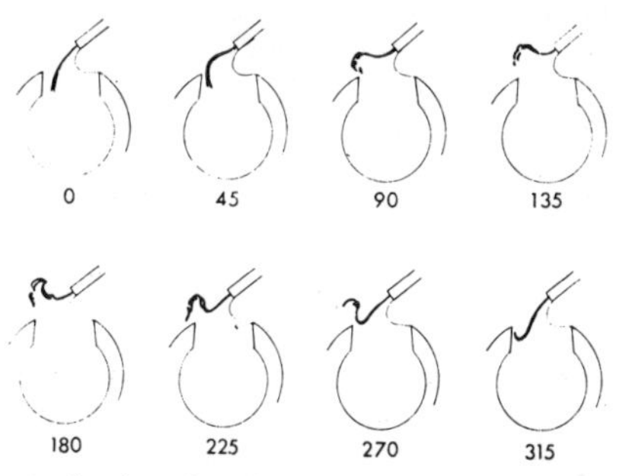


FIG. 1. Sketches of smoke-laden jet viewed stroboscopically. The labels are phase angles of the acoustic current (volume velocity) at the hole; 0° is zero current, 90° maximum current blowing out. Frequency 437 Hz, blowing pressure 0.5 in. of water, acoustic volume velocity 130 cm³/sec.

## II. APPROACH

Much of the previous work on organ pipes has been complicated by the fact that the oscillating system is only weakly under the control of the experimenter—the feedback mechanisms at work permit it to take up a state of oscillation appropriate to the imposed external conditions, and as these are varied, the oscillator alters its frequency and amplitude and may jump hysteretically from one mode to another. In the present work, the feedback loop was disconnected. The ability of the blown embouchure to convert the direct current of the air stream into an alternating acoustic pressure was measured under conditions where the stimulating acoustic vibrations were separately produced at a known amplitude by an electrically driven piston. The embouchure was treated then as a two-terminal impedance connected in series with the equivalent transmission line at the plane of the mouthhole, and whose value was a function of the blowing conditions and of the acoustic current flowing through it. This impedance is complex, and in the region of interest has a negative real component. When the magnitude of this component is larger than the positive resistance of the resonator, oscillation can take place. It will be maintained at an amplitude and frequency determined by the condition that the impedance looking into the embouchure is the negative of the impedance looking into the resonator. The latter was determined with the same apparatus, and also turns out to be nonlinear.

The nonlinear nature of both these impedances has two implications. First, a certain degree of harmonic generation is encountered—i.e., an impressed sinusoidal current gives rise to a nonsinusoidal pressure. Fortunately, the harmonic content in the sound of the flute is not large, and since the radiated power goes up as the frequency squared, we find the harmonic content of the oscillation within the tube is quite moderate. Oscilloscope observation of the sound pressure at the stopped end of the artificially blown head rarely showed harmonic content more than 20% in amplitude. For the purposes of this experiment, the harmonic generation was ignored and only the fundamental pressures measured. This means that the theory presented does not deal with an important aspect of a musical instrument, the tone quality. The second aspect of the nonlinearity is that, since impedances change with amplitude, each measurement must be carried out at some specified oscillation amplitude. We shall find, in fact, that the blown embouchure acts more nearly like a constant-pressure generator than like a constant negative resistance. The impedance concept is, however, a convenient method of expressing the results. It is employed here with the caution that the word *impedance* is used merely to express the ratio of the fundamental of the pressure generated to an impressed sinusoidal volume velocity of a given value.

### III. APPARATUS

Figure 2 shows schematically the arrangement used to measure the impedances of the flute sections, and of the jet. It consists of a short length of copper pipe of $\frac{3}{4}$ in. i.d., to which sections like the cylindrical flute head (1) could be affixed. It is closed at one end by a piston (3), whose mass (18 g) is large as compared to that of the air in the tube. This piston is sealed with a thin rubber diaphragm, and may be driven by the loudspeaker motor (4) to provide a variable driving acoustic current. The value of this current could be measured with a pickup coil (5), which moves with the piston in a separate magnetic yoke. Closely adjacent to the closed end is a rigid microphone (6), made from two thin disks of oppositely polarized barium titanate. The microphone, which was calibrated in another laboratory, measures the acoustic pressure close to the closed end. The ratio of the microphone signal to the pickup-coil signal is proportional to the acoustic impedance looking up the pipe. This impedance could always be made real by tuning the system to resonance, and it was thus possible to provide a null-balancing circuit in the form of potentiometer (8), from which the acoustic resistance at resonance could be read directly. The detector took the form of an oscilloscope whose $x$ axis was driven sinusoidally by the audio oscillator that drove the loudspeaker. The resultant Lissajous figure showed the presence of nonlinearities, and permitted visual balancing of the fundamental to zero, even with harmonics present.

In order to damp the resonator so that it would not oscillate under the action of the air jet alone, an acoustic resistor (7) was provided. In an attempt to make this resistor noninductive, a bundle (more accurately, a disk) of several thousand glass capillaries, each 0.01 cm in diameter and 0.1 cm long, was used. While the length and diameter of each of these tubes were such as to make its resistance outweigh its inductance by a large factor at all frequencies of interest, the assemblage of tubes taken as a whole had an end correction of the order of the diameter of the entire disk, so that an appreciable inductive effect was measured. The assemblage of tubes could be partially covered by a rubber pad to vary the acoustic resistance. This resistor was used as a test object for calibrating the null circuit. With a quarter-wavelength of open pipe connected and the resistor partly opened, the potentiometer reading at resonance was obtained. The $Q$ of the resonator was then measured by running a frequency-response curve. To avoid problems from acoustic nonlinearities, the driving current was adjusted at each frequency to give a constant pressure, rather than employing the usual technique of keeping the drive constant and measuring the response. Because the loudspeaker motor was driving a mass whose amplitude of vibration would fall off with frequency for a constant driving force, the electrical oscillator was coupled to the amplifier with a small capacitor to give a voltage rising with frequency in compensation.

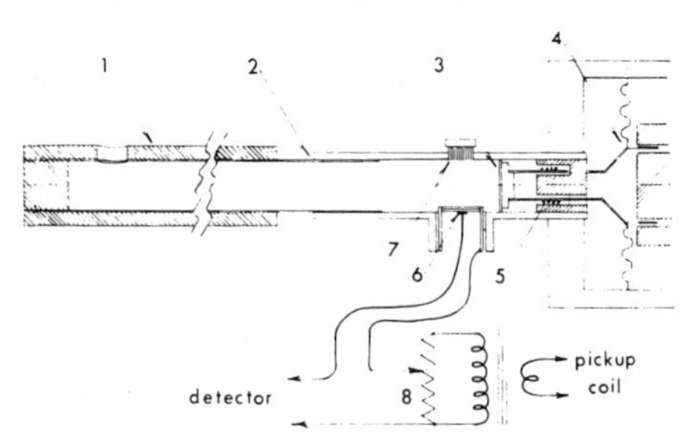


FIG. 2. Apparatus for measuring acoustic impedance: (1) flute head with mouthhole, (2) tuning slide, (3) piston, (4) loudspeaker motor, (5) velocity pickup coil, (6) microphone, (7) acoustic resistor, (8) null potentiometer.

The effective resistance $R$ as seen at the closed end of a resonant length of tube is related to the $Q$ of the resonator by

$$R = 4QZ_0/n\pi. \quad (1)$$

Here $Q$ is the quality factor, $n$ the number of quarter-wavelengths on the line, and $Z_0$ the characteristic impedance of the tube:

$$Z_0 = \rho c/S, \quad (2)$$

where $\rho$ is the density of air, $c$ the velocity of sound, and $S$ the cross-sectional area of the tube.

The potentiometer was found to give readings directly proportional to the effective resistance, independent of frequency, as it should. Readings were repeatable, the resistance read on successive balances rarely varying as much as 1%.

The procedure for making a measurement of the jet impedance was as follows. With the acoustic resistor capped (i.e., not in the circuit), the jet blowing tube geometry and blowing pressure were adjusted as desired; for example, to produce the loudest possible tone for some chosen blowing pressure. The microphone could be used to measure the acoustic pressure at the velocity node. The acoustic current at the mouthhole is found by dividing the microphone pressure by $Z_0$, and multiplying by $\sin\theta$, where $\theta/2\pi$ is the distance to the mouthhole in wavelengths. The acoustic resistor was then introduced and adjusted until oscillation ceased. With the jet turned off, the driving piston was activated by the electrical oscillator, the frequency tuned to near resonance, and the amplitude adjusted to give some chosen amplitude of acoustic oscillation as measured by the microphone. The potentiometer and frequency were then adjusted to give a null output at the detector and the potentiometer reading was taken as a measure of the resistance seen at the plane of the piston.

This resistance reflects all of the acoustic losses in the system at the particular amplitude of oscillation chosen; the acoustic power loss is given by the square of the microphone pressure divided by this measured resistance. The blowing jet was then turned on at a given blowing pressure, and the measurement repeated. The effect of the jet is to induce an additional acoustic pressure of some unknown phase and amplitude. A null is obtained again by changing the length of the tube at the tuning slide to take care of the reactive component, and balancing again the potentiometer setting. The piston drive must be changed also to return the system to the original amplitude, since some parameters are nonlinear. The change in length of the tuning slide, and the change in potentiometer readings suffice to calculate the effective impedance of the jet. In order to simplify the procedure, a cylindrical rather than a tapered head joint was used.

## IV. CALCULATION OF THE JET IMPEDANCE

The electrical circuit analogous to the acoustic system of Fig. 2 is shown in Fig. 3. The flute head tube is represented by a length $l$ of transmission line, terminated at the left by the parallel combination of the mouthhole inductance $L_h$ and the small capacitance $C_s$ of the cavity between the mouthhole and stopper. The effect of the blowing jet is represented by an unknown impedance $Z_j$, arbitrarily placed in series with the transmission line at the plane of the mouthhole. We do not really know the details of the interaction of the jet with the flow at this point—all that this placing of $Z_j$ signifies is that to get the effective acoustic back pressure sustaining the fundamental of the oscillation we multiply $Z_j$ by the calculated line current at this point.

At the right end, the circuit is driven by a constant current $i$ through the essentially infinite inductance $L_d$ representing the mass of the driving pistion.

The voltmeter $V$ represents the microphone, while the resistor $R_a$ represents the artificial acoustic resistor. The other acoustic losses in the system are not specifically shown in the diagram, but their effect is felt as a real component $R_{in}$ of the impedance $Z_{in}$ looking up the line at the plane of the piston.

The potentiometer, which measures $V/i$ when $Z_{in}$ is real, reads the value of $R_{in}$ shunted by $R_a$ if the artificial resistor is being used.

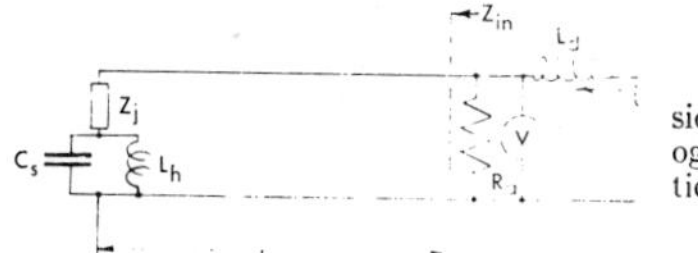


FIG. 3. Transmission-line circuit analogous to the acoustic system of Fig. 2.

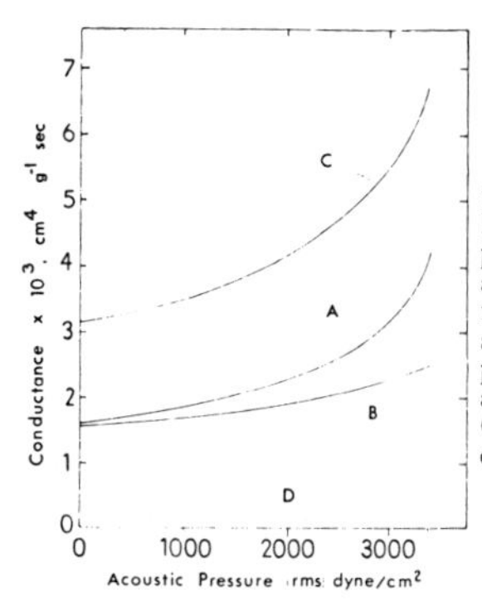


FIG. 4. Acoustic losses for the flute sounding G (392 Hz). The losses are expressed as the conductance as seen at the velocity node, as a function of acoustic pressure at this point. Curve A, head joint alone; Curve B, body alone; Curve C, sum; Curve D, calculated radiation loss.

Calculations of effective impedance are based on the equation for a lossless transmission line:

$$Z_{in}=(Z_L+j\tan\theta)/(1+Z_L\tan\theta). \quad (3)$$

Here, and in the following discussions, all impedances are relative to the characteristic impedance of the line as given by Eq. 2 and are dimensionless. $Z_{in}$ is the impedance as measured looking into a line of length $l$ terminated by a load impedance $Z_L$, and $\theta=2\pi l/\lambda$, where $\lambda$ is the wavelength on the line. For the measurement described above, the system is tuned so that $Z_{in}$ is real, i.e., $Z_{in}=R_{in}$. Inverting Eq. 3 and using the condition that $Z_{in}=R_{in}$, we find:

$$Z_L=\frac{R_{in}(1+\tan^2\theta)+j(R_{in}^2-1)\tan\theta}{1+R_{in}^2\tan^2\theta}. \quad (4)$$

In our case, $R_{in}^2\tan^2\theta\gg 1$, i.e., the $Q$ of the system without the acoustic resistor is quite high. Making this approximation and taking $Z_i$ as the change in $Z_L$ when the jet is introduced, we find the jet impedance to be

$$Z_j\cong(G_1-G_0)(\cot^2\theta_0+1)+j(1-G_1^2)(\cot\theta_1-\cot\theta_0). \quad (5)$$

$G_1$ and $G_0$ are the conductances $(1/R_{in})$ measured by the potentiometer with and without the jet blowing. The angles $\theta_1$ and $\theta_0$ correspond to the lengths of the turned line with and without the jet blowing. Because the acoustic resistor introduced some inductance, a separate measurement was made of the change in line length necessitated by its introduction, and this correction was applied before calculating $\theta_0$ and $\theta_1$. Since only small changes in $l$ are produced by the jet, differential methods were used to evaluate Eq. 5.

## V. ACOUSTIC LOSSES

Before describing the jet effects, we report measurements made of losses in flute tubes with the above-described apparatus. These are directly proportional to the conductance $(1/R_{in})$ measured with the potentiometer.

In Fig. 4 are given measurements of the conductance, as seen at the velocity node, of a Haynes flute head

(A) and body (B). The nonlinear effects are apparent in the functional dependence of the conductance on the oscillation amplitude. The flute head shows the most pronounced nonlinearity. The loss coefficient at a typical playing amplitude (2100 dyn/cm$^2$ at the velocity node) is about 50% larger than the small-signal value, and rises very rapidly beyond this point. The effects arise almost entirely at the mouthhole, which was partially covered with a modeling-clay "lip" as in normal playing. A cylindrical open-end pipe of the same diameter and resonance frequency shows practically no increase in conductance with amplitude.

Acoustic nonlinearities in small apertures have been treated by Ingard and Ising.[8] They show that the nonlinear effects result from acceleration of masses of air that do not entirely return through the hole on the reverse cycle. The results in Curve A agree with their measurements within 10%, when the mouth hole area (0.63 cm$^2$) is used to calculate the acoustic particle velocity and specific resistance at this point. The flute body shows also some nonlinearity (Curve B, Fig. 4), though it is not as pronounced as for the head. The tone holes are doubtless responsible for this. It is evident that in any quantitative treatment of the flute as an oscillating system, these nonlinear losses must be taken into account. Calculations based on small-signal $Q$ values would not be representative of what goes on at normal playing amplitude.

## VI. IMPEDANCE OF THE JET

By use of the technique described above, a number of measurements were made of the effective jet impedance as a function of blowing pressure, distance from the end of the blowing tube to the edge of the embouchure hole, and frequency and amplitude of the exciting acoustic oscillation. An effective way of describing the results is to plot, in the complex plane, the impedance of the jet as a function of blowing pressure, all the other parameters being held constant. Sets of these plots are then made for other values of the fixed parameters.

A typical plot of this kind is shown in Fig. 5. Impedance values are relative to the characteristic impedance of the tube, 15.3 g cm$^{-4}\cdot$sec$^{-1}$. The sign convention is that appropriate to the impedance as seen from inside the tube, i.e., a positive real value represents a resistive loss, a negative real value, an energy generator, a positive imaginary value, an inductive (mass) loading, and a negative imaginary value, a capacitance or compliance. In the particular measurement reported in Fig. 5, the acoustic pressure $p_m$ at the microphone was held constant at an rms value of 450 dyn cm$^{-2}$. The calculated acoustic volume velocity at the plane of the mouthhole, a distance $l=\lambda\theta/2\pi$ away, is given by $(p_m/Z_0)\sin\theta$. For Fig. 5, its value was 28 cm$^3$ sec$^{-1}$ rms. These values, about $\frac{1}{4}$ those for loud playing, were chosen for presentation here because the resulting diagram

[8] U. Ingard and H. Ising, J. Acoust. Soc. Amer. **42**, 6–17 (1967).

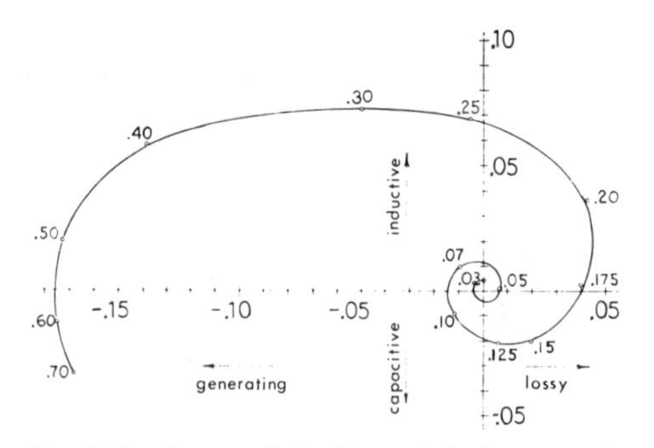


FIG. 5. Complex acoustic impedance of the jet as seen from inside the tube at the mouthhole. Impedances are relative to the characteristic impedance of the tube, 15.3 g cm$^{-4}$. sec$^{-1}$. Labels on the points are blowing pressure in inches of water. Acoustic current at the mouthhole constant at 28 cm$^3$ sec$^{-1}$ rms. Frequency: 440 Hz. Jet orifice area: 0.072 cm$^2$.

exhibits all of the essential features of the cases examined. Each point on the curve corresponds to a particular jet blowing pressure, measured and labeled in inches of water. The geometry of the blowing tube was held fixed throughout this set of measurements.

It can be seen that the impedance ascribable to the jet is a smooth, well-behaved function of blowing pressure over the entire range, the magnitude decreasing monotonically as the pressure is reduced, and the phase rotating clockwise over more than two complete cycles. The impedance values can lie in any quadrant of the complex plane. Starting at the outer edge where the blowing pressure is about 0.56 in. of water, we see that the impedance is real and negative; such a condition would overcome the losses in the tube were the artificial resistance removed, and would result in oscillation at large amplitude at the natural resonance frequency of the tube. At a higher blowing pressure, the impedance has a capacitive component that will make the frequency sharp: at lower pressure, 0.3 in., the inductive effect makes it go flat, and the real component is less negative—i.e., it could not generate so much power. At about 0.25 in., the phase crosses into the positive real domain—the jet now represents a loss mechanism and could not possibly sound the flute. At about 0.11 in., however, we are back into the negative resistance region, which persists down to about 0.06 in., where the curve crosses over again into the positive domain.

It is evident that while the jet impedance varies smoothly with blowing pressure, in principle spiraling indefinitely around the origin as the pressure is reduced, it represents a possible sound-generating mechanism only when it lies in the negative half-plane, which it periodically occupies as the blowing pressure is reduced. In traversing the negative resistance region, the impedance crosses the real axis, going from capacitive to inductive reactance. In the flute under test, oscillation at 440 Hz was obtainable for only two such pressure régimes, separated as expected by a zone of silence,

TABLE I. Propagation velocity of a disturbance of the jet. Frequency, 440 Hz. Transverse sound field particle velocity: 28 cm/sec rms; peak to peak displacement amplitude: 0.028 cm.

| Blowing pressure (in. water) | Initial jet velocity $u$ (cm/sec) | Phase velocity of disturbance (cm/sec) | Velocity ratio |
|---|---|---|---|
| 1.0 | 1920 | 670 | 0.35 |
| 0.6 | 1460 | 600 | 0.41 |
| 0.3 | 1000 | 390 | 0.39 |
| 0.15 | 770 | 370 | 0.49 |

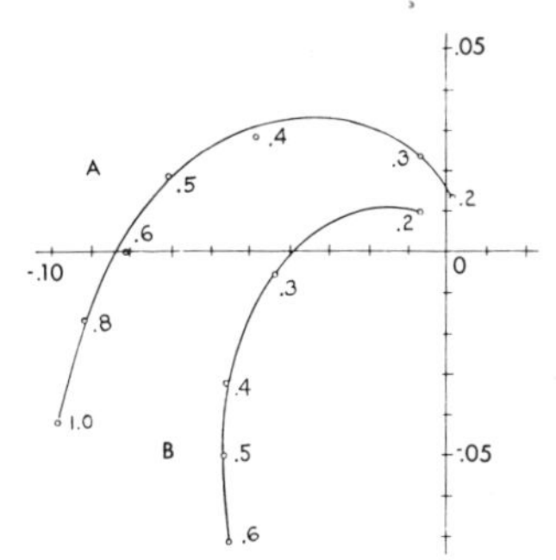


FIG. 7. Acoustic impedance of the jet for two lip-to-edge distances: Curve A for 7 mm and Curve B for 5 mm. Labels as in Fig. 5. Acoustic current at the mouthhole 74 cm$^3$ sec$^{-1}$ rms. Frequency 440 Hz. Jet orifice area 0.072 cm$^2$.

with the generated frequency going from sharp to flat with lowering pressure with each régime. In organ pipes, oscillation at the same frequency for several distinct pressures may be observed.[6,7] While in principle there are an indefinite number of turns as the pressure is lowered, there is a last turn for high pressures. This is because the phase of the impedance depends on the travel time of a wave of the jet across the mouthhole. As the velocity decreases, the travel time can become indefinitely long, encompassing an arbitrary number of cycles before reaching the splitting edge. With increasing velocity, the travel time can only approach zero. This last turn is the large one to the left. It terminates at high blowing pressures (in Fig. 5 at 0.7 in. of water) with the onset of a noisy turbulence. Only this major turn of the curve is used in music, and we devote most of our attention to an examination of its properties.

## VII. PHASE OF THE JET IMPEDANCE

The rotation of the impedance vector with pressure is associated with the travel time of a jet disturbance across the mouthhole. If we plot the phase of the points in Fig. 5 against the inverse of the initial airstream velocity $u$, an essentially straight line results. The slope of this line, together with the known distance across the hole, gives a phase velocity—i.e., the velocity of a disturbance on the jet, about 0.4 the initial jet velocity $u$. To check this inference, an experiment was conducted with a jet stream from the same blowing tube injected into the strong transverse sound field existing between two opposed quarter-wave resonant pipes driven by the oscillating piston. Movies of the stroboscopically illuminated, smoke-laden jet were examined frame-by-frame to measure the propagation velocity of the disturbances on the jet. Typical frames are shown in Fig. 6. The measured velocities were remarkably constant along the path; there was no evidence of any slowing down on the propagation velocity right up to the point where the smoke trace broke up. Table I lists the values found.

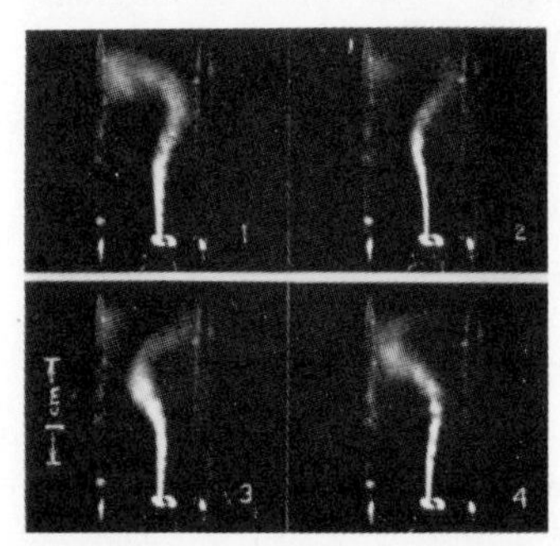


FIG. 6. Snapshots of jet in sound field. Four frames $\frac{1}{4}$ cycle apart in time. Blowing pressure 1.0 in., initial jet velocity 1920 cm sec$^{-1}$. Acoustic peak particle velocity 38 cm/sec.

The values found check well those inferred from the rotation of the impedance vector. Experiments measuring rotation of the impedance vector as the lip-to-edge distance is changed give closely concordant values. Sato[3] and Brown[2] discuss the theoretical and experimental aspects of this wave propagation. Cremer and Ising[5] derive an equation for the expected jet motion and compare it with observations on an organ pipe jet. It suffices to say here that even for the relatively strong disturbances acting in the case of the flute and organ pipe, the wave-propagation velocity stays very close to 0.3 $u$ to 0.4 $u$, as these authors find.

The phase of the impedance vector, which is so important in determining the strength and frequency deviation of the resultant oscillation, is thus determined by the initial jet velocity—i.e., the blowing pressure, and the lip-to-edge distance. Figure 7 shows two spirals like that of Fig. 5. Curve A was obtained with a 7-mm lip-to-edge distance, Curve B with 5 mm. The effect of changing the distance is to rotate the entire diagram, which gives rise to a pronounced change in the oscillation condition. With a 5-mm distance and 0.6-in. blowing pressure, the jet wave gets there too soon; its capacitive reactance would make the flute sound half a semitone sharp. Reducing the pressure to 0.3 in. to avoid this would give a weak oscillation. By pulling the lip back to 7 mm, however (Curve A), the arrival time is delayed, and a strong in-tune oscillation could be produced at 0.6-in. blowing pressure. There is no pressure on Curve B that could match this oscillation strength.

The necessity for adjusting the lip-to-edge distance is further brought out by examining the effect of frequency change. Figure 8 shows two impedance plots

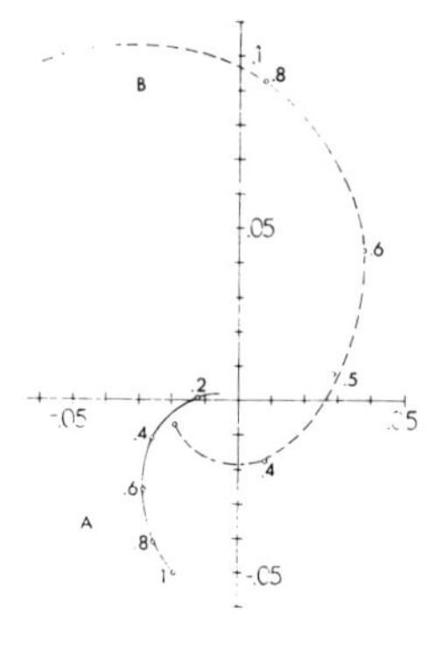

FIG. 8. Acoustic impedance of the jet for two modes of the resonant pipe. Curve A: first mode, 300 Hz, acoustic current 135 $cm^3\ sec^{-1}$. Curve B: second mode, 900 Hz, acoustic current 82 $cm^3\ sec^{-1}$.

taken for identical blowing geometries and pressures; Curve A for the 300-Hz first mode of a stopped pipe, and Curve B for its second mode, at 900 Hz. It can be seen that the phases are markedly different. At a blowing pressure of 0.6 in. of water, the jet impedance vectors for the two modes are about 180° apart. At this pressure, the jet impedance for the second mode (900 Hz) lies in the real half-plane—it could not produce oscillation at this frequency. As the pressure is increased, the impedance vector rotates counterclockwise (note that its rotation rate is three times faster for 900 Hz than for 300 Hz, as expected) so that at a blowing pressure of 1.0 in., it lies well in the generating quadrant, and the upper mode would be sounded. Transition to the upper mode could be greatly favored by moving the lip closer to the edge; this would rotate both diagrams counterclockwise so as to put the upper-mode vector in the generating region over most of the curve, and displace the lower-frequency mode toward the lossy region. Conversely, retraction of the lip would place the low-frequency mode in a favored position, and disadvantage the other. Curves run for the conditions of Fig. 8, but with a lip-to-edge distance of 9 mm instead of 7 mm, show that exactly this happens, Curve B being rotated completely into the nongenerating half-plane, while Curve A rotates one-third as much toward the generating axis.

This adjustment of the lip-to-edge distance by the flute player, and its effect on intonation and tone production have been discussed by Coltman.[9] It is apparent from the above that the flute player adjusts both the blowing pressure and lip-to-edge distance in such a manner as to control the arrival phase of the jet, and that this phase is a more important variable in determining which mode will be sounded than is the magnitude of the blowing pressure.

## VIII. ACOUSTIC PRESSURE GENERATED BY THE JET

It is important to point out that the magnitudes of the measured jet impedances such as shown in Figs. 5, 7, and 8 depend markedly on the value chosen for the magnitude of oscillation. If the jet impedance is multiplied by the current at the plane of the mouthhole, one gets the complex acoustic backpressure generated by the jet, which may be plotted in a similar diagram. Such curves are much less dependent on the value of the current chosen, and we conclude from this that the jet action can be best described in terms of the magnitude and phase of the acoustic pressure that it generates. The way in which the phase varies has already been discussed; we give attention now to the mechanisms that determine the acoustic driving force that the jet can provide.

In the following discussion, we neglect certain refinements in quantitatively dealing with flow—namely, we presume that viscous and friction effects at the walls are absent. This is a reasonable approximation for the precision sought here.

A jet of air issuing from an orifice of area $s_1$ under the influence of a blowing pressure $p$, will have an initial velocity $u$ given by Bernoulli's law:

$$p=\rho u^2/2. \tag{6}$$

It will carry a volume of air $us_1$ per second. Consider such a jet blowing axially into the open end of a long tube of larger cross-section area $s_2$ whose far end is closed. The jet stream will mingle with the still air, slowing down not only to zero, but in fact reversing direction and re-emerging from the open end with a velocity $-us_1/s_2$. The mass flow is $\rho us_1$, the velocity change is $u+us_1/s_2$, and the total force exerted on the large tube is thus $\rho u^2 s_1(1+s_1/s_2)$. Dividing by the area of the large tube, and making use of Eq. 6, we find the pressure in the large tube is

$$p_2=2p(s_1/s_2)(1+s_1/s_2). \tag{7}$$

Experiments of this sort, carried out with jets similar to those used to blow the flute, bear out Eq. 7 for a variety of pressures and tube areas. The pressure built up in the large tube is independent of small changes in the direction and position of the jet, whether or not it is playing against the wall of the tube, thus justifying the neglect of wall friction. Because the acoustic particle velocity in the flute is small as compared to the jet velocity, and because the jet stream slows down in a distance short as compared to the wavelength, the situation in the flute during each half-cycle is quite comparable to the static incompressible situation described above.

While the force available from the jet is thus known from the rate of momentum transfer, the pressure which this force will develop depends on the cross-section area of the region in which the jet slows down. In the flute, this region is ill defined; the jet acts partly in the mouthhole, whose uncovered area may be 0.5 $cm^2$, and partly in the tube, whose area is about 2.5 $cm^2$. To examine situations of this sort experimentally, the

[9] J. W. Coltman, J. Acoust. Soc. Amer. **40**, 99–107 (1966).

arrangement sketched in Fig. 9 was made. A long tube of 1.9 cm i.d. was provided with necks of varying length having a diameter of about 0.8 cm. The shortest "neck" was simply a hole in a thin metal end plate. The pressures built up in the large tube by a jet of 0.315-cm diameter, carrying 338 dyn of thrust, are plotted in Fig. 9 as functions of the length of neck. The three curves are for various spacings of the nozzle, including a case where the nozzle extends 4 mm inside the tube. Broken Line A is calculated by Eq. 7 for a long tube of the small diameter. It is seen that when the neck is 3 cm or longer, all the important action seems to be taking place in the small tube. For shorter necks, the pressures drop drastically, but do not reach, even for "zero" length, the low pressure (Line B) calculated for the large-diameter tube with a back-flow velocity dictated by the small-area aperture. It thus appears that an aperture in a thin plate still has an effective length. Or put another way, there is a transition region in the neighborhood of the hole in which velocities of motion are changing from that characteristic of the large diameter to that of the small diameter, and momentum transferred here can result in larger pressures that are transmitted uniformly throughout the volume. In the flute then, we can expect an acoustic pressure to be developed that lies somewhere between that calculated using the area of the tube, and that using the area of the mouthhole.

The smoke traces show that the transverse jet motion is large, and it seems reasonable to consider the jet to be blowing into the tube for a complete half-cycle, transferring its momentum all during this time. It interacts with a sinusoidal acoustic current of some unknown phase $\phi$ with respect to the square wave of pressure, and the effective rms value of such a square wave of pressure, with regard to power delivered to the fundamental, will be $\sqrt{2}/\pi$ times the maximum pressure $p_2$. Using Eq. 7, we can write the magnitude of the rms acoustic pressure generated by the jet as:

$$p_j = \frac{2\sqrt{2}}{\pi} p \left(\frac{s_1}{s_2}\right)\left(1+\frac{s_1}{s_2}\right). \quad (8)$$

Here $p$ is the blowing pressure, $s_1$ the area of the lip aperture, and $s_2$ an effective area that lies somewhere between that of the flute-tube cross section and that of the embouchure hole.

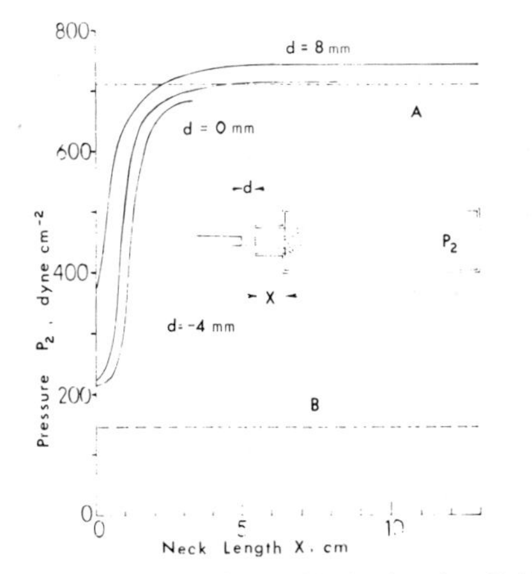


FIG. 9. Pressure produced by a jet blowing into the cylindrical can as a function of neck length. Jet pressure 1.0 cm water, average initial velocity 1944 cm sec$^{-1}$, flow 145 cm$^3$ sec$^{-1}$. Curve A, pressure calculated for infinite neck length. Curve B, pressure calculated for zero neck length. Jet spacings $d$ as marked.

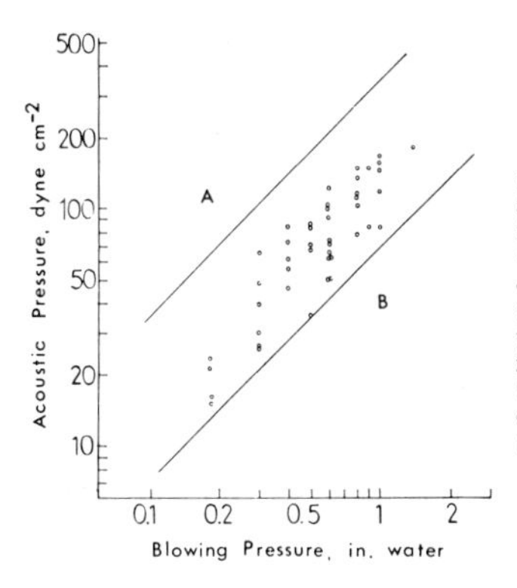


FIG. 10. Acoustic oscillation pressures as a function of blowing pressure for a variety of blowing conditions and frequencies. Curve A: pressure calculated from mouthhole area. Curve B: pressure calculated from flute-tube area.

Equation 8 is plotted as the two straight lines in Fig. 10, with $s_1$ the blowing-tube area. The upper line represents a choice for $s_2$ of 0.5 cm$^2$ (the embouchure-hole area) and the lower line an area of 2.81 cm$^2$, the flute-tube area. The points between are the actual observed values of rms acoustic pressure generated. These are obtained from the jet-impedance experiments described earlier and represent values obtained using a wide variety of lip spacings, oscillation pressures, and operating frequencies. All these fall between the lower and upper bounds given by Eq. 8; a mean line through the set lies about a factor of 2 above the lower bound, a value consistent with the findings displayed in Fig. 9 for a short neck. Measurement of the static pressure built up in a flute head by the blowing jet directed just below the embouchure edge, gave a value about 1.5 times that calculated from Eq. 7 when the flute-tube diameter was used for $s_2$, again showing the influence of the restricted mouthhole in raising the pressure. No measurable suction is developed when the jet is directed across the hole and above the embouchure edge.

While exact values undoubtedly depend somewhat on the particular geometry of the mouthhole and the blowing conditions, it seems safe to state that the acoustic pressure generated by the jet will lie in the neighborhood of twice the blowing pressure, times the ratio of the area of the lip aperture to the area of the flute-tube cross section.

## IX. SOUND-POWER PRODUCTION

The oscillation pressure in the sounding flute will reach an equilibrium when the jet impedance, as defined earlier, equals the negative of the impedance looking into the flute at the plane of the mouthhole. At the natural passive resonance frequency of the system, this impedance will be real. If the phase of the jet impedance is such that it in turn is real and negative (which requires a specific combination of jet velocity and lip distance), the oscillation will take place at the resonance frequency of the system and will build up in amplitude until the magnitudes of the impedances match. Since the jet provides a nearly constant-pressure system, its apparent impedance falls inversely as the acoustic current rises. At the same time, the nonlinear effects described in Fig. 4 cause the resonator resistance to rise so the two come to a definite equilibrium point. If the acoustic oscillating current at this point is $v_0$, the acoustic power generated is $p_j v_0$. The power expended in blowing is $pus_1$. The generating efficiency is the ratio of these two, and using $p_j = 2ps_1/s_2$, we find:

$$\text{GENERATING EFFICIENCY} \cong 2v_0/s_2u. \tag{9}$$

Now $2v_0/s_2$ is just the sound particle velocity in the region where the jet is interacting. The generating efficiency is thus equal to the ratio of the sound-particle velocity to the jet velocity. It is clear that the energy loss takes place because in slowing down the rapidly moving jet, momentum is conserved, but energy is necessarily lost. The actual value that $v_0$ attains is set by the losses in the flute tube. Calculations from the acoustic pressure measured by the microphone and the measured jet impedance show the generating efficiency is low—about 2.4 % at A-440. Even if the resonator were completely lossless, however, $v_0$ could not rise much beyond the point where the acoustic particle velocity in the mouthhole equaled the jet velocity, for at this point there would no longer be anything to push against. We estimate the efficiency at this point at about 4%, so the mechanism of sound generation in the flute is inherently a very inefficient one.

Of the acoustic power generated, only a small fraction is radiated. The radiation resistance of a small isolated source is $\pi\rho c/\lambda^2$. The flute, under most circumstances, has two sources, one at each end. The one at the mouthhole has slightly less current, owing to the taper and the end correction, but is partially baffled by the player's head. Over the first two octaves, it is nearly as strong a source as the open end. The two interfere to some extent; but the effects are not large, amounting to an increase of 20% or so in the radiation resistance. Using these calculated values, and the total losses measured as in Fig. 4, we find that at 440 Hz only 3.3% of the acoustic power generated is radiated as sound. The over-all efficiency at this frequency then comes to $8\times10^{-4}$, a value lying within the range reported by Bouhuys.[10] The efficiency will rise with frequency because of the increased radiation resistance.

## X. FREQUENCY PULLING

When the jet velocity and lip-to-edge distance are not such as to make the jet impedance real, the steady-state condition will be one in which the frequency is shifted to introduce a reactive component equal and opposite to that of the jet. Inspection of the spirals of Figs. 5, 7, and 8 makes it apparent that reactive components as large as the real components—i.e., jet phases 45° away from the negative real axis—may readily occur and still leave enough real component to sustain the losses. Since the real (loss) part of the resonator impedance must equal the negative real component of the jet impedance, the frequency shift in this case will be such as to introduce a reactive component equal to the resistive component of the resonator impedance, or a shift $\Delta f = f/2Q$. We may thus expect frequency shifts of at least this much as blowing conditions are varied. From Fig. 4 and Formula 1, we find the $Q$ at 440 Hz to be about 30, and thus we expect to find frequency shifts of about ±30 cents. This is quite consistent with those measured on an artificially excited flute.[9] We may also infer from Ref. 9 that the flutist ordinarily operates so as to maintain the phase of the jet impedance at 180°.

While the impedance spirals, and the measurements of frequency shift show clearly that a specific arrival phase of the impulse is required for zero frequency shift, they do not tell us what the required phase is. This is because the actual momentum transfer takes place over a distributed region of the tube, and selection of a particular arrival time is arbitrary. Since it is known, however, that a sound field produces its major influence on the jet immediately after the jet leaves the aperture, we might ask what travel times, from the jet to the edge, are required to produce an acoustic pressure in phase with the ingoing (negative) current.

An examination of the data from many experiments shows that the 180° phase condition is obtained when the travel time of a jet particle across the gap is about 0.2 of a period. Remembering that the jet wave travels at about 0.4 the initial stream velocity, this corresponds to a travel time of $\frac{1}{2}$ a period for a jet disturbance. The oval mouthhole geometry did not lend itself to a more precise determination of this number.

## XI. DISCUSSION

Cremer and Ising[5] have approached the description of the organ pipe in a manner similar to that of this paper. In their model, they consider the resonator and jet as coupled systems whose transfer functions must combine to unity. The jet is assumed to inject its pulsating current into the resonant system in such a way as to create a driving pressure against the impedance of the

[10] A. Bouhuys, J. Acoust. Soc. Amer. 37, 453-456 (1965).

mouthhole. Such a model leads to a driving pressure directly proportional to the jet volume velocity. To account for their experimental result that the driving pressure was directly proportional to the square of the initial jet velocity (Fig. 10 of Ref. 5), they hypothesized that entrainment of air by the jet increased the injected current over that of the jet alone, and that this entrainment varied with jet velocity in just such a way as to give a square-law result. The momentum concept presented here in Sec. VIII, however, gives directly the square-law dependence, whether or not entrainment takes place. In a current-drive concept, there is an uncertainty as to the proper place to insert the jet current in an equivalent electrical circuit. In the real case, it is distributed over the region conventionally represented by the lumped reactance of the mouthhole mass, and alternately, flows in either direction through a portion of this region. Cremer's assumption that it is injected between the main resonant column and the mouthhole impedance is hard to justify. The quantitative results to date indicate that the main features of the drive mechanism can be accounted for by the jet momentum, and the volume of gas inserted does not play a major role.

Ingard and Ising[8] show that nonlinear acoustic losses in an orifice are affected by a superimposed steady flow. This raises the question of whether part of the measured effect of the jet represents a modification of the turbulent losses, which are certainly present at the mouthhole. There is also a question of the extent to which the puffs of air from the jet passing outside the wedge contribute directly to the radiated sound. The volume velocities of the jet current and the oscillating sound current are quite comparable in many cases. Neither of these questions has been investigated.

As pointed out in Sec. III, the present work was restricted as much as possible to the case of sinusoidal oscillations. While this is helpful in simplifying the physical picture of what is going on, and is not too bad a model for the flute, the organ pipe is ordinarily constructed to be rich in harmonics and to operate with a jet configuration giving short impulses. Elder and Fasnacht[11] have investigated the velocity and pressure conditions at the mouth of a diapason organ pipe, and point out the importance of the complex waveform in influencing the jet. The interaction of complex sinuous waves on the jet (which show some variation of phase velocity with frequency[5]) with the waveform from a resonator whose modes are not exact harmonics, is a subject whose scope is attested to by the variety of tone colors achieved in the pipe organ. Benade and Gans[12] have investigated for reed and brass instruments the effect of inharmonicity of the modes of the resonator on the regeneration, and find that it is greatly facilitated in a horn whose resonance frequencies are close to a harmonic series. Detailed treatment of regeneration in the case of nonsinusoidal oscillations has yet to be attempted.

[11] S. A. Elder and W. F. Fasnacht, J. Acoust. Soc. Amer. 42, 1217(A) (1967).

## XII. CONCLUSION

The acoustic driving force represented by the momentum of the blowing jet is converted into an alternating acoustic pressure on the oscillating air column in the immediate neighborhood of the mouthhole. The phase of this alternating pressure with respect to the alternating acoustic current depends on the lip-to-edge distance and the propagation velocity of a wave on the jet, which is approximately 0.4 the initial jet velocity. The magnitude of the driving pressure is directly proportional to the blowing pressure and the area of the lip aperture. In order to maintain the driving force in proper phase relation with the acoustic current, the flutist increases the blowing pressure and decreases the lip-to-edge distance with ascending frequency. He can independently control the amplitude of oscillation by varying the area of the lip aperture. The octave jump can readily be controlled by choosing pressures and lip-to-edge distances such that the phase condition for oscillation in the desired mode is satisfied, while that for the other mode is not. The momentum transfer concept, and recognition of the phase condition for jet arrival, provides a theoretical basis for the description of the sound generating mechanism of acoustic oscillators of the flute family.

[12] A. H. Benade and D. J. Gans, "Sound Production in Wind Instruments," Proc. Conf. Sound Production in Man, New York Acad. Sci. (Nov. 1966).

# 26

*Copyright © 1973 by the Acoustical Society of America*

Reprinted from *J. Acoust. Soc. Am.*, **54**(2), 417–420 (1973)

## Mouth resonance effects in the flute

**John W. Coltman**

*3319 Scathelocke Road, Pittsburgh, Pennsylvania 15235*

(Received 21 March 1973)

**Resonance of the mouth cavity while playing the flute has been found to occur near 1000 Hz. Experiments with an artificial mouth show the $Q$ of this cavity is less than two when air is passing through the lips. The presence of this coupled cavity can affect the flute frequency by as much as 10 cents, and may increase the losses in the system by as much as one-third.**

**Subject Classification: 6.8.**

Conversations among players of the recorder occasionally refer to the desirability of holding the player's mouth cavity at certain volumes in order to affect the tone. Bak[1] has made some measurements on an artificially blown recorder looking for the effect of varying the volume of a resonator placed before the mouthpiece slit. Only very slight changes in the frequency were observed. Benade and French[2] have provided a mathematical analysis of what might be expected to happen to flute frequency due to coupling of a resonant mouth cavity with the vibrating air column at the mouthhole.

Because the effects predicted by Benade and French appeared to be substantial, and yet no clear identification of them in flute playing is generally recognized, it appeared worthwhile to investigate experimentally the nature and magnitude of any mouth resonance effects which may be present.

First we may ask, does mouth resonance occur, and at what frequencies? Benade and French hypothesized that it would be in the neighborhood of the lowest formant for vowel sounds like "ah," "aw," and "oh," and therefore in the range of 500-600 Hz. They observed, presumably by ear, "an appreciable shift" in flute frequency in the neighborhood of G# and A (near 430 Hz) when the tongue was moved from the "ee" to "oh" positions. Such a frequency seems extraordinarily low for the mouth cavity resonance frequency in the position for playing the flute. If one attempts to whistle a note without markedly changing mouth position from that used in playing the flute, frequencies in the neighborhood of 1000 Hz are more typical.

To pin this down, a small microphone was constructed that could be placed inside the mouth, with the lead coming out the mouth corner. It was possible to play the flute reasonably well with the microphone in place. Readings of the output of this microphone were taken as the scale was ascended. The resulting curve showed a peak and dip in the neighborhood of 1000 Hz, the remainder of the readings following a generally ascending trend with frequency. Later it was found that a piezoceramic disk microphone directly in contact with the outside of the player's cheek produced a nearly identical curve, while the playing was more comfortable. The combined results of a series of such trials are reproduced in Fig. 1. The points are averages of sound-pressure levels in decibels, and while the scatter is rather large, the peak and dip seem very real, especially since each trial, consisting of a chromatic scale, exhibited similar behavior. The driving force is not constant with frequency it can be expected to rise quite rapidly with frequency as the blowing pressure increases, accounting for the rising trend of the whole curve. From the extent in frequency of the perturbation, we see the cavity $Q$ is quite low.

No such perturbation was found in the region of 500 Hz. It is possible that the effects of tongue movement reported by Benade and French in this region were caused by the mouth cavity acting on the second harmonic of the flute tone, which is quite prominent in the spectrum. Of course, mouth sizes will vary with individuals, so we must consider Fig. 1 to represent only a single sample, though there is no reason to believe it is atypical.

To investigate in more detail the effect of the mouth cavity on the frequency of the flute, an artificial mouth

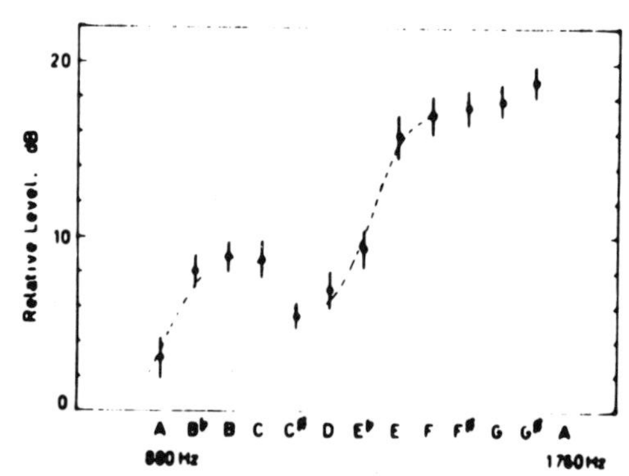


Fig. 1. Response of a mouth-coupled microphone to various notes played on the flute.

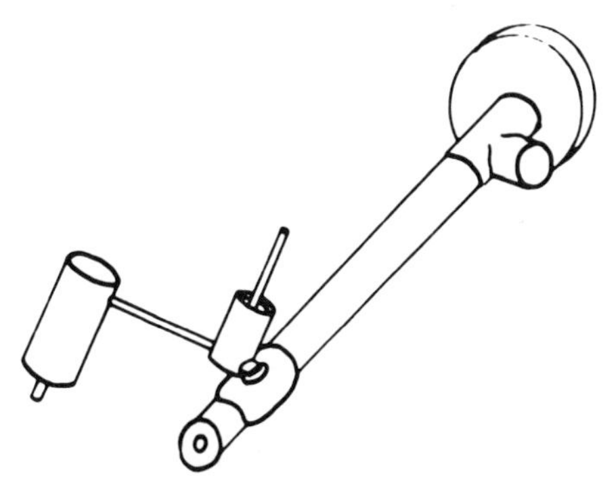

FIG. 2. Arrangement of the flute and artificial mouth. Not shown are the modeling-clay "lips" formed around the blowing tube.

was constructed. This consisted of a cylindrical cavity 1.9 cm in diameter whose volume could be varied by a movable plunger. Air could be introduced into the cavity through a small-diameter tube approximately ¼-wavelength long at the frequency of interest. This tube, leading into a wind chest, presented a high impedance so that the cavity resonance was not altered much by it. A short (6 mm long) brass tube, flattened to 1 mm×6 mm at its outer end, formed the blowing slit, and modeling clay was used to imitate the external geometry of the player's lips. The flute could be sounded adequately (if not charmingly) with this arrangement. The passive resonance frequency of the Helmholz resonator formed by the cavity and lip could be varied with the plunger from 750 to 1300 Hz, covering the range of perturbation observed in the first experiment. When resonant at 1000 Hz, the volume of the cavity was 3.6 cm³. The player's (author's) mouth, when playing this note had a quite similar volume, as measured by imbibing water.

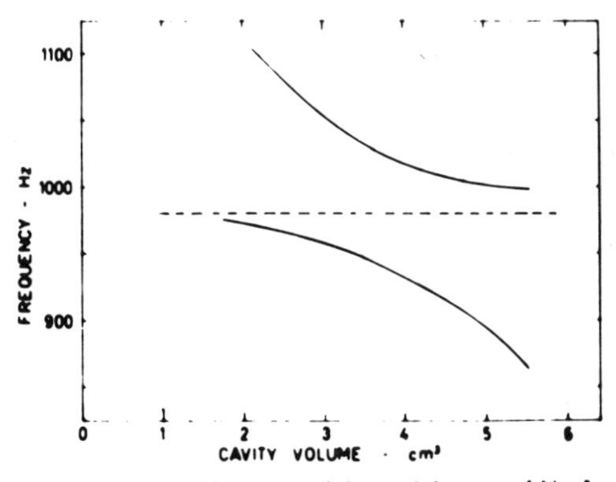


FIG. 3. Resonance frequencies of the coupled system of Fig. 2, as a function of volume of the mouth cavity. Dashed line is with cavity stuffed with cotton wool.

The cavity was placed as shown in Fig. 2 at the embouchure of a cylindrical flute head-joint, and this in turn was connected to a piston driver. A microphone in the tube nearby the driver was used to measure the response of the flute. The passive resonance frequency in the second mode was adjusted to about 1000 Hz with the mouth cavity tuned off resonance. Tuning the mouth cavity through resonance gave very pronounced perturbations in the resonance frequency of the head joint. The resonance in fact was split into two, as can be expected when two resonant circuits are coupled. Figure 3 shows the two branches of the observed curve. When the cavity is tuned to the flute resonance at 994 Hz, the splitting is about 80 Hz. Such effects are enormous compared to any frequency shifts observed in practice, and it was apparent that something was drastically wrong.

What was left out in this experiment was the effect of the air stream passing through the lip aperture, which forms the "neck" of the Helmholz resonator for the mouth cavity. Ingard and Ising[3] have shown that the acoustic resistance of an aperture is markedly affected by the passage of a continuous stream of air through the aperture. By putting a piezo-ceramic driver in the

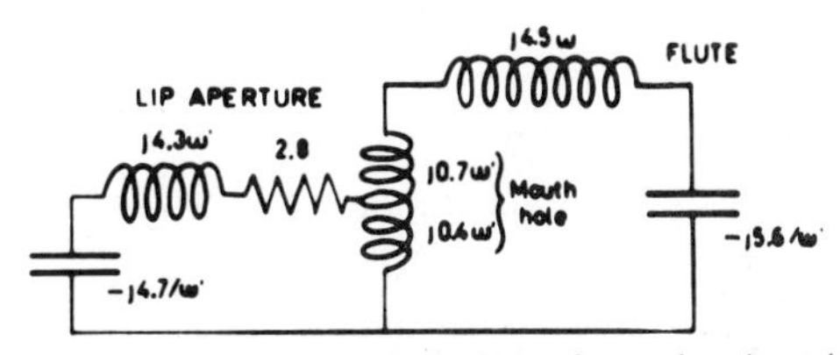


FIG. 4. Equivalent circuit characterizing the mouth cavity and flute near resonance.

plunger of the cavity, and coupling a microphone through a hole in the wall, one can measure the resonance frequency and $Q$ of the mouth cavity itself. The value is about 10 when the air is not blowing. Even a small velocity of blowing air lowered the $Q$ so drastically that it was difficult to measure. Accordingly, tubing was added to the cavity to extend it a half wavelength, greatly increasing the stored energy for a given volume velocity at the neck. With this it was possible to measure, by the usual resonance width method, the $Q$ with and without air blowing, and also with the neck blocked, so that the wall dissipation could be subtracted off.

The $Q$ of this extended cavity, together with the known geometry of the tubular portion of the cavity, can be used to calculate the effective acoustic resistance of the lip aperture in the following manner: The tubular portion is considered as a transmission line of length $L$ and cross-section area $S$. The tube is closed at one end and is terminated at the other by a restricted aperture whose impedance shortens the resonant line from its ideal length of $\frac{1}{2}\lambda$ by an end correction $e$. The acoustic resistance of this aperture is $r$, and its ratio to the characteristic impedance $\rho c/S$ of the line we designate as $R = rS/\rho c$.

Calculation of the energy stored at resonance in the tube and in the aperture for a given acoustic volume velocity $i$ in the aperture, and comparison of this with $2\pi$ times the energy lost per cycle in $R$ for the same $i$, gives the value of $Q$. It is found that

$$Q = (\pi L/\lambda + \tfrac{1}{2}\sin 4\pi e/\lambda)(R\cos^2 2\pi e/\lambda)^{-1}. \quad (1)$$

Expression 1 was used to obtain from measurements of $Q$ the value of $R$ in the lip with various blowing wind velocities. For zero wind velocity $R$ was found to be 0.44 while at the blowing pressure of 1.5 in. of water, $R$ increased manyfold to 2.7. The variation was, except at the beginning, linear with the square root of the blowing pressure, as predicted by Ingard and Ising.[3] To find the $Q$ of the original (unextended) cavity, Eq. 1 can again be used with the original length for $L$ and the above determined values of $R$. For the length which tuned to 994 Hz, and a value of $R = 2.7$, the $Q$ is calculated to be 1.7.

The observed values of frequency splitting with the passive cavity (Fig. 3), the measured value of $R$ for the lip and measurements of the flute head dimensions suffice to determine values for the equivalent circuit given in Fig. 4. This is essentially the circuit proposed by Benade and French, in which the resonant mouth cavity is tapped across a portion of the end correction inductance. In the frequency range treated, a simple LC circuit represents the flute, rather than using a transmission line, and the refinement of a stopper cavity reactance has also been omitted. We have chosen here a dimensionless frequency unit $\omega' = \omega/\omega_0$, where $\omega$ is the actual angular frequency and $\omega_0$ is the angular resonance frequency of the flute head joint in the absence of the cavity.

Dimensionless impedance values are relative to the characteristic impedance of the flute tube, $\rho c/S$. The tube diameter for both cavity and flute head was 1.9 cm, the normal dimension of a modern flute. The stopped flute head is represented by a simple resonant series LC circuit, with an inductance calculated by using the stored energy implied by Eq. 1. An end correction of 4.7 cm was assumed, and the inductive reactance equivalent to this ($1.1\,\omega'$) was assigned to the mouth-hole. The frequency-splitting results of Fig. 3 dictate $j0.4\omega'$ as the value where the lip aperture is exposed to the acoustic pressure. No wall losses are shown, since they do not enter into what is to be calculated. The value of the capacitive reactance assigned to the mouth cavity in Fig. 4 corresponds to the cavity tuned to $\omega_0$.

This equivalent circuit can be used to predict the frequency shifts and added losses due to the mouth cavity. The $Q$ of the mouth cavity is now so low that no

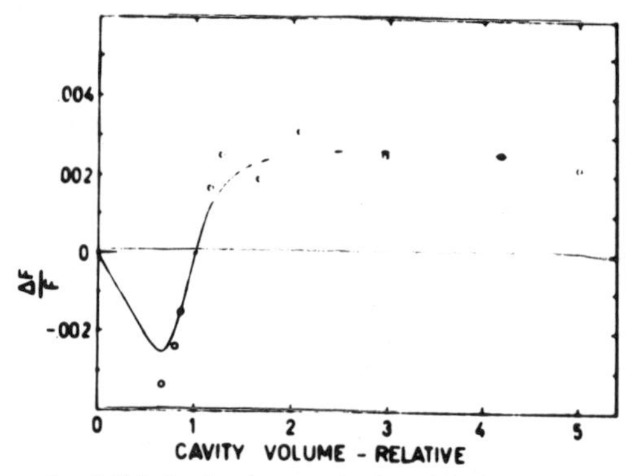


FIG. 5. Calculated and measured values of the frequency shift caused by varying the mouth-cavity volume.

frequency splitting occurs. We take the resonance frequency as the point where the series reactance of the right hand loop is zero. In Fig. 5 the solid curve plots the calculated change in resonance frequency of the flute as the size of the mouth cavity is varied. The effect is only a few parts per thousand, and the major change occurs over a ±50% change in cavity volume. Also plotted here are experimental points taken by measuring the actual frequency of the artificially blown flute as the cavity volume was varied. Considering the small size of the effect, the agreement is very good. It was not possible to observe the expected rise as the cavity approaches zero size because the plunger cut off the air supply below the last point taken.

Plotted in Fig. 6 are calculated values of the expected change in flute end correction due to a fixed cavity as a function of frequency at which the flute is played. This follows the course predicted by Benade and French. The entire effect amounts to about 3 mm, and the change

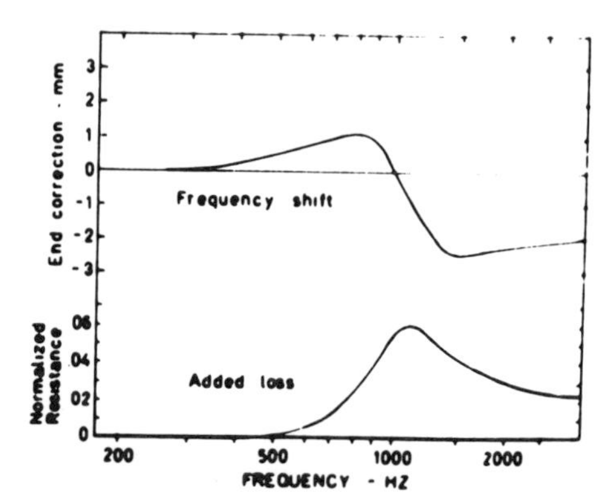


FIG. 6. Calculated effects of a fixed mouth cavity for various played frequencies. The resistance is relative to the characteristic impedance of the tube.

takes place over a whole octave. An increase in losses is also present, represented by the equivalent series resistance plotted in the same figure. The losses rise to a peak near the cavity resonance. The value of inserted resistance here is such as to give the experimental flute head a $Q$ of 100 due to this resistance alone. This is not negligible, since typical wall-losses give $Q$'s about 30. Measurements of the oscillation amplitude of the artificially blown flute show a drop in amplitude to about 70% of the normal value as the cavity is tuned through resonance.

It is concluded that mouth resonance does occur, somewhere in the neighborhood of 1000 Hz. Its effects on frequency when the flute is played are overall about 10 cents, and would be manifested as a slight upward perturbation as the cavity resonance frequency is approached from below, followed by a downward shift as the resonance frequency is passed. It takes more than an octave to go through this region, so these small effects are likely to be masked by other irregularities.

When air is not passing through the lips, the effects of mouth cavity resonance can be very much more pronounced. Measurements of passive resonance of the flute with the player's mouth in position, as reported by Coltman[4] and Nederveen[5] may therefore have been affected by a variable that was not controlled during the experiments. It is possible that this contributed to some of the discrepancies reported by Nederveen.

[1]N. Bak, Acustica 22, 295–299 (1969).
[2]A. H. Benade and J. W. French, J. Acoust. Soc. Am. 37, 679–691 (1965).
[3]U. Ingard and Ising, J. Acoust. Soc. Am. 42, 6–17 (1967).
[4]J. W. Coltman, J. Acoust. Soc. Am. 40, 99–107 (1966).
[5]C. J. Nederveen, Acustica 28, 12–23 (1973).

# 27

*Copyright© 1974 by the Acoustical Society of America*

Reprinted from *J. Acoust. Soc. Am.*, **56**(2), 645–652 (1974)

# Nonlinear interactions in organ flue pipes

N. H. Fletcher

*Department of Physics, University of New England, Armidale, N.S.W. 2351, Australia*

(Received 5 March 1973; revised 10 September 1973)

The ideas introduced by Coltman and Benade are developed into a quantitative formalism for treating the oscillatory behavior of an air column in nonlinear interaction with an air jet, as in an organ flue pipe or a flute. Explicit solutions are given for the case when the pipe has only two resonances and the nonlinearity is described up to cubic terms. The results of illustrative calculations are discussed.

Subject Classification: 75.60.

## INTRODUCTION

The scaling of ranks of organ flue pipes to produce a coherent, characteristic, and tonally balanced ensemble is a problem which has confronted organ builders for many centuries. The solutions which they developed were initially empirical and the more satisfactory ones were then refined into scaling laws of which several exist.[1] The precise relationships between attack, intensity, and harmonic development of the pipes which are necessary to constitute a satisfactory rank design are still not well understood, except in a qualitative way, and a great deal depends upon the experience and skill of the designer and voicer.

When we try to attack this problem we find that many things about the behavior of a single flue pipe are not well understood either. Even leaving aside the musically most important attack transient, the way in which the spectrum of the sound radiated by a pipe depends upon its scale (length to diameter ratio) and upon the geometry of mouth and jet is known only in qualitative outline.

Much of the reason for this lack of detailed understanding comes from the fact that the problem is essentially nonlinear. The linear theory has been explored by many workers, particularly for the related cases of the flute[2,3] and the clarinet.[4-6] (References 5 and 6, which are books, give copious additional references.) Unfortunately, the linear theory gives information primarily about the frequency of the fundamental and tells us very little about the relative amplitudes of the upper partials.

Almost the only studies of nonlinear effects in pipes have been those of Benade.[7,8] He proposed a treatment in which the normal resonance modes of the air column within the pipe are coupled together through nonlinear interaction with the air jet (or reed in the case of reed pipes). In principle, provided the interaction law and the separate characteristics of the pipe and jet are known, this approach allows calculation of the amplitudes of all the harmonics of the oscillation. Even without such a calculation, Benade has shown that these considerations allow general predictions of the change with amplitude of harmonic content and of frequency to be made.

The purpose of the present paper is to develop in quantitative form the nonlinear interaction theory put forward by Benade. In subsequent papers, we hope to present the results of an experimental study of some of the predictions of the theory and finally to relate our conclusions to the initial problem of the tonal design of a rank of flue pipes. We shall see that the results also have relevance to tone development in the flute.

## I. THE JET AS AN EXCITATION MECHANISM

The interaction between sound waves and an air jet issuing from an orifice has been studied in some detail by Brown.[9] He showed that interaction takes place almost exclusively at the point where the jet emerges from the orifice and that the interaction induces the formation of vortices which progress along the jet with a velocity rather less than that of the fluid.

Coltman[3] has carried out detailed measurements of the acoustic impedance of such a jet when it travels a relatively short distance and then impinges upon an edge which is part of the embouchure hole of a flute. In this study, he was able to measure the acoustic impedance at a given frequency as a function of jet velocity and found a behavior of the sort illustrated in Fig. 1. The real part of the impedance was negative (corresponding to a supply of acoustic energy to the tube resonator) over several discrete ranges of airjet velocity. He pointed out that only the outermost loop of the spiral is in fact used in practical flute playing and that, unless the velocity is such as to make the impedance exactly real, its reactive part will cause a correction to the natural tube resonance, making the sounding tone either sharp or flat.

For our present purposes, we require an approximate treatment of the acoustic impedance of such a jet (in this case for an organ pipe rather than a flute) as a function of frequency. It is, unfortunately, out of the question to attempt any sort of complete solution. Rayleigh[10] long ago gave attention to this problem and it has also been studied more recently by Cremer and Ising[11] and by Powell.[12] The behavior of the jet is both nonlinear and dispersive, but we shall concentrate, for the moment, on a linear approximation and simplify the discussion as much as we can.

Suppose that inside the organ pipe there is an acoustic disturbance with angular frequency $\omega$ so that at time $t$ the acoustic particle velocity out of the pipe mouth near the jet orifice is $v\exp(i\omega t)$. Following the work of Brown[9] and of Coltman,[3] we know that this acoustic ve-

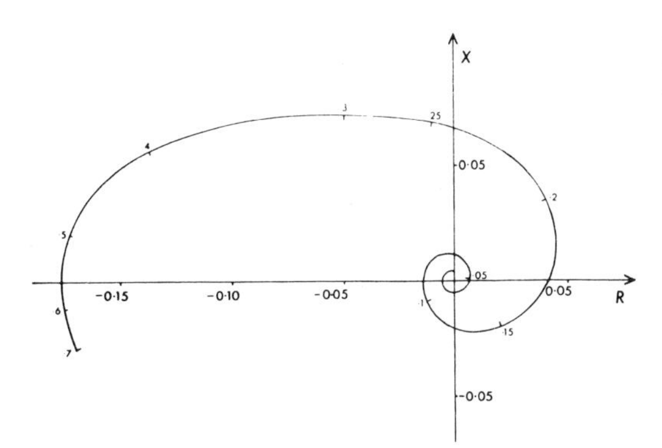


FIG. 1. Acoustic impedance $Z=R+iX$ of the blowing jet of a flute as measured by Coltman[3] for a particular jet configuration. The impedance is given in units of the characteristic impedance of the tube, the parameter on the curve is the blowing pressure in inches of water, and the sounding frequency is 440 Hz.

locity interacts with the jet and provokes a disturbance near the orifice which is essentially wave-like in character and which travels along the jet with a velocity $u$. Coltman's measurements show that $u$ is about 0.4 times the fluid velocity in the jet but it also varies somewhat with frequency. In addition, over a reasonably large frequency range, the amplitude of the jet disturbance increases with distance from the orifice.[9,11] Taking all these effects into account, if the distance from the jet mouth to the pipe lip is $d$, then the jet disturbance reaches the lip after a time $d/u$. At the lip it generates a pressure fluctuation, due to its blowing either into or out of the tube, whose magnitude by Bernoulli's theorem is proportional to the square of the jet velocity and hence to the pressure $P$ in the blowing reservoir.

In the linear approximation which we are using, the amplitude of the jet deflection is proportional to the acoustic disturbance $v\exp(i\omega t)$ which causes it, though we cannot immediately say whether or not any phase change is involved in the interaction, nor exactly what the coupling constant is. We can, however, absorb both these uncertainties into an effective interaction constant $\gamma$ to write[13] the pressure disturbance $p$ generated when the jet strikes the pipe lip as

$$p=-\gamma P v \exp[i\omega(t-d/u)] . \tag{1}$$

The interaction constant $\gamma$ depends in detail upon the geometry of the jet, the pipe mouth, and the pipe lip and is in general complex, of the form $\gamma_0\exp(-i\delta)$.

The acoustic impedance $Z$ of the jet is now obtained by dividing this pressure fluctuation $p$ by the acoustic volume velocity $Av\exp(i\omega t)$ out of the pipe mouth, where $A$ is the effective area of the mouth opening. Thus,

$$Z=-(\gamma_0 P/A)\exp[-i(\omega d/u+\delta)] . \tag{2}$$

Measurements by Coltman[3] on flute jets led him to the conclusion that $Z$ is real and negative, so that the flute tube sounds at its normal resonance frequency when the path length $d$ of the jet is about half a wavelength. This implies a value close to $\pi$ for the phase lag $\delta$ under the particular conditions chosen. The jet photographs of Cremer and Ising[11] suggest a similar result for the organ pipe jet which they studied. Finally, measurements by the present author, to be reported in detail in a later paper, indicate quite directly that $\delta\simeq\pi$ for both the fundamental and the next mode of a small organ pipe.

It is fairly easy to identify the approximate origin of this phase shift. The interaction between the jet and the acoustic current occurs at the jet aperture and the jet, if we assume it to be mass controlled, acquires a transverse velocity component which lags behind the forcing acoustic velocity by $\pi/2$. In the interaction between the jet and the pipe lip, there is a phase lag because the pressure is generated by a volume flow and the cross section of the jet is very much smaller than that of the pipe. In the limit of a very small jet and a very large pipe, the pressure should tend to follow the integral of the jet flux into the pipe and therefore lag behind the jet deflection by $\pi/2$. For a larger jet and smaller pipe, this phase lag should be smaller. The total phase lag $\delta$, being the sum of these two contributions, should therefore approach $\pi$ for a typical pipe geometry. The real situation is, of course, much more complex than this in its details.

If we adopt the value $\pi$ for $\delta$, then the impedance $Z$, given as a function of blowing pressure by Eq. 2, is as shown in Fig. 2. Because of the unknown magnitudes in $\gamma_0$ and the dependence of $A$ upon the particular physical system involved, the absolute magnitude of the complex impedance $Z$ is undetermined and we have simply drawn Fig. 2 to the same size as Fig. 1 so that a shape comparison can be made. The parameter on the curve giving blowing pressure (in inches of water for comparison with Coltman's data) is however calculated directly on the assumption of a jet length of 7 mm, a sounding fre-

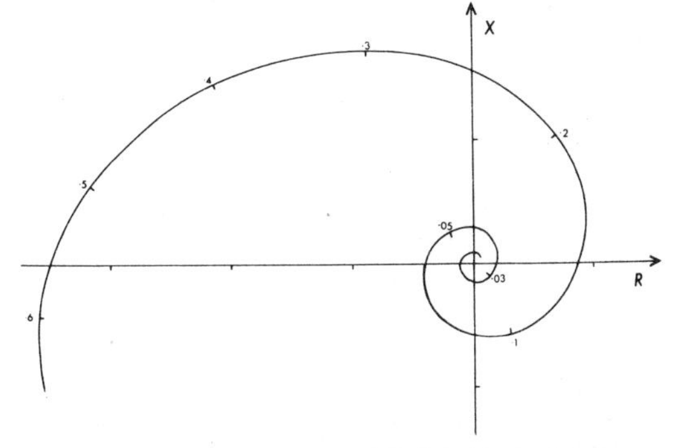


FIG. 2. Acoustic impedance $Z=R+iX$ of the blowing jet of an organ pipe as described by Eq. 2. As discussed in the text, the impedance units are undetermined but the figure has been drawn the same size as Fig. 1 for qualitative comparison. The parameter on the curve is the blowing pressure in inches of water assuming a jet length of 7 mm, a sounding frequency of 440 Hz, and a wave-propagation velocity along the jet of 0.4 times the jet air velocity, again for comparison with Fig. 1.

quency of 440 Hz, and a wave-propagation velocity along the jet of 0.4 times the airstream velocity, so that these figures are directly compar· ·le with those of Fig. 1.

From a comparison of the two figures it is clear that, apart from the unknown scale factor which can be accommodated in the parameter $\gamma_0$, the semiquantitative agreement between theory and experiment is good. There are of course some minor discrepancies and there remains the possibility that ultimate experimental determination of $\gamma_0$ might not give the expected agreement in magnitude, but with these reservations we can go on to use the more general form of Eq. 2, which includes frequency dependence, as a basis for our further development of the theory.

We shall not discuss the linear theory further except to point out that the condition for maintenance of a pipe oscillation near its fundamental resonance frequency $\omega_1$ is that the jet impedance $Z(\omega_1)$ at this frequency should have a negative real part of sufficient magnitude to overcome the pipe losses. If the blowing pressure is increased or the jet length decreased, the real part of the jet impedance can be made negative for the second pipe resonance at frequency $\omega_2$, but positive for the first resonance, and the pipe will overblow. This has been discussed in more detail by Coltman.[3]

## II. NONLINEAR JET EXCITATION

The theory we have set out above is linear: the pressure disturbance $p$ generated by the jet and given by Eq. 1 is simply related to the velocity disturbance $v\exp(i\omega t)$ through the impedance $Z$ given by Eq. 2. In reality, the situation is much more complicated than this and, in particular, there is a maximum pressure that can be generated by the jet (when it is blowing entirely inside the lip), as well as a minimum pressure (when it is blowing entirely outside the lip). Thus, the static $(p, v)$ relation for the jet looks rather like the full curve in Fig. 3, instead of being simply a straight line.

A detailed experimental or theoretical study could, in

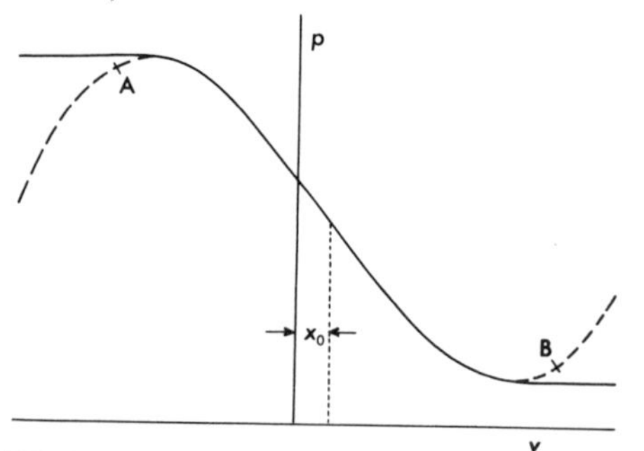


FIG. 3. Static interaction curve for a jet exciting an organ pipe. An acoustic particle velocity $v$ out of the pipe mouth causes a pressure $p$ due to interaction of the jet with the pipe lip. $x_0$ is the static offset in the position of the jet relative to the lip, as defined in Sec. 6. The broken curve is a cubic approximation to the interaction curve, valid within the range $A$ to $B$.

principle, elucidate the form of this curve, but we shall not attempt this here. Instead we shall assume a general static characteristic of the form

$$p=\sum_{n=0}^{\infty} a_n' v^n , \tag{3}$$

where the zeroth-order term $a_0'$ represents a static pressure produced by the jet and the linear term $a_1' v$ was written in Eq. 1 as $-\gamma P v$. Higher terms describe the saturation behavior shown in Fig. 3.

If we take all the coefficients $a_n'$ to be real and follow a development similar to that leading to Eq. 1, then we find, for a velocity disturbance $v\exp(i\omega t)$, the jet-generated pressure disturbance

$$p=\sum_{n=0}^{\infty} a_n' v^n \exp[in\omega(t-d/u)-i\delta] , \tag{4}$$

where the jet phase shift $\delta$ is now incorporated explicitly in the argument. Any possible dispersive behavior of wave-propagation velocity along the jet is immaterial at this stage since the higher harmonics are generated only in the interaction of the jet with the lip edge, rather than propagating along the jet. This statement does not hold true, however, for the next step in the development.

We can now extend this analysis further to suppose that the original velocity disturbance has a Fourier series spectrum

$$v(t)=\sum_{m=-\infty}^{\infty} c_m \exp(im\omega t) . \tag{5}$$

In this expression, the coefficients $c_m$ satisfy[13]

$$c_{-m}=c_m^* , \tag{6}$$

and $\omega$ is positive. The resulting pressure disturbance is then

$$p(t)=\sum_{n=0}^{\infty} a_n' \exp(-i\delta)\left\{\sum_{m=-\infty}^{\infty} c_m \exp[im\omega(t-d/u)]\right\}^n . \tag{7}$$

In Eq. 7, in distinction from Eq. 4, the individual pipe modes whose amplitudes are $c_m$ are interacting with the jet at its orifice and the wave-like disturbance of frequency $m\omega$ then propagates along the jet and interacts with the lip. If there is an appreciable dispersion in wave velocities along the jet as a function of frequency, then the velocities $u$ appearing in Eq. 7 should be subscripted to $u_m$ and the velocity appropriate to frequency $m\omega$ used in each case. As in Eq. 4, there is no further complication of this type introduced by the nonunity exponents $n$ and we only have to keep track algebraically of the individual velocities $u_m$ involved. This is perfectly feasible if $u$ is known as a function of frequency and the number of modes considered is not too large. For our present purposes, and in absence of detailed knowledge of dispersion in the propagation velocity, we shall assume $u$ to be independent of frequency.

It now no longer makes sense to try to define an effective impedance for the jet because the nonlinearity leads to a great deal of frequency conversion. Rather, let us consider in a more detailed way the interaction between the jet and the resonant modes of the pipe.

## III. THE JET-PIPE INTERACTION

The oscillating air column in an organ pipe is a continuous system, but for our present purposes it is most convenient to consider its behavior as resolved into an infinite sequence of normal modes. Because of the damping associated with each mode and arising from viscous, thermal, and radiation losses, the resonances are not sharp but exhibit finite $Q$ values. If $\psi_n$ is the acoustic displacement associated with the $n$th normal mode and $B$ is a constant equal to the cross-sectional area of the pipe divided by the effective vibrating mass of the air column, then the equation of motion has the form

$$\frac{d^2\psi_n}{dt^2} + k_n \frac{d\psi_n}{dt} + \omega_n^2\psi_n = -p(t)B , \tag{8}$$

where $\omega_n$ is its resonance frequency and $k_n$ its characteristic damping. The forcing term $p(t)$ arises from the pressure fluctuations produced by the jet and its sign is negative because displacements have been taken as positive in a direction out of the pipe mouth.

To solve the set of Eqs. 8 is a formidable task, but we can simplify them considerably if we assume the pipe resonances to be sufficiently sharp that they are essentially nonoverlapping. This is a good approximation for the first few resonances of all reasonably shaped pipes and is valid up to at least $n \simeq 10$ for pipes with reasonably narrow scales like diapasons. For cylindrical pipes, the resonance frequencies $\omega_n$ form an approximately harmonic series so that they each select from the pressure spectrum of Eq. 7 a single harmonic with which to interact. If we denote by $\omega$ the angular frequency of the fundamental component of $p(t)$, which approximately corresponds with the pipe fundamental $\omega_1$, then Eq. 8 can be written as

$$\frac{d^2\psi_n}{dt^2} + k_n \frac{d\psi_n}{dt} + \omega_n^2\psi_n = -p_n B \exp(in\omega t) , \tag{9}$$

where $p_n$ is the complex amplitude associated with the $n$th harmonic of $p(t)$. The fundamental mode is not necessarily the strongest, or even excited at all, but, because of the nearly harmonic relation between the $\omega_n$, Eq. 9 is still a convenient formulation in most cases.

From Eq. 7, defining $a_n = Ba_n'$, we can write formally for this pressure amplitude:

$$Bp_n = \sum_m \sum_{s=1}^{\infty} a_s c_{m(1)} c_{m(2)} \cdots c_{m(s)} \exp(-in\omega d/u - i\delta) , \tag{10}$$

where $\sum_m$ implies a sum over all possible sets of $m(i)$ satisfying

$$m(1) + m(2) + \cdots + m(s) = n , \tag{11}$$

and, of course, the individual $m(i)$ may be either positive or negative integers.

Now the velocity disturbance $v(t)$ of Eq. 5 which interacts with the jet is simply the time derivative of the displacement $\psi$. But from Eq. 9, the form of the forcing term is such that the mode $\psi_n$ is constrained to vibrate with the forcing frequency $n\omega$, so that

$$\psi_n = (c_n/in\omega)\exp(in\omega t) . \tag{12}$$

If we use this self-consistency condition in Eq. 9, then we find immediately the solution

$$c_n = \frac{-in\omega p_n B}{\omega_n^2 - (n\omega)^2 + in\omega k_n} . \tag{13}$$

Equations 10–13, when taken only to some finite value of $s$, constitute with their real and imaginary parts a set of $2s$ equations for the $s$ complex velocity amplitudes $c_1, \ldots, c_s$ and the angular frequency $\omega$. We can, however, without loss of generality, choose the origin of time so that the phase of the fundamental $c_1$ is zero, so that the $2s+1$ unknowns reduce to $2s$ and an explicit solution becomes possible.

## IV. PIPE WITH A SINGLE RESONANCE

To gain some feeling for the behavior to be expected, let us first examine the behavior of a jet coupled to a pipe with only a single resonant mode of angular frequency $\omega_1$. If the pipe resonance is sufficiently narrow, we can concentrate our attention on the behavior of the fundamental pipe mode and neglect the amplitude of higher modes in the pipe, even though they may be present in the jet.

For our later development, we shall be forced to truncate the power series expansion of Eq. 3 for the jet characteristic and it is important to find what limits this places on the range of validity of the solution. The analysis is simplified by noting that neither $a_0$ nor $a_2$ enter into the solution. The linear term $a_1$ is insufficient to yield a finite solution, so we investigate the behavior when Eq. 3 is truncated after the cubic term $a_3v^3$. The broken curve in Fig. 3 shows this cubic approximation and it is clear that, while the approximation is good for small amplitudes $v$ and the saturation behavior is well reproduced, the curve becomes entirely incorrect for amplitudes outside the range $AB$. We note that, necessarily, $a_1 < 0$ and $a_3 > 0$.

Proceeding with the formal solution of Eq. 13 and 10 and writing

$$\theta \equiv \omega d/u , \tag{14}$$

we find

$$(\omega_1^2 - \omega^2 + i\omega k_1)\, c_1 = -i\omega(a_1 c_1 + 3a_3 c_1^3)\, e^{-i(\theta+\delta)} , \tag{15}$$

the factor 3 arising in the cubic term since there are three terms in the summation on $m$ in Eq. 10. The imaginary part of this equation gives

$$c_1^2 = -[a_1\cos(\theta+\delta) + k_1]/3a_3\cos(\theta+\delta) , \tag{16}$$

so that oscillations occur provided $\cos(\theta+\delta)$ is positive and $-a_1\cos(\theta+\delta) > k_1$. This solution lies in the range of validity $AB$ provided that $|a_1| \lesssim 2k_1$. The real part of Eq. 15 gives the sounding frequency and, neglecting smaller terms, we find

$$\omega \simeq \omega_1 - \tfrac{1}{2}k_1\tan(\theta+\delta) . \tag{17}$$

In the "center" of the range of blowing pressures producing this fundamental, $\theta+\delta = 2\pi$ and $\omega = \omega_1$. As the blowing pressure is increased, $u$ rises and $\theta$ decreases, so that the sounding frequency $\omega$ increases above $\omega_1$.

Conversely, for pressures less than that for the center of the range, $\omega$ becomes progressively less than $\omega_1$.

The solutions of Eqs. 16 and 17 are mathematically and physically correct provided that the condition

$$|a_1| \lesssim 2k_1 \tag{18}$$

is met. This allows for an excursion of the jet from entirely inside to entirely outside the pipe lip, as well as all smaller excursions, and therefore represents a physically interesting range of situations. We must be carefuly, however, not to apply the solutions blindly to strongly blown pipes with very small damping coefficients $k_1$ or we may exceed their range of validity. We shall examine this criterion again after considering the more general case.

It is also worthwhile noting two other apparent solutions which arise from Eq. 15. The first is the quiescent situation with $c_1 = 0$. This is physically legitimate but unstable and any small perturbation of the jet will cause a transition to the situation described by Eqs. 16 and 17. The second is an artifact which arises from Eq. 16 if $\cos(\theta + \delta)$ is negative, and does not correspond to a real physical situation. It is easily eliminated by the requirement that $\cos(\theta + \delta)$ is positive.

## V. PIPE WITH MANY RESONANCES

In this section we proceed as far as possible without restricting the generality of the problem. Finally then, we shall make some more explicit assumptions to treat a particular case as an example.

The Eqs. 10–13 can be simplified to some extent by writing the complex amplitudes $c_n$ in the form

$$c_n = d_n \exp(i\phi_n) , \tag{19}$$

where the $d_n$ are real positive quantities and, by Eq. 7,

$$d_{-n} = d_n ; \quad \phi_{-n} = -\phi_n . \tag{20}$$

Using this form and substituting from Eqs. 10, 12, and 14 into Eqs. 13, we deduce, after a little manipulation, the equations

$$\begin{aligned} -d_n(\omega_n^2 - n^2\omega^2)/n\omega &= a_1 d_n \sin(n\theta + \delta) \\ &+ a_2 \sum_m d_m d_{n-m} \sin(n\theta + \phi_n - \phi_m - \phi_{n-m} + \delta) \\ &+ a_3 \sum_l \sum_m d_l d_m d_{n-l-m} \sin(n\theta + \phi_n - \phi_l - \phi_m \\ &\qquad - \phi_{n-l-m} + \delta) + \cdots \end{aligned} \tag{21}$$

and

$$\begin{aligned} -k_n d_n &= a_1 d_n \cos(n\theta + \delta) \\ &+ a_2 \sum_m d_m d_{n-m} \cos(n\theta + \phi_n - \phi_m - \phi_{n-m} + \delta) \\ &+ a_3 \sum_l \sum_m d_l d_m d_{n-l-m} \cos(n\theta + \phi_n - \phi_m \\ &\qquad - \phi_{n-l-m} + \delta) + \cdots . \end{aligned} \tag{22}$$

Straightforward solution of these equations for the $d_n$, $\phi_n$, and $\omega$, given that $\phi_1 = 0$, now provides a solution to our problem. Usually one or other of the first two or three harmonics will have the dominant amplitude and the $p(v)$ series, subject to the criterion of Eq. 18, can be approximated by its first few terms. We can therefore proceed by truncating the problem to a relatively small order and, after solving this, proceed to the full solution by means of successive approximations.

To this end, let us represent the interaction $p(v)$ by the first three terms of its series expansion of Eq. 3, as discussed in the previous section. Let us also suppose that the physical situation (jet velocity and tube resonances) is such that either the first or the second harmonic is dominant. We therefore proceed to a solution for these two components only, neglecting all $d_n$ for $n > 2$.

After a good deal of tedious algebra, we find the solutions

$$d_1^2 = -F_2 H , \tag{23}$$

$$d_2^2 = F_1 H , \tag{24}$$

$$\sin\phi_2 = (1/2\omega a_2)(F_1/H)^{1/2} , \tag{25}$$

$$\cos\phi_2 = (1/2\omega a_2)(F_1 H)^{-1/2}[G_1 + \omega a_1 + \omega a_3 H(3F_1 - F_2)] , \tag{26}$$

where

$$F_1 = (\omega_1^2 - \omega^2)\cos(\theta + \delta) - \omega k_1 \sin(\theta + \delta) , \tag{27}$$

$$F_2 = (\omega_2^2 - 4\omega^2)\cos(2\theta + \delta) - 2\omega k_2 \sin(2\theta + \delta) , \tag{28}$$

$$G_1 = (\omega_1^2 - \omega^2)\sin(\theta + \delta) + \omega k_1 \cos(\theta + \delta) , \tag{29}$$

$$G_2 = (\omega_2^2 - 4\omega^2)\sin(2\theta + \delta) + 2\omega k_2 \cos(2\theta + \delta) , \tag{30}$$

$$H = \frac{\omega a_1(2F_1 + F_2) + F_2 G_1 + F_1 G_2}{\omega a_3(F_2^2 + 3F_1 F_2 - 2F_1^2)} . \tag{31}$$

One of the Eqs. 25 and 26 would appear to be redundant, but in fact the allowed values of $\omega$ are determined by the consistency condition

$$\cos^2\phi_2 + \sin^2\phi_2 = 1 . \tag{32}$$

These Eqs. 23–31 thus determine the coefficients $c_1$ and $c_2$ in the Fourier series spectrum of Eq. 5 of the pipe oscillation. With these two components known, in the form $(d_n, \phi_n)$ and provided that our original assumption that one or the other of them is the dominant mode is justified, we can determine $c_3$ as $(d_3, \phi_3)$ from Eqs. 21 and 22. We can proceed in this way to find all the Fourier components $c_n$.

This procedure effectively takes into account the coupling of a given mode $c_n$ with all modes $c_m$ for which $m < n$. Coupling with modes for which $m > n$ is neglected. It is, however, now possible to refine the result obtained above by using these first approximations in Eqs. 21 and 22. If the initial result or the refinement suggests that the dominant mode is not $c_1$ or $c_2$ but some other $c_n$, then the initial solution to find the oscillation frequency should be carried out for this $c_n$ and the next most intense mode. For a stopped pipe, for example, $c_1$ and $c_3$ should be used and, for an overblown open pipe, $c_2$ and $c_3$ or $c_4$.

## VI. FURTHER CONSIDERATION OF JET INTERACTION

To apply this theory to a real situation we must first define a reasonable set of parameters to describe the jet and its interaction with the acoustic particle velocity $v$ and with the lip of the pipe. This we now proceed to do.

As shown in Fig. 4, the jet emerges from a reservoir under pressure $P$ through a slit of length $L$ and width $2W$ at the mouth of the pipe. It is a reasonable approximation to describe the velocity distribution across the jet in the direction of its thickness $W$ by an expression of the form

$$V = V_0 \exp[-(x-x_0)^2/W^2] . \tag{33}$$

From Bernoulli's theorem we expect

$$P = \tfrac{1}{2}\rho V_0^2 , \tag{34}$$

where $\rho$ is the density of the air. We do not interpret the velocity distribution as implying a distribution in the disturbance velocity $u$ (although this may happen), but rather simply as a blurring of the edges of the jet.

In a real situation, the jet will spread and its velocity decrease as it moves across the mouth to the lip, but for simplicity, we shall ignore this complication and assume it to remain as a sheet of thickness $W$. The jet travels across the mouth a distance $d$ and then impinges on the sharp lip of the pipe on the plane $x=0$ at a transverse distance $x_0$ (which we shall call the offset) from the plane of symmetry of the jet. We now further assume that, when a steady airflow of particle velocity $v$ is flowing out of the pipe mouth, the jet is deflected outwards by an amount $\alpha v$ to be intercepted by the pipe lip at a distance $x_0 + \alpha v$ from the jet symmetry plane. The coefficient $\alpha$, with the addition of a phase shift as discussed before, then measures the sensitivity of the jet to acoustic disturbance.

For the purposes of our present calculation it is helpful to dissect this parameter $\alpha$ a little further to display in approximate form its dependence on other physical parameters of the system. We should expect, for example, that $\alpha$ should vary inversely with the mass of the jet per unit length and directly with the travel time to the lip (i.e., directly with $\theta/\omega_1$). It is therefore a reasonable approximation to write

$$\alpha = \beta\theta/\omega_1 W , \tag{35}$$

where $\beta$ is a more fundamental parameter measuring the interaction strength and depending upon quantities like the Reynold's number of the jet.

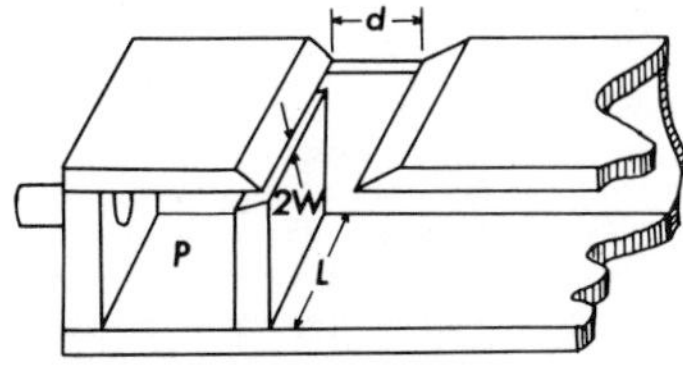


FIG. 4. Schematic diagram of the mouth of an organ flue pipe showing the jet thickness $2W$, jet width $L$, and lip cut-up $d$.

TABLE I. Assumed values of parameters.

| | |
|---|---|
| $\omega_1 = 1000\ \text{sec}^{-1}$ | $\omega_2 = 2100\ \text{sec}^{-1}$ |
| $k_1 = 50\ \text{sec}^{-1}$ | $k_2 = 50\ \text{sec}^{-1}$ |
| $W = 0.1$ cm | $L = 3$ cm |
| $S = 10\ \text{cm}^2$ | $x_0/W = 0.1$ |
| $P = 10$ mbar | $\theta = \pi$ |
| $\beta = 0.4$ | $\delta = \pi$ |

Coltman[2] has analyzed the pressure produced by a jet of cross section $s$ and velocity $V$ blowing into the end of a pipe of cross sections $S$ and finds, for $s \ll S$, that the pressure generated is

$$p = \rho V^2 s/S . \tag{36}$$

We can apply this equation to the portion of the jet entering the pipe when the intercept position is $x_0 + \alpha v$ as above and, after some algebra, we find, for the first three coefficients in the expansion of Eq. 3, the values

$$\begin{aligned} a_1 &= -C\alpha , \\ a_2 &= 2C\alpha^2 W^{-2} x_0 , \\ a_3 &= \tfrac{2}{3} C\alpha^3 W^{-2}(1 - 4x_0^2 W^{-2}) , \\ C &= 2PLS^{-1}\exp(-2x_0^2 W^{-2}) . \end{aligned} \tag{37}$$

This description of the jet and the nonlinear character of its interaction with the air column of the pipe is manifestly incomplete and oversimplified and we make no claim for its general validity except as a heuristic approximation suitable for our present purposes. A more detailed description must clearly take into account some of the points raised, for example, by Powell.[12]

## VII. CALCULATION FOR PIPE WITH TWO RESONANCES

In Sec. V we set out the formal solution of our problem for a pipe with two resonances and showed how this could be extended to treat more general systems. To examine the predictions of the theory we now solve Eqs. 19–32 together with Eqs. 35 and 37 for a representative system with two pipe resonances. The assumed values of the physical parameters are those set out in Table I, these parameters being varied one at a time to observe their effect on the solutions. In all cases, the overtones present are true harmonics of the fundamental and the condition in Eq. 18 is satisfied for the whole range of the variables displayed, so that truncation of the nonlinear expansion is a valid approximation, as discussed in Sec. IV.

The phenomenon of overblowing requires some separate comment. A pipe is said to be overblown when the amplitude at the pipe fundamental frequency falls to zero. The behavior of the second mode is then given by Eqs. 16 and 17 with $(c_2, \omega_2, k_2, 2\theta)$ in place of $(c_1, \omega_1, k_1, \theta)$. This oscillation state can occur when $\theta$, as defined in Eq. 14, lies between $\pi/4$ and $3\pi/4$, provided now that $-a_1\cos(2\theta+\delta) > k_2$, and the solution is quantitatively

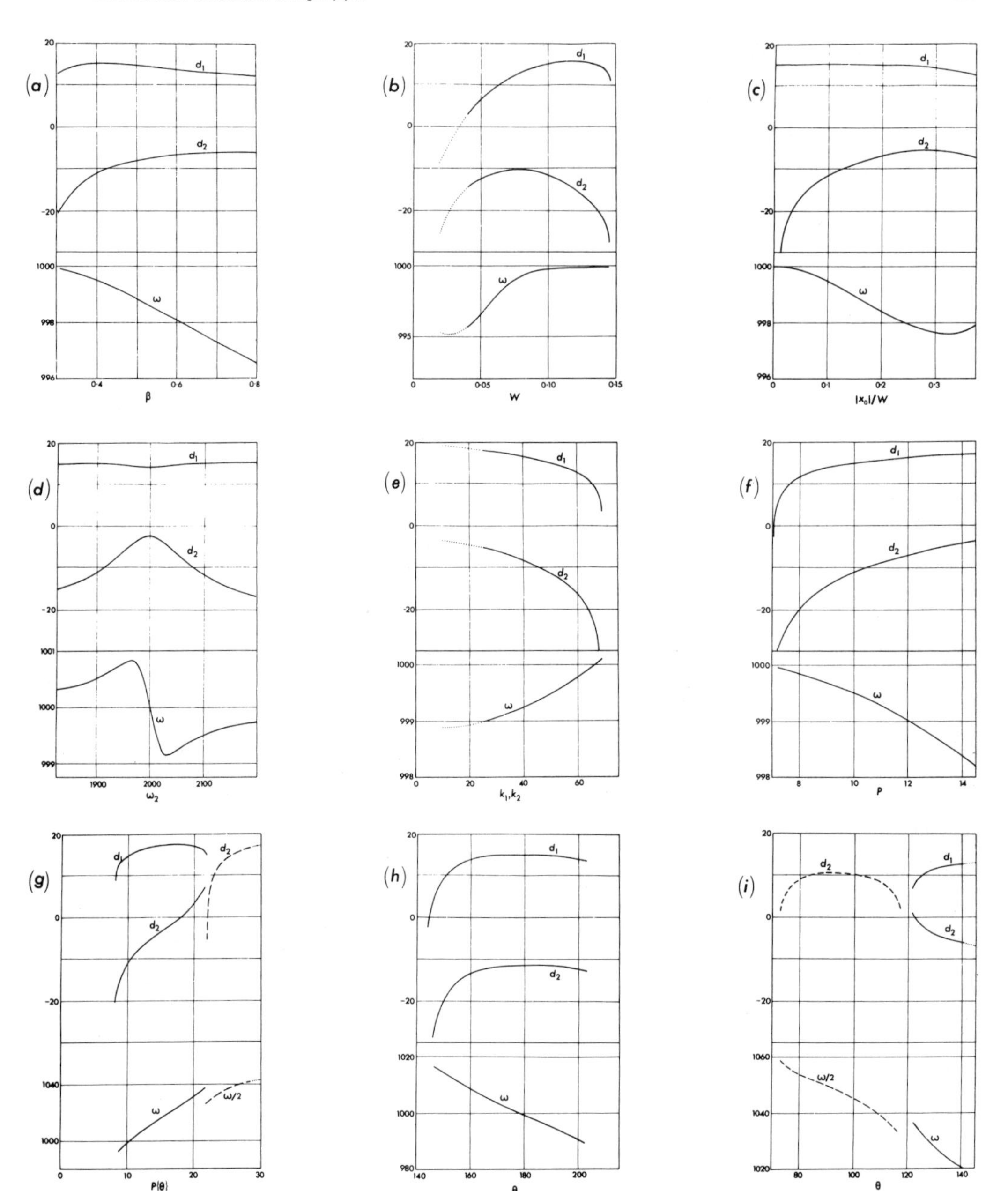


FIG. 5. (a)–(f) Effects on the oscillation behavior of a two-mode pipe caused by varying individual physical parameters while keeping the others fixed at the values given in Table I. (g) Behavior of the pipe of Table I as a function of blowing pressure with the lip cut-up held fixed at the value giving $\theta=\pi$ for $P=10$ mbar. (h) Behavior of the pipe of Table I as a function of lip cut-up distance as reflected in the phase parameter $\theta$. (i) As for (h), but with the coupling parameter $\beta$ doubled to 0.8. In each part of the figure, a broken line indicates an overblown condition and a dotted line indicates a region where the truncation criterion of Eq. 18 is no longer valid. ($P$ = blowing pressure in millibars, $\theta$ = phase shift in degrees for the fundamental as determined by propagation time across the lip cut-up, $2W$ = jet thickness and $x_0$ = jet offset both in centimetres, $\omega$ = sounding frequency in radians per second, $k_1$ and $k_2$ = damping coefficients for first and second resonances in seconds$^{-1}$, $d_1$ and $d_2$ are velocity levels of first and second harmonics of the pipe oscillation, in decibels, relative to 1 cm sec$^{-1}$.)

valid if $|a_1| < 2k_2$.

The results of these calculations are shown in Fig. 5, which is largely self explanatory. In Fig. 5(g), the phase $\theta$ is appropriately related to the blowing pressure $P$, so that the behavior shown is that of a pipe as the blowing pressure is increased, without other adjustments. The broken line indicates an overblown condition. In Fig. 5(i), the coupling is doubled and the pipe overblows to the octave for small $\theta$. Note also that the phase lag $\theta$, which is related to the jet travel time, is most appropriately thought of as specifying the pipe cut-up, or distance from the jet orifice to the pipe lip.

From these calculations several important conclusions arise.

(1) For a note which is reasonably well above its sounding threshold, the amplitude of the fundamental is most largely controlled by the thickness $W$ ot the jet. The amplitude of this fundamental increases steadily with $W$ until, at a critical value (in this case $W \simeq 1.5$ mm), the pipe ceases to speak.

(2) The amplitude of the second partial (which is, in fact, the second harmonic of the pipe tone), in contrast decreases as the thickness $W$ of the jet increases. The amplitude of this second harmonic increases very markedly, for a given pipe, as the blowing pressure $P$ is increased and has its maximum value at a pressure just below that at which the pipe overblows. The amplitude of the second harmonic is greatest when the frequency of the second resonance is equal to twice the sounding frequency.

(3) The relative amplitude of the second harmonic also depends upon the asymmetry of the jet, as measured by the parameter $x_0$. In our simplified model the second harmonic component vanishes for a symmetric jet, $x_0 = 0$. For a real jet, it is likely that the difference in pressure environment for a jet blowing into or out of the pipe mouth is such that considerable asymmetry is always present.

(4) For a given blowing pressure, the sounding frequency of a pipe depends strongly upon the cut-up of the lip (as reflected in the phase parameter $\theta$) and decreases as the cut-up distance is increased.

(5) For a given pipe, the sounding frequency depends strongly upon the blowing pressure and increases as this is increased. When overblowing occurs, the frequency jumps by a little less than a factor of 2, despite the fact that the upper resonance is at more than twice the frequency of the lower.

## VIII. CONCLUSIONS

The approach to the nonlinear pipe excitation developed in this paper is a quite general one but its predictions in particular cases are quite explicit. The example displayed in the previous section is an arbitrary one, but its qualitative agreement with the accumulated experience of organ pipe voicers[14] and the subjective analysis of flute players is encouraging. A detailed experimental program is, however, clearly necessary to study the predictions of the theory and to clarify some of the physical parameters involved. Such a study is at present in progress in this laboratory.

## ACKNOWLEDGMENT

This work is part of a study of musical acoustics supported by the Australian Research Grants Committee.

[1]P. G. Andersen, *Organ Building and Design* (George Allen and Unwin, London, 1969).
[2]J. W. Coltman, J. Acoust. Soc. Am. 40, 99–107 (1966).
[3]J. W. Coltman, J. Acoust. Soc. Am. 44, 983–992 (1968).
[4]J. Backus, J. Acoust. Soc. Am. 33, 806–809 (1961).
[5]J. Backus, *The Acoustical Foundations of Music* (John Murray, London, 1970).
[6]C. J. Nederveen, *Acoustical Aspects of Woodwind Instruments* (Frits Knuf, Amsterdam, 1969).
[7]A. H. Benade, J. Acoust. Soc. Am. 40, 247–249 (1966).
[8]A. H. Benade, "On the tone and response of wind instruments from an acoustical viewpoint," AAAS Acoustics Symposium, Philadelphia, 1971 (private communication, to be published).
[9]G. B. Brown, Proc. Phys. Soc. Lond. 47, 703–732 (1935).
[10]J. W. S. Rayleigh, *The Theory of Sound* (Macmillan, London, 1896; reprinted by Dover, New York, 1945), Vol. 2, pp. 376–414.
[11]L. Cremer and H. Ising, Acustica 19, 143–153 (1967/68).
[12]A. Powell, J. Acoust. Soc. Am. 33, 395–409 (1961).
[13]Throughout this paper we adopt the convention of representing oscillatory disturbances by exponentials $\exp(in\omega t)$ associated with complex amplitudes. Here, $n$ is an integer which is not apparent when its value is unity. The real physical quantities, together with their phases, can be recovered either by taking the real and imaginary parts of any equation or by taking the sum and difference of the two equations for $+n$ and $-n$.
[14]D. M. A. Mercer, J. Acoust. Soc. Am. 23, 45–54 (1951).

# 28

Copyright © 1975 by the Acoustical Society of America

Reprinted from *J. Acoust. Soc. Am.*, **57**(1), 233–237 (1975)

# Acoustical correlates of flute performance technique

N. H. Fletcher

*Department of Physics, University of New England, Armidale, New South Wales 2351, Australia*
(Received 21 March 1974; revised 1 August 1974)

Measurements of physical parameters of performance technique for a group of experienced flute players are reported. Blowing pressure is found to be consistent among the players and intermediate between previous measurements by Bouhuys [J. Acoust. Soc. Am. **37**, 453–456 (1965)] and by Coltman [J. Acoust. Soc. Am. **40**, 99–107 (1966); **44**, 983–992 (1968)]. Jet-length measurements agree with those of Coltman. Blowing pressure and jet length come near to satisfying the expected relationship but with some discrepancy which may be significant. Harmonic analysis of flute tone shows that amplitude variations from *piano* to *forte* are largely confined to the upper partials, particularly for notes in the low octave. A study of vibrato shows that this normally consists of an amplitude modulation of the upper partials of the tone with little change in the fundamental. The vibrato frequency is consistently about 5 Hz and is associated with a 10% variation in blowing pressure at that frequency. Physiological vibrato mechanisms are discussed and the acoustical nature of the vibrato is shown to be determined by the nonlinear jet excitation mechanism and the stabilizing effect of the narrow fundamental pipe resonance.

Subject Clasification: 75.35.

## INTRODUCTION

The particular techniques used by a performer to elicit musical sounds from an instrument are governed both by the acoustical nature of the instrument and by the performer's artistic criteria. Sounds can, indeed, be produced in other ways but will generally be judged to be musically unsatisfying.

During the course of a study with a pedagogic end in view,[1] a considerable amount of data was collected on flute performance technique by means of measurements made on four experienced players. Two of these (C. E. and L. V.), to be denoted by A and B, were experienced professional players, the third (N. F.), denoted by C, was an experienced semiprofessional, and the fourth, D, an advanced student (D. M.). To indicate the range of the sample, A and C were men and B and D were women; A and B were trained predominantly in Australia, while C and D studied both in the United States and in Australia. Measurements should not, therefore, show obvious bias towards a particular school of playing.

The purpose of the present note is to present the results of the measurements, and the conclusions to be drawn from them, in some quantitative detail, and to discuss their relationship to established acoustical principles.

## I. BLOWING PRESSURE

The correct lip configuration and blowing pressure to be used in playing the flute have been matters of conflicting advice for at least 200 years,[2] and only recently have careful measurements been made. Bouhuys[3] has reported measurements of blowing pressure for a variety of wind instruments, including the flute, and Coltman[4] has given the results of a rather more extensive series for the flute. Each set, however, involved measurements on one player only and, since the reported pressures differ by almost an order of magnitude, they leave the situation uncertain.

In the present study the air pressure in the player's mouth was measured using a 1-mm catheter tube inserted into one corner of the lip opening. The tube led to a sensitive aneroid pressure gauge which had been calibrated by comparison with a water column. The measurements made on the four players are detailed in Fig. 1. There was some variation in the measurements for the lowest few notes but otherwise the players used consistent pressures for given notes on different occasions. Also shown for comparison are the results of Coltman.

From Fig. 1 it is clear that the blowing pressure used increases roughly linearly with frequency and that there is a good measure of agreement between the four players A, B, C, and D. The median blowing pressure $p$ (in millibars), in excess of atmospheric pressure, to sound a note of frequency $\nu$ (in hertz) is

$$p \simeq 0.008\nu , \quad (1)$$

the maximum observed deviation being mostly ±50%. Measurements on player C show that this relation also applies for performance on the alto (G) flute.

The results reported by Coltman lie just on the lower edge of this range, but those of Bouhuys (7.5–13 mbar for $C_4$ and 27–40 mbar for $A_6$) are so much higher that they lead to questions. Bouhuys's measurement technique involved insertion of a small latex balloon in the player's mouth, which may have upset the technique or given misleading results. Experiments by the present author suggest that it is simply not possible to produce the lowest notes on the flute with pressures as high as those reported.

Returning to the results shown in Fig. 1 we observe that players B and C used substantially the same blowing pressure for a given note for dynamic levels from pianissimo to fortissimo, while A and D varied their blowing pressure by about a factor of 2 over this range. Subjectively, players B and C appeared to maintain a bright "ringing" tone quality for quiet playing while A and D used a much "softer" tone for quiet passages.

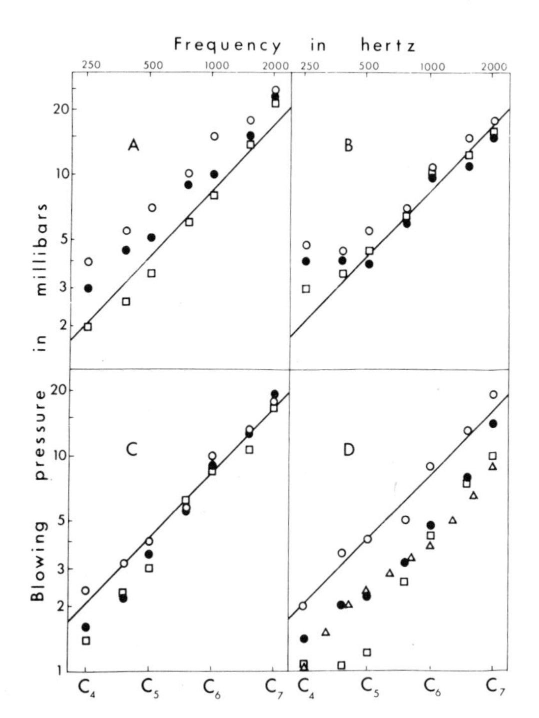


FIG. 1. Blowing pressures $p$ (in millibars) used by flute players A, B, C, and D to produce the notes shown: ○ *fortissimo*, • *mezzoforte*, □ *pianissimo*. Measurements by Coltman are also shown: Δ (*mezzoforte*). The curve drawn is the relation $p = 0.008\ \nu$.

This distinction is brought out in the spectral analyses to be discussed later.

## II. LIP CONFIGURATION

The principal variables to be controlled in the lip configuration, or embouchure, are the width and height of the aperture in the lips producing the air jet, the distance between this aperture and the edge of the flute embouchure hole (the jet length), the fraction of the flute embouchure hole covered by the lower lip, and the angle at which the air jet strikes the flute embouchure edge.

Some of these variables were studied, for each of the four players, by taking photographs, both full face and in profile, and subsequently measuring these. The same technique was used by Coltman[4] in a similar, though more limited, series of measurements.

Jet length, defined to be the distance measured on a profile photograph from the apparent point of emergence of the jet from the player's lips to the target edge of the flute embouchure hole, is perhaps the most important and consistent variable. There is a slight arbitrariness about definition of the point of emergence from the lips, but, as we see later, this is not important.

The results of measurements of the four players are shown in Fig. 2. Once more there is good consistency between all four sets of measurements. The median relation between jet length $l$ (in millimeters) and note frequency $\nu$ (in hertz) is

$$l \simeq 1.8 + 100\,\nu^{-1/2} \quad (2)$$

and all measurements lie within about $\pm 20\%$ of this relation, the players making little or no adjustment to $l$ with dynamic level of their playing. The analytical form assumed for Eq. 2 is derived from subsequent discussion. The precision of the measurements and range of frequency involved is certainly not sufficient to distinguish between Eq. 2 and a simple linear relation between $l$ and $\nu$.

Coltman[4] has not reported measurements of jet length directly, but instead has plotted the width of the flute embouchure hole left uncovered by the lower lip. This ranges from 6 mm for $C_4$ to 3.5 mm for $G_6$ and, since it is typically 1–2 mm less than the jet length, his measurements are in substantial agreement with those reported above.

Analysis of the full-face photographs of the four players in this study again shows a good measure of consistency among them in the matter of embouchure shape. The lip opening approximates an oval with an axial ratio between 10:1 and 20:1, although its shape is slightly irregular and varies from player to player. Its maximum width is about 12 mm, equal to the width of the flute embouchure hole, for low notes played loudly, and its size is reduced to produce soft sounds or to play high notes. For very high notes played softly, the embouchure width decreases to about 5 mm, its axial ratio remaining between 10:1 and 20:1.

## III. RELATION TO THEORY

All these observations are in general agreement with what we should expect from acoustical principles. Coltman[4] has made careful measurements of the impedance of an air jet interacting with a flute, after the fashion of

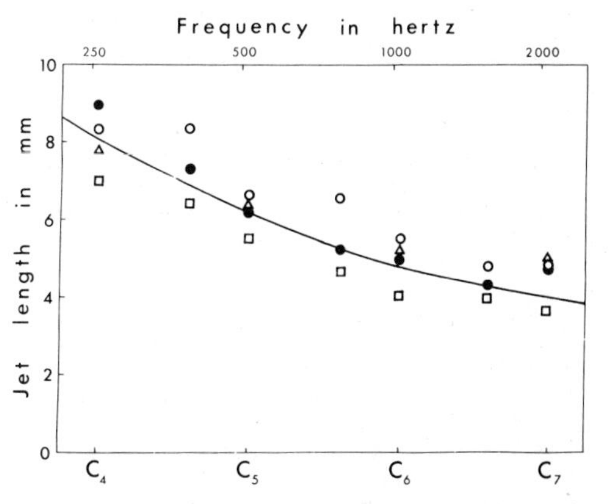


FIG. 2. Air jet lengths $l$ (in millimeters) measured from photographs for the players A, ○; B, •; C, □; D, Δ. The curve drawn is the relation $l = 1.8 + 100\,\nu^{-1/2}$.

a normal player, and has identified regions where the jet impedance is negative, leading to sustained oscillation. The pure negative resistance region corresponds to a particle travel time along the length of the jet of about 0.2 of an oscillation period. The apparent fact that the displacement wave velocity along the jet is about 0.4 of the particle velocity, together with an additional phase shift of $\pi$, gives the correct phase relationship for regeneration.

If we assume that jet velocity is determined by Bernoulli's equation and require that the travel time be 0.2 of an oscillation period, then we are led to the relation

$$lp^{-1/2} = 2700\nu^{-1}, \tag{3}$$

where $l$ is in millimeters, $p$ in millibars, and $\nu$ in hertz. More realistically, however, we must allow for the fact that the jet velocity decreases with its travel distance, due to entrainment of stationary air, so that we should replace Eq. 3 by

$$lp^{-1/2} = 2700\,\alpha\nu^{-1}, \tag{4}$$

where $\alpha < 1$. To compare this with our measurements, we see that a simple manipulation of Eqs. 1 and 2 gives the relation

$$(l - 1.8)p^{-1/2} = 1100\,\nu^{-1}. \tag{5}$$

The two results, Eqs. 4 and 5, can be reconciled if we recognize that the measured length $l$ contains a dead interval of 1.8 mm which is effectively shielded from the acoustic field and assume that the factor $\alpha$ has a value near 0.4 so that the average jet speed is a little less than half that predicted from Bernoulli's equation.

There are, however, other possibilities. Coltman's measured blowing pressures[4] are only half those found in the present study for nearly the same jet length, which would increase the right-hand side of Eq. 5 by a factor 1.4, leading to closer agreement. There is also a distinct feeling among flute players that, rather than blowing the "center" of a note, which might correspond to the optimum phase condition Eq. 4, one actually blows just short of the condition which would give overblowing to the next octave. In this way the harmonic development of the tone is enriched and sensitive adjustment of embouchure hole coverage prevents increase in frequency. Coltman's experiments[4] with an artificially blown flute suggest that this increase in frequency should be a sensitive test of blowing condition, but the present author's experiments with organ pipes (to be reported later) show a stable frequency regime for an energetically blown pipe. The details of this point therefore remain to be resolved.

Another point of disagreement concerns the way in which increases of dynamic level from *piano* to *forte* are achieved. Our measurements show that, while some players may make adjustments of blowing pressure, there is a universal adjustment of the lips to increase the cross section of the jet when a *forte* level is required. Coltman,[4] on the other hand, found that, with his artificially blown flute, "radiated power turned out to be a function mostly of blowing pressure, and was not very dependent on the note being produced or the size of the blowing tube." The subtle factor involved here may well be the shape of the cross section of the blowing jet, since calculations[6] have shown this to be of considerable importance in determining the amplitudes of the upper partials, as well as of the fundamental.

## IV. HARMONIC DEVELOPMENT

Many texts on musical acoustics characterize flute tone as being of weak harmonic development and imply that the fundamental is always dominant. The harmonic development of flute tone is, of course, much less rich than that of oboe tone, but in the lowest octave the fundamental is by no means dominant.

To clarify these matters and to seek for possible correlation between harmonic development and performance technique, the sounds produced by each of the four players in this study were recorded and analyzed. A dynamic microphone having a hypercardioid response pattern was used at a distance of about 1 m from the player in a normal living room. The same room was used for A and B while C and D were in different but rather similar rooms. The recordings were judged subjectively to give a faithful reproduction of the sound as heard, but may obviously contain some emphasis of certain frequencies due to standing waves. They are, however, probably preferable to recordings made in anechoic surroundings because of the effect of such an unusual environment on the player.

Figure 3 shows the results of harmonic analysis of the sounds produced by each of the four players for three different notes, each played both loudly and softly. Again, there is good general agreement among all players, but some differences. The main conclusions are as follows, all partials being strictly harmonic.

In the lowest octave of the flute, and for loud playing, the fundamental is lower in level than either the second or third harmonics, and may be lower than the fourth and fifth harmonics as well. When the playing is soft in this octave, the level of the fundamental is the same as for loud playing but the relative levels of all higher harmonics are decreased. This decrease is much more pronounced for players A and D, who reduce wind pressure for soft playing, than for B and C, who use a constant wind pressure.

For the middle octave of the flute, the fundamental becomes the dominant partial for both loud and soft playing, though second and third harmonics are within 10 dB of it in relative level. The sound-pressure level of the fundamental changes little with dynamic level and most of the change is represented by changes in the upper partials.

In the third octave the fundamental is clearly dominant and all upper partials are more than 10 dB below it in relative level. The fundamental changes considerably with dynamic level, though still not as much as do the upper partials.

If we were to seek to describe a formant for flute tone on the basis of these measurements, then we would in

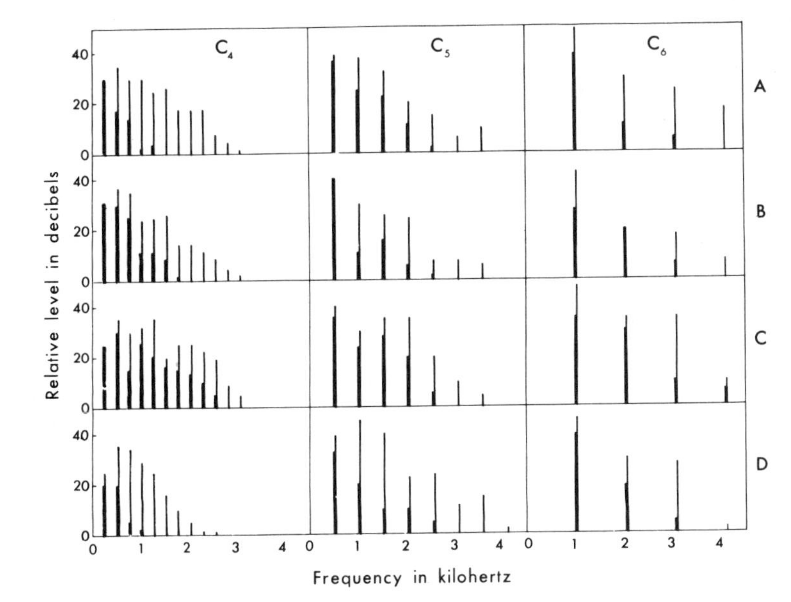


FIG. 3. Harmonic analysis of *forte* and *piano* notes played by A, B, C, and D. Absolute sound-pressure levels were not determined and relative levels of partials are given in decibels consistently for each player separately.

fact need different formants for loud and soft playing. For *forte* tone the formant rises at about 12 dB/octave up to 500 Hz, is constant from 500 to 1000 Hz, and above this falls at about 12 dB/octave. For *piano* playing the upper roll-off point is reduced to about 500 Hz and the rising lower portion of the formant curve is either reduced in extent or even eliminated.

The nonlinear mechanism responsible for hamonic generation in flutes and organ pipes is not yet fully understood, but an approximate theory has been developed by the present author[5] based on some more qualitative arguments by Benade.[6] To maximize harmonic development it appears desirable to use a very thin lamellar jet to maximize the nonlinearity of its interaction with the embouchure edge. It is also desirable to operate at a wind pressure just short of that giving overblowing to the octave. In this regime, indeed, the level of the fundamental may even decrease with increased blowing pressure, while the levels of most of the upper partials increase. This is in general agreement with the results of our measurements, though any detailed calculation for upper partials must await a further development of the theory.

## V. VIBRATO

The various components of flute vibrato can be readily dissected from recorded sounds by using a wave analyzer, provided that the bandwidth of the analyzer is much larger than either the amplitude-modulation frequency (the pulsation frequency) or the frequency deviation in the vibrato. For a normal flute vibrato the pulsation frequency is about 5 Hz and the frequency deviation is less than 1%, so that the measurement conditions for the first few harmonics are met by using a heterodyne wave analyzer (GR 1900-A) with a fixed 50-Hz bandwidth.

The vibrato of subjects A, B, and C of the present study was analyzed in this way and found to be very similar. Subject C was then further analyzed as discussed below.

Analysis of the individual partials of flute tone with vibrato shows frequency modulation of less than 1%, but substantial amplitude modulation which varies from one partial to another. The amplitude variation is only roughly sinusoidal but we can define an approximate modulation index $\delta_n$ for the $n$th harmonic by writing its behavior as $a_n(1+\delta_n \sin\Omega t)\sin n\omega t$ for its sound pressure. The modulation frequency $\Omega$ is very close to 5 Hz while the $a_n$ (sound-pressure amplitude in unspecified units) and $\delta_n$ have the values given in Table I for a low note ($C_4 = 262$ Hz nominally) and a midrange note ($C_5 = 524$ Hz).

From this table it is apparent that flute vibrato consists largely of an amplitude modulation of the upper partials of the tone, causing a periodic variation both in loudness and, more importantly, in timbre. Once this is realized, the timbre vibrato aspect of the tone quality is immediately apparent to the listener.

Nearly all flute players produce vibrato by an oscillation of the diaphragm muscles to produce a rhythmic fluctuation in blowing pressure. Direct measurements by a pressure transducer, linked to the player's mouth cavity by a 1-mm catheter tube, confirm that the pres-

TABLE I. Amplitudes $a_n$ and modulation indices $\delta_n$ for vibrato.

| Note | $a_1$ | $\delta_1$ | $a_2$ | $\delta_2$ | $a_3$ | $\delta_3$ | $a_4$ | $\delta_4$ |
|---|---|---|---|---|---|---|---|---|
| $C_4$ | 4 | 0.1 | 12 | 0.2 | 7 | 0.4 | 6 | 0.7 |
| $C_5$ | 11 | 0.2 | 2 | 0.5 | 4 | 0.5 | 4 | 0.5 |

sure fluctuations have a frequency of 5 Hz and an amplitude about 10% of the blowing pressure. A few players are known to use a lip-driven or throat-driven vibrato but this is unusual and is not generally regarded as being very satisfactory.

Experience shows that it is not very easy for the player to vary his vibrato frequency and that this frequency is very nearly the same for all players. This suggests that some sort of resonant mechanism may be involved and there seem to be two possibilities, one mechanical and one neurophysiological.

In the first place we note that the lung cavity contains a volume $V \sim 10^{-2}$ m$^3$ of air maintained under a pressure $p \sim 10^5$ Pa slightly above atmospheric by an elastic diaphragm of area $A \sim 3\times10^{-2}$ m$^2$. The diaphragm is loaded by the mass $m \sim 10$ kg of the contents of the abdomen. The resonant frequency of this system is $\nu = (1/2\pi)\,(pA^2/mV)^{1/2} \simeq 5$ Hz, which corresponds closely to the observed vibrato frequency. It is therefore reasonable that one can play with a "straight" tone without vibrato, but that, once vibrato is allowed to develop, it tends to run at the resonant frequency.

The second possibility is that the diaphragm is maintained in the correct state of tension by opposing sets of muscles which are controlled by both voluntary and involuntary neurological feedback loops. The oscillation frequency of such loops, as observed in various nervous disorders, is also not far from 5 Hz. It is most likely, of course, that both mechanisms are involved, but experiments are being planned to try to separate these.

Returning to the acoustical effects of the periodically varying blowing pressure, we find that the effects shown in Table I can readily be accounted for. The data of Fig. 1 show that variations in loudness are achieved through variation in amplitude of the upper partials rather than of the fundamental. Wormann,[8] in a study of clarinet tone, has shown that, over a limited range, the amplitude of the $n$th harmonic varies as the $n$th power of the amplitude of the fundamental, and calculations by the present author[6] show that, for a strongly blown pipe, the amplitude of the fundamental remains constant or even decreases with increased blowing pressure, while the amplitude of the second harmonic increases sharply.

In addition to these steady-state effects, the time-varying nature of the vibrato must be taken into account. Using the method described by Benade,[7] we have measured the acoustic resonances of a flute tube and head joint with simulated lips in position. Because of the narrow tube diameter (19 mm) and the presence of the correcting cavity and taper in the head joint,[9] the resonances are in harmonic relation to a very good approximation. For the tube fundamental $C_4 = 262$ Hz, the resonance half-widths at 3-dB points are $\Delta_1 = \pm 4$, $\Delta_2 = \pm 6$, $\Delta_3 = \pm 7$, $\Delta_4 = \pm 8$ Hz, corresponding to quality factors ($Q$ values) for these resonances in the range 40–70. The small width of the fundamental resonance will attenuate the side bands at $\pm 5$ Hz carrying amplitude-modulation information and thus smooth the output. Because of their greater widths, the upper resonances will have a smaller smoothing effect. This phenomenon reinforces the effect of the blowing mechanism in favoring modulation of upper partials and, indeed, the reverberant nature of the rooms in which the recordings were made has a similar effect.

## ACKNOWLEDGMENTS

This work is part of a program, aimed at elucidating second-order effects in the design and performance of traditional musical instruments, which is supported by the Australian Research Grants Committee.

[1]N. H. Fletcher, Instrumentalist 28(7), 57–61 (1974).
[2]J. J. Quantz, *On Playing the Flute* (1752), transl. by E. R. Reilly (Faber and Faber, London, 1966), pp. 49–59.
[3]A. Bouhuys, J. Acoust. Soc. Am. **37**, 453–456 (1965).
[4]J. W. Coltman, J. Acoust. Soc. Am. **40**, 99–107 (1966).
[5]J. W. Coltman, J. Acoust. Soc. Am. **44**, 983–92 (1968).
[6]N. H. Fletcher, J. Acoust. Soc. Am. **56**, 645–652 (1974).
[7]A. H. Benade, J. Acoust. Soc. Am. **40**, 247–249 (1966).
[8]W. Wormann, Ph. D. thesis, Case Western Reserve University, (1970), p. 53.
[9]A. H. Benade and J. W. French, J. Acoust. Soc. Am. **37**, 679–691 (1965).

# SELECTED BIBLIOGRAPHY

(See also the Bibliography at end of Paper 12.)

Aebi, W. 1969. Das Waldhorn und seine innere Akustik. *Schweizerische Bauzeitung,* **87,** 38.

Ancell, J. E. 1960. Sound Pressure Spectra of a Muted Cornet. *J. Acoust. Soc. Am.,* **32,** 1101–1104.

Archibald, F. R., and A. G. Einslie. 1958. The Vibration of a String Having Uniform Motion Along Its Length. *J. Appl. Mech.,* **80,** 347--348.

Aschoff, V. 1936. Experimentalle Untersuchungen an einer Klarinette. *Akust. Z.,* **1,** 77–93.

Baakes, F. 1974. *Piano Tone Building.* Vestal, N.Y.: Vestal Press.

Backhaus, H. 1932. Über die Bedeutung der Ausgleichsvorgänge in der Akustik. *Veit. f. techn. Physik,* **8.**

Backus, J. G. 1960. Studies of the Vibrations of Clarinet Reeds. *J. Acoust. Soc. Am.,* **32,** 935(A).

———.1961a. Vibration of the Air Column and the Reed in the Clarinet. *J. Acoust. Soc. Am.,* **33,** 806–809.

———.1961b. Influence of the Reed on the Vibration Frequency of Clarinet Tones. *J. Acoust. Soc. Am.,* **33,** 862(A).

———. 1961c. Behavior and Properties of Clarinet Reeds. *J. Acoust. Soc. Am.,* **33,** 1652(A).

Backus, J. G. 1962a. Variation with Loudness of the Harmonic Structure of the Clarinet and Bassoon Tones. *J. Acoust. Soc. Am.,* **34,** 717(A).

———. 1962b. Experimental Check of the Theoretical Expressions for Frequency Shift and Maximum Blowing Pressure in the Clarinet. *J. Acoust. Soc. Am.,* **34,** 1994(A).

———. 1963a. Acoustical Investigation of the Clarinet. *Sound,* **2,** 22–25.

———. 1963b. Frequency Shift for Loud Tones of the Clarinet. *J. Acoust. Soc. Am.,* **35,** 771(A).

———. 1963c. Vibration of the Clarinet Body and Its Contribution to the Clarinet Tone. *J. Acoust. Soc. Am.,* **35,** 190(A).

———. 1964a. Effect of Wall Material on the Steady-State Tone Quality of Woodwind Instruments. *J. Acoust. Soc. Am.,* **36,** 1881–1887.

———. 1964b. Effect of Steady Flow on the Response Frequencies and Q's of the Clarinet. *J. Acoust. Soc. Am.,* **36,** 2014(A).

———. 1965. Measurement of Clarinet Resonance Frequencies. *J. Acoust. Soc. Am.,* **37,** 1203(A).

———. 1966a. Clarinet Reed Parameters. *J. Acoust. Soc. Am.,* **39,** 1220(A).

———. 1966b. Effect of Warping of the Reed Tip on Clarinet Tones. *J. Acoust. Soc. Am.,* **40,** 1252(A).

———. 1967. Resonances in the Bassoon. *J. Acoust. Soc. Am.,* **41,** 1608(A).

———. 1968a. Resonance Frequencies of the Clarinet. *J. Acoust. Soc. Am.,* **43,** 1272–1281.

———. 1968b. Resonances in the Brass Instruments and the Hand Stopping of Horns. *J. Acoust. Soc. Am.,* **44,** 367(A).

———. 1969. *The Acoustical Foundations of Music.* New York: W. W. Norton.

———. 1971a. Harmonic Generation in the Trumpet. *J. Acoust. Soc. Am.,* **49,** 509–519.

———. 1971b. Improved equipment for Plotting Resonance Curves for Wind Instruments. *J. Acoust. Soc. Am.,* **50,** 128(A).

———. 1972. Interaction of the Clarinet Reed with an Air Column Having a Single Resonance. *J. Acoust. Soc. Am.,* **52,** 147(A).

———. 1974a. Input Impedance Curves for the Reed Instruments. *J. Acoust. Soc. Am.,* **56,** 1266–1279.

———. 1974b. Composite Woodwind Reed. *J. Acoust. Soc. Am.,* **56,** 1664(P).

———. 1975a. Input Impedance Curves for the Brass Instruments and the Behavior of Mutes. *J. Acoust. Soc. Am.,* **57,** 522(A).

———. 1975b. Acoustic Impedance of an Annual Cavity. *J. Acoust. Soc. Am.,* **58,** 1078–1081.

———, and T. C. Hundley. 1966. Wall Vibrations in Flue Organ Pipes and Their Effect on Tone. *J. Acoust. Soc. Am.,* **39,** 936–945.

———, and T. C. Hundley. 1970. Trumpet Air-Column Overloading. *J. Acoust. Soc. Am.,* **47,** 131(A).

Bahnert, H. 1958. *Metallblasinstrumente..* Leipzig: Fachbuch-Verlag.

Baines, A. 1957. *Woodwind Instruments and Their History.* New York: Norton.

Bak, N. 1969. Pitch, Temperature, and Blowing-Pressure in Recorder Playing. *Acustica,* **22,** 295–299(L).

Barducci, I., and G. Pasqualini. 1975. Measurement of the Internal Friction and the Elastic Constants of Wood. Translated by Elizabeth B. Abetti in *Musical Acoustics, Part I,* Carleen Hutchins, ed. Stroudsburg, Pa.: Dowden, Hutchinson & Ross, pp. 410–423.

Bartholomew, W. T. 1942. *Acoustics of Music.* Englewood Cliffs, N.J.: Prentice-Hall.
Barton, E. H. 1919. *A Textbook on Sound.* New York: Macmillan.
Barton, E. H., and S. C. Laws. 1902. Air Pressure Used in Playing Brass Instruments. *Phil. Mag.,* s6, **3,** 385–393.
Bate, A. E. 1933. Resonance in Coupled Pipes. *Phil. Mag.,* s7, **16,** 562–574.
Bate, A. E. 1937. End Correction of an Unflanged Pipe. *Phil. Mag.,* s7, **24,** 453–458.
Beauchamp, J. W. 1969. Nonlinear Characteristics of Brass Tones. *J. Acoust. Soc. Am.,* **46,** 98(A).
Beldie, I. P. 1975. Die Bestimmung der Schubmoduln des Fichtenholzes. In *Musical Acoustics, Part I,* edited by Carleen Hutchins. Stroudsburg, Pa.: Dowden, Hutchinson & Ross, pp. 438–444.
Bell, E. R.; E. C. Peck; and N. T. Krueger. n.d. *Modulus of Elasticity of Wood Determined by Dynamic Methods,* USDA Forest Products Laboratory Report No. 1977, Madison, Wisconson.
Benade, A. H. 1960. *Horns, Strings and Harmony,* New York: Doubleday.
———. 1963. Thermal Perturbations in Woodwind Bores. *J. Acoust. Soc. Am.,* **35,** 190(A).
———. 1966a. Formulation of the Brass-Instrument Bore Problem. *J. Acoust. Soc. Am.,* **39,** 1220(A).
———. 1966b. Radiation of Air-Column Resonance to Sound Spectra Produced by Wind Instruments. *J. Acoust. Soc. Am.,* **40,** 247–249(L).
———. 1968. On the Propagation of Sound Waves in a Cylindrical Conduit. *J. Acoust. Soc. Am.,* **44,** 616–623.
———. 1969. Effect of Dispersion and Scattering on the Startup of Brass Instrument Tones. *J. Acoust. Soc. Am.,* **45,** 296(A).
———. 1970. Acoustic Criteria and Procedures for Adjusting Tone and Response in Woodwinds. *J. Acoust. Soc. Am.,* **48,** 89(A).
———. 1972. Brass Instrument Design and the Theory of Horns. *J. Acoust. Soc. Am.,* **52,** 138(A).
———. 1973a. Flute Headjoint Cork Position and Damping of Higher Order Modes. *J. Acoust. Soc. Am.,* **54,** 310(A).
———. 1973b. Register Hole Design for Cone Woodwinds. *J. Acoust. Soc. Am.,* **54,**, 310(A).
———. 1973c. Characterization of Woodwinds by Tone-Hole Cutoff Frequency. *J. Acoust. Soc. Am.,* **54,** 311(A).
———. 1974a. Mechanism of Multiphonic Tone Production in Woodwinds. *J. Acoust. Soc. Am.,* **55,** S49(A).
———. 1974b. Nonlinear Aspects of Wind Instrument Regeneration. *J. Acoust. Soc. Am.,* **55,** S69(A).
———.. 1976. *Fundamentals of Musical Acoustics.* New York: Oxford University Press.
———, and J. M. Bebler. 1974. Reed Cavity and Neck Proportions in Conical Woodwinds. *J. Acoust. Soc. Am.,* **55,** 458(A).
———, and J. J. Cuddeback. 1974. Quasi-Turbulent Damping at Wind Instrument Joints and Tone Holes. *J. Acoust. Soc. Am.,* **55,** 457(A).
———, and J. W. French. 1965. Analysis of the Flute Head Joint. *J. Acoust. Soc. Am.,* **37,** 679–691.
———, and J. S. Murday. 1967. Measured End Correction for Woodwind Tone-Holes. *J. Acoust. Soc. Am.,* **41,** 1609(A).

Benade, A. H., and W. E. Worman. 1967. Search-Tone Measurements in Blown Wind Instruments. *J. Acoust. Soc. Am.,* **42,** 1217(A).

———, and W. E. Worman. 1971. Schematic Representation of Wind Instrument Oscillation. *J. Acoust. Soc. Am.,* **49,** 127(A).

———, and W. E. Worman. 1972. Spectrum Development with Playing Level in Wind Instruments. *J. Acoust. Soc. Am.,* **52,** 148(A).

Beranek, L. L. 1949. *Acoustic Measurements.* New York: Wiley.

———. 1954. *Acoustics.* New York: McGraw-Hill.

Bert, P. A. 1969. Correlations Between Theoretical and Measured Standing-Wave Patterns in a Cylinder. *J. Acoust. Soc. Am.,* **45,** 313(A).

Bhargova, S., and R. N. Ghosh. 1924. Elastic Impact of Pianoforte Hammer. *Phil. Mag.,* s6, **47,** 1141–1148.

Bilhuber, P. H. 1936. Soundboard for Pianos and Other Instruments or Devices Using Soundboards. *U.S. Patent 2,051,633,* Aug. 18, 1936.

Blaikley, D. J. 1878. On Brass Instruments as Resonators. *Phil. Mag.,* s5, **6,** 119–128.

———. 1879. Experiments for Determining the Correction to Be Added to the Length of a Cylindrical Resonant Tube to Find the True Wavelength and the Velocity of Sound in Small Tubes. *Phil. Mag.,* s5, **7,** 339–343.

———. 1890. *Acoustics in Relation to Wind Instruments.* London: Boosey.

Blocker, W. 1974. A Theory of Edgetone Production. *J. Acoust. Soc. Am.,* **55,** 458(A).

Boehm, W. M. 1910. Determination of the Correction for the Open End of Cylindrical Resonator. *Phys. Rev.,* **31,** 332–341.

Boethius, A. M. S. 1973. Concerning the Principles of Music, 1867. Translated by R. Bruce Lindsay in *Acoustics: Historical and Philosophical Development,* R. Bruce Lindsay, ed. Stroudsburg, Pa.: Dowden, Hutchinson & Ross, pp. 35–39.

Boner, C. P., and R. B. Newman. 1940. The Effect of Wall Materials on the Steady-State Acoustic Spectrum of Flue Pipes. *J. Acoust. Soc. Am.,* **12,** 83–89.

Bonvallet, G. L. 1940. Some Factors Involved in Cornet Tone Quality. Master's thesis, Northwestern University.

Bouhuys, A. 1965. Sound-Power Production in Wind Instruments. *J. Acoust. Soc. Am.,* **37,** 453–456.

———. 1968. Pressure-Flow Events During Wind Instrument Playing. *Ann. N.Y. Acad. Sci.,* **155,** 264–275.

———. 1969. Human Factors in Wind-Instrument Performance. *J. Acoust. Soc. Am.,* **45,** 296(A).

Briggs, G. A. 1951. *Pianos, Pianists and Sonics.* Bradford Yorks, England: Wharfedale Wireless Works.

Bürck, W., and H. Lichte. 1938. Über die Schallfortpflanzung in Rohren. *Akust. Z.,* **3,** 259–270.

Campbell, R. A. 1954. A Study of the Effect of Selected Interior Contours of the Trombone Mouthpiece upon the Tone Quality of a Trombone. Master's thesis, University of Texas.

Cardwell, W. T., Jr. 1966. Working Theory of Trumpet Air-Column Design. *J. Acoust. Soc. Am.,* **40,** 1252(A).

———. 1969. Trumpet Intonation Improvements with Multiple Helmholtz Resonator Terminations. *J. Acoust. Soc. Am.,* **45,** 296(A).

Cardwell, W. T., Jr. 1974. Trumpet Acoustics: The Tuning Effect of the Mouthpiece and Leaderpipe. *J. Acoust. Soc. Am.,* **55,** 457(A).

Carse, A. 1939. *Musical Wind Instruments.* London: Macmillan.

Caughey, T. K. 1960. Random Excitation of a Loaded Nonlinear String. *J. Appl. Mech.,* 575.

Chlandi, E. F. F. 1973. Discoveries in the Theory of Sound. 1787. Translated by R. Bruce Lindsay in *Acoustics: Historical and Philosophical Development,* R. Bruce Lindsay, ed. Stroudsburg, Pa.: Dowden, Hutchinson & Ross, pp. 156–165.

Chotteau, M. 1971. The Isospectrum Clarinet System. Master's thesis, Case Western Reserve University.

Coltman, J. W. 1966. Resonance and Sounding Frequencies of the Flute. *J. Acoust. Soc. Am.,* **40,** 99–107.

———. 1968. Acoustics of the Flute. *Phys. Today,* **21,** 25–32.

———. 1971. Effect of Material on Flute Tone Quality. *J. Acoust. Soc. Am.,* **49,** 520–523.

Colwell, R. C., and L. H. Gipsons. 1941. Sound Velocity in Gases Under Different Pressures. *J. Acoust. Soc. Am.,* **12,** 436–437.

Coppens, A. B., and J. W. Saunders. 1968. Finite-Amplitude Standing Waves in Rigid Walled Tubes. *J. Acoust. Soc. Am.,* **43,** 516–529.

Cremer, L. 1950. *Die Wissenschaftl. Grundlg. der Raumakustik.* Leipzig: Hirzel-Verlag.

———, and H. Ising, 1967–1968. Die selbsterregten Schwingungen von Orgelpfeifen. *Acustica,* **19,** 143–153.

Culver, C. A. 1956. *Musical Acoustics.* 4th ed. New York: McGraw-Hill.

d'Alembert (Jean le Rond). 1973. Investigation of the Curve Formed by a Vibrating String, 1747. Translated by R. Bruce Lindsay in *Acoustics: Historical and Philosophical Development,* R. Bruce Lindsay, ed. Stroudsburg, Pa.: Dowden, Hutchinson & Ross, pp. 119–123.

Das, P. 1931. Theory of the Clarinet. *Indian J. Phys.,* **6,** 225–232.

Davy, N.; J. H. Littlewood; and M. McCraig. 1939. The Force-Time Law Governing the Impact of a Hammer on a Stretched String. *Proc. Roy. Soc. (London),* s7, **27,** 133–143.

Deditius, K. 1896–1897. Die Fehler des Blechblasinstruments. *Mus. Instr. Z.*

Dhar, S. C. 1936. The Study of the Duration of Contact of a Pianoforte String with a Hard Hammer Striking Near the End. *Indian J. Phys.* **10,** 305–311.

Drechsel, F. A. 1927. *Zur Akustik der Blasinstrumente..* Leipzig: Paul de Vib.

Drow, J. T., and R. S. McBurney. n.d. The Elastic Properties of Wood. USDA Forest Products Laboratory, Report No. 1528-A, Madison Wisconson.

Edwards, P. H. 1911. A Method for the Quantitative Analysis of Musical Tone. *Phys. Rev.,* **32,** 23–37.

Elder, S. A. 1962. Physical Basis of Woodwind-Recorder Voicing. *J. Acoust. Soc. Am.,* **35,** 1901(A).

Euler, L. 1973. Dissertation on Sound, 1727. Translated by R. Bruce Lindsay in *Acoustics: Historical and Philosophical Development, R. Bruce Lindsay, ed. Stroudsburg, Pa.: Dowden, Hutchinson & Ross, pp. 104–117.*

Fay, R. D. 1931. Plane Sound Waves of Finite Amplitude. *J. Acoust. Soc. Am.,* **3,** 222–241.

———. 1940. Attenuation of Sound in Tubes. *J. Acoust. Soc. Am.,* **12,** 62–67.

Feldman, W. C. 1961. Mechanics of Piano Strings Exitation. Bachelor's thesis, Massachusetts Institute of Technology.

Fenner, K. 1960. Inharmonicity and the Piano Tuner. Translated by J. Englehardt in *Das Musikinstrument,* **9,** 607–609.

———. 1961. The Calculation of the Transition From Wound Strings to Wire. Translated by J. Englehardt in *Das Musikinstrument,* **10,** 60, 62, 64, 70, 102–104.

———. 1962. On the Calculation of the Tension of Wound Strings. Translated by J. Engelhardt in *Das Musikinstrument,* **11,** 810, 341–344.

———. 1966. Unterschiede in der Stimmbarkeit unserer heutigen Klaviere. *Europiano Kongress Berlin 1965 Dokumentation.* Frankfurt am Main: Fördergemeinschaft Klavier e.V., pp. 200–212.

———, and H. Fuchs. 1967. Further Research in the Sound of the Pianoforte. *Instrument. Z.,* 30–31.

Fickenscher, A. 1941. Polytone and the Potentials of Purer Intonation. *Musical Quart.,* **27.**

Finch, T. L., and A. H. Benade. 1974. Transient Analyzer for Wind Instrument Tones. *J. Acoust. Soc. Am.,* **55,** 457(A).

Freedman, M. D. 1967. Analysis of Musical Instrument Tones. *J. Acoust. Soc. Am.,* **41,** 793–806.

Fuchs, H. 1964a. Klavierstimmung und akustische Forschung. *Das Musikinstrument,* **13,** 151–153.

———. 1964b. Piano Tuning and Acoustical Research. *Das Musikinstrument,* **13,** 575–577.

———. 1966. Einige akustische und asthetische Aspekte des Klavierklangs. *Europiano Kongress Berlin 1965 Dokumentation.* Frankfurt am Main: Fördergemeinschaft, Klavier e.V., pp. 425–436.

Fukada, E. 1975. The Vibrational properties of Wood, Parts I and II. 1950/1951. In *Musical Acoustics, Part I,* edited by Carleen Hutchins. Stroudsburg, Pa.: Dowden, Hutchinson, & Ross, pp. 425–436.

Galilei, G. 1973. Dialogues on Music and Acoustics. 1638. In *Acoustics: Historical and Philosophical Development,* edited by R. Bruce Lindsay. Stroudsburg, Pa.: Dowden, Hutchinson & Ross, pp. 41–61.

George, W. H., and H. E. Beckett. 1927. Energy of a Struck String: Part I *Proc. Roy. Soc. (London),* **A114,** 111–137.

Ghelmeziu, H., and I. P. Beldie. 1975. On the Characteristics of Resonance Spruce Wood 1972. In *Musical Acoustics, Part I,* edited by Carleen Hutchins. Stroudsburg, Pa.: Dowden, Hutchinson & Ross, pp. 445–454.

Ghosh, R. N. 1935. On the Quality of Pianoforte. *J. Acoust. Soc. Am.,* **7,** 27–28.

———. 1936. Elastic Impact of Pianoforte Hammer. *J. Acoust. Soc. Am.,* **7,** 254–260.

———.1938a. Dynamics of the Pianoforte String and the Hammer: I Hard Hammer. *Indian J. Phys.,* **12,** 317–330.

———. 1938b. Theory of the Clarinet. *J. Acoust. Soc. Am.,* **9,** 225–264.

———. 1948. Elastic Impact of a Pianoforte Hammer. *J. Acoust. Soc. Am.,* **20,** 324–328.

———, and H. G. Mohammad. 1935. Kinks on Impact Diagram of Struck String. *Phil. Mag.,* s7, **19,** 260–277.

Goldstein, S., and N. W. McLachlen. 1935. Sound Waves of a Finite Amplitude in an Exponential Horn. *J. Acoust. Soc. Am.,* **6,** 275–278.

Haines, D. W. 1975. Mechanical Properties of Wood and Varnish of Importance in Radiating Panels. *Catgut Acoust. Soc. Newsletter,* **24,** 8–11.

Hall, J. C. 1954. A Radiographic, Spectrographic and Photographic Study of the Non-Labial Physical Changes Which Occur in the Transition from Middle to Low and Middle to High Registers During Trumpet Performance. Ph.D. thesis, Indiana University.

———. 1955. Effect of the Oral and Pharyngeal Cavities on Trumpet Tone Qaulity. *J. Acoust. Soc. Am.,* **27,** 996(A).

———. 1963a. The Proper Selection of Cup Mouthpieces. Elkhart, Ind.: C. G. Conn, Ltd.

———. 1963b. Analysis of the Resonance Patterns Obtained with Mouthpieces of Varying Dimensions. *J. Acoust. Soc. Am.,* **35,** 1902(A).

———. 1963c. System for Measuring the Acoustical Response of Wind Instruments. *J. Acoust. Soc. Am.,* **35,** 1902(A).

———, and E. L. Kent. 1959. Effect of Temperature on the Tuning Standards of Wind Instruments. Elkhart, Ind.: C. G. Conn, Ltd.

———, and E. L. Kent. 1960. Relationship Between Wind Instrument Timbre and Sound Spectra. *J. Acoust. Soc. Am.,* **32,** 935(A).

———, and C. E. Lockwood. 1959. Effect of Mutes on Cornet Tone Quality. *J. Acoust. Soc. Am.,* **31,** 130(A).

———, and C. E. Lockwood. 1963. Characteristics of the Tone Quality of Wind Instruments. *J. Acoust. Soc. Am.,* **35,** 1902(A).

Hall, W. M. 1932. An Investigation of Sound Fields Within Regions Restricted by Finite Boundaries. Thesis, Massachusetts Institute of Technology.

———. 1939. An Acoustic Transmission Line for Impedance Measurement. *J. Acoust. Soc. Am.,* **11,** 140–146.

Hanson, L. H. 1967. Overstretching of Piano Strings and Inharmonicity. Master's thesis, Brigham Young University.

Hardy, H. C.; D. Telfair; and W. H. Pielemeier. 1942. The Velocity of Sound in Air. *J. Acoust. Soc. Am.,* **13,** 226–233.

Harker, G. F. H. 1937. The Principles Underlying the Tuning of Keyboard Instruments to Equal Temperament. *J. Acoust. Soc. Am.,* **8,** 243–256.

Hart, H. C.; M. W. Fuller; and W. S. Lusby. 1934. A Precision Study of Piano Touch and Tone. *J. Acoust. Soc. Am.,* **6,** 80–94.

Hartjes, R. N. 1960. On Experimental Investigation of the Tone Quality of a Single-Reed Mouthpiece for Oboe and Bassoon. Thesis, University of Colorado.

Hearmon, R. F. S. 1943. The Significance Between Shear and Extension in the Elastic Behavior of Wood and Plywood. *Proc. Phys. Soc. (London),* **55,** 67–80.

———. 1946. The Fundamental Frequency of Vibration of Rectangular Wood and Plywood Plates. *Proc. Phys. Soc. (London),* **58,** 78–92.

Helmholtz, H. 1954. *On the Sensation of Tone.* New York: Dover.

Henderson, H. W. 1942. An Experimental Study of trumpet Embouchure. *J. Acoust. Soc. Am.,* **13,** 58–64.

Hofman, H. 1956. *Über den Ansatz der Blechbläser.* Kassel and Basel: BVK.

Hundley, T. C.; D. W. Martin; and H. Benioff. 1956. Factors Contributing to the Multiple Decrement of Piano Tone Envelope. *Proc. 2nd ICA Cong.,* 158(A).

Igarashi, J., and M. Koyasu. 1953. Acoustical Properties of Trumpets. *J. Acoust. Soc. Am.*, **25,** 122–128.

Ingard, U., and H. Ising. 1967. Acoustic Nonlinearity of an Orifice. *J. Acoust. Soc. Am.*, **42,** 6–17.

———, and S. Labate. 1950. Acoustic Circulation Effects and the Nonlinear Impedance of Orifices. *J. Acoust. Soc. Am.*, **22,** 211–218.

Jeans, Sir J. 1961. *Science and Music.* London: Cambridge University Press.

Jensen, C. C. 1950. The Experimental Control of Clarinet Profile. Master's thesis, Illinois State Normal University.

Jones, A. T. 1939. Resonance in Certain Nonuniform Tubes. *J. Acoust. Soc. Am.*, **10,** 167–172.

Joseph, J. J. 1967. *The Physics of Musical Sound.* New York: Van Nostrand.

Jung, K. 1962. Zur Theorie der Seitenbohrungen an Blechblasinstrumenten. *Das Musikinstrument,* **11,** 332–333.

———. 1964. Harmonic and Inharmonic Piano String Overtones. *Das Musikinstrument,* **13,** 773–774.

Junghanns, H. 1971. *Junghanns Der Piano-und Flügelbau.* Frankfurt am Main: Verlag Das Musikinstrument.

Kalähne, A. 1927. Schallerzeungung mit mechanischen Mitteln. *Handb. Phys.*, **8.**

Karal, F. C. 1953. The Analogous Acoustical Impedance for Discontinuities and Constrictions of Circular Cross Section. *J. Acoust. Soc. Am.*, **25,** 327–334.

Kaufmann, W. 1895. Über die Bewegungen geshagener Saiten. *Ann. Physik,* **54,** 675–712.

Kemp, G. T., and A. W. Nolle. 1953. The Attenuation of Sound in Small Tubes. *J. Acoust. Soc. Am.*, **25,** 1083–1086.

Kent, E. L. 1955. Some Related and Objective Measurements on Cornet Tones. *J. Acoust. Soc. Am.*, **27,** 209(A).

———. 1963a. Comparison of a Mathematically Derived Effective Length of a Cornet Bell with Experimental Data. *J. Acoust. Soc. Am.*, **35,** 1902(A).

———. 1963b. System for Measuring the Acoustical Response of Wind Instruments of Portions of Instruments. *J. Acoust. Soc. Am.*, **35,** 1902(A).

———. 1963c. Influence of Irregular Patterns in Inharmonicity of Piano Tone Partials upon Tuning Practice. *J. Acoust. Soc. Am.*, **35,** 1909(A).

———. 1967. An Objective Appraisal of Piano Tone Quality. *Audio Eng. Soc.*, Preprint No. 505.

———. 1971a. Basic Elements in Piano Scale Design with Plain Strings. *J. Acoust. Soc. Am.*, **50,** 128(A).

———. 1971b. Der Einfluss der Inharmonizität auf die Stimmpraxis. *Junghanns Der Piano-und Flügelbau.* Frankfurt am Main: Verlag Das Musikinstrument, pp. 100–110.

———, and J. C. Hall. 1956. Characteristics of Cornet Tones. *J. Acoust. Soc. Am.*, **28,** 768(A), and *Proc. 2nd Int. Congr. Acoust.*, 158A.

Kinsler, L. E., and A. R. Frey. 1950. *Fundamentals of Acoustics.* 2nd ed. New York: Wiley.

Knaüss, H. P., and W. J. Yeager. 1941. Vibration of the Walls of a Cornet. *J. Acoust. Soc. Am.*, **13,** 160–162.

Kollman, F., and H. Krech. 1960. Dynamic Measurement of the Damping Capacity and Elastic Properties of Wood. Forest Products Laboratory, Madison, Wisconson.

Krüger, W. 1965. Zur Stimmung der Metallblasinstrumente. *Das Musikinstrument,* **14,** 479–481.
———, and E. Rohloff. 1975. Über die innere Reibung von Holz. 1938. In *Musical Acoustics, Part I,* edited by Carleen Hutchins. Stroudsburg, Pa.: Dowden, Hutchinson & Ross, pp. 340–351.
Kunitz, H. 1966. Gedanken zur klanglichen Struktur des Klaviers. *Europiano Kongress Berlin 1965 Dokumentation.* Frankfurt am Main: Fördergemeinschaft Klavier e.V., pp. 44–51.
Kurka, M. J. 1958. A Study of the Acoustical Effects of Mutes on Wind Instruments. Master's thesis, University of South Dakota.
Laible, U. 1964/1965. Selecting the Dimensions of Soundboard Ribs. *Das Musikinstrument,* **13,** 29–32, 688–692 and **14,** 35–36.
Lamb, H. 1960. *The Dynamical Theory of Sound.* New York: Dover.
Lambert, R. F. 1953. A Study of the Factors Influencing the Damping of an Acoustical Cavity Resonator. *J. Acoust. Soc. Am.,* **25,** 1068–1083.
Lange, T. 1955. Die Eigenfrequenzen von Trichtern. *Acustica,* **5,** 323–330.
Lange, W. 1935. Zur Physik des Konzertflügels. *Hochfr. Elektroakust.,* **45,** 118–128, 159–167.
Lehman, P. R. 1964. Harmonic Structure of the Tone of the Bassoon. *J. Acoust. Soc. Am.,* **36,** 1649–1653.
Leipp, E. 1962. Die Mundhöhle, ein empfindlicher Parameter der von Blasinstrumenten augestrahlten Spektren. *Vortrag 4th Int. Congr. Acoust., Copenhagen,* and *Das Musikinstrument,* **12,** 463–464 (1963).
———. 1964. New Method of Evaluating the Quality of a Clarinet. *Das Musikinstrument,* **13,** 22–24.
———. 1965. Testing a Clarinet. *Das Musikinstrument,* **14,** 22–26.
———. 1966. Qu'est-ce Qu'un Son de Piano? *Europiano Kongress Berlin 1965 Dokumentation.* Frankfurt am Main: Fördergemeinschaft Klavier e.V., pp. 118–126.
———. 1967. Was ist ein Musikinstrument? *Das Musikinstrument,* **16,** 700–704.
———. 1971. Was ist ein Klavierton? *Junghann's Der Piano-und Flügelbau,* Frankfurt am Main: Verlag Das Musikinstrument, pp. 93–99.
———, and M. Castellengo. 1964. Was ist Klarinettenklag? *Das Musikinstrument,* **13,** 671–673.
Lieber, E. 1960. Ermittlung der Naturtonlagen bei Metallblasinstrumenten. *Hochfr. Electroakust,* **69,** 29.
———. 1966. Der Einfluss des Resonanzbodens auf den Pianoklang. *Das Musikinstrument,* **15,** 858–846.
Lindsay, R. B. 1929. Connectors in Acoustical Conduits. *Phys. Rev.,* **34,** 808–816.
Lottermoser, W. 1936. Klanganalytische Untersuchungen an Zungenpfeifen. *Neuedeutsche Forshung,* **105.**
———. 1937. Der Eifluss des Materials von Orgel-Metallpfeifen auf ihre Tongebung. *Akust. Z.,* **2,** 129–134.
Louden, M. E. L. 1964. Untersuchungen von Reflexionsvorgängen in Rohren mit Hilfe akustischer Impulse. Dissertation, TH Braunschweig.
Luce, D., and M. Clark, Jr. 1967. Physical Correlates of Brass-Instrument Tones. *J. Acoust. Soc. Am.,* **42,** 1232–1243.

Mang, W. 1948. Zur Tonreinheit der Blechblas instrumente. *Instrumentenbau Z.*, **2.**

Martin, D. W. 1941. A Physical Investigation of the Performance of Brass Musical Instruments. Ph.D. dissertation, University of Illinois.

———. 1942. Directivity and the Acoustic Spectra of Brass Instruments. *J. Acoust. Soc. Am.*, **13,** 309–313.

———. 1960. Research Problems and Progress in Musical Acoustics. *J. Acoust. Soc. Am.*, **32,** 935(A).

———, and W. D. Ward. 1961. Subjective Evaluation of Musical Scale Temperament in Pianos. *J. Acoust. Soc. Am.*, **33,** 582–585.

Mateev, A., and A. Rimski-Korsakov. 1937. An Investigation of the Influence of Internal Friction on the Quality of Wood for Sounding Boards (in Russian). *J. Tech. Phys.*, **7,** 1273–1282.

Mawardi, O. K. 1949. On the Propagation of Sound Waves in Narrow Conduits. *J. Acoust. Soc. Am.*, **21,** 482–486.

McCracken, G. 1969. Practical Design of Brass Wind Instruments. *J. Acoust. Soc. Am.*, **45,** 297(A).

McGinnis, C. S., and C. Gallager. 1941. Mode of Vibration of a Clarinet Reed. *J. Acoust. Soc. Am.*, **12,** 529–531.

———; H. Hawkins; and N. Sher. 1943. Experimental Study of the Tone Quality of the Boehm Clarinet. *J. Acoust. Soc. Am.*, **14,** 228–237.

Meinel, H. 1954. Zur Stimmung der Musikinstrumente. *Acustica*, **4,** 233–236.

———. 1955. Zum Einfluss der Tonsysteme auf dem Normstimmton. *Acustica*, **5,** 284–288.

Meyer, E., and G. Buchmann. 1931. Die Klangspektren der Musikinstrumente. Berlin: Verlag Der Akademie Der Wissenschaft Bei Walter de Gruyter & Co.

Meyer, J., 1961. Über die Messung der Frequenzskalen von Holzblasinstrumenten. *Das Musikinstrument*, **10,** 614–616.

———. 1962. Uber die Stimmung von Klarinetten. *Das Musikinstrument*, **11,** 540–544.

———. 1964. Die Klangspektren von Klarinetten. *Das Musikinstrument*, **13,** 133–138.

———. 1965a. Die Richtcharakteristiken von Klarinetten. *Das Musikinstrument*, **14,** 21–25.

———. 1965b. Die Richtcharakteristiken des Flügels. *Das Musikinstrument*, **14,** 1085–1090.

———. 1966a. Die Richtcharakteristiken von Oboen und Fagotten. *Das Musikinstrument*, **15,** 958–964.

———. 1966b. *Akustik der Holzblasinstrumente in Einzeldarstellungen.* Frankfurt am Main: Verlag Das Musikinstrument.

———. 1967. Akustische Untersuchungen über den Klang des Hornes. *Das Musikinstrument*, **16,** 32–37, 199–203.

———. 1969. Über die Intonation bei den Klarinetten. *Instrumentenbau Z.*, **23,** 480.

———, and W. Lottermoser. 1961. Über die Moglichkeiten einer Klanglichen von Flügen. *Akust. Beihefte*, no. 1, 291–297.

———, and W. Lottermoser. 1965. On the Feasibility of Evaluating the Tone of Grand Pianos. *Piano Tech. J.*, 11–15.

———, and K. Wogram. 1969. Die Richtcharakteristiken des Hornes. *Das Musikinstrument*, **18.**

Meyer, J., and K. Wogram. 1970. Die Richtcharakteristiken von Trompete, Posaune, und Tuba. *Das Musikinstrument,* **19,** 171–180.

Meissner, B. F. 1961. Piano Sounding Board Vibration. *J. Acoust. Soc. Am.,* **33,** 539–540(L).

Miller, D. C. 1916. *Science of Musical Sounds.* New York: Macmillan.

Miller, F., Jr. 1949. Proposed Loading of Piano Strings for Improved Tone. *J. Acoust. Soc. Am.,* **21,** 318–322.

Mokhtar, M., and H. Yousef. 1952. Observations on Edge Tones. *Acustica,* **2,** 135–139.

Morse, P. M., and K. U. Ingard. 1968. *Theoretical Acoustics.* New York: McGraw-Hill.

Muhle, C. 1966. Untersuchungen über die Resonanzeigen schaften der Blockflöte. Ph.D. dissertation, TH Braunchweig.

Nagarkar, B. N., and R. D. Finch. 1971. Sinusoidal Horns. *J. Acoust. Soc. Am.,* **50,** 23–31.

Nederveen, C. J. 1969a. *Acoustical Aspects of Woodwind Instruments.* Amsterdam: Fritz Kunt.

———. 1969b. Influence of Reed Motion on the Resonance Frequency of Reed-Blown Woodwind Instruments. *J. Acoust. Soc. Am.,* **45,** 513(L).

———. 1973. Blown, Passive and Calculated Frequencies of the Flute. *Acustica,* **28,** 12–23.

———, and A. Bruijn. 1967. Hole Calculations for an Oboe. *Acustica,* **18,** 47–57.

———, and D. W. Wulfften. 1963. Resonance Frequency of a Gas in a Tube with a Short Closed Side Tube. *Acustica,* **13,** 65–70.

Neustadt, H. M., 1963a. Transients in Woodwinds and Brasses. *J. Acoust. Soc. Am.,* **35,** 771(A).

———. 1963b. Transients in Woodwind and Brass Musical Instruments. *U.S. Naval Acad. Sci. Lab. Research Report S-4.*

———. 1967. Acoustical Negative Resistance. *J. Acoust. Soc. Am.,* **41,** 1608(A).

Ohm, G. S. 1973. On the Definition of a Tone with Associated Theory of the Siren and Similar Sound Producing Devices. 1843. Translated by R. Bruce Lindsay in *Acoustics: Historical and Philosophical Development,* R. Bruce Lindsay, ed. Stroudsburg, Pa.: Downden, Hutchinson & Ross, pp. 243–247.

Oplinger, D. W. 1960. Frequency Response of a Nonlinear Stretched String. *J. Acoust. Soc. Am.,* **32,** 1529–1538.

Ortman, O. 1925. *The Physical Basis of Piano Touch and Tone.* New York: Dutton.

Parker, S. E. 1947. Analysis of the Tones of Wooden and Metal Clarinets. *J. Acoust. Soc. Am.,* **19,** 415–419.

Peirce, B. 1836. *An Elementary Treatise on Sound.* Boston: Munroe.

Pielmeir, W. H. 1939. Acoustic Effect of Humidity in Gases. *J. Acoust. Soc. Am.,* **10,** 87(A).

Plitnik, G., and W. J. Strong. 1972. Impedance Calculations for Oboe and Oboe-Like Structures. *J. Acoust. Soc. Am.,* **51,** 137(A).

Powell, A. 1961. On the Edgetone. *J. Acoust. Soc. Am.,* **33,** 395–409.

———. 1965. Aspects of Edgetone Experiment and Theory. *J. Acoust. Soc. Am.,* **37,** 535–539(L).

Pyle, R. W., Jr. 1964. Pitch Change of the Stopped French Horn. *J. Acoust. Soc. Am.,* **36,** 1025(A).

———. 1969. Mathematical Model of the Brass-Player's Embouchure. *J. Acoust. Soc. Am.,* **45,** 296(A).

Railsback, O. L. 1938a. Scale Temperament as Applied to Piano Tuning. *J. Acoust. Soc. Am.,* **9,** 274(A).

———. 1938b. A Study in the Tuning of Pianos. *J. Acoust. Soc. Am.,* **10,** 86(A).

Raman, C. V. 1927. Musik-instrumente und ihre Klang. *Handb. Phys.,* **8,** 240.

———, and B. Banerji. 1920. On Kaufmann's Theory of the Impact of the Pianoforte Hammer. *Proc. Roy. Soc. (London),* sA, **97,** 99–110.

Redfield, J. 1931. Minimizing Discrepancies of Intonation in Valve Instruments. *J. Acoust. Soc. Am.,* **3,** 292–296.

———. 1934. Certain Anomolies in the Theory of Air Column Behavior in Orchestral Wind Instruments. *J. Acoust. Soc. Am.,* **6,** 34–36.

Reichardt, W. 1968. *Grundlagen der Technischen Akustic,* Leipzig: Akademische Verlagsgesellschaft.

Richardson, E. G. 1929. *The Acoustics of Orchestral Instruments and of the Organ,* New York: Oxford University Press.

———. 1954. The Transient Tones of Wind Instruments. *J. Acoust. Soc. Am.,* **26,** 960–962.

Rimski-Korsakov, A. 1937. The Problem of the Striking of Strings by the Hammer of a Pianoforte and the Energy Spectrum of a String Struck by a Pianoforte Hammer (in Russian). *J. Tech. Phys.,* **7,** 43–74, 225–241.

Risset, J. C. 1965. Computer Study of Trumpet Tones. *J. Acoust. Soc. Am.,* **38,** 912(A).

Rschevkin, S. N. 1963. *Theory of Sound,* London: Pergamon.

Russell, M. E. 1953. The Oboe: A Comparison Study of Specifications with Musical Effectiveness. Ph.D. dissertation, Iowa State Teachers College.

Sabine, H. J. 1960. Decay Characteristics of Piano Tones. *J. Acoust. Soc. Am.,* **32,** 1493(A).

Saunders, F. A. 1946. Analysis of the Tones of a Few Wind Instruments. *J. Acoust. Soc. Am.,* **18,** 395–401.

Sauveur, J. 1973. General System of Sound Intervals and Its Application to Sounds of All Systems and All Musical Instruments, 1701. Translated by R. Bruce Lindsay in *Acoustics: Historical and Philosophical Development,* R. Bruce Lindsay, ed. Stroudsburg Pa.: Dowden, Hutchinson & Ross, pp. 88–94.

Schimmel, K. 1966. *Piano-Nomenclatur.* (German, English, French, Italian, Norwegian.) Frankfurt am Main: Verlag Das Musikinstrument.

Schwartz, D. M. 1960. Excitation and Overtone Structure of the Vibrating String of Musical Instruments. Bachelor's thesis, Massachusetts Institute of Technology.

Sharman, R. V. 1961. A Vibrating String Analogy with an Electrical Transmission Line. *J. Electronics and Control,* **11,** 233–239.

Shaw, A. E. G. 1972. Impedance-Transforming Wave Systems with Spatially Varying Density or Elasticity. *J. Acoust. Soc. Am.,* **52,** 138(A).

Shields, F. D.; K. P. Lee; and W. J. Wiley. 1965. Numerical Solution of Sound Velocity and Absorption in Cylindrical Tubes. *J. Acoust. Soc. Am.,* **37,** 724–729.

Sivian, L. J. 1935. Acoustic Impedance of Small Orifices. *J. Acoust. Soc. Am.,* **7,** 94–101.

Sivian, L. J.; H. K. Dunn; and S. D. White. 1931. Absolute Amplitudes and Spectra of Certain Musical Instruments and Orchestras. *J. Acoust. Soc. Am.,* **2,** 330–371.

Skudrzyk, E. 1954. *Die Grundlagen der Akustik,* Vienna: Springer-Verlag.

Small, A., and D. W. Martin. Musical Acoustics: Aims, Problems, Progress, and Forecast. *Proc. 2nd Int. Congr. Acoust.,* 68–75.

Stauffer, D. W. 1968. Role of Oral Cavities in the Support of Tone Production in Wind Instruments. *J. Acoust. Soc. Am.,* **44,** 367(A).

Stevenson, A. F. 1951. Theory of Electromagnetic Horn. *J. Appl. Phys.,* **22,** 1447–1460.

Stewart, G. W., and R. B. Lindsay. 1930. *Acoustics,* New York: Van Nostrand.

Strong, W. J. 1965. Spectrum-Envelope Method for Synthesis of Oboe Tones. *J. Acoust. Soc. Am.,* **37,** 1202(A).

Strutt, J. W. (Lord Rayleigh) 1973. On the Theory of Resonance. In *Acoustics: Historical and Philosophical Development,* edited by R. Bruce Lindsay. Stroudsburg, Pa.: Dowden, Hutchinson & Ross, pp. 376–398.

Struve, K. V. 1936. The Acoustics of Musical Pipes. *J. Tech. Phys.,* **6,** 1363–1373.

———. 1937. The Acoustics of Wind Instruments. *J. Tech. Phys.,* **7,** 75–80.

Stubbins, W. H.; C. P. Lillya; and J. R. Frederick. 1956. Effects of Blowing Pressure and Embouchure Factors on Trumpet Tone Production. *J. Acoust. Soc. Am.,* **28,** 769(A).

Tang, R. C., and N. N. Hsu. 1972. Dynamic Young's Moduli of Wood Related to Moisture Content. *Wood Sci.,* **5,** 7–14.

Taylor, B. 1973. Concerning the Motion of a Stretched String, 1713. Translated by R. Bruce Lindsay in *Acoustics: Historical and Philosophical Development,* R. Bruce Lindsay, ed. Stroudsburg, Pa.: Dowden, Hutchinson & Ross, pp. 96–102.

Taylor, C. A. 1965. *Physics of Musical Sounds,* New York: Elsevier.

Thomma, L. 1967. On Calculating the Diameter and Tension of Wound Strings. *Das Musikinstrument,* **16,** 274.

Trendelenburg, F. 1935. *Klänge und Geräuche,* Berlin: Springer-Verlag.

———. 1961. *Einfuhrüng in die Akustik,* Berlin: Springer-Verlag.

Trimmer, J. D. 1939. Resonant Frequencies of Certain Pipe Combinations. *J. Acoust. Soc. Am.,* **11,** 129–133.

Van Wye, J. R. 1966. Wrapped String Weights and Tension Calculations. *Das Musikinstrument,* **15,** 820–822.

Vitruvius, P. 1973. Acoustics of the Theatre. In *Acoustics: Historical and Philosophical Development,* edited by R. Bruce Lindsay. Stroudsburg, Pa.: Dowden, Hutchinson & Ross, pp. 26–33.

Vogel, M. 1961. Das Problem der Ventilkombination in Metallblasinstrumenten. *Das Musikinstrument,* **10,** 617–618.

Voots, R. J., and P. L. West. 1959. Report on an Investigation of Certain Flute "Blow-Hole" Parameters. *J. Acoust. Soc. Am.,* **31,** 1565(A).

Webster, A. G. 1973. Acoustical Impedance and the Theory of Horns and of the Phonograph, 1919. In *Physical Acoustics,* edited by R. Bruce Lindsay. Stroudsburg, Pa.: Dowden, Hutchinson & Ross, pp. 58–65.

Webster, J. C. 1949. Internal Tuning Differences Due to Players and the Taper of Trumpet Bells. *J. Acoust. Soc. Am.,* **21,** 208–214.

———. 1954. Intonation Errors Due to Discontinuities in the Valve Mechanism of Trumpets. *J. Acoust. Soc. Am.,* **26,** 932(A).

Wehner, W. 1962. The Effect of Interior Shape and Size of Clarinet Mouthpieces on Intonation and Tone Quality. Thesis, University of Kansas.
Weibel, E. S. 1955. On Webster's Horn Equation. *J. Acoust. Soc. Am.,* **27,** 726–727.
Weiner, S. 1966. Standing Waves of Finite Amplitude. *J. Acoust. Soc. Am.,* **40,** 240–243.
White, W. B. 1930. The Human Element in Piano Tone Production. *J. Acoust. Soc. Am.,* **1,** 357–365.
———. 1941. The Problem of a Stringing Scale for Small Vertical Pianofortes. *J. Acoust. Soc. Am.,* **12,** 409–411.
———. 1943. *Piano Tuning and Allied Arts.* 4th ed. Boston: Tuner's Supply Co.
Wilson, T. A., and G. S. Beavers. 1974. Operating Modes of the Clarinet. *J. Acoust. Soc. Am.,* **56,** 653–658.
Wogram, K. 1972. Ein Beitrag zur Ermittlung Der Stimmung von Blechblasinstrumenten, Ph.D. thesis, Tech. Universität Carolo-Wilhemina, Braunschweig.
Wolf, D., and H. Muller. 1968. Normal Vibration Modes in Stiff Strings. *J. Acoust. Soc. Am.,* **44,** 1093–1097.
Wolf, S. K. and W. J. Sette. 1935. Some Applications of Modern Acoustical Apparatus. *J. Acoust. Soc. Am.,* **6,** 160–168.
Wood, A. 1944. *The Physics of Music.* London: Methuen.
Woodward, J. G. 1942. Resonance Characteristics of a Cornet. *J. Acoust. Soc. Am.,* **13,** 156–159.
Worman, W. E. 1969. Spectral Component Coupling in Wind Instruments. *J. Acoust. Soc. Am.,* **45,** 313(A).
———. 1970. Self-Sustained Oscillations in Clarinet-Like Systems—Qualitative Results. *J. Acoust. Soc. Am.,* **48,** 88(A).
———. 1971a. A Comparison of Boehm's Design of the Flute with That of Rockstro. *J. Acoust. Soc. Am.,* **50,** 128(A).
———. 1971b. Self-Sustained Nonlinear Oscillations of Medium Amplitude in Clarinet-Like Systems. Ph.D. thesis, Case Western Reserve University.
———. 1972. Spectrum Development with Playing Level in Wind Instruments. *J. Acoust. Soc. Am.,* **52,** 148(A).
———. 1975. Boehm's Design of the Flute: A Comparison with That of Rockstro. *Galpin Society J.,* Spring 1975, 107–120.
Young, F. J. 1961. Impedance of Tapered Structure. *J. Acoust. Soc. Am.,* **33,** 1206–1210.
———. 1966. Open Tones of Musical Horns. *J. Acoust. Soc. Am.,* **40,** 1252(A).
———, and B. H. Young. 1961. Smoothly and Step-Tapered Structures. *J. Acoust. Soc. Am.,* **33,** 813(L).
Young, R. W. 1934. A Study of the Standing Wave System Formed in the Boehm Flute. Ph.D. dissertation, University of Washington.
———. 1936. Standing Sound Waves in the Boehm Flute Measured by the Hot Wire Probe. *J. Acoust. Soc. Am.,* **7,** 178–189.
———. 1939. Terminology for Logarithmic Frequency Units. *J. Acoust. Soc. Am.,* **11,** 134–139.
———. 1942. Some Characteristics of the Tuning of Valved Wind Instruments. *J. Acoust. Soc. Am.,* **13,** 333(A).
———. 1944. Some Problems for Postwar Musical Acoustics. *J. Acoust. Soc. Am.,* **16,** 103–107.

Young, R. W. 1946. Dependence of Tuning Wind Instruments on Temperature. *J. Acoust. Soc. Am.*, **17,** 187–191.
———. 1948. On the Performance of Cup Mouthpiece Instruments. *J. Acoust. Soc. Am.*, **20,** 345–346(L).
———. 1949. Influence of Humidity on the Tuning of a Piano. *J. Acoust. Soc. Am.*, **21,** 580–585.
———. 1952a. *A Table Relating Frequency to Cents.* 2nd ed. Elkhart, Ind.: C. G. Conn, Ltd.
———. 1952b. Inharmonicity of Plain Wire Piano Strings. *J. Acoust. Soc. Am.*, **24,** 267–273.
———. 1954a. Inharmonicity of Piano Strings. *Acustica,* **4,** 259–262.
———. 1954b. Inharmonicity of Piano Bass Strings. *J. Acoust. Soc. Am.*, **26,** 144(A).
———. 1954c. Twenty-Five Years of Musical Acoustics. *J. Acoust. Soc. Am.*, **26,** 955–959.
———. 1954d. Tuning: Pianoforte. *Groves Dictionary of Music and Musicians,* Vol. 8, 5th ed. New York: St. Martins Press, pp. 595–599.
———. 1957a. Die Stimmung der Flöte. *Gravesaner Blatter II,* **7/8,** 87–91.
———. 1957b. Tuning of the Oboe. *Gravesaner Blatter III,* **9,** 116–119.
———. 1959a. Sur l'Intonation de Divers Instruments de Musique. *Acoustique Musicale,* Paris: Editions du Centre National de la Recherche Scientifique, pp. 169–184.
———. 1959b. Intonation of an Alto and Tenor Saxophone. *J. Acoust. Soc. Am.*, **31,** 1565(A).
———. 1959c. Intonation of Musical Instruments IV: The Alto Saxophone. *Gravesaner Blatter IV,* **14,** 124–134.
———. 1963. A Decade of Musical Acoustics. *Report II 4th Int. Congr. Acoust., Copenhagen,* pp. 231–250.
———. 1966. Musical Acoustics, Musical Instruments, and Nine Related Articles on Acoustics. *McGraw-Hill Encyclopedia of Science and Technology,* 2nd ed. New York: McGraw-Hill.
———. 1967. Optimum Lengths of Valve Tubes for Brass Wind Instruments. *J. Acoust. Soc. Am.*, **42,** 224–235.
———, and H. K. Dunn. 1957. On the Interpretation of Certain Sound Spectra of Musical Instruments. *J. Acoust. Soc. Am.*, **29,** 1070–1073.
———, and A. Loomis. 1938. Theory of the Chromatic Stroboscope. *J. Acoust. Soc. Am.*, **10,** 112–118.
———, and D. H. Loughridge. 1935. Relative Measurments of the Standing Wave System in a Mechanically Blown Flute Tube. *Phys. Rev.*, **47,** 258(A).
———, and J. C. Webster. 1958. The Tuning of Musical Instruments: The Clarinet. *Gravesaner Blatter IV,* **11/12,** 182–186.
———, and J. C. Webster. 1959. Some Factors Affecting the Intonation of a Clarinet. *J. Acoust. Soc. Am.*, **31,** 839(A).

# AUTHOR CITATION INDEX

# SUBJECT INDEX

# ABOUT THE EDITOR

Earle L. Kent is former Director of Research, Development, and Design with C. G. Conn, Ltd., where his work was related to the manufacture of electronic organs, wind instruments, and pianos. Since retiring from that position his work as a consulting engineer has included architectural acoustics, piano technology, patent litigation, and data processing. He received both the B.S. and M.S. from Kansas State University and earned the Ph.D. in electrical engineering from the University of Michigan.

Dr. Kent has received Distinguished Service Awards from Kansas State University; the University of Michigan; and Kappa Kappa Psi, National Honorary Fraternity for College Bandsmen. He is a member of numerous honorary and professional societies, the author of many technical articles, and is the patentee of 27 patents.

LIBRARY
eConte Hall